Reinforced

Concrete

Fundamentals

Reinforced Concrete Fundamentals

WITH   EMPHASIS

New York · John Wiley & Sons, Inc.

London

ON ULTIMATE STRENGTH

PHIL M. FERGUSON

*Professor of Civil Engineering
The University of Texas*

FIFTH PRINTING, JULY, 1962

Library of Congress Catalog Card Number: 58–13459

Printed in the United States of America

Preface

A text should be forward-looking, leading the student toward improved methods rather than simply recording present practice. Forward-looking methods now include (1) emphasis upon the results of research and physical testing, and (2) the use of ultimate strength design methods; and in prospect, probably limit design and the yield-line method for slabs. Ultimate strength design represents an entirely new philosophy which utilizes proven strengths established from earlier research.

This text emphasizes both the physical behavior of reinforced concrete members and the approved ultimate strength theory. It is desirable that reinforced concrete, as an inelastic material, be taught differently from a simple junior course in strength of materials. Wherever appropriate, topics are introduced with descriptions of member action under steadily increasing loads with pictures of failure at ultimate load. Although design specifications can change, failure patterns represent permanent knowledge.

The ultimate strength theory is founded upon the proven behavior of reinforced concrete members as revealed in numerous laboratory investigations. Long used in some form in several countries (and in the United States in modified form in column design), the general ultimate strength theory received the support of a joint ASCE-ACI Committee in 1955. In 1956 the most widely used North American specification for reinforced concrete, the ACI Building Code, incorporated provisions for ultimate strength as an alternate method. As engineers become better acquainted with its merits, ultimate strength design will undoubtedly become the predominant design procedure.

Although this text, designed for a beginning course in reinforced concrete, emphasizes ultimate strength theory, it still retains adequate coverage of the working stress method. Chapter 1 explains the physical properties which make ultimate strength design the most practical. Chapter 2, dealing with "axially" loaded columns, introduces the student to the major problems created by shrinkage and creep of concrete. Column behavior at failure is described and shown in photographs. The ACI working load specification for axially loaded columns is then introduced as a slight modification of an ultimate strength formula. Chapter 3 describes how beams fail and develops the ultimate strength theory for flexural members. Chapter 13 presents ultimate strength as applied to eccentrically loaded columns, along with working stress methods.

Since the rigorous elastic analysis of flat slabs and slabs supported on four sides is too complex for ordinary use, Chapters 9 and 11 emphasize only the general action of such slabs and the statics involved in each case.

With future developments in mind, and to present a slab analysis easily understood, Chapter 10 is devoted to an elementary treatment of the yield-line theory for slabs. This is an ultimate strength method, or more exactly a limit design method. Likewise, Appendix C develops limit design ideas as applied to frames. A joint ACI-ASCE committee has already started a study of what portions of limit design may be applied to reinforced concrete structures.

For teachers who may wish to defer the study of ultimate strength theory, the text is written in such a way that a class may proceed directly from Chapter 1 to Chapter 4 on working load analysis without generally being conscious of the material passed over. Presumably, such a treatment would shift Chapter 2 on axially loaded columns just ahead of Chapter 13 on eccentric loading. With this approach, ultimate strength can be introduced wherever the teacher desires.

In the preparation of this text I have drawn upon material presented in one form or another by many authors and upon my own experience of thirty-five years as a designer, teacher, and research man. I acknowledge my indebtedness to the authors of the textbooks I have used in the past, particularly to F. E. Turneaure and E. R. Maurer and to H. Sutherland and R. C. Reese. But my greatest inspiration has come from my colleagues and associates in the American Concrete Institute who were ever anxious to share their information, as well as their friendship, with all who were interested. To those who organized the American Concrete Institute, to those who carried its responsibilities during troubled times, and to those who have contributed the many distinguished papers it has published, I am most deeply in debt.

Finally, a request to the reader, whether he be a teacher, a student, or a professional engineer. Whenever so many details are presented, some errors usually creep in. I would appreciate having them called to my attention.

PHIL M. FERGUSON

Austin, Texas
March, 1958

Contents

Materials
and
Specifications

1.1. CONCRETE MATERIALS AND PRODUCTION

Concrete for reinforced concrete consists of aggregate bonded together in a paste made from portland cement and water. The paste fills the voids in the aggregate and after the concrete is placed it hardens to form a solid structural material. A typical cross section of concrete is shown in Fig. 1.1a.

Although there are five standard portland cements, most concrete for buildings is made from Class I ordinary or standard cement (for concrete where strength is needed in something like 28 days) or from Class III high-early strength cement (for concrete where strength is required in a few days). The heat generated by the different types of cements during the setting and hardening process varies widely, as indicated in Fig. 1.2. Where shrinkage and temperature stresses are important in the design, these heat differences become significant. Air-entraining cement or

1

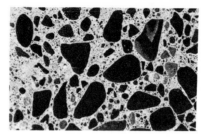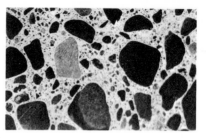

(a)

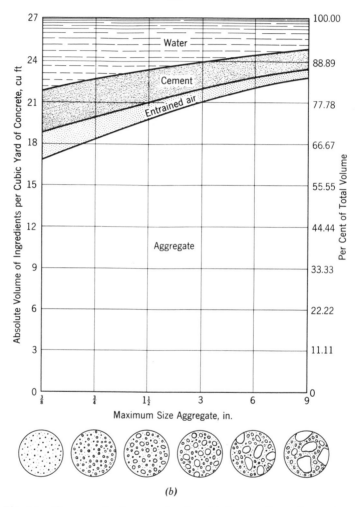

(b)

Fig. 1.1. Components of a concrete mix. (a) Cross sections of concrete showing coarse and fine aggregate separated by cement paste. (Courtesy Bureau of Reclamation.) (b) Quantities of each material in 1 cu yd of concrete. (From Ref. 1, Bureau of Reclamation.)

REINFORCED CONCRETE FUNDAMENTALS

admixtures for entraining air in the concrete are frequently used for greater workability or durability; air-entrained concrete should have more general usage.

Aggregate consists of both fine and coarse aggregate, usually sand for the fine and gravel or crushed stone for the coarse aggregate. Many other aggregates, such as slag or lightweight aggregates, are also used. The size (and also the grading) of aggregate has an important influence on the

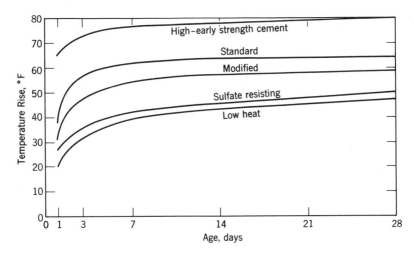

Fig. 1.2. Temperature rise in concrete for various types of cement, when no heat is lost. One barrel of cement per cubic yard. (From Refs. 2 and 1, ACI and Bureau of Reclamation.)

amount of cement and water required to make 1 cu yd of concrete (Fig. 1.1*b*).

The quantity of water relative to that of the cement is the most important item in determining concrete strength. The effect of the water-cement ratio on strength is indicated in Fig. 1.3. The water is sometimes controlled indirectly and approximately by specifying the cement content in terms of sacks per cubic yard of concrete.

It is important that concrete have a workability adequate to assure its consolidation in the forms without excessive voids. This property is usually measured in the field by the slump test (Fig. 1.4*a*) or the Kelly ball test (Fig. 1.4*b*). The necessary slump may be small when vibrators are used to consolidate the concrete. For methods of designing concrete mixes the student is referred to the American Concrete Institute's "Recommended Practice for Selecting Proportions for Concrete" (ACI 613–54)[4] or the Portland Cement Association booklet "Design and Control of Concrete Mixes."[3]

Proper curing of concrete requires that the water in the mix not be allowed to evaporate from the concrete until the concrete has gained its

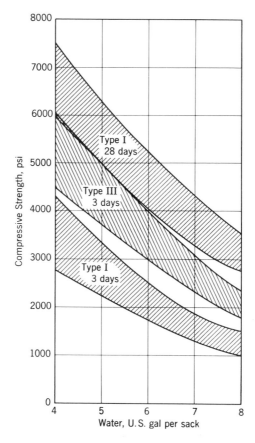

Fig. 1.3. Effect of water-cement ratio on strength of concrete at different ages. All specimens moist cured at 70°F. (Modified from Ref. 3, Portland Cement Assn.)

strength. Figure 1.5 is representative of the variations in strength which can result from differences in curing. Temperature is also an important element in the rate at which concrete gains strength, low temperatures slowing up the process. Early high temperatures lead to rapid setting and some permanent loss of strength potential.

                                      REINFORCED CONCRETE FUNDAMENTALS

(a)   (b)

Fig. 1.4. Testing for workability of concrete. (*a*) Slump test. (Courtesy Portland Cement Assn.) (*b*) Kelly ball test. The "ball" penetration is read on the graduated shaft by Professor Kelly of the University of California. This mix is quite stiff.

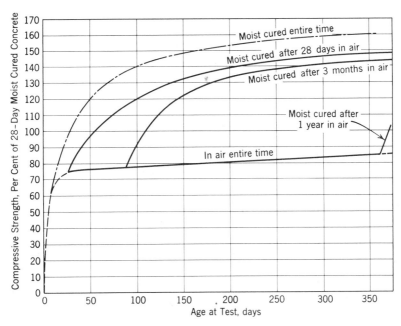

Fig. 1.5. Effect of curing conditions on strength of concrete. (From Ref. 3, Portland Cement Assn.)

1.2. COMPRESSIVE STRENGTH

Depending upon the mix (especially the water-cement ratio) and the time and quality of the curing, compressive strengths of concrete can be obtained up to 8000 psi or 10,000 psi. Commercial production of concrete with ordinary aggregates is usually in the 2500-psi to 6000-psi range with the most common near 3000 psi. On the other hand, highway departments often expect strengths of 4000 to 6000 psi. Because of the difference in aggregates, and to a lesser degree in cements, the same mix proportions result in substantially lower strengths in some sections of the country. In these sections a lower water-cement ratio must be used.

Compressive strength f_c' is based on standard 6-in. by 12-in. cylinders cured under standard laboratory conditions and tested at a specified rate of loading at 28 days of age. The designer should note that building concrete cured in place on the job will rarely develop as much strength as these standard cured cylinders. The job-specified concrete strength should be increased above the desired or design f_c' by an amount which should vary with the mixing control that is used. The author would suggest that this increase be at least 15% when the control is good, that is, that a mix design never be made for less than 3500 psi when the design f_c' is 3000 psi. The ACI Code,* Art. 304c, among other requirements, says that "not more than one strength test in ten shall have an average value less than 90 per cent of the specified strength." Additional cylinders cured on the job may be used to check on the quality of the job curing.

The ASCE-ACI Committee Report on Ultimate Strength Design quoted in essence in the ACI Code Appendix, Art. A602f, sets up a very desirable specification form for concrete strength where sampling is adequate:

> The quality of concrete shall be such that not more than one test in ten shall have an average strength less than the strength assumed in the design, and the average of any three consecutive tests shall not be less than the assumed design strength. Each test shall consist of not less than three standard cylinders.

This requirement is stricter than that for working load design in Art. 304.

When better methods of mix design are not used, the ACI Code assumes that various water-cement ratios with natural aggregates lead to the strengths shown in Art. 302a. These are conservative estimates of strength, except in a few regions.

With lightweight aggregates, strengths will be lower and a mix design should be made on the basis of trial batches. Many lightweight aggregates can produce 3000 psi concrete and some give 5000 psi concrete when under proper control.

* The larger part of the Code is reprinted in Appendix D.

1.3. TENSILE STRENGTH

The tensile strength of concrete is relatively low, about 10% to 15% of the compression strength, occasionally 20%. This strength is more difficult to measure and the results vary more specimen to specimen than those from compression cylinders.

1.4. SIGNIFICANCE OF LOW TENSILE STRENGTH

In a homogeneous elastic beam subjected to bending moment, one can calculate the bending stresses from $f = Mc/I$. The extreme fiber on one face carries compression, on the opposite face tension. If the beam is rectangular (or of any shape symmetrical about the centroidal axis), the maximum tensile stress equals the maximum compressive stress. In concrete construction, except in massive structures such as gravity dams and sometimes heavy footings, it is not economical to limit the beam strength by the low tensile strength of plain concrete. It is generally more economical to make up a beam with compressive bending stresses carried by concrete and tensile bending stress carried entirely by steel reinforcing bars. It is not possible for concrete to cooperate with steel in carrying these tensile stresses except at very low and uneconomical values of steel stress. When the steel stress reaches some 6000 psi, the tensile concrete starts to crack and the steel must soon thereafter pick up essentially all the tension necessary to provide for the applied moment. Hence, in ordinary reinforced concrete beams the tensile concrete is not assumed to assist at all in resisting the moment.

1.5. SHEAR STRENGTH

The shear strength of concrete is large, variously reported as from 35% to 80% of the compression strength. It is difficult to separate shear from other stresses in testing and this accounts for some of the variation reported. The lower values represent attempts to separate friction effects from true shears. The shear value is significant only in rare cases, since shear must ordinarily be limited to much lower values in order to protect the concrete against diagonal tension stresses (Secs. 6.10 and 6.12).

Diagonal tension stresses are often referred to as shear stresses, but this is actually a misnomer. If the student will keep in mind that true shear strength is rarely in question, it will not matter that the term "shear" is often loosely used for diagonal tension.

1.6. STRESS-STRAIN CURVE

Typical stress-strain curves for concrete cylinders on initial loading are shown in Fig. 1.6. The first part of each curve is nearly a straight line, but there is some curvature at f_c equal to half the maximum value. The maximum stress is designated as f_c' (Sec. 1.2). The curve for low strength concrete has a long and relatively flat top. For high strength concrete the peak is sharper. Special techniques are necessary to establish these curves

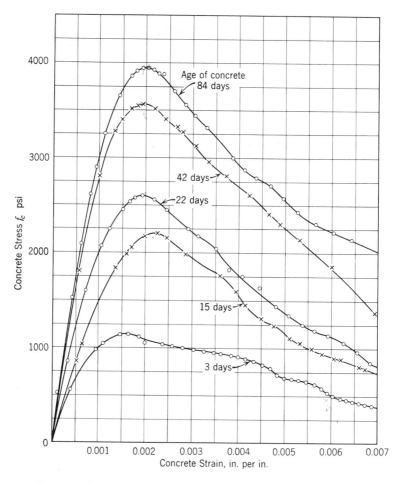

Fig. 1.6. Concrete stress-strain curves from compression cylinders. (From Ref. 5, Bureau of Reclamation.)

REINFORCED CONCRETE FUNDAMENTALS

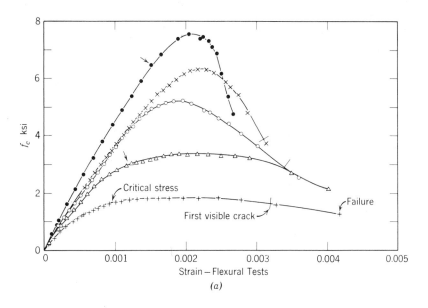

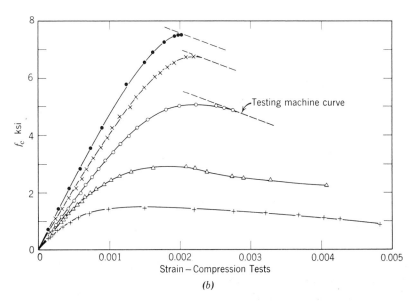

Fig. 1.7. Compression stress-strain curves at age of 28 days. (From Ref. 6, ACI.) (*a*) From flexural tests on 5 by 8 by 16-in. prisms. (*b*) From direct compression tests on 6 by 12-in. cylinders.

on the steep downward sections beyond the peak stress. Otherwise the testing machine characteristics result in sudden instead of gradual failure. Figure 1.7b illustrates this difficulty with high strength concretes.

At strains beyond the peak value of stress, considerable strength still exists. It will be noted that the strain occurring near maximum stress is nearly the same for all strengths of concrete, being roughly 0.002 in./in. In a cylinder a maximum strain of something like 0.0025 measures the useful limit for all concretes except those of low strength or those made with lightweight aggregate. In beams of ordinary concrete, observations show that unit strains of 0.0035 to 0.0045 normally occur before the beam fails; with f_c' over 5000 psi, the maximum observed strains are from 0.0025 to 0.0030. Recent tests[6] have proved conclusively that the stress-strain curve for the compression face of a beam is essentially identical with that for a standard test cylinder, as shown in Fig. 1.7.

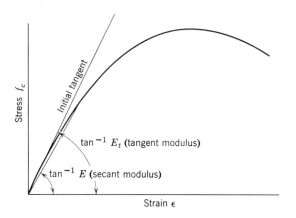

Fig. 1.8. Tangent and secant modulus of elasticity determinations.

Strictly speaking, concrete on initial loading has no fixed ratio of f_c/ϵ which truly justifies the term "modulus of elasticity." The initial slope of the stress-strain curve defines the initial or tangent modulus used with the parabolic stress method and occasionally elsewhere. The slope of the chord (up to about $0.5f_c'$) determines the secant modulus of elasticity which is generally used in straight-line stress calculations (Fig. 1.8). When E or the term "modulus of elasticity" is used without further designation, it is usually the secant modulus which is intended.

The secant modulus is often taken as $1000f_c'$ but it is known that this is low for moderate strength concrete and high for high strength concrete.

REINFORCED CONCRETE FUNDAMENTALS

The ASCE-ACI Joint Committee on Recommended Practice for Prestressed Concrete recommends the relation

$$E = 1,800,000 + 500f_c'$$

but states that actual values may differ as much as 25% from these.

A reduced modulus is necessary to account for the time effects as discussed in the next section.

1.7. CREEP OF CONCRETE

The initial strain in concrete on first loading at low unit stresses is nearly elastic but this strain increases with time even under constant load (Fig. 1.9a). This increased deformation with time is called creep or plastic flow and under ordinary conditions it may amount to more than the elastic deformation. Factors tending to increase creep are loading at an early age (while the concrete is still "green"), using concrete with a high water-cement ratio, and exposing the concrete to drying conditions. Concrete completely wet or completely dried out creeps little, and in general creep decreases with the age of the concrete.

At stresses up to the usual working stresses, creep is directly proportional to the unit stress; hence elastic and creep deformations are essentially proportional in plain concrete members. Under overload conditions this proportionality no longer holds; and in reinforced concrete the constant modulus of the steel causes minor strain readjustments with time.

Creep is more rapid when the load is first applied and decreases somewhat exponentially with time, as shown in Fig. 1.9b.

Creep is one common cause of deflections which increase with time. In reinforced concrete, without compressive steel, the final deflection will usually be from 2.0 to 2.5 times the initial deflection. It has been suggested that long-time deflections be calculated on the basis of a reduced modulus having a value one-third that of the instantaneous modulus.

1.8. SHRINKAGE OF CONCRETE

As concrete loses moisture by evaporation, it shrinks. Since moisture is never uniformly withdrawn throughout the concrete, the differential moisture changes cause differential shrinkage tendencies and internal stresses. Stresses due to differential shrinkage can be quite large and this is one of the reasons for insisting on moist curing conditions.

In plain concrete completely unrestrained against contraction, a uniform

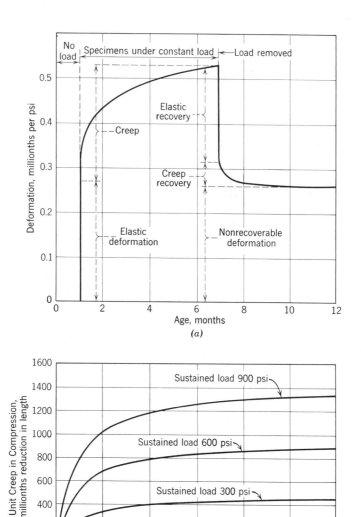

Fig. 1.9. Creep of concrete. (From Ref. 1, Bureau of Reclamation.) (*a*) Creep and elastic deformation. (*b*) Effect of unit stress upon unit creep, for identical concretes.

shrinkage would cause no stress; but complete lack of restraint and uniform shrinkage are both theoretical terms, not ordinary conditions. With reinforced concrete even uniform shrinkage causes stresses, compression in the steel, tension in the concrete.

The amount of shrinkage will depend on the exposure and the concrete.

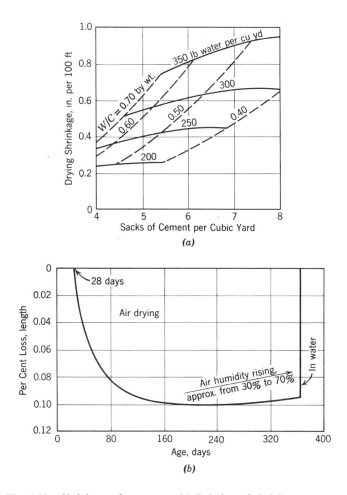

Fig. 1.10. Shrinkage of concrete. (*a*) Relation of shrinkage to water content. (From Ref. 2, ACI.) (*b*) Typical shrinkage-time curve starting with water-cured specimen (3 by 3 by 40-in.) 28 days old. Note recovery when again placed in water; constant volume reached in about 24 hours of soaking. (Replotted from Ref. 7, The Engineering Foundation.)

Exposure to wind greatly increases the shrinkage rate. A humid atmosphere will reduce shrinkage; a low humidity will increase shrinkage. Shrinkage is usually expressed in terms of the shrinkage coefficient s, which is the shortening per unit length. This coefficient varies greatly, with values commonly 0.0004 to 0.0006 and in some cases as much as 0.0010. An indication of how shrinkage varies with the water and cement content is given in Fig. 1.10a with shrinkage there expressed in terms of inches per 100 ft. This figure can only show trends since the amount of shrinkage differs with materials and drying conditions.

Shrinkage is, to a considerable extent, a reversible phenomenon. If concrete is soaked after it has shrunk, it will expand to nearly its original size, as indicated in Fig. 1.10b.

Shrinkage is another common cause of deflections which increase with time. Only symmetrical reinforcement can prevent curvature and deflection from shrinkage.

1.9. REINFORCING STEEL

Reinforcing bars are made from billet steel in intermediate or hard grade, and occasionally in structural grade. Rail steel (rerolled from old rails) and axle grade steel bars are also available. The various steels have these specified yield points* and ultimate strengths.

	Min. Yield Point f_y, ksi	Ultimate f_u, ksi
Billet steel (and axle steel)		
Structural	33	55 to 75
Intermediate	40	70 to 90
Hard	50	80
Rail steel	50	80

To increase the bond between concrete and steel, projections called deformations are rolled on the bar surface as shown in Fig. 1.11, the pattern of these varying with the manufacturer. The deformations shown satisfy ASTM Spec. A 305;[8] such bars are called *deformed* bars. The ACI Building Code treats bars with any lesser deformations as plain bars.

---

* As this goes to press it appears that the designations of structural, intermediate, and hard grade will be eliminated. Reinforcing steel will then be specified as B33, B40, A50, B60, R60, and B75, where B designates billet steel, A axle steel, R rail steel, and the associated number the specified minimum yield point. This change in effect raises the yield point of the present hard grade billet steel and of the present rail steel from 50 ksi to 60 ksi.

REINFORCED CONCRETE FUNDAMENTALS

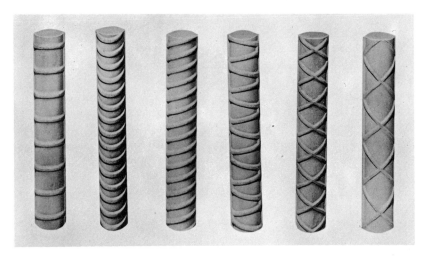

Fig. 1.11. Various types of deformed bars. (Courtesy Concrete Reinforcing Steel Inst.)

TABLE 1.1. Weight, Area, and Perimeter of Individual Bars

Current Bar Designation No.	Unit Weight per Foot, lb	Nominal Dimensions—Round Sections		
		Diameter in.	Cross-Sectional Area, sq in.	Perimeter, in.
2	0.167	0.250	0.05	0.786
3	0.376	0.375	0.11	1.178
4	0.668	0.500	0.20	1.571
5	1.043	0.625	0.31	1.963
6	1.502	0.750	0.44	2.356
7	2.044	0.875	0.60	2.749
8	2.670	1.000	0.79	3.142
9	3.400	1.128	1.00	3.544
10	4.303	1.270	1.27	3.990
11	5.313	1.410	1.56	4.430

ASTM in 1957 approved a tentative specification for two larger sizes which are outside the scope of ASTM Specs. A 15[9] and A 305.[8] The bond strength and other properties of these bars have not yet been established:

14S	—	1.693	2.25	—
18S	—	2.257	4.00	—

MATERIALS AND SPECIFICATIONS   15

All standard bars are round bars, designated by size as #2 to #11, this number corresponding roughly to the bar diameter in eighths of an inch. The #2 bars are plain $\frac{1}{4}$-in. round bars, with #3 to #11 usually deformed bars. The bar weights and nominal areas, diameters, and circumferences or perimeters are tabulated in Table 1.1. Since the area is calculated from the weight, including that of the deformations, it is a nominal area as far as minimum cross section is concerned. The perimeter is the circumference of this nominal circular area. Bars 14S and 18S are not yet fully standard bars.

Welded wire mesh is also used for reinforcing. This is made of cold drawn wires running in two directions and welded together at intersections.

1.10. DESIGN CODES

A specification for reinforced concrete design may take the form of a code or a recommended practice. A code is written in the form of a law, for enactment by public bodies such as city councils. It represents, usually, the minimum requirements necessary to protect the public from danger. It makes no attempt to specify the best practice, although it usually attempts to eliminate the most common mistakes, especially those involving safety. A recommended practice, on the other hand, attempts to define the best practice or at least to state satisfactory design assumptions and procedures. It may state reasons as well as methods.

The most significant code in the United States is the "Building Code Requirements for Reinforced Concrete" (ACI 318–56). Most of this code is reprinted in Appendix D. Its requirements are frequently quoted in the chapters following. It will be referred to hereafter simply as the Code or the ACI Code and references to its requirements will be made by noting the article number without naming the code.

Two other codes have considerable usage: the Pacific Coast Building Officials Conference's "Uniform Building Code" and the Building Officials Conference of America "Basic Building Code." In addition, many cities write their own codes, making some modifications in these more standard codes. The designer must at the beginning of any project determine the code under which he is required to operate.

The Joint Committee's "Recommended Practice for Concrete and Reinforced Concrete" was last rewritten in 1940. Although it was once highly regarded, it is now obsolete. Since the ACI Code is answering current needs, further Joint Committee action is not probable.

Highway bridges are normally designed under specifications prepared by the American Association of State Highway Officials (AASHO).

The American Railway Engineering Association (AREA) has a specification covering masonry structures, including those of reinforced concrete.

1.11. ELASTIC AND ULTIMATE STRENGTH DESIGN

The curved stress-strain diagram for concrete complicates theoretical analysis. In this country some of the prominent early investigators favored calculations based on ultimate strength, the assumption being made that the beam compressive stress at failure had a parabolic distribution, from zero at the neutral axis to the ultimate f_c' at the extreme fiber,

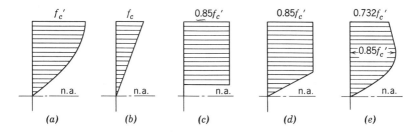

Fig. 1.12. Stress distributions assumed on compression side of beam. (*a*) Simple parabola (ultimate). (*b*) Straight line (working stress). (*c*) Rectangular stress block (ultimate). (*d*) Trapezoidal stress block (ultimate). (*e*) Parabolic, with straight line (ultimate).

as shown in Fig. 1.12*a*. But instead of this, the early specifications adopted the idea of working stresses and the elastic or straight-line stress distribution shown in Fig. 1.12*b*, which idea has remained dominant until recently. All of the specifications named above are essentially elastic design specifications.

In 1940 the Joint Committee Recommendation, and in 1941 the ACI Code, adopted a modified ultimate strength specification for axially loaded columns. Subsequently the ACI Code modified the requirements for compression steel in beams in related fashion.

In 1956 the ACI Code added Art. 601*b*, as follows:

> The ultimate strength method of design may be used for the design of reinforced concrete members.

Although the remainder of the Code defines a type of analysis which is predominantly straight line, this sentence permits the designer to use ultimate strength procedures. This authorization followed the issuance in October 1955 of the Report of the ASCE-ACI Joint Committee on Ultimate Strength Design. This report does not specify an exact shape for the compressive stress distribution but permits "a rectangle, trapezoid, parabola, or any other shape which results in ultimate strength in reasonable agreement with tests." Some of these distributions are pictured in Fig. 1.12c, d, e. Ultimate strength discussions in this text are in terms of the rectangular stress block (Fig. 1.12c), a stress block pioneered in this country by Whitney.* This somewhat simpler procedure complies fully with the Report and gives sufficiently accurate results. In fact, the practical differences obtained from the several suggested stress distributions are rather minor.

It is probable that the next revision of the ACI Code will incorporate more detailed rules governing ultimate strength design. At the present time it merely summarizes the Joint Committee recommendations in the Code Appendix.

1.12. FACTORS OF SAFETY AND LOAD FACTORS

Structural members are designed to have some reserve strength beyond their ordinary working loads. This is necessary to allow for variation in quality of materials, for possible overloads, for stresses not calculated (secondary stresses), and for errors introduced by simplifications and approximations in calculation procedures. When elastic (straight-line) stress calculations are used with working loads, a factor of safety is provided by the use of stresses much below the failure stresses. The factor of safety is the ratio of the load that would cause failure (collapse) to that used as the working or service load. In reinforced concrete, this factor of safety is far different from the ratio of ultimate stress to working stress, but some writers have not been careful to maintain the distinction. The result is that the term "factor of safety" may be ambiguous unless defined each time it is used.

The term "load factor" has been introduced in connection with ultimate strength design to eliminate any possible ambiguity. When ultimate strength design is used, the ultimate load, moment, or shear upon which design is based must be greater than the working load, moment, or shear in order to provide a factor of safety. Accordingly, the working values are multiplied by a load factor in order to obtain the desirable ultimate design

* Univ. of Ill. Eng. Exp. Sta. *Bull. No. 399*, 1951, shows numerous stress assumptions that have been made, including one use of the rectangular stress block as early as 1912.

values. Load factors also serve a second function, namely, to assure that strains under working loads will not be so large as to cause excessive cracking.

The ASCE-ACI Committee recommends load factors of 1.2 for basic (dead) loads, 2.4 for live loads and impact, and 2.4 for wind or earthquake loading. This is modified as follows for various load combinations.

These terms are used in the load factor equations:

U = ultimate strength of section

B = effect of basic load consisting of dead load plus volume change due to plastic and elastic actions, shrinkage, and temperature

L = effect of live load plus impact

W = effect of wind load

E = effect of earthquake forces

K = load factor equal to 2 for columns and members subjected to combined bending and axial load, and equal to 1.8 for beams and girders subjected to bending only.

For those structures in which, due to location or proportions, the effects of wind and earthquake loading can properly be neglected:

$$U = 1.2B + 2.4L \qquad (I)$$

$$U = K(B + L) \qquad (II)$$

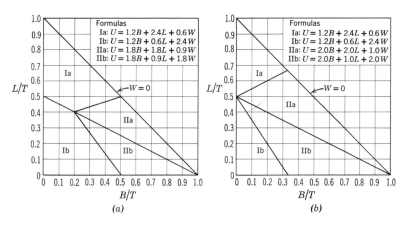

Fig. 1.13. Charts showing governing load factor equations. $T = B + L + W$, as defined in Sec. 1.12. (Courtesy of Mr. Alfred M. Parme, Portland Cement Assoc.) (a) For bending alone. (b) For combined direct stress and bending.

MATERIALS AND SPECIFICATIONS 19

For those structures in which wind loading should be considered:

$$U = 1.2B + 2.4L + 0.6W \qquad (Ia)$$

$$U = 1.2B + 0.6L + 2.4W \qquad (Ib)$$

$$U = K(B + L + W/2) \qquad (IIa)$$

$$U = K(B + L/2 + W) \qquad (IIb)$$

For those structures in which earthquake loading should be considered, substitute E for W in the preceding equations. In case there is doubt as to the importance of wind or earthquake loading, it can be tested by making a trial calculation using these equations.

The choice between these equations is much simplified by the use of the charts of Fig. 1.13. There the coordinates are in terms of L/T and B/T where $T = B + L + W$.

1.13. ADVANTAGES OF ULTIMATE STRENGTH DESIGN

The ASCE-ACI Joint Committee lists five advantages which result from ultimate strength design and the use of load factors. These can be summarized as follows:

1. Elastic or straight-line theory does not give a reliable prediction of ultimate strength, and thus leaves the actual factor of safety somewhat uncertain.

2. Ultimate strength design permits the use of a lower load factor for loads definitely known, such as dead load, and a higher load factor for less certain loadings. This gives a total factor of safety consistent with the type of loading.

3. Ultimate strength design applied to all members eliminates certain inconsistencies in the design of members carrying axial load and bending. (The straight-line stress concept for beams conflicts somewhat with the modified ultimate strength approach for axially loaded columns.)

4. A better evaluation of the critical moment-thrust ratio for members subject to combined bending and axial load is obtained by ultimate design procedure. (For example, in arches the thrust due to dead load may tend to offset the effect of moment due to live load.)

5. For prestressed concrete members, ultimate strength calculations are absolutely necessary to establish the factor of safety, since cracking of the concrete changes the relationship between loads and stresses.

Whether ultimate strength design will lead to economy in cross sections depends upon the load factors used. The load factors proposed by the

ASCE-ACI Joint Committee give added economy in beams only when higher yield strength steel is used or when compression steel would be required by straight-line procedures. In column design, somewhat smaller columns are permitted because load factors lower than the factors of safety in the main body of the ACI Code have been recommended.

1.14. LIMITATIONS ON ULTIMATE STRENGTH DESIGN

The author considers that ultimate strength design gives a better balanced design than can result from the general straight-line procedures outlined in detail in the ACI Code. But certain unsatisfactory aspects should be recognized at the start.

1. Ultimate strength procedures for shear and bond have not yet been developed. Hence this part of design has to be based on working stresses and working shears. Working stress methods for shear and bond are currently the weakest link in our design procedure by any method.

2. Design must still be based on moments and shears established by elastic analysis rather than limit design procedures. This sounds slightly contradictory, but the use of moments determined elastically from loads which have been multiplied by their load factor is on the safe side, that is, it calls for a larger member than limit design (see Appendix C) moments would require. A committee is currently investigating the possibility of adapting limit design procedures to reinforced concrete design.

3. Deflections must be given more attention; yet present deflection theory is only reasonably satisfactory for reinforced concrete.

4. More basic data on lightweight aggregate concrete is required to establish the proper constants for use in ultimate strength methods.

The following chapters develop both ultimate strength and straight-line design procedures, the former strictly in accord with the ASCE-ACI Joint Committee Report, and the latter strictly in accord with the ACI Code except where specifically noted otherwise.

1.15. CALCULATION ACCURACY

Reinforced concrete theory is not a precise theory. In view of this fact, judgment is always an important factor in the application of this theory. A distinguished engineer and the present chairman of the ACI Building Code Committee, Raymond C. Reese, introduces his *CRSI Design Handbook*[10] with these comments on the accuracy of calculations:

If the somewhat involved mathematical methods used in rigid frame analysis lead one to believe that the design of reinforced concrete structures requires a high degree of precision, the reverse is the case. Concrete is a job-made material, and control cylinders that do not vary more than 10% are remarkably good. Reinforcing bars are shop-made; yet variations in strength characteristics run 3% to 5%; rolled weights can vary $3\frac{1}{2}$%. Formwork is field-built; frequently a 2 × 8 or 2 × 10 (measuring, respectively, $7\frac{5}{8}$ in. and $9\frac{1}{2}$ in.) is used to form the soffit of an 8 in. or 10 in. beam. Bars that are held in place to an accuracy of between $\frac{1}{8}$ in. and $\frac{1}{4}$ in. are extremely well placed. Two-figure accuracy is sufficient for almost all problems in reinforced concrete design.

Concrete is weak in tension; reinforcing steel is supplied to make up that deficiency; the time and effort of the designer is best spent in recognizing and providing for such tensions wherever they may exist, not in striving for a high degree of precision by carrying figures to an unmeaning number of significant places.

On the other hand, the bulk of present computing is done on a 10-in. slide rule, reading easily to three significant figures. When numbers are subtracted, significant figures are often lost. It is, therefore, recommended, more for control of the computations, for ready checking, and to keep the computer alert, rather than for any effect on the completed structure, that figures be carried to three significant places or to the extent of a 10-in. slide rule. There is no point in computing loads to a fine determination only to lose the results in a moment computation, nor is it logical to carry moments to the suggested three significant figures when the loads were guessed to one-figure precision. For that reason, the following table is suggested as a rough guide, not as any hard and fast rule, but only to give some indication of a satisfactory procedure.

RECORD VALUES TO THE FOLLOWING PRECISION

Loads to nearest 1 psf; 10 plf; 100 lb concentration
Span lengths to about 0.01 ft ($\frac{1}{8}$ in. = 0.01 ft)
Total loads and reactions to 0.1 kip
Moments to nearest 0.1 kip-in., if readable
Individual bar areas to 0.01 in.²
Concrete sizes to $\frac{1}{2}$ in.
Bar spacings to $\frac{1}{2}$ in. (supports are crimped at 1-in. intervals)
Effective beam depth to 0.1 in.

1.16. HANDBOOKS

Since this book is written primarily as a textbook, it does not concern itself greatly with office practice and the use of design aids. Nevertheless, the student should be aware that curves and tables can speed up design considerably. Two handbooks are in wide usage.

The Reinforced Concrete Design Handbook,[11] published by ACI, has many useful tables and curves, including some valuable moment coefficient tables in its Appendix. The *CRSI Design Handbook*,[10] published by the Concrete Reinforcing Steel Institute, includes many tables of valuable data, some of which represent complete designs of typical members, such as beams, eccentrically loaded columns, and footings.

In the detailing of structures the *Manual of Standard Practice for Detailing Reinforced Concrete Structures* (ACI 315–57)[12] is most helpful as a guide to the clear presentation of the necessary details. It is a drafting rather than a design manual, although it calls attention to some important considerations in designing reinforced concrete.

SELECTED REFERENCES

1. *Concrete Manual*, U.S. Bureau of Reclamation, Denver, Colo., 6th ed., 1956.
2. ACI Committee 611, Lewis H. Tuthill, Chairman, *ACI Manual of Concrete Inspection*, ACI, Detroit, 3rd ed., 1957.
3. "Design and Control of Concrete Mixes," Portland Cement Association, Chicago, 10th ed., 1952.
4. ACI Committee 613, Walter H. Price, Chairman, "Recommended Practice for Selecting Proportions for Concrete (ACI 613–54)," *ACI Jour.*, **26**, Sept. 1954; *Proc.*, **51**, p. 49.
5. David Ramaley and Douglas McHenry, "Stress-Strain Curves for Concrete Strained Beyond Ultimate Load," *Lab. Rep. No. SP-12*, U.S. Bureau of Reclamation, Denver, Colo., 1947.
6. Eivind Hognestad, N. W. Hanson, and Douglas McHenry, "Concrete Stress Distribution in Ultimate Strength Design," *ACI Jour.*, **27**, Dec. 1955; *Proc.*, **52**, p. 455.
7. J. L. Savage, Ivan E. Houk, H. J. Gilkey, and Fredrik Vogt, *Arch Dam Investigation*, Vol. II, *Tests of Models of Arch Dams and Auxiliary Concrete Tests*, Engineering Foundation, New York, 1934.
8. "Tentative Specifications for Minimum Requirements for the Deformations of Deformed Steel Bars for Concrete Reinforcement," *ASTM Spec. A 305–53T*, ASTM, Philadelphia, 1953.
9. "Tentative Specifications for Billet-Steel Bars for Concrete Reinforcement," *ASTM Spec. A 15–54T*, ASTM, Philadelphia, 1954.
10. Raymond C. Reese, *CRSI Design Handbook*, Concrete Reinforcing Steel Institute, Chicago, 2nd ed., 1957.
11. ACI Committee 317, Thor Germundsson, Chairman, *Reinforced Concrete Design Handbook*, ACI, Detroit, 2nd ed., 1955.
12. *Manual of Standard Practice for Detailing Reinforced Concrete Structures*, ACI 315–57, ACI, Detroit, 1957.
13. ACI Committee 214, Wm. A. Cordon, Chairman, "Recommended Practice for Evaluation of Compression Test Results of Field Concrete (ACI 214–57)," *ACI Jour.*, **29**, July 1957; *Proc.*, **54**, p. 1.

14. ACI Committee 313, Clyde T. Morris, Chairman, "Effect of Plastic Flow and Volume Changes on Design," *ACI Jour.*, **8,** Nov.–Dec. 1936; *Proc.*, **33,** p. 123.
15. ACI-ASCE Committee 327, Leo H. Corning, Chairman, "Ultimate Strength Design," *ACI Jour.*, **27,** Jan. 1956; *Proc.*, **52,** p. 505.
16. "Report of ASCE-ACI Joint Committee on Ultimate Strength Design," *ASCE Proc.-Separate 809*, Oct. 1955.

"Axially" Loaded Columns

2.1. TYPES OF COLUMNS

Plain concrete is not used for columns, but may be used for pedestals in which the height does not exceed three times the least lateral dimension (Fig. 2.1*a*).

Reinforced concrete columns normally contain longitudinal steel bars and are designated by the type of lateral bracing provided for these bars. *Tied columns* (Fig. 2.1*b*) have the bars braced or tied at intervals by closed loops called ties. *Spiral columns* have the bars (and the core concrete) wrapped with a closely spaced helix or spiral of small diameter wire or rod (Fig. 2.1*c*).

Composite columns contain a steel or cast-iron structural member encased in concrete which is reinforced with both spiral and longitudinal reinforcement (Fig. 2.1*d*).

A *combination column* may be either a structural steel column encased in a concrete cover reinforced with mesh or a pipe column filled with concrete.

Tied and spiral columns are the most common forms. Either may be made circular, octagonal, square, or rectangular in cross section, as desired.

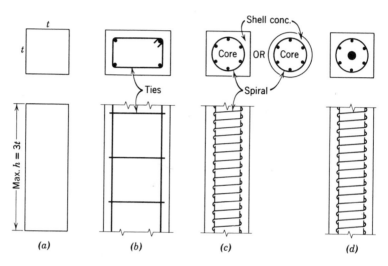

Fig. 2.1. Types of columns. (*a*) Plain concrete pedestal. (*b*) Tied column. (*c*) Spiral column. (*d*) Composite column.

2.2. COLUMN TESTS

Since about 1930, or possibly earlier, it has been evident that one could not calculate f_c, the actual unit stress on the concrete, nor f_s, the actual unit stress on the steel, in a reinforced concrete column under sustained axial load. If the materials were really elastic it would be possible to equate the unit deformations of the two materials and establish the ratio of steel stress to concrete stress as in Sec. 2.10. However, actual observations show that the steel stress is much larger than this calculation would indicate, due both to shrinkage and creep of the concrete under load.

Starting about 1930, a very large research project on columns was carried out at the University of Illinois[1] and at Lehigh University.[2] These tests indicated clearly that there was no fixed ratio of steel stress to concrete stress in the ordinary column. The ratio of these stresses depended upon the amount of shrinkage which in turn depended upon the age of the concrete and the method of curing. It also depended upon the amount of creep in the concrete. Creep is greater when the load is applied

REINFORCED CONCRETE FUNDAMENTALS

at an early stage of the hardening or curing process. The amount of creep is influenced by any of the factors which determine the quality of concrete, such as cement content, water content, curing, and even the type of aggregates used.

A load applied for only a short time, such as the ordinary live load, causes very little creep, especially after the concrete is well cured. The usual live load thus produces an increment or increase of stress in steel and concrete which can be calculated reasonably well by use of transformed area methods associated with elastic materials (Sec. 2.10). However, stresses produced by dead load or any permanent or semipermanent load depend upon the entire history of the column. It is even possible to have a loaded column with tension in the concrete and compression in the steel under very special circumstances (such as a large percentage of steel and a heavy initial loading which is later greatly reduced in amount).

Although the tests showed that actual working stresses could not be determined or estimated with any reasonable accuracy, they also showed that *ultimate* column strength did *not* vary appreciably with the history of loading. If, as loading was increased, the steel reached its elastic limit first, the increased deformation then occurring built up stress in the concrete until its ultimate strength was reached. If the concrete approached its ultimate strength before the steel reached its elastic limit, the increased deformation of the concrete near its maximum stress forced the steel stress to build up more rapidly. Thus, regardless of loading history, a column reached what might be called its yield point only when the load became equal to approximately 85% of the ultimate strength of the concrete (as measured by standard cylinder tests) plus the yield-point strength of the longitudinal steel. The 85% factor for the concrete is probably due to less ideal compaction of concrete in columns (around the steel) than in cylinders, together with the reduction in apparent strength caused by the slower application of load and the longer specimen.

Up to the column yield point, tied columns and spiral columns act almost identically and the spiral adds nothing measurable to the yield-point strength. The stress-strain curves for the tied column and the spiral column up to this point are essentially identical, similar to Fig. 2.2.

After the yield-point load is reached, a tied column immediately fails with a shearing diagonal failure of the concrete (as in a test cylinder) and a buckling failure of the column steel between ties as shown in Fig. 2.3. The yield point and ultimate strength of a tied column are thus the same thing. In the case of a spiral column, the yield-point load results in cracking or complete destruction of the shell of concrete outside the spiral (Fig. 2.4). The spiral comes into effective action only with the large increased deformation which follows yielding of the column and loss of

ultimate Load for spiral column may be higher than Yield-point

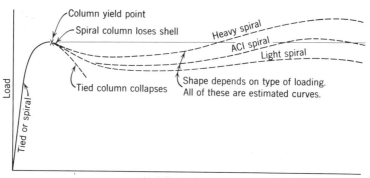

Fig. 2.2. - Comparison of strains in tied and spiral columns.

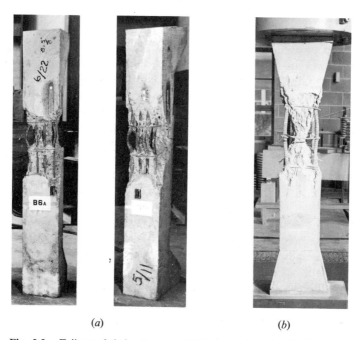

(a)   (b)

Fig. 2.3. Failure of tied columns. (a) Note the bars buckled between ties. $h/t = 7.5$. Special ends were cast to permit comparative tests with eccentric loads. (From Ref. 3, Univ. of Ill.) (b) Column in which a tie seems to have failed after yield point of column was reached. (Courtesy Portland Cement Assn.)

       REINFORCED CONCRETE FUNDAMENTALS

(a)
(b)
(c)

Fig. 2.4. Spiral column tests under concentric loads. (From Univ. of Ill. tests, Ref. 3, 4, and 5.) (*a*) Failure of 32-in. diameter column; $h/t = 6.6$. (*b*) Failure of 12-in. diameter column; $h/t = 7.3$. Shell has completely spalled off. (The special ends were cast to permit comparative tests with eccentric loads.) (*c*) Failure of column with thin cover or shell; $h/t = 10.0$.

"AXIALLY" LOADED COLUMNS   29

the shell concrete. Figure 2.4 shows spiral column failures. At this stage the spiral provides radial compressive forces on the concrete within the core of the column and these confining stresses add significantly to the load the core concrete can carry. It is interesting to note that, pound for pound, steel in the spiral has been found to be from 2.0 to 2.4 times as effective as longitudinal steel in contributing to the ultimate strength of the column. However, excessive deformations are involved (Fig. 2.2) which make this spiral steel of questionable value except as a factor of safety against complete collapse. The spiral steel never becomes significantly effective until after the destruction of the shell concrete which covers it.

A heavy spiral can add more strength to the column than that lost in the spalling or failure of the shell, in which case the column will carry an ultimate load greater than the yield-point load. However, this extra load is available only with very large deformations which are totally unsuitable in a structure. If too light a spiral is used, the column will continue to carry some load beyond the column yield point, but not as much as that which caused the spalling of the shell. The ACI Building Code specifies that amount of spiral steel which will just replace* the strength lost when the shell concrete spalls. The initial cracking of the shell gives some warning of overload prior to failure. The spiral also adds a considerable element of toughness to the column. Toughness is valuable in resisting explosion or blast since toughness measures the energy which can be absorbed before complete failure.

2.3. ULTIMATE STRENGTH OF "AXIALLY" LOADED COLUMNS

Since all concrete columns are subject to some end moment and some lateral deflection at failure, the ASCE-ACI Joint Committee recommends that no columns actually be designed for axial load alone. Instead, they recommend a minimum eccentricity of 0.10 of the column thickness for tied columns and 0.05 of the column diameter for spiral columns. Hence all columns are to be designed as eccentrically loaded. Such design is discussed in Chap. 13.

Nevertheless, the ultimate strength of an axially loaded column does have significance: (1) as the basis for the working load design formula used in the ACI Code; (2) as a limiting case in the ultimate strength analysis of eccentrically loaded columns.

---

* Actually, an estimated 10% in excess of the shell strength is used to be sure the strength after spalling is not less than before.

The tests discussed in the preceding section established the ultimate strength of either a tied or a spiral column,* "axially" loaded, as:

$$P_0 = 0.85f_c'A_c + f_yA_{st}$$
$$= 0.85f_c'(A_g - A_{st}) + f_yA_{st} \tag{2.1}$$

where P_0 = ultimate load capacity (yield-point strength) of tied or spiral column when eccentricity is zero

A_c = net area of concrete = $A_g - A_{st}$

A_g = gross area of concrete, in.^{2}

A_{st} = area of vertical column steel, in.^{2}

f_c' = standard cylinder strength of concrete, psi

f_y = yield-point stress for steel, psi.

The ASCE-ACI Joint Committee on Ultimate Strength Design[7, 8] endorses the above relationship for axially loaded short columns, that is, for length-to-depth ratios up to 15. The student will note that a majority of columns fall in this group where buckling is not a problem. The reduction in ultimate strength for larger length-to-depth ratios is discussed in Chap. 13 where ultimate strength design of columns is treated in detail.

2.4. WORKING LOAD THEORY FOR COLUMNS

The ACI Code column formula for axially loaded columns is a working *load* formula, not a working *stress* formula. The Code simply modifies the ultimate strength formula (Eq. 2.1) of Sec. 2.3, reducing the coefficients enough to provide the desired factor of safety. The actual working stresses in concrete and steel are unknown, owing to the uncertainties introduced by creep and shrinkage.

The coefficients specified in Eq. 2.2 provide a factor of safety from 2.75 to 3.60 for spiral columns, the larger value when the reinforcement is small. For tied columns, the factor of safety is made 25% larger in consideration of the sudden failure of this type of column.

For spiral columns, the allowable working load is:

$$P = 0.225f_c'A_g + f_sA_s \tag{2.2}$$
$$= A_g(0.225f_c' + f_sp_g) \tag{2.2a}$$

* More exactly, the yield-point strength of the spiral column. Under the ACI Code method of spiral design, the ultimate strength will not be significantly greater. See Ref. 6.

where P = allowable working load on spiral column

A_g = gross area of the column (for any shape)

A_s = area of vertical column steel

f_s = nominal allowable stress in vertical column reinforcement, 16,000 psi for intermediate grade steel, 20,000 for rail or hard grade steel

f_c' = standard cylinder strength of concrete

$p_g = A_s/A_g$.

The student should study Art. 1103 of the ACI Code to learn the detailed requirements which apply to such columns. Among these is a requirement that p_g be between 0.01 and 0.08, a minimum of six bars, and #5 bars as a minimum bar size.

The spiral reinforcement is specified by the formula in Art. 1103d:

$$p' = 0.45(A_g/A_c - 1)f_c'/f_s' \qquad (2.3)$$

where p' = ratio of volume of spiral reinforcement to volume of concrete core (out to out of spiral)

A_c = area of core of column

f_s' = useful limit stress of spiral reinforcement: 40,000 psi for hot rolled rods of intermediate grade; 50,000 psi for rods of hard grade; 60,000 psi for cold drawn wire.

This relation can be arranged as follows:

$$p'A_cf_s' = 0.45(A_g - A_c)f_c'$$
$$2p'A_cf_s' = 0.90f_c'(A_g - A_c)$$

Since $A_g - A_c$ is the shell area, which spalls off, the right-hand side represents the assumed ultimate strength of the shell with an increase in the coefficient from 0.85 to 0.90. The quantity $p'A_c$ represents the spiral steel reduced to equivalent longitudinal steel. This steel can develop a stress f_s' and because it is in spiral form it is roughly twice as effective as longitudinal steel. Thus the spiral is designed to replace the strength of the shell with a very slight extra allowance for safety.[6]

For tied columns, the allowable load is specified as 0.80 of that permitted by Eq. 2.2 for a spiral column:

$$P = 0.8(0.225f_c'A_g + f_sA_s) \qquad (2.4)$$
$$= A_g(0.18f_c' + 0.8f_sp_g) \qquad (2.4a)$$

The value of p_g is restricted to the range 0.01 to 0.04, with a minimum of four bars, and #5 bars as a minimum bar size. The detailed specifications

REINFORCED CONCRETE FUNDAMENTALS

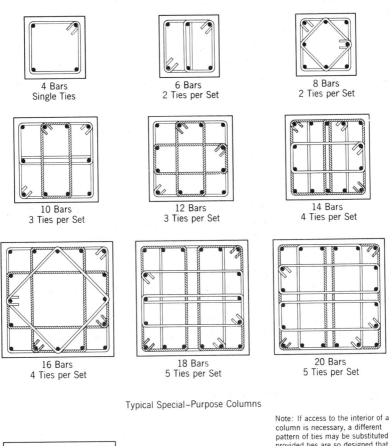

4 Bars
Single Ties

6 Bars
2 Ties per Set

8 Bars
2 Ties per Set

10 Bars
3 Ties per Set

12 Bars
3 Ties per Set

14 Bars
4 Ties per Set

16 Bars
4 Ties per Set

18 Bars
5 Ties per Set

20 Bars
5 Ties per Set

Typical Special-Purpose Columns

Note: If access to the interior of a column is necessary, a different pattern of ties may be substituted provided ties are so designed that each vertical bar is securely braced against movement in any direction

Column Steel
Arranged for
Bending and Direct Stress

Alternate Method
of Tie Arrangement
for Elongated Columns

Typical Arrangement
of Corner Columns

Fig. 2.5. Arrangement of column ties. (From Ref. 9, ACI.)

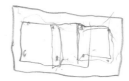

"AXIALLY" LOADED COLUMNS

33

are covered in Art. 1104. Bars must be held firmly in place by ties. The ACI *Manual of Standard Practice for Detailing Reinforced Concrete Structures* (ACI 315–57)[9] suggests the tie arrangements shown in Fig. 2.5 for various numbers of bars.

Neither of the allowable load equations includes an L/r term such as is normally used with steel columns. A large majority of reinforced concrete columns have unsupported lengths not over ten times their least dimensions, the maximum the ACI Code permits with the above formulas. This limit corresponds to an L/r of from 33 to 37. For longer columns Art. 1107 lowers the allowable load from P, as above, to a reduced value

$$P' = P(1.3 - 0.03h/t) \tag{2.5}$$

in which h is the unbraced height and t the least lateral dimension. This formula agrees satisfactorily with test results obtained at the University of Illinois,[5] being considerably on the conservative side for tied columns.

All these design formulas, although empirical, are simple in form and allow the designer wide latitude in choosing the portions of load to be assigned to steel and concrete.

It is never quite proper to design a column simply as axially loaded; Art. 1108 requires that the bending moment acting on the column be included in the design. The following examples of columns *without* eccentricity are given here only because design for an "equivalent axial load" is one of the more satisfactory approaches to the design of eccentrically loaded columns (Secs. 13.4c and 13.5d).

2.5. ALLOWABLE COLUMN LOAD EXAMPLES

For $f_c' = 3000$ psi and intermediate grade steel, find the allowable "axial" loads on these columns by the ACI Code.

(a) A 16-in. square tied column with $A_s = 4$–#11 bars, Fig. 2.6. Unsupported length = 13 ft. Ties are assumed adequate.

SOLUTION

$h/t = 13 \times 12/16 < 10$. ∴ short column.

$A_s = 4$–#11 $= 4 \times 1.56 = 6.24$ in.²

$0.01 < p = 6.24/16^2 < 0.04$. ∴ qualifies as tied column.

From Eq. 2.4 (or ACI Code Arts. 1104a and 1103a):

Allowable $P = 0.8 (0.225 f_c' A_g + f_s A_s)$

$\qquad = 0.8 (0.225 \times 3000 \times 16^2 + 16{,}000 \times 6.24)$

$\qquad = 0.8 (173{,}000 + 99{,}800) = 218{,}000$ lb $= 218$ k (*b*) A 16-in. square spiral column with $A_s = 8$-#8 bars, Fig. 2.7. Unsupported length = 20 ft. Spiral is assumed adequate.

SOLUTION

$h/t = 20 \times 12/16 = 15.$ ∴ long column.

$A_s = 8$-#8 $= 8 \times 0.79 = 6.32$ in.^{2}

$0.01 < p = 6.32/16^2 < 0.08.$ ∴ qualifies as spiral column.

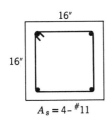

$A_s = 4$-#11

Fig. 2.6. Tied column of Sec. 2.5*a*.

$A_s = 8$-#8

Fig. 2.7. Spiral column of Sec. 2.5*b*.

From Art. 1103*a*:

$P = 0.225f_c'A_g + f_sA_s$

$= 0.225 \times 3000 \times 16^2 + 16,000 \times 6.32 = 173,000 + 101,000$

$= 274,000$ lb $= 274$ k

From Art. 1107:

Allowable $P' = P(1.3 - 0.03\,h/t)$

$= 274\,(1.3 - 0.03 \times 15) = 274 \times 0.85 = 233$ k

2.6. DESIGN OF TIED COLUMN BY ACI CODE

Design a square tied column for an "axial" load of 300 k, $f_c' = 2500$ psi, intermediate grade steel, using p about 2%. Unsupported height 10 ft.

SOLUTION

For given materials and 2% steel, from Eq. 2.4:

$P = 0.8A_g\,(0.225f_c' + f_sp_g)$

$= 0.8A_g\,(0.225 \times 2500 + 16,000 \times 0.02) = 705A_g$

Reqd. $A_g = P/705 = 300,000/705 = 425$ in.^{2} $= 20.6$ in. $\times$ 20.6 in.

Could use 20-in. square column with more than 2% steel.
Could use 21-in. square column with less than 2% steel.

USE 21-in. × 21-in. column.

$h/t = 10 \times 12/21 < 10.$ ∴ short column.

Load P $\qquad\qquad\qquad\qquad\qquad\quad$ = 300,000 lb

Value of conc. = $21^2 \times 0.225 \times 2500 \times 0.8$ = 199,000

Value for steel = $0.8 \times 16,000 A_s$ $\qquad\quad$ = 101,000 lb

Reqd. $A_s = 101,000/12,800 = 7.88$ in.^{2} $p > 0.01$ O.K.

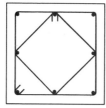 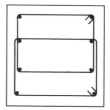

Fig. 2.8. Tied column design of Sec. 2.6.

Symmetry requires an even, rather than an odd, number of bars. Bars are placed near the outside face of column in order to be available for accidental bending moments. Specification minimum is four bars, at least #5 in size.

$\qquad$ 6–#11 = 9.36 in.^{2}

USE 8–#9 = 8.00 in.^{2}

Assume $\frac{1}{4}$-in. bars for ties. $\qquad\qquad$ (Art. 1104c)

$\qquad$ 48 tie diam. = 12 in. $\qquad$ USE $\frac{1}{4}$-in. ties at 12 in. vertically.
$\qquad$ 16 bar diam. = 18.1 in. $\qquad$ Art. 1104c requires two ties at
$\qquad$ Col. width   = 21 in. $\qquad\qquad$ each level for eight bars, as in
$\qquad\qquad\qquad\qquad\qquad\qquad\qquad\qquad$ Fig. 2.8.

2.7. DESIGN OF SPIRAL COLUMN BY ACI CODE

Design a round spiral column for an "axial" load of 300 k, $f_c' = 2500$ psi, intermediate grade steel, using p about 2%. Unsupported height 10 ft.

SOLUTION

For given materials and 2% steel, from Eq. 2.2a:

$\qquad P = A_g(0.225 \times 2500 + 16,000 \times 0.02) = 882 A_g$

$\qquad$ Reqd. $A_g = P/882 = 300,000/882 = 340$ in.$^2 = \pi t^2/4$

$\qquad$ Reqd. $t = 20.8$ in.

Could use 20-in. diam. with $p_g > 0.02$.
Could use 21-in. diam. with $p_g < 0.02$.

USE 21-in. diam. column, core $= 21 - 2 \times 1.5 = 18$-in. diam.

$h/t = 10 \times 12/21 < 10$. $\therefore$ short column.

$A_g = 0.786 \times 21^2 = 347$ in.² $A_c = 0.786 \times 18^2 = 255$ in.²

P $= 300,000$ lb

Value conc. $= 347 \times 0.225 \times 2500 = 195,000$

Value steel $= 16,000 A_s$ $= 105,000$ lb

Reqd. $A_s = 6.56$ in.² $p > 0.01$ O.K.

Either even or odd number of bars may be used, but minimum is six bars, of #5 size.

6-#10 $= 7.62$ in.²

USE 7-#9 $= 7.00$

9-#8 $= 7.11$

The #10 bars would give fewer bars to handle but slightly more area and slightly longer splices.

Bars are normally spliced just above floor level, with a splice or stub bar in contact and alongside each column bar. Between each such pair the spacing rule of Art. 1103b applies, namely, a clear space of 1.5 in. or 1.5 times the maximum aggregate size. If a $\frac{1}{2}$-in. spiral rod is used, the main steel will lie on a circle of $18 - 2 \times 0.5 - 1.13 = 15.87$-in. diam. with a spacing of $\pi \times 15.87/7 = 7.11$ in. on centers. This compares to a minimum permissible of $2 \times 1.13 + 1.5 = 3.76$ in., assuming 1-in. aggregate or less and the splice bars in contact by the side of the main steel.

The spiral steel according to Art. 1103d must provide, for intermediate grade steel,

$$p' = 0.45 \left(\frac{A_g}{A_c} - 1\right) \frac{f_c'}{f_s'} = 0.45 \left(\frac{347}{255} - 1\right) \frac{2,500}{40,000} = 0.0101$$

By definition, $p' = $ (vol. of spiral in one round) $\div$ (vol. of core in height b), where b is the pitch as shown in Fig. 2.9. The pitch b is small enough for the

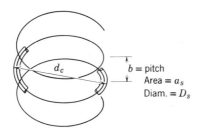

Fig. 2.9. Spiral notation.

volume of one round of the spiral to be taken as $a_s\pi(d_c - D_s)$. The volume of the core in height b is $b\pi d_c^2/4$.

$$p' = a_s\pi(d_c - D_s) \div (b\pi d_c^2/4) = 4a_s(d_c - D_s) \div (bd_c^2)$$

(Many designers ignore the difference between $d_c - D_s$ and d_c, and use $p' = 4a_s \div bd_c$.) It is recommended that the size of spiral wire be assumed and b then be calculated, since the wire will usually be $\frac{1}{4}$ in., $\frac{3}{8}$ in., $\frac{1}{2}$ in., or occasionally $\frac{5}{8}$ in., a rather narrow range of values. The spacing b can be specified as closely as desired, usually to quarter inches.

Try $\frac{1}{2}$-in. round spiral rod, $a_s = 0.20$ in.^{2}

$$p' = 0.0101 = 4 \times 0.20(18 - 0.5) \div (b \times 18^2)$$
$$b = 4.30 \text{ in. } (3.80 \text{ in. clear})$$

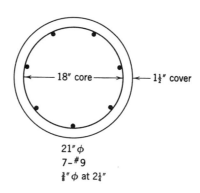

18″ core — 1½″ cover

21″ φ
7-#9
¾″ φ at 2¼″

Fig. 2.10. Spiral column design of Sec. 2.7.

Specification maximums: $\frac{1}{6}$ of 18 = 3.00 in. on center
3 in. clear spacing
Specification minimums: $1\frac{3}{8}$ in. clear
1.5 max. aggregate size, clear

It would be uneconomical to use the $\frac{1}{2}$-in. round at 3.00 in. on center.
Try $\frac{3}{8}$-in. round, $a_s = 0.11$ in.^{2}

$$p' = 0.0101 = 4 \times 0.11(18 - 0.38) \div (b \times 18^2)$$
$$b = 2.37 \text{ in.}$$

USE $\frac{3}{8}$-in. round at $2\frac{1}{4}$ in.
The design would be as shown in Fig. 2.10.

2.8. ECONOMY

Economy in column design favors the use of higher strength concrete on well-controlled jobs, since extra concrete strength costs only slightly

REINFORCED CONCRETE FUNDAMENTALS

more than low strength. Concrete will generally be cheaper than steel. Hard grade or rail steel is cheaper than intermediate grade because of its higher f_s value. Tied columns will generally be cheaper than spiral columns, particularly if square columns are needed rather than round. However, the cost of the column can rarely be considered alone. Spiral columns and heavy steel save floor space which has an annual rental value. Form costs are also a major item and beam forms can be reused from floor to floor most simply if column sizes are kept constant. Hence it is quite common practice to keep the column size constant over several stories and take care of increasing load with increasing steel, stronger concrete, or the use of spiral steel.

2.9. REDUCTION IN COLUMN LIVE LOADS

Building codes specify uniform live loads large enough to represent ordinary local concentrations of loading. Over larger areas the probability that this same load intensity will exist everywhere is reduced. Codes usually permit some reduction in the assumed live load on floor areas in excess of 100 to 150 sq ft. Many codes permit such reductions only in cases where the live load is 100 psf or less; heavier loads imply storage or machinery loads which are easily concentrated over large areas.

The live load on columns may also be reduced under the same reasoning. The reductions permitted vary considerably in the different codes and it will be necessary for the designer to consult the particular code which governs his design. The magnitude of the reduction depends both upon the occupancy, or size of the unit live load, and upon the number of floors carried by the column; it may vary from none to as much as 60% of the total live load.

2.10. LIVE LOAD STRESSES AND TRANSFORMED AREA

Although stresses in columns due to long-time loads can scarcely be calculated, the changes in these stresses due to short-time loads can be determined by elastic procedures. The simplest process uses the transformed area concept.

For short-time live loads, Hooke's law holds both for steel and concrete, that is, both materials may be considered elastic with unit stresses proportional to unit strains. Consider a concrete column (Fig. 2.11) reinforced with steel and carrying a compression live load P which causes it to shorten uniformly with a unit deformation ϵ.

Let A_g = gross area of concrete = t^2

A_s = steel area

A_c = net area of concrete = $A_g - A_s$

f_c = unit stress on concrete due to load P

f_s = unit stress on steel due to load P

E_c = modulus of elasticity of concrete

E_s = modulus of elasticity of steel

$n = E_s/E_c$ = modular ratio.

$$P = A_c f_c + A_s f_s \qquad \epsilon = f_s/E_s = f_c/E_c \qquad f_s = (E_s/E_c)f_c = nf_c$$

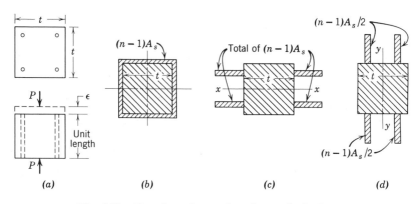

Fig. 2.11. Transformed area of a column, elastic theory.

Substituting this value of f_s in the equation for P,

$$P = A_c f_c + A_s(nf_c) = f_c(A_c + nA_s)$$

The last term of this equation associates n with the steel area instead of with the steel stress. It shows that the steel area A_s acts identically as would a concrete area nA_s. This concrete area is called the transformed area of the steel. When the steel is thus replaced by its transformed area, the result is a total area of homogeneous material, in this case concrete, which is relatively easy to analyze for stress or deformation. For the compressive area shown in Fig. 2.11a, a more usable form results when A_c is replaced by its equivalent, $A_g - A_s$. Then

$$P = f_c(A_c + nA_s) = f_c(A_g - A_s + nA_s) = f_c[A_g + (n - 1)A_s]$$

This indicates that, although the transformed area of the steel is nA_s, the *effective* transformed area is only $(n - 1)A_s$, because the steel itself

REINFORCED CONCRETE FUNDAMENTALS

displaces useful concrete (A_s square inches) which would have carried some load. Similarly, $f_s = nf_c$, but since the steel displaces concrete that would carry a stress f_c, the gain in strength due to A_s is measured by the *effective* $f_s'' = nf_c - f_c = (n - 1)f_c$.

It should be noted that the transformed area of the column steel in Fig. 2.11a may be sketched as shown in Fig. 2.11b, c, or d, at any point around the cross section of the column provided symmetry is maintained. This is true only because the unit deformation ϵ is everywhere the same. The same freedom does not exist with an eccentrically loaded column or a beam where ϵ is not uniform. The ϵ of the transformed area must correspond to that of the concrete adjacent to the steel. The transformed area of a beam is discussed in Sec. 4.1.

Although the use of transformed area as above should be limited to changes in stresses caused by short-time live loads, it has been suggested[10] that the effect of long-time loads such as dead load might be approximated by using some multiple of n such as $3n$ or $4n$. The Code in Arts. 706b and 1109d suggests the use of $2n$ on compression steel, this to be used with combined dead and live load.*

2.11. OTHER COLUMN FORMULAS

Although the ACI Code formulas for columns are widely used, there are also other strength relations in use. For example, the 1953 AASHO *Standard Specifications for Highway Bridges*[11] specifies the following unit stresses to be applied on the gross concrete area:

Tied column: $f_c = 0.25f_c'[1 + (n - 1)p]$

Spiral column: $f_c = (0.25 + 12p')f_c'[1 + (n - 1)p]$

where p' is the per cent of spiral steel based on the volume of the core and p is the per cent of longitudinal steel based on gross column area. The new seventh edition expected in 1958 will use the ACI Code formulas essentially as given earlier in this chapter.

2.12. DESIGN TABLES

The simple form of the column formula makes it easy to show in a single table the "axial" load capacity of the concrete for tied (or spiral) columns of most practical sizes for the common values of f_c'; also the load capacity

* The Code might be more consistent if $2n$ were also used in the calculation of f_b in Arts. 1109a and 1100, but the present intention of the Code is to calculate this stress from a transformed area where steel is replaced by an $(n - 1)A_s$ area of concrete.

of the minimum steel and maximum steel for each column. A separate table can show the load value of different numbers or combinations of bars. In Appendix E two such tables are reproduced from the ACI *Reinforced Concrete Design Handbook.* Table E.1 shows the data for tied columns and Table E.2 for spiral columns. With such tables, design becomes simply the choice of a concrete load capacity and a steel load capacity which together are adequate for the given load.

For example, consider the selection of a square tied column of 3000 psi concrete and intermediate grade steel to carry an "axial" load of 400 k. Article 1103a fixes the steel stress at 16,000 psi. Table E.1 indicates that a 20-in. by 20-in. column with maximum steel has a capacity of 216 k on the concrete plus 205 k on the steel to give a total possible of 421 k. Also possible with less steel are columns 22 in. square and 24 in. square. If one chooses the 24-in. square column, the value of the concrete is 311 k, leaving $400 - 311 = 89$ k for the steel. This is satisfactory since it is more than the minimum, which is listed as 74 k, based on $p = 0.01$. In the lower left part of Table E.1, it is noted that the 89 k can be provided by 6–#10 bars (98 k), 8–#9 (102 k), 10–#8 (101 k), or 12–#7 (92 k).

Attention is again called to the requirement that columns be designed for moment as well as for axial load. The above designs are correct only if the axial load has been increased to represent the equivalent axial load discussed in Sec. 13.4c or Sec. 13.5d.

SELECTED REFERENCES

1. F. E. Richart and G. C. Staehle, "Column Tests at University of Illinois," *ACI Jour.*, **2**, Feb., Mar. 1931; *Proc.*, **27**, pp. 731, 761; *Jour.*, **3**, Nov. 1931, Jan. 1932; *Proc.*, **28**, pp. 167, 279.
2. W. A. Slater and Lyse, "Column Tests at Lehigh University," *ACI Jour.*, **2**, Feb., Mar. 1931; *Proc.*, **27**, pp. 677, 791; *Jour.*, **3**, Nov. 1931, Jan., 1932; *Proc.* **28**, pp. 159, 317.
3. Eivind Hognestad, "A Study of Combined Bending and Axial Load in Reinforced Concrete Members," Univ. of Ill. Eng. Exp. Sta. *Bull. No. 399,* 1951.
4. Frank E. Richart and Rex L. Brown, "An Investigation of Reinforced Concrete Columns," Univ. of Ill. Eng. Exp. Sta. *Bull. No. 267,* 1934.
5. Frank E. Richart, Jasper O. Draffin, Tilford A. Olson, and Richard H. Heitman, "The Effect of Eccentric Loading, Protective Shells, Slenderness Ratios, and Other Variables in Reinforced Concrete Columns," Univ. of Ill. Eng. Exp. Sta. *Bull. No. 368,* 1947.
6. ACI Committee 105, F. E. Richart, Chairman, "Reinforced Concrete Column Investigation, Tentative Final Report," *ACI Jour.*, **4**, Feb. 1933; *Proc.*, **29**, p. 275.
7. "Report of ASCE-ACI Joint Committee on Ultimate Strength Design," *ASCE Proc.-Separate 809*, Oct. 1955.

8. ACI-ASCE Committee 327, Leo H. Corning, Chairman, "Ultimate Strength Design," *ACI Jour.*, **27**, Jan. 1956; *Proc.*, **52**, p. 505.
9. ACI Committee 315, Raymond C. Reese, Chairman, *Manual of Standard Practice for Detailing Reinforced Concrete Structures, ACI 315–57*, ACI, Detroit, 1957.
10. ACI Committee 313, Clyde T. Morris, Chairman, "Effect of Plastic Flow and Volume Change on Design," *ACI Jour.*, **8**, Nov.–Dec., 1936; *Proc.*, **33**, p. 123.
11. *Standard Specifications for Highway Bridges*, AASHO, Washington, 6th ed., 1953.

PROBLEMS

Prob. 2.1.

(a) If a spiral and a tied column of the same areas and materials have equal yield strengths, why does the ACI Code permit more load on the spiral column?

(b) Explain why, when live load stresses in a column can be found by use of the transformed area, the same procedure is not permissible for dead load stresses.

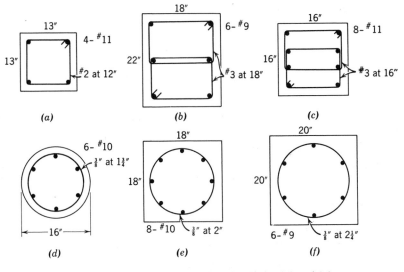

Fig. 2.12. Column cross sections for Probs. 2.2 and 2.3.

Prob. 2.2. Calculate the allowable "axial" loads on the columns of Fig. 2.12. Verify that ties or spirals are adequate and consider h/t ratios that exist as well as limiting percentages of steel. All columns have 1.5-in. clear cover.

(a) Column of Fig. 2.12a has $f_c' = 3000$ psi, rail steel, $h = 10$ ft.
(b) Column of Fig. 2.12b has $f_c' = 3750$ psi, intermediate grade steel, $h = 11$ ft.
(c) Column of Fig. 2.12c has $f_c' = 3000$ psi, intermediate grade steel, $h = 14$ ft.

(*d*) Column of Fig. 2.12*d* with $f_c' = 3000$ psi, intermediate grade steel for bars and spiral, $h = 12$ ft.

(*e*) Column of Fig. 2.12*e* with $f_c' = 3750$ psi, hard grade steel bars, cold drawn spiral, $h = 12$ ft.

(*f*) Column of Fig. 2.12*f* with $f_c' = 3750$ psi, intermediate grade steel bars, cold drawn spiral, $h = 10$ ft.

Prob. 2.3. Calculate the ultimate "axial" load capacity of the columns of Prob. 2.2. Establish the factor of safety in each case as the ratio of ultimate to allowable load.

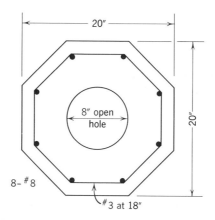

Fig. 2.13. Pile cross section for Prob. 2.4.

Prob. 2.4. Find the allowable "axial" load on the regular octagonal pile of Fig. 2.13 if $f_c' = 4000$ psi and intermediate grade steel is used. What unsupported length can be used without reduction in this load?

Prob. 2.5. Design "axially" loaded square tied columns for the conditions stated, sketch each cross section, and specify ties. Use a column size in full inches.

(*a*) $P = 400$ k, $f_c' = 3000$ psi, intermediate grade steel, p approximately 0.03, $h = 12$ ft.

(*b*) $P = 400$ k, $f_c' = 3750$ psi, rail steel, p approximately 0.03, $h = 12$ ft.

(*c*) $P = 250$ k, $f_c' = 3000$ psi, hard grade steel, p approximately 0.015, $h = 12$ ft.

Prob. 2.6. Design "axially" loaded spiral columns for the conditions stated. Sketch cross sections and specify spirals. Sizes should be specified in full inches.

(*a*) Circular column, $P = 400$ k, $f_c' = 3000$ psi, intermediate grade steel for bars and spiral, p approximately 0.03, $h = 12$ ft.

. (*b*) Square column, $P = 400$ k, $f_c' = 3750$ psi, rail steel for bars, cold drawn wire for spiral, p approximately 0.03, $h = 12$ ft.

(*c*) Circular column, $P = 500$ k, $f_c' = 3750$ psi, hard grade steel and cold drawn spiral, p approximately 0.015, $h = 15$ ft.

Prob. 2.7. Redesign the column of Prob. 2.6*b* for $h = 22$ ft.

Ultimate Strength Theory For Beams

3.1. THE RESISTING COUPLE IN A BEAM

Statics shows that an external bending moment on any beam must be resisted by internal stresses which can be indicated as a resultant tension T and a resultant compression C. Unless there is axial load, summation of horizontal forces (Fig. 3.1) indicates that T must equal C and that together they form a couple. In a reinforced concrete beam the reinforcing steel is assumed to carry all the tension T (Sec. 1.4) and thus T is located at the level of the steel. The compressive force C is the resultant of compression stresses over some depth of beam and thus its location is not established from statics alone. Let the arm or distance between these T and C forces be designated as jd, as shown in Fig. 3.1. (This is standard reinforced concrete notation, where d is the depth of beam to center of steel and j is a constant, less than unity; j and d will not be considered separately at this time.) The depth below the steel is useful chiefly to fireproof the steel and protect it from moisture; it does not influence these calculations. Further information is required to evaluate j or jd.

The resisting couple idea can be applied to homogeneous beams. It is simpler for rectangular beams with straight-line distribution of stresses than is the use of $f = Mc/I$. For steel I-beams it is more awkward, but is useful for rough estimates based on neglect of the web area. For reinforced concrete beams it has definite advantages, whether straight-line distribution of stresses or ultimate strength is under consideration.

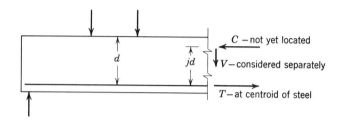

Fig. 3.1. Internal resisting couple in a beam.

3.2. DISTRIBUTION OF COMPRESSIVE STRESS

In reinforced concrete beams the compressive stress varies from zero at the neutral axis to a maximum at or near the extreme fiber. How it actually varies and where the neutral axis actually lies depend both upon the amount of the load and upon the history of past loadings. This variation is the result of several factors: (1) The spacing and depth of tension cracks depend upon whether the beam has been loaded before, and how heavily. (2) Shrinkage stresses and creep of concrete are important factors in relation to stress distribution, factors very difficult to include in an analysis. (3) Most important, the stress-strain curve for concrete as indicated in Figs. 3.2 and 1.8 is not a straight line.

The curve of Fig. 3.2 indicates that the compressive stress distribution on the first application of loading (without any shrinkage) would go through several stages and the neutral axis would shift location with the stress pattern. For heavy reinforcement, and neglecting the tension in the concrete, these stages are shown in Fig. 3.3.

Because of these complications, it probably is not feasible (and it may not even be possible) to do more than estimate rather crudely the approximate magnitude of real stresses under working loads. Certainly these depend upon shrinkage and upon how much cracking has been induced by previous loadings. Although present-day specifications emphasize stresses at working loads, laboratory tests of reinforced concrete beams show that actual deformations and stresses at working loads only faintly resemble values conventionally calculated on the basis of straight-line stresses (Fig. 3.3*a*). These working stress calculations are not representative of the real action of reinforced concrete beams under working loads; nor do they attempt to be representative of ultimate load conditions. They are entirely artificial and have been developed with allowable unit stresses empirically adjusted to give safe results.

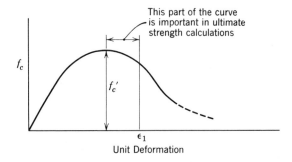

Fig. 3.2. Stress-strain curve for concrete of medium strength.

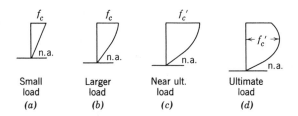

Fig. 3.3. Shifting stress pattern with increasing moment up to failure in compression. (Tension in concrete below neutral axis has been neglected.)

Fortunately, the *ultimate* strength of reinforced concrete beams can be predicted or calculated with quite satisfactory accuracy. Design on the basis of ultimate strength, as an alternate procedure, was authorized by the ACI Building Code in 1956 (Art. 601*b*). Such design is based upon the way beams actually fail under overload.

ULTIMATE STRENGTH THEORY FOR BEAMS   47

3.3. TENSION AND COMPRESSION FAILURES DUE TO BENDING MOMENT

Beams may fail from moment due to weakness in the tension steel or weakness in the compression concrete. Failure due to stresses primarily related to shear will be considered later and separately, as in the case of steel construction, since it is only in very deep and relatively short beams that these influence bending strength.

Most beams are weaker in their reinforcing steel than in their compression concrete. Such beams fail under a load slightly larger than that making $T = f_y A_s$, where f_y is the yield-point strength of the steel and A_s is the area of the steel. Since $f_y A_s$ normally represents the entire usable strength of steel, the further increase in moment resistance needs explanation. When the steel first reaches its yield point, the compressive stress distribution may be like that previously illustrated in Fig. 3.3b or c. A slight additional load causes the steel to stretch a considerable amount. The increasing steel deformation in turn causes the neutral axis to rise (when the tension is on the bottom) and the center of compression C therefore moves upward. This increase in the jd arm between C and T gives an increased resisting moment Tjd even though T is essentially unchanged. The rising of the neutral axis also reduces the area under compression and thereby increases the unit compressive stress required to develop the nearly constant value of C. This process continues until the reduced area fails in compression, as a secondary effect. These changes (neglecting any tension in the concrete) are summarized in Fig. 3.4a. This type of failure (inverted because in a negative moment region) is shown in Fig. 3.4b.

Such an underreinforced beam shows greatly increased deflection after the steel reaches the yield point, giving adequate warning of approaching beam failure; the steel, being ductile, will not actually pull apart even at failure of the beam. The increase in jd will rarely be more than a few per cent, say 3% to 5%. If the concrete stress is very high before the steel stress f_s reaches the yield-point value of f_y, the increase in jd may be very small.

If the concrete reaches its full compressive strength just as the steel reaches its yield-point stress, the beam is said to be a balanced beam at failure. A beam thus balanced requires much more steel than the usual working stress specifications would indicate; and this amount of steel is rarely economical.

Before a beam fails from weakness in compression, the top elements of the beam shorten considerably under the final increments of load, causing

REINFORCED CONCRETE FUNDAMENTALS

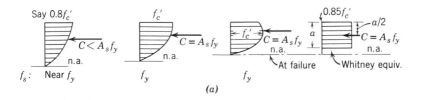

f_s: Near f_y f_y f_y

(a)

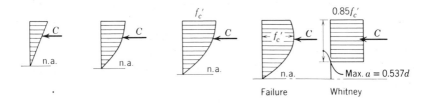

(b)

Fig. 3.4. Flexural failure in tension. (a) Variation in compressive stresses as beam approaches failure in tension. (b) Beam after failure under negative moment (tension on top).

the neutral axis to move lower down in the beam. Such movement of the neutral axis increases the area of concrete carrying compression and importantly increases the total C that can be carried. The greatly increased C is offset slightly by a reduced arm jd. The concrete finally fails in compression, and the steel stress remains below the yield point unless the beam is exactly balanced. These stress changes, again ignoring any tension in the concrete, are summarized in Fig. 3.5. Such a beam is called an overreinforced beam.

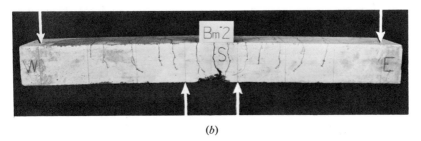

Failure   Whitney

Fig. 3.5. Variation in compressive stresses as beam approaches failure in compression.

ULTIMATE STRENGTH THEORY FOR BEAMS   49

3.4. WHITNEY'S ULTIMATE STRENGTH ANALYSIS— RECTANGULAR BEAMS

For concrete having $f_c' = 3000$ psi or more, Charles S. Whitney[1] has empirically established that the ultimate strength of rectangular *balanced* beams is, closely enough,

$$M_{\text{ult.}} = 0.333 f_c' b d^2$$

where b is the width of beam and d is the depth to center of steel. However, the steel required for such a balanced beam appears to be considerably more than is economical at the present time. A larger beam with less steel will carry the same moment and be cheaper.

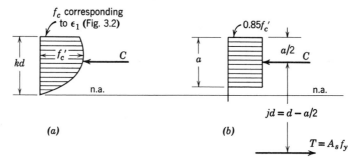

Fig. 3.6. The Whitney compressive stress block.

Beams with less reinforcement than required for a balanced section, that is, underreinforced beams, he analyzes as follows. Such beams as discussed above, will fail finally in compression after the neutral axis rises as a result of the stretching of the steel. Since $T = C$, the ultimate moment is reached when the compressive area has been reduced to where it can just support a C equal to $A_s f_y$, where A_s is the area of the steel and f_y is its yield-point stress. For a rectangular beam this means that the beam fails when the extreme fiber deformation reaches some critical value, such as that represented by ϵ_1 on the stress-strain curve of Fig. 3.2, which corresponds to the stresses shown in Fig. 3.6a. Whitney's simplification is to replace this distribution of compressive stress, for calculation purposes, by an equivalent block of uniform stress, of intensity $0.85f_c'$ and height a (Fig. 3.6b), which is supposed to give the same location of the resultant C. Since $C = T$:

$$0.85 f_c' a b = A_s f_y$$

$$a = \frac{A_s f_y}{0.85 f_c' b} = \frac{p f_y d}{0.85 f_c'}$$

REINFORCED CONCRETE FUNDAMENTALS

where $p = A_s/bd$. The arm between C and T is $d - a/2$. Hence

$$M_u = Tjd = A_s f_y(d - a/2)$$

where M_u is the ultimate resisting moment and the value of a is found from the relation above.

Whitney assumes that beams having steel greater than required for a balanced beam, that is, overreinforced beams, are unable to develop the yield point of the excess steel and hence give only the balanced beam strength:

$$M = 0.333f_c'bd^2$$

Whitney established this value of balanced M by first determining an empirical value of the depth of stress block a accompanying the compression failure, $a = 0.537d$ as diagrammed in Figs. 3.5 and 3.7a. This led to

$$jd = d - 0.537d/2 = 0.732d, \qquad C = 0.85f_c'b \times 0.537d$$

$$M = Cjd = (0.85f_c'b \times 0.537d)0.732d = 0.333f_c'bd^2$$

$$p = A_s/bd = C/(f_y bd) = (0.85f_c'b \times 0.537d) \div (f_y bd) = 0.456f_c'/f_y$$

3.5. ASCE-ACI JOINT COMMITTEE RECOMMENDATIONS

The next ACI Code will probably include more specific recommendations for ultimate strength design of beams. The 1956 Code permits ultimate strength design as an alternate and in the Code Appendix summarizes the Report of the ASCE-ACI Joint Committee on Ultimate Strength Design[2, 3] already briefly discussed in Sec. 1.11. It assumes the use for design of bending moments calculated as though all members were elastic. This Report is the current best authority for ultimate strength design. It permits the use of any assumed stress block in compression that predicts ultimate strengths reasonably in agreement with tests. The rectangular stress block used in the Whitney method satisfies this requirement and is the one selected for presentation in this text. However, the Report defines f_c' more rigorously (Sec. 1.2) and imposes two limitations not included in the original Whitney proposals.

First, the maximum yield-point stress f_y to be used in calculating ultimate strength shall not exceed 60,000 psi. The intent seems to be to limit tension crack size at working loads. Second, the maximum steel percentage is limited to $p = 0.40f_c'/f_y$, with the 0.40 coefficient to be reduced by 0.025 for each added 1000 psi concrete strength in excess of 5000 psi.

Since Whitney's balanced design requires $p = 0.456f_c'/f_y$, the somewhat lower Report limit will avoid the sudden compression type of failure and cause all moment failures to be initiated by yielding of the steel. The reduced p limits the maximum depth of stress block to $(0.400/0.456) \times 0.537d = 0.471d$, as sketched in Fig. 3.7b. However, it should be noted that the difference between the 0.40 limit and the 0.456 balanced coefficient is not large; a compression failure could result if the actual f_c' should fall as much as 13% lower than expected or if the actual f_y were as much as 15% larger than assumed. As an example of the latter case, a 70,000-psi yield strength steel might be used at the maximum permissible f_y value of 60,000 psi.

The reason for the gradual reduction in the 0.40 coefficient for p with f_c' above 5000 psi lies in the more triangular or less curved nature of the stress-strain curve for these higher strength concretes (Fig. 1.7a).

Under these provisions all beam design is on the basis of tension failure.

The Report gives the ultimate moment formula for rectangular beams in two forms, each exactly equivalent to the Whitney tension failure equation given in Sec. 3.4:

$$M_u = A_s f_y d \left(1 - \frac{0.59 p f_y}{f_c'} \right)$$

$$M_u = f_c' b d^2 q (1 - 0.59q)$$

in which $q = p f_y / f_c'$, with a maximum value of $q = 0.40$.

When the maximum p or q is used in this equation, it becomes

Max. $M_u = f_c' b d^2 \times 0.40(1 - 0.59 \times 0.40) = 0.306 f_c' b d^2$

which is slightly below the Whitney balanced section moment value of $0.333 f_c' b d^2$. The corresponding depth of stress block a is $0.40(f_c'/f_y) b d f_y \div (0.85 f_c' b) = 0.471d$, as established above and shown in Fig. 3.7b.

The Report states that "attention should be given to the deflection of members, including the effect of creep, especially whenever the net ratio of reinforcement which is defined as $(p - p')$ or $(p_w - p_f)$ in any flexural member exceeds $0.18 f_c'/f_y$." Without here defining each of these steel ratios, it can be stated that this simply calls attention to the increased deflections that will result when beams are made smaller than those designed under current working stress methods.*

When $p = 0.18 f_c'/f_y$ or $q = 0.18$ is substituted in the Report formula, the equation becomes

$$M_u = f_c' b d^2 \times 0.18(1 - 0.59 \times 0.18) = 0.161 f_c' b d^2$$

or slightly more than half of the maximum moment $0.306 f_c' b d^2$. The lower moment corresponds to a depth of stress block

$$a = (0.18/0.40)0.471d = 0.212d$$

* The straight-line method under the ACI Code, with $f_c' = 3000$ psi and intermediate grade steel, leads to $p = 0.181 f_c'/f_y$ for a balanced rectangular beam.

as shown in Fig. 3.7c. These criteria are helpful in warning about the need for special attention to deflections. This must not be interpreted to mean that deflections are necessarily unimportant when members are designed with less steel. Long span slabs, cantilever construction, and shallow members, under any design procedure, require consideration of deflection. The Report simply says that deflections become a larger problem when p exceeds $0.18 f_c'/f_y$.

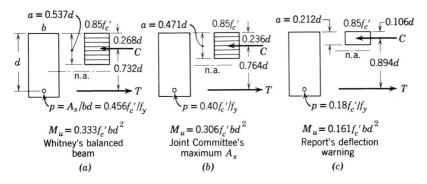

Fig. 3.7. Critical reinforcing in rectangular beams.

The corresponding requirements for beams with compression steel and for T-beams will be discussed in Secs. 3.7 and 3.9.

3.6. RECTANGULAR BEAM EXAMPLES

(a) A rectangular beam has $b = 11$ in., $d = 20$ in., $A_s = 3$-#8, $f_c' = 3000$ psi, $f_y = 40,000$ psi. Calculate the ultimate moment capacity.

SOLUTION

Ultimate $T = A_s f_y = 3 \times 0.79 \times 40,000 = 95,000$ lb $= C$

$95,000 = 0.85 f_c' ba = 0.85 \times 3000 \times 11a$

$a = 3.38$ in. $<$ maximum of $0.471d = 9.42$ in.   O.K.

$jd = d - a/2 = 20 - 3.38/2 = 18.31$ in.

$M_u = Tjd = 95,000 \times 18.31/12,000 = 145$ k-ft

The fact that tension controls this ultimate could have been established by two other methods: (1) by showing that $p < 0.40 f_c'/f_y$; (2) by showing that

$M_u < 0.306f_c'bd^2$. Since $a < 0.212d = 4.24$ in., deflections are probably no problem.

(b) If in (a) the steel is changed to 5-#11, calculate the ultimate moment capacity and corresponding f_s.

SOLUTION

$\quad$ Ultimate $T = A_s f_y = 5 \times 1.56 \times 40,000 = 312,000$ lb $= C$

$\quad$ $312,000 = 0.85 \times 3000 \times 11a$

$\quad\quad a = 11.1$ in. $> 0.471 \times 20 = 9.42$ in. $\quad$ N.G.

This calculation is not acceptable because a and A_s exceed the Report maximum shown in Fig. 3.7b. M_u could be calculated from C based on the maximum a of 9.42 in., but the limiting ultimate moment expression is more direct.

$\quad$ $M_u = 0.306f_c'bd^2 = 0.306 \times 3000 \times 11 \times 20^2/12,000 = 337$ k-ft

$\quad$ $jd = d - a/2 = 20 - 9.42/2 = 15.29$ in.

$\quad$ At M_u, $f_s = M_u/(A_s jd) = 337,000 \times 12/(5 \times 1.56 \times 15.29) = 33,900$ psi

Deflections may be large since $p > 0.18f_c'/f_y$.

(c) How much steel can be effectively used in the beam of (a)? What is M_u for this case?

SOLUTION

By Whitney theory the balanced $a = 0.537d = 10.74$ in., but the Report does not permit the use of a balanced section. The maximum permissible p is $0.40f_c'/f_y$.

$\quad$ $A_s = pbd = 0.40 \times 3000 \times 11 \times 20/40,000 = 6.60$ in.^{2}

$\quad$ $M_u = 0.306f_c'bd^2 = 0.306 \times 3000 \times 11 \times 20^2/12,000 = 337$ k-ft

As an alternate, maximum $a = 0.471d = 9.42$ in.

$\quad$ $C = 0.85 \times 3000 \times 11 \times 9.42 = 264,000$ lb

$\quad$ $A_s = T/f_y = C/f_y = 264,000/40,000 = 6.60$ in.^{2}

$\quad$ $M_u = Cjd = 264(20 - 9.42/2)/12,000 = 337$ k-ft

Deflection should be investigated.

(d) Design a rectangular beam for minimum depth and a working moment of 100 k-ft, using $b = 11$ in., $f_c' = 3000$ psi, $f_y = 40,000$ psi, and a load factor of 2.

SOLUTION

$\quad$ $M_u = $ (working moment)(load factor) $= 100 \times 2 = 200$ k-ft

$\quad$ $M_u = 0.306f_c'bd^2$

$\quad$ $200,000 \times 12 = 0.306 \times 3000bd^2$, $\quad$ reqd. $bd^2 = 2620$ in.^{3}

$\quad$ If $b = 11$ in., reqd. $d = 15.40$ in., $a = 0.471 \times 15.40 = 7.25$ in.

$\quad$ $40,000 A_s = C = 0.85 \times 3000 \times 11 \times 7.25$

$\quad$ Reqd. $A_s = 5.09$ in.^{2}, $b = 11$ in., $d = 15.40$ in. (theoretical size)

Alternate solution:
$$jd = 15.40 - 7.25/2 = 11.78 \text{ in.}$$
$$T = M/jd = 200 \times 12/11.78 = 204 \text{ k}$$
$$A_s = T/f_y = 204/40 = 5.08 \text{ in.}^2$$

(e) If the beam of (d) is used with $b = 11$ in., $d = 16$ in., find the required A_s.

SOLUTION

$$T = 40,000A_s = C = 0.85f_c'ba = 0.85 \times 3000 \times 11a$$
$$a = 1.426A_s$$
$$M_u = 200,000 \times 12 = T(d - a/2) = 40,000A_s(16 - 1.426A_s/2)$$
$$2,400,000 = 640,000A_s - 28,500A_s^2$$
$$A_s^2 - 22.44A_s + 11.22^2 = -84.3 + 11.22^2 = 41.6$$
$$A_s = \pm 6.44 + 11.22 = 4.78 \text{ in.}^2 \text{ (or } 17.66 \text{ in.}^2)$$

USE $A_s = 4.78 \text{ in.}^2$

Check:
$$a = 1.426A_s = 6.82 \text{ in.}, \quad jd = 16 - 6.82/2 = 12.59 \text{ in.}$$
$$M = A_s f_y jd = 4.78 \times 40,000 \times 12.59/12,000 = 200.5 \text{ k-ft} \quad \text{say O.K.}$$

An alternate solution for A_s by successive approximations would probably be preferred by the experienced designer, as follows:

Try $a = 6$ in., $d - a/2 = 16 - 3 = 13$ in.

Approx. $A_s = T/f_y = M/13f_y = 200,000 \times 12/(13 \times 40,000) = 4.62 \text{ in.}^2$
$$a = 1.426A_s = 1.426 \times 4.62 = 6.57 \text{ in.}$$
$$d - a/2 = 16 - 3.28 = 12.72 \text{ in.}$$
$$A_s = 200,000 \times 12/(12.72 \times 40,000) = 4.72 \text{ in.}^2$$
$$a = 1.426 \times 4.72 = 6.72 \text{ in.}, \quad d - a/2 = 16 - 3.36 = 12.64$$
$$A_s = 4.72 \times 12.72/12.64 = 4.76 \text{ in.}^2$$

This answer is probably more accurate than the quadratic solution.

(f) Design a rectangular beam for a working moment of 100 k-ft using $b = 11$ in., $f_c' = 3000$ psi, $f_y = 40,000$ psi, and a load factor of 2. Make the depth such that p is approximately $0.18f_c'/f_y$ in order to reduce deflections.

SOLUTION

For $p = 0.18f_c'/f_y$, $M_u = 0.161f_c'bd^2$.

Design $M_u = 100 \times 2 = 200$ k-ft.

$$200,000 \times 12 = 0.161 \times 3000 \times 11d^2, \quad d = \sqrt{453} = 21.2 \text{ in.}$$

USE $b = 11$ in., $d = 22$ in.

Estimate $jd = 21$ in., $A_s = M/(f_y jd) = 200,000 \times 12/(40,000 \times 21) = 2.87 \text{ in.}^2$
$$a = 2.87 \times 40,000/(0.85 \times 3000 \times 11) = 4.08 \text{ in.}$$
$$jd = 22 - 4.08/2 = 19.96 \text{ in.}$$

The smaller jd will increase A_s and a and further reduce jd.

Try $jd = 19.80$ in., $A_s = 200,000 \times 12/(40,000 \times 19.80) = 3.03$ in.[2]
$$a = 3.03 \times 40,000/(0.85 \times 3000 \times 11) = 4.32 \text{ in.}$$
$$jd = 22 - 4.32/2 = 19.84 \text{ in.} \qquad \text{say O.K.}$$

USE $A_s = 3.03$ in.[2]

3.7. BEAMS WITH COMPRESSION STEEL

Beams are occasionally restricted in size to such an extent that steel is needed to help carry the compression. In ultimate strength analysis both

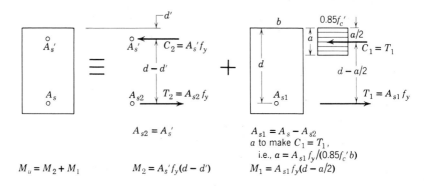

$$M_u = M_2 + M_1 \qquad M_2 = A_s'f_y(d - d')$$

Fig. 3.8. Analysis of double-reinforced beam.

the tension and the compression steels are assumed to develop their yield-point stress and the concrete must provide such additional compression as is required for the given ultimate moment.

The Report limits the f_y used in the calculations to a maximum of 60,000 psi and limits the tension steel to $p - p' = 0.40f_c'/f_y$, where the tension steel A_s defines $p = A_s/bd$ and the compression steel A_s' defines $p' = A_s'/bd$. This limitation is equivalent to the limitation of $p = 0.40f_c'/f_y$ already noted for rectangular beams. The following analysis gives the same results as the Report formula and is recommended for student use. The cases of analysis and design will be considered separately.

For analysis, as indicated in Fig. 3.8, the tension steel is subdivided into parts, $A_{s2} = A_s'^*$ and $A_{s1} = A_s - A_{s2}$, and the total moment is computed in corresponding parts as M_2 and M_1.

$$M_2 = A_s'f_y(d - d') \qquad M_1 = A_{s1}f_y(d - a/2)$$

* If it is desired to consider concrete displaced by A_s', this equality is replaced by the relation $T_2 = C_2$ or $A_{s2}f_y = A_s'(f_y - 0.85f_c')$, which makes A_{s2} slightly less than A_s'.

The depth of stress block a is calculated from $C_1 = T_1$ or $0.85f_c'ba = A_{s1}f_y$.

For design, Fig. 3.9 assumes that the M_1 couple is the maximum permitted on a rectangular beam, namely, $M_1 = 0.306f_c'bd^2$. This value results from the Report limitation of $p - p' = p_1 = A_{s1}/bd$ to $0.40f_c'/f_y$. The remainder of the moment $M_2 = M_u - M_1$ is carried by the necessary extra tension steel A_{s2} and compression steel A_s', each at f_y; or, if concrete displaced by A_s' is considered, A_s' is calculated at an effective stress of $f_y - 0.85f_c'$.

Special attention is directed by the Report to deflections when $p_1 = p - p'$ is in excess of $0.18f_c'/f_y$.

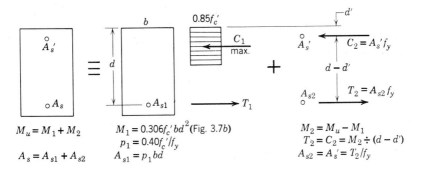

$$M_u = M_1 + M_2$$
$$A_s = A_{s1} + A_{s2}$$

$$M_1 = 0.306f_c'bd^2 \text{ (Fig. 3.7b)}$$
$$p_1 = 0.40f_c'/f_y$$
$$A_{s1} = p_1 bd$$

$$M_2 = M_u - M_1$$
$$T_2 = C_2 = M_2 \div (d - d')$$
$$A_{s2} = A_s' = T_2/f_y$$

Fig. 3.9. Design of double-reinforced beam.

It should also be noted that ultimate strength design is less apt to need the use of compression steel than is design by working stresses.

3.8. DOUBLE-REINFORCED BEAM EXAMPLES

(a) A rectangular beam has $b = 11$ in., $d = 20$ in., $A_s = 5$–$\#11 = 7.80$ in.^{2}, $f_c' = 3000$ psi, $f_y = 40,000$ psi, $A_s' = 2$–$\#11 = 3.12$ in.^{2}, with d' (cover to center line of A_s') of 2 in. Calculate the ultimate moment.

SOLUTION

Neglecting concrete displaced by A_s', consider A_{s2} equal to A_s', namely, 3.12 in.^{2}

$$M_2 = A_s'f_y(d - d') = 3.12 \times 40,000(20 - 2)/12,000 = 187 \text{ k-ft}$$

The remainder of the tension steel, $A_{s1} = A_s - A_{s2} = 7.80 - 3.12 = 4.68$ in.^{2}, works with the concrete, as in any rectangular beam, to develop an ultimate moment M_1. Since $T_1 = C_1$,

$4.68 \times 40{,}000 = 0.85 \times 3000 \times 11a$

$a = 6.70$ in. $< 0.471d = 9.42$ in.   O.K.

$j_1 d = 20 - 6.70/2 = 16.65$ in.

$M_1 = A_{s1} f_y j_1 d = 4.68 \times 40{,}000 \times 16.65/12{,}000 = 260$ k-ft

$M_u = M_1 + M_2 = 260 + 187 = 447$ k-ft

Allowable $p - p' = 0.40 f_c'/f_y = 0.40 \times 3000/40{,}000 = 0.030$

$p = 7.80/(11 \times 20) = 0.0355$

$p' = 3.12/(11 \times 20) = 0.0142$

$p - p' \qquad\qquad = 0.0213 < 0.030$ O.K., although deflections may be large

(b) A double-reinforced beam with $b = 11$ in., $d = 20$ in., $f_c' = 3000$ psi, $f_y = 40{,}000$ psi must carry a dead load moment of 116.7 k-ft and a live load moment of 150 k-ft. Calculate the required steel if the load factors are 1.2 for dead load and 2.4 for live load.

SOLUTION

Reqd. $M_u = 116.7 \times 1.2 + 150 \times 2.4 = 140.0 + 360 = 500$ k-ft

As a rectangular beam without A_s', the maximum steel for A_{s1} is limited by $p_1 = 0.40 f_c'/f_y$, which provides

$M_1 = 0.306 f_c' bd^2 = 0.306 \times 3000 \times 11 \times 20^2/12{,}000 = 336$ k-ft

$A_{s1} = 0.40 \times 3000 \times 11 \times 20/40{,}000 = 6.60$ in.²

or $j_1 d = d - a/2 = 20 - 0.471 \times 20/2 = 15.29$ in.

$A_{s1} = M_1/ f_y j_1 d) = 336{,}000 \times 12/(40{,}000 \times 15.29) = 6.60$ in.²

$M_2 = M_u - M_1 = 500 - 336 = 164$ k-ft

$T_2 = C_2 = M_2/(d - d') = 164{,}000 \times 12/18 = 109{,}000$ lb

on the assumption that $d' = 2$ in., that is, that the center line of A_s' is 2 in. from the compression face of the beam.

$A_{s2} = T_2/f_y = 109{,}000/40{,}000 = 2.72$ in.²

$A_s = A_{s1} + A_{s2} = 6.60 + 2.72 = 9.32$ in.²

$A_s' = C_2/f_y = 109{,}000/40{,}000 = 2.72$ in.²

If it is desired to recognize the compression concrete displaced by A_s':

Effective $f_s'' = f_y - 0.85 f_c' = 40{,}000 - 0.85 \times 3000 = 37{,}450$ psi

$A_s' = 109{,}000/37{,}450 = 2.91$ in.²

$p - p' = (9.32 - 2.91)/(11 \times 20)$

$\qquad\qquad = 0.0292 <$ allowable of $0.40 \times 3000/40{,}000 = 0.030$ O.K.

Deflections may be large since $p - p' \gg 0.18 f_c'/f_y$.

3.9. ULTIMATE STRENGTH OF T-BEAMS

Because slabs and beams are ordinarily cast together as shown in Fig. 3.10, the beams are automatically provided with an extra width at the top

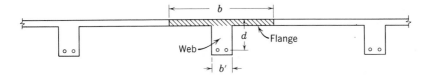

Fig. 3.10. T-beam as part of a floor system.

which is called a flange. Such beams are known as T-beams. The portion below the slab is called the web. The Report limits the flange width to be used in calculations to a maximum projection of six times the slab thickness on each side of the web.

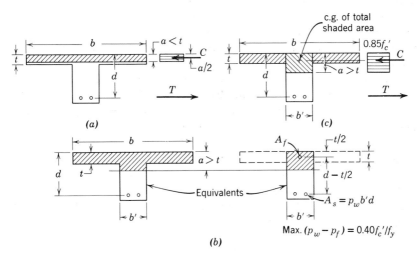

Fig. 3.11. Design of T-beams. (*a*) Acts as rectangular beam. (*b*) Report replaces flange with A_f to give equivalent double-reinforced rectangular beam. (*c*) Direct analysis as T-beam.

T-beams are analyzed in much the same way as rectangular beams. For a tension failure, which is the common case, the uniform stress block is assumed to be just deep enough to provide a compression C equal to the critical tension $T = A_s f_y$. If the resulting depth of stress block a is less than the slab (flange) thickness t, as shown in Fig. 3.11a, the analysis is identical with that of a very wide rectangular beam of width b.

If the area within the flange depth does not provide enough compression, the form of the calculation must be modified to take account of the narrower web width b' below the flange (Fig. 3.11c). The Report suggests an indirect approach to the analysis of such T-beams. The Report proposal is to consider the overhanging part of the flange, shown dotted in Fig. 3.11b, as removed and replaced by an imaginary area of compression steel A_f having the same compression strength and located opposite the middle of the overhanging flange. Thus

$$A_f f_y = 0.85 f_c' t(b - b')$$

$$A_f = 0.85 f_c' t(b - b')/f_y{}^*$$

The resulting "double-reinforced rectangular beam" shown in Fig. 3.11b is analyzed or designed exactly as indicated in Secs. 3.7 and 3.8.

Presumably, if a T-beam could fail in compression, the depth a would be approximately the $0.537d$ value used by Whitney for a balanced rectangular beam. This value of a would lead to an ultimate moment different from the $0.333 f_c' b d^2$ value for a rectangular beam, but one that could easily be calculated. Compression failures will rarely occur and this case is probably not important from a practical point of view. However, the Report sets a limit on the tension steel, in exactly the same fashion as on rectangular beams, to avoid the possibility of a compression failure. The ratios of steel are defined as $p_w = A_s/b'd$ and $p_f = A_f/b'd$; and the maximum steel is limited to $p_w - p_f = 0.40 f_c'/f_y$. Deflection should receive special attention when $p_w - p_f$ exceeds $0.18 f_c'/f_y$. These are the same limits as were used on rectangular beams and they will be interpreted in this fashion in the alternate solution in Sec. 3.10a.

A more direct approach to the T-beam problem is also possible, as indicated in Fig. 3.11c. The total tension can be equated to the total compression to establish the depth of the stress block.

$$A_s f_y = 0.85 f_c' [ab' + t(b - b')]$$

$$a = \frac{A_s f_y - 0.85 f_c' t(b - b')}{0.85 f_c' b'}$$

The resultant compression C acts at the centroid of the shaded area in Fig. 3.11c. This procedure gives results identical with the Report method.

---

* Since this is an imaginary area of steel, no concrete is actually displaced and no deduction from f_y should be made for displaced concrete.

REINFORCED CONCRETE FUNDAMENTALS

3.10. T-BEAM EXAMPLES

(*a*) For the T-beam shown in Fig. 3.12*a*, find the ultimate moment if $A_s = 3.00$ in.^{2}, $f_y = 60,000$ psi, $f_c' = 3000$ psi.

SOLUTION

Max. flange overhang $= 6t = 12$ in. $=$ actual   O.K.
Ultimate $T = 3.00 \times 60,000 = 180,000$ lb
Max. C within depth $t = 0.85 \times 3000 \times 32 \times 2 = 163,000$ lb

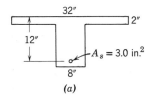

(*a*)

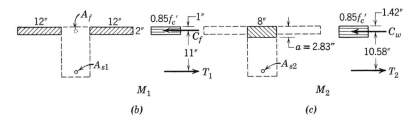

(*b*)   (*c*)

Fig. 3.12. T-beam of Sec. 3.10*a*.

Since $180,000 > 163,000$, the stress block extends below the flange far enough to pick up the remaining compression. The Report replaces the overhanging flange with A_f, as indicated in Fig. 3.11*b*.

$$A_f \times 60,000 = 0.85 \times 3000 \times 2(32 - 8)$$
$A_f = 2.04$ in.^{2} acting at $t/2 = 1$ in. from top of beam
$$p_w - p_f = (3.00 - 2.04)/(8 \times 12) = 0.010$$
Allowable $p_w - p_f = 0.40 \times 3000/60,000 = 0.020$ O.K.

However, $p_w - p_f$ exceeds $0.18f_c'/f_y$ and deflection may be large.
   In the "double-reinforced beam" the A_s of 3.00 in.^{2} may be treated as $A_{s1} = A_f = 2.04$ in.^{2} and $A_{s2} = 3.00 - 2.04 = 0.96$ in.^{2} A_f and A_{s1} form a couple M_1; A_{s2} and the compression concrete form a couple M_2.

$$M_1 = 2.04 \times 60,000 (12 - 1)/12,000 = 112.4 \text{ k-ft}$$
$$a = A_{s2}f_y/(0.85f_c'b') = 0.96 \times 60,000/(0.85 \times 3000 \times 8) = 2.83 \text{ in.}$$
$$M_2 = 0.96 \times 60,000 (12 - 2.83/2)/12,000 = 50.8 \text{ k-ft}$$
Total $M_u = M_1 + M_2 = 112.4 + 50.8 = 163.2$ k-ft

ULTIMATE STRENGTH THEORY FOR BEAMS   61

Alternate solution: As above, the stress block must extend below the flange to pick up a compression of $180,000 - 163,000 = 17,000$ lb.

$$17,000 = 0.85 \times 3000 \times 8(a - 2)$$
$$a - 2 = 0.83 \text{ in.}, \qquad a = 2.83 \text{ in.}$$

The resultant C acts at the centroid of the compression area, which establishes jd and leads to $M_u = Tjd$ or Cjd, as indicated in Fig. 3.11c. As an equivalent procedure, the moment will be calculated as the sum of two couples. The compression C_f on the outstanding flanges pairs with a corresponding tension to form couple M_1, as shown in Fig. 3.12b. The remainder of the tension paired with the compression C_w in the 8-in. web width will form the second couple M_2, as sketched in Fig. 3.12c.

$$C_f = (32 - 8)2 \times 0.85 \times 3000/1000 = 122.7 \text{ k}$$
$$M_1 = 122.7(12 - 2/2)/12 = 112.6 \text{ k-ft}$$
$$C_w = 8 \times 2.83 \times 0.85 \times 3000/1000 = 57.6 \text{ k}$$
$$M_2 = 57.6(12 - 2.83/2)/12 = 50.8 \text{ k-ft}$$
$$M_u = M_1 + M_2 = 112.6 + 50.8 = 163.4 \text{ k-ft}$$

This solution is simple but does not lead to a direct check on maximum permissible steel exactly as stated in the Report. However, precisely the same results can be obtained by relating the M_2 (web) couple to the rectangular beam requirements. The maximum moment, based on $p = 0.40 f_c'/f_y$, is then $M_u = 0.306 f_c' b d^2 = 0.306 \times 3000 \times 8 \times 12^2/12,000 = 88.2 \text{ k-ft} > M_2 = 50.8$, which is satisfactory. However, by inspection it is seen that M_2 is much more than half of $0.306 f_c' b d^2$ and hence p must be in excess of $0.18 f_c'/f_y$. Therefore deflection should be investigated.

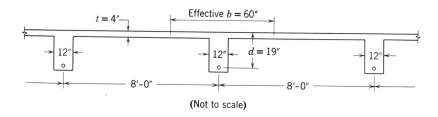

Fig. 3.13. Floor of Sec. 3.10b.

(b) The floor of Fig. 3.13 consists of a 4-in. slab supported by beams cast monolithically with the slab at a spacing of 8 ft center to center. These beams have webs which are 12 in. wide and a depth of 19 in. to the center of steel plus the necessary cover over the steel. Dead load moment is 50 k-ft and live load moment is 120 k-ft. Using $f_c' = 3000$ psi, $f_y = 50,000$ psi, and the load factors recommended in the Report (Sec. 1.12), calculate the required steel.

SOLUTION

$$M_u = 50 \times 1.2 + 120 \times 2.4 = 60 + 288 = 348 \text{ k-ft}$$

Since $M_D < M_L$, the 1.8 load factor on total moment will not control. For $6t$ overhang,

$$b = 12\text{-in. web} + 2 \times 6 \times 4 = 60 \text{ in.} < 96\text{-in. beam spacing} \qquad \text{O.K.}$$

It must be determined whether the stress block is as deep as the flange.
If $a = t$, available $C = 0.85 \times 3000 \times 60 \times 4 = 614{,}000$ lb.

$$jd = 19 - a/2 = 17 \text{ in.}$$

$$\text{Reqd. } C = M/jd = 348{,}000 \times 12/17 = 245{,}000 \text{ lb} < 614{,}000$$

Hence $a < t$ and the beam must be designed as a rectangular beam, exactly as in Sec. 3.6e.

Estimate $jd = 18$ in., $A_s = M_u/f_y jd = 348{,}000 \times 12/(50{,}000 \times 18) = 4.64$ in.^{2}

$$a = 4.64 \times 50{,}000/(0.85 \times 3000 \times 60) = 1.52 \text{ in.}$$

$$jd = 19 - 1.52/2 = 18.24 \text{ in.}$$

Try $jd = 18.26$ in., $A_s = 4.64 \times 18/18.26 = 4.58$ in.^{2}

$$a = 1.52 \times 4.58/4.64 = 1.50 \text{ in.}$$

$$jd = 19 - 0.75 = 18.25 \text{ in.} \qquad \text{O.K.}$$

USE $A_s = 4.58$ in.^{2}

(c) Calculate A_s if the loads in the above example are increased to give $M_u = 1000$ k-ft.

SOLUTION

If $a = t$, available $C = 614{,}000$ lb, as above.

Approx. reqd. $C = 1000 \times 12{,}000/17 = 706{,}000 \qquad$ (approx. $jd = d - t/2$)
Therefore $a > t$. Design as true T-beam.

$$A_f = 0.85 \times 3000 \times 48 \times 4/50{,}000 = 9.80 \text{ in.}^2 = A_{s2}$$

$$M_2 = 9.80 \times 50{,}000(19 - 4/2)/12{,}000 = 695 \text{ k-ft}$$

$$M_1 \text{ on } b' \text{ width} = 1000 - 695 = 305 \text{ k-ft}$$

$$\text{Permissible } M_1 = 0.306 f_c' b' d^2$$

$$= 0.306 \times 3000 \times 12 \times 19^2/12{,}000$$

$$= 332 \text{ k-ft} > 305$$

The web is large enough for moment, but deflection may be large.
For A_{s1} calculation, estimate $j_1 d = 19 - 3 = 16$ in.

$$A_{s1} = (305{,}000 \times 12)/(50{,}000 \times 16) = 4.57 \text{ in.}^2$$

$$a = 4.57 \times 50{,}000/(0.85 \times 3000 \times 12) = 7.45 \text{ in.}$$

$$j_1 d = 19 - 7.45/2 = 15.28 \text{ in.}$$

Try $j_1 d = 15.10$ in., $A_{s1} = 4.57 \times 16/15.10 = 4.83$ in.^{2}

$$a = 7.45 \times 4.83/4.57 = 7.88 \text{ in.}$$

$$j_1 d = 19 - 7.88/2 = 15.06 \text{ in.} \qquad \text{say O.K.}$$

$$\text{Reqd. } A_s = A_{s1} + A_{s2} = 4.83 + 9.80 = 14.63 \text{ in.}^2$$

3.11. BEAMS WITH REINFORCING AT SEVERAL LEVELS

When reinforcing is placed in two layers, it is usually satisfactory to consider the resultant stress at the centroid of the steel, as in working load analysis (Chap. 4). However, if the bars are generally scattered over the depth, as in the column sections of Figs. 2.12b–f and 2.13, some bars will be near the neutral axis and have a stress less than f_y. In such cases strains as well as stresses must be considered.

For ultimate moment calculations in such cases, the report is not specific as to the necessary assumptions. However, it would be reasonable to adopt the assumptions used for columns under eccentric loads. The maximum unit deformation on the compression concrete would then be limited to 0.003 in./in. and a straight-line variation in deformations would be used. It would also be assumed that the depth of the rectangular stress block a is 0.85 of the depth to the neutral axis. This procedure applied to columns is discussed briefly in Sec. 13.7d and is illustrated in Fig. 13.17.

3.12. CURVE FOR ULTIMATE STRENGTH OF RECTANGULAR BEAMS

Calculations for rectangular beams are slightly simplified[4] by use of the curve in Fig. E.1, which was adapted[5] from the Report.

(*a*) For analysis of a given beam, one can enter on the right with the steel ratio p, move horizontally to the proper f_y curve, thence vertically to the f_c' curve, and finally horizontally to read M_u/bd^2. This establishes the ultimate moment for the beam.

(*b*) For a given beam size, the steel is established by the reverse procedure, going from M_u/bd^2 on the left horizontally to f_c', vertically to f_y, and finally horizontally to read the required p.

(*c*) To choose a beam size corresponding to a given p and given M_u, one proceeds exactly as in (*a*) and solves the required M_u/bd^2 for required bd^2 instead of for M_u. With practical values of b and d chosen, the procedure of (*b*) establishes the exact p.

(*d*) For the absolute minimum size of beam (probably not the most economical one), the limiting value of $p = 0.40 f_c'/f_y$ would be used. The f_c' curves terminate on the right against a dashed line corresponding to this maximum p. Hence one can shorten the process a little by starting at this terminus of the f_c' curve and then reading M_u/bd^2 directly to the left.

For example, using the data of Sec. 3.6d:

$$M_u = 2 \times 100 = 200 \text{ k-ft}$$

Start on the $f_c' = 3000$ curve where it intersects the dashed line on the right and proceed horizontally to the left to read $M_u/bd^2 = 900$.

$$bd^2 = M_u/900 = 200 \times 12{,}000/900 = 2670 \text{ in.}^3$$

If $b = 11$ in., $d = \sqrt{2670/11} = 15.35$ in. If d is increased to 16 in., $M_u/bd^2 = 200 \times 12{,}000/(11 \times 16^2) = 854$. On the curve M_u/bd^2 of 854 leads (through $f_c' = 3000$ and $f_y = 40{,}000$) to $p = 0.027$.

$$A_s = 0.027 \times 11 \times 16 = 4.75 \text{ in.}^2$$

compared to 4.78 and 4.76 in.^{2} found in Sec. 3.6e. USE $b = 11$ in., $d = 16$ in., $A_s = 4.75$ in.^{2}

SELECTED REFERENCES

1. Charles S. Whitney, "Plastic Theory of Reinforced Concrete Design," *ASCE Trans.*, **107**, 1942, p. 251.
2. "Report of ASCE-ACI Joint Committee on Ultimate Strength Design," *ASCE Proc.-Separate 809*, Oct. 1955.
3. ACI-ASCE Committee 327, Leo H. Corning, Chairman, "Ultimate Strength Design," *ACI Jour.*, **27**, Jan. 1956; *Proc.*, **52**, p. 505.
4. Phil M. Ferguson, "Simplification of Design by Ultimate Strength Procedures," *Jour. ASCE*, Structural Div., **82**, No. ST4, July 1956.
5. Charles S. Whitney and Edward Cohen, "Guide for Ultimate Strength Design of Reinforced Concrete," *ACI Jour.*, **28**, Nov. 1956; *Proc.*, **53**, p. 455.

PROBLEMS

Note: Section 1.9 lists yield points of the more common reinforcing steels; Table 1.1 lists bar sizes and areas; Sec. 1.12 lists recommended load factors.

Prob. 3.1. If $f_c' = 3000$ psi and steel is intermediate grade, find the ultimate moment capacity of the beam of Fig. 3.14 by Whitney's ultimate strength theory, if A_s is:

(a) 2-#8.   (c) 4-#11.

(b) 4-#8.   (d) 6-#11.

Prob. 3.2. Recalculate any of the ultimate moments in Prob. 3.1 which would be different if calculated according to the Joint Committee recommendations (Code Appendix).

Prob. 3.3. If $f_c' = 3000$ psi and steel is hard grade, calculate the permissible service or working moment on the beam of Fig. 3.15 according to the Code Appendix, assuming the load factor is 1.8 and steel as follows:

(a) 3–#8. (c) 4–#11.

(b) 6–#8. (d) 6–#11.

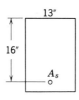

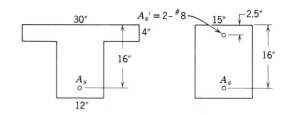

Fig. 3.14. Beam for Probs. 3.1 and 3.2.

Fig. 3.15. Beam for Prob. 3.3.

Fig. 3.16. Beam for Prob. 3.4.

Prob. 3.4. If $f_c' = 4000$ psi, steel is rail steel, over-all load factor is 2, calculate the permissible service moment on the beam of Fig. 3.16 according to Code Appendix, assuming A_s is:

(a) 3–#8. (c) 4–#11.

(b) 6–#8. (d) 7–#11.

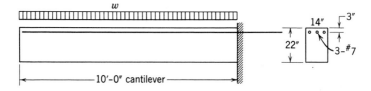

Fig. 3.17. Beam for Prob. 3.5.

Prob. 3.5. Check the adequacy of the beam of Fig. 3.17 in flexure under the Joint Committee recommendations, assuming $f_c' = 3000$ psi, rail steel, service live load of 1000 plf and dead load (including beam weight) of 500 plf. (Suggestion: Compare calculated M_u with required M_u.)

Prob. 3.6. In Prob. 3.5 calculate the exact steel that is needed for the loads given.

Prob. 3.7. In Prob. 3.5 calculate the exact steel that is needed if intermediate grade steel is used.

REINFORCED CONCRETE FUNDAMENTALS

Prob. 3.8. A simple span rectangular beam 20 ft long is to carry a service load of 3000 plf made up of 1600 plf dead load (including beam weight) and 1400 plf live load. Use $f_c' = 3000$ psi, hard grade steel, and design a beam, subject to later check on shear and bond, for p approximately $0.18f_c'/f_y$. Make $b = 13$ in. and keep d in full inches. Choose bars.

Prob. 3.9. Assuming deflections are not considered serious for the usage contemplated, redesign the beam of Prob. 3.8 with $b = 13$ in. and the minimum effective depth (full inches) permitted under the Code Appendix.

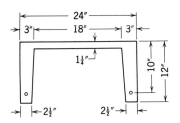

Fig. 3.18. Beam for Prob. 3.12.

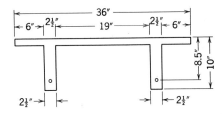

Fig. 3.19. Precast section for Prob. 3.14.

Prob. 3.10. A continuous rectangular beam with $b = 14$ in., $d = 24$ in., $f_c' = 3750$ psi, rail steel, must care for $M_u = -900$ k-ft. Design the necessary steel, using $d' = 3$ in. if A_s' is necessary.

Prob. 3.11. A rectangular beam has $b = 15$ in., $d = 18$ in., $f_c' = 3000$ psi, intermediate grade steel, $A_s = 6\text{–}\#11$, $A_s' = 3\text{–}\#11$ with cover d' to center of steel $= 2.5$ in.

(a) Calculate the ultimate moment.

(b) Calculate the ultimate moment if A_s' were omitted.

(c) Could the nine bars be redistributed between A_s and A_s' to develop a larger ultimate moment than in (a)?   Yes

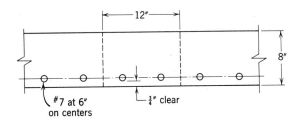

Fig. 3.20. Slab for Prob. 3.15.

Prob. 3.12. If $f_c' = 5000$ psi and steel is intermediate grade, what is the ultimate moment capacity of the beam of Fig. 3.18 when each leg is reinforced with:

(a) 1–#8.

(b) 1–#11.

ULTIMATE STRENGTH THEORY FOR BEAMS

Prob. 3.13. Design the steel for the channel section of Prob. 3.12 if $M_u = 120$ k-ft and the steel is changed to hard grade.

Prob. 3.14. If the precast section of Fig. 3.19 has $f_c' = 5000$ psi, rail steel, 1–#8 bar in each leg, calculate the ultimate moment capacity. Flange $t = 1.5$ in.

Prob. 3.15.

(a) Calculate the ultimate moment (Fig. 3.20) on a strip of slab 12 in. wide if $f_c' = 3000$ psi and the steel is intermediate grade.

(b) What would be the service or working live load per square foot if the slab were used on a 10-ft simple span? Use the load factors in the Joint Report and the ACI Appendix. Concrete weight may be taken at 150 pcf which includes the weight of reinforcement.

Beams—
Analysis for Moment
by
Conventional Theory

4.1. TRANSFORMED AREA CONCEPT FOR BEAMS

The conventional working stress theory of reinforced concrete assumes that Hooke's law holds both for concrete and steel, that is, that both materials are elastic and have unit stresses directly proportional to unit strains.   Where two different materials, such as concrete and steel, are subject to related deformations, the transformed area concept is a simplifying idea which is very helpful.

The basic idea of transformed area has been discussed in Sec. 2.10 in connection with live loads on axially loaded columns.   It was shown that a steel area A_s could be replaced in an analysis with an equivalent area of concrete equal to nA_s; and that the steel stress f_s would equal nf_c, where $n = E_s/E_c$.   The steel area and its substituted transformed area must be subject to the same unit deformation; and $f_s = nf_c$ only when the unit deformations are the same.

In a beam, it should be apparent that f_s again equals nf_c *provided* f_c is the concrete stress immediately adjacent to the steel, that is, at exactly the same distance from the neutral axis. Likewise, the transformed area of the steel is again nA_s, but this area must be sketched in position at a uniform distance from the neutral axis corresponding to the location of A_s. Thus, if the column of Fig. 2.11a were eccentrically loaded, that is, if moment as well as axial load were acting, the transformed area would have to be sketched parallel to the axis of bending as shown in Fig. 2.11c for moment or eccentricity about axis x-x, and as shown in Fig. 2.11d for moment or eccentricity about axis y-y. Bars in different planes would then carry different stresses in accordance with their locations.

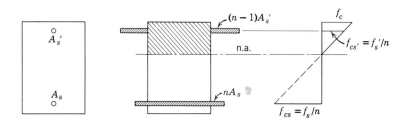

Fig. 4.1. Transformed area when tension is present, elastic analysis (nearly obsolete for compression steel).

If bending alone existed, or if a column load were eccentric enough to produce tension on one set of bars, the tension concrete would be assumed as cracked and would be omitted from the calculations. Thus the transformed area of a double-reinforced beam (if under assumed elastic action) would be as shown in Fig. 4.1, with $A_s{}'$ replaced by an effective transformed area of $(n - 1)A_s{}'$ and A_s replaced by nA_s, there being no useful concrete displaced on the tension side. In this case the compression steel stress $f_s{}' = nf_{cs'}$, the effective $f_s{}'' = (n - 1)f_{cs'}$, and the tension steel stress $f_s = nf_{cs}$. This elastic type of analysis would be correct only for the effects of short-time loads.

For most loads and especially for dead loads or long-time loads, the elastic stresses discussed above are complicated by the presence of shrinkage stresses and creep in the concrete, somewhat as in a column (Sec. 2.2). These inelastic effects are most significant in the case of compression steel, which tends to pick up a stress much in excess of $nf_{cs'}$. Under these conditions $f_s{}'$ cannot be calculated accurately. As an approximation the ACI Code suggests that $f_s{}'$ may be taken as $2nf_{cs'}$.* This is equivalent to an effective compressive stress $f_s{}''$ of $(2n - 1)f_{cs'}$ and a transformed area of

$(2n - 1)A_s'$ as indicated in Fig. 4.2. The use of this area in analysis is recommended as more in line with present practice than the real elastic approach. Some refer to this as plastic analysis but the author considers semielastic analysis as more descriptive.

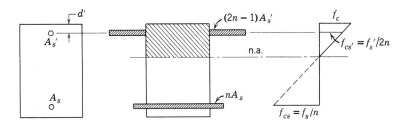

Fig. 4.2. Transformed area for semielastic analysis as required by the ACI Code.

4.2. ANALYSIS OF REINFORCED CONCRETE BEAM AS A HOMOGENEOUS BEAM

The proper use of the transformed area concept makes it possible to replace any reinforced concrete member with an equivalent member of homogeneous elastic material. This in turn permits the use of simple strength of materials relationships in the analysis. It should be obvious that the "concrete" which replaces tension steel is assumed to carry tension and to have the same modulus of elasticity in tension as in compression.

The most common analysis for reinforced concrete beams employs directly the resisting couple idea of Sec. 3.1. The external bending moment M is resisted by a tensile force T and a resultant compressive force C (Fig. 3.1), which form a couple $(T = C)$ when the member is free from axial load.† Where a straight-line stress distribution is assumed, mechanics shows that the relationship $T = C$ requires a neutral axis at the centroid of the effective cross section. The word *effective* is used here to call attention to the fact that concrete in tension is neglected and thus the effective area of concrete is divided from the ineffective area by the

* An upper limit is placed on the compressive stress to be used in design. When $2nf_{cs'}$ exceeds the allowable stress in tension, the tension stress value controls. This complication is discussed in Sec. 4.8c, d.

† It should be noted that $T = C$ is a perfectly general relation of statics applying equally well to the Whitney analysis, to straight-line stress distribution, or to any other pattern of stress.

neutral axis itself. The effective area cannot be fully dimensioned until the neutral axis has been located.

When the neutral axis has been located (at the centroid), the calculation either of actual stresses for a given moment or the allowable moment for given permissible stresses can be determined by evaluating the internal couple or by using the conventional flexure formula

$$Mc = fI$$

where M = bending moment, usually in.-lb or in.-k

c = distance to extreme fiber, in.

f = bending stress, psi or ksi, at extreme fiber (at distance c from neutral axis). This term is used as s in engineering mechanics notation, but f is standard notation in reinforced concrete

I = area moment of inertia, $\int y^2 \, dA$, about the neutral axis, in.[4]

The internal couple solution gives a clearer picture of beam action and is commonly used. The flexure formula is particularly useful for irregular shapes, especially those involving curved surfaces.

Neither method of analysis is theoretically correct for members with a cross section which varies along the axis, particularly sharply varying cross sections. Neither applies to concrete stresses anywhere near the ultimate, because the straight-line stress distribution is then invalid. Both analyses assume concrete (in effect) cracked in tension to the neutral axis, a condition more nearly approached at high loads and stresses than at working loads. This cracking assumption could be modified, but the actual cracking at working loads depends upon the history of earlier loading. The usual assumption of complete cracking is probably the safest for general use. Both analyses commonly ignore stresses due to shrinkage of concrete and changes in stress due to creep (flow) of concrete, except in the $2n$ arbitrary correction for compression steel. It follows that the stresses thus calculated are nominal rather than real stresses. One would not expect to find these stresses in the laboratory.

4.3. ALLOWABLE WORKING STRESSES IN FLEXURE

Stresses calculated on this nominal basis can provide reasonably adequate controls for safe design of conventional construction when the allowable stresses are properly correlated with ultimate strength tests. The ACI Building Code, Arts. 305 and 306, specifies such stresses for beams, f_c on concrete, f_s on steel:

$$\text{Allowable } f_c = 0.45 f_c'$$

where f_c' is the minimum specified compressive strength (cylinder strength) of concrete,

Allowable f_s = 20,000 psi on rail steel, intermediate and
hard grade billet steel, and cold drawn wire*

Allowable f_s = 18,000 psi on structural grade steel

Code Table 305(a) also specifies values of n.

The AASHO[1] specifies essentially the same f_s but a lower f_c:

Allowable f_c = $0.4f_c'$

4.4. ANALYSIS AND DESIGN NEED DIFFERENT PROCEDURES

There is very little basic difference between calculating beam stresses under a given moment, for comparison with allowable stress values, and calculating an allowable moment based on these allowable stresses. Desirable procedures for such analyses are illustrated in terms of the numerical problems which follow.

The design of beams for moment, on the other hand, is a process considerably different from analysis. This subject is treated in the next chapter.

4.5. RECTANGULAR BEAM ANALYSIS

(a) Find f_c and f_s for the rectangular beam shown in Fig. 4.3 for M = 100 k-ft. Use the internal couple procedure.

$$f_c' = 4000 \text{ psi} \qquad E_c = 4 \times 10^6 \text{ psi}$$

$$E_s = 30 \times 10^6 \text{ psi} \qquad \text{Rail steel}$$

SOLUTION

$$n = E_s/E_c = 30 \times 10^6 \div (4 \times 10^6) = 7.5$$

The transformed area is first sketched (Fig. 4.3b) and the neutral axis indicated at the unknown depth kd (standard notation), where k is a constant less than unity and usually less than 0.5. The neutral axis lies at the centroid of the transformed area. The moment of the areas about the neutral axis† gives

---

* Article 306b permits more for a special case of one-way slabs.

† Although moments about an axis not yet located may seem awkward, it should be noted that this gives a simpler equation. In general, $\bar{y}\int dA = \int y\, dA$. If y is measured from the centroid, $\bar{y} = 0$ and the equation becomes simply $\int y\, dA = 0$.

a quadratic equation for which a solution by completing the squares is recommended.

$$(13kd)kd/2 = 60(20 - kd)$$

$$6.5(kd)^2 + 60kd = 1200$$

$$(kd)^2 + 9.24kd + (9.24/2)^2 = 184.8 + (9.24/2)^2 = 206.1$$

$$kd + 4.62 = \pm 14.36$$

$$kd = +9.74 \text{ in. (or negative).}$$

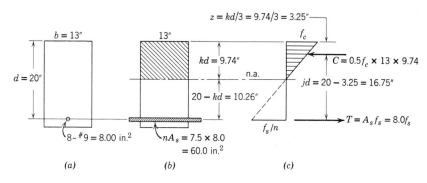

(a)   (b)   (c)

Fig. 4.3. Analysis of a rectangular beam.

The triangle of stress on a uniform width in Fig. 4.3b, c locates the resultant C at $z = kd/3$ from the top and gives the arm jd of the resulting couple as $d - z = 20 - 3.25 = 16.75$ in.

$$T = C = M/jd = 100,000 \times 12/16.75 = 71,500 \text{ lb}$$

$$T = A_s f_s$$

$$f_s = T/A_s = 71,500/8.0 = 8940 \text{ psi}$$

or

$$f_s = \frac{M}{A_s jd} = \frac{100,000 \times 12}{8.0 \times 16.75} = 8950 \text{ psi}$$

The latter form is the more convenient for general usage.

It should be noted that the *average* steel stress has been calculated. Ordinarily the maximum is not calculated. (Here the maximum would be some 5% higher since this steel area implies two layers of steel.)

$$C = \frac{f_c}{2} bkd$$

$$71,500 = 0.5f_c \times 13 \times 9.74$$

$$f_c = 1129 \text{ psi}$$

It is well worthwhile to check these results using the similar triangles of the unit stress distribution with one of the calculated stresses as a means of checking the other:

$$\frac{f_c}{f_s/n} = \frac{kd}{d - kd}, \qquad \frac{f_c}{8950/7.5} = \frac{9.74}{20 - 9.74}$$

$$f_c = 1130 \text{ psi vs. } 1129 \qquad \text{O.K.}$$

(b) Find the stresses in the beam of (a) using $Mc = fI$.

SOLUTION

The transformed area and neutral axis location must first be calculated as in (a). Then from Fig. 4.3b:

$$
\begin{aligned}
I: \ 13 \times 9.74^3/12 \ &= \ 1,002 \\
13 \times 9.74 \times 4.87^2 \ &= \ 3,000 \\
60 \times 10.26^2 \ &= \ 6,320 \\
\text{Total } I \ &= \ 10,320 \text{ in.}^4
\end{aligned}
$$

The transformed area of the steel is considered negligibly thin, such that its moment of inertia about its centroidal axis can be neglected.

$$f_c = Mc_1/I = 100,000 \times 12 \times 9.74/10,320 = 1130 \text{ psi}$$
$$f_s/n = Mc_2/I = 100,000 \times 12 \times 10.26/10,320 = 1192$$
$$f_s = 7.5 \times 1192 = 8950 \text{ psi}$$

(c) Find the allowable moment for the beam of (a), using the allowable stresses of ACI Code, Arts. 305 and 306.

SOLUTION

The allowable moment can be found from simple proportion *after* a solution for stresses as in (a). The unit stresses increase in direct proportion to the moment.

Allowable $f_c = 0.45f_c' = 0.45 \times 4000 = 1800$ psi

Allowable $f_s = 20,000$ psi

Based on compression alone, moment can be increased above 100 k-ft until the f_c of 1129 psi of (a) becomes the 1800 psi allowable:

Allowable $M_c = (1800/1129)100 = 159.5$ k-ft

Based on tension alone, similarly,

Allowable $M_T = (20,000/8950)100 = 223$ k-ft > 159.5

∴ compression controls

Allowable $M = 159.5$ k-ft

(d) Find the allowable moment for the beam of (a), using the allowable stresses of the ACI Building Code but assuming no earlier analysis is available.

SOLUTION

As before, the neutral axis is at centroid of the effective cross section. Area moments about the neutral axis give $kd = 9.74$ in.

The neutral axis location fixes the ratio between f_c and f_s (actually f_s/n). As the moment varies, f_c and f_s change proportionally to maintain this specific ratio. At the allowable moment, the unit stress picture fits one of the conditions sketched in Fig. 4.4. Either *one* of these sketches* (the *two* sketches are

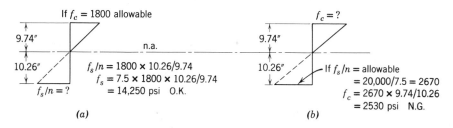

Fig. 4.4. Determination of governing stress for allowable moment.

totally unnecessary) indicates that the allowable moment is limited by $f_c = 1800$ psi (not by $f_s = 20,000$ psi).

Allowable $M = Cjd = Tjd$

$jd = 20 - 9.74/3 = 16.75$ in.

Allowable $C = 0.5f_cbkd = 0.5 \times 1800 \times 13 \times 9.74 = 114{,}000$ lb

or   Allowable T (to protect f_c) $= 8.0 \times 14{,}250 = 114{,}000$ lb $= 114.0$ k

Allowable $M = 114.0 \times 16.75/12 = 159.1$ k-ft

For the rectangular beam, an alternate procedure is practical. After the neutral axis is located, the allowable C and allowable T can be evaluated entirely independently of each other. Since the actual T equals actual C at all times, the smaller allowable (T or C) limits the allowable moment.

Allowable $C = 0.5 \times 1800 \times 13 \times 9.74 = 114{,}000$ lb $= 114$ k

Allowable $T = 8.0 \times 20{,}000 = 160{,}000$ lb

Allowable C limits M

Allowable $M = 114 \times 16.75/12 = 159.1$ k-ft

* The student should be careful to note that the two allowable stresses (1800 and $20{,}000/n$) do not occur simultaneously and should not be shown on the same sketch. Here the cross section fixes the neutral axis; the allowable stresses have no influence on it. The student might contrast this with Chap. 5 where the steel is chosen to fit a desirable neutral axis determined from similar triangles using both the allowable stresses.

4.6. SLABS

A one-way slab is simply a wide, shallow, rectangular beam insofar as stress analysis is concerned. The reinforcing steel is usually spaced uniformly over its width. For convenience a 1-ft width is generally taken for analysis or design, since loads are frequently specified in terms of load per

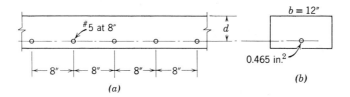

Fig. 4.5. Design strip and effective steel area in slab analysis. (*a*) Slab cross section. (*b*) Design strip.

square foot; on a 1-ft strip, this unit load becomes the load per linear foot. Since the slab can average the effect of steel over some width, the effective A_s may well correspond to a fractional number of bars in the 1-ft width. For example, #5 bars at 8-in. spacing, as in Fig. 4.5a, give A_s/ft = 0.31 × 12/8 = 0.465 in.²/ft for the 1-ft design strip, Fig. 4.5b.

4.7. T-BEAM ANALYSIS

(a) Comparison with rectangular beams

The theory of T-beam analysis is exactly the same as for rectangular beams, but several practical differences justify some discussion.

The T-beam usually results from placing beams and slabs monolithically, as indicated in Fig. 3.10. Since the slab is continuous over several beams, the effective flange width to be used must be established. Proper limits are set out in the ACI Code, Art. 705a, b, and these will be discussed briefly in Chap. 5.

The flange area is usually more than adequate to care for compressive stresses; hence allowable moments are usually limited by the steel stress. Furthermore, the large compression area in the flange often pulls the centroid of the transformed area up into the flange itself. When this occurs, the analysis for moment is exactly that for a wide rectangular beam of width *b*, since the missing area below the flange would have been a tension area which would be considered as cracked in rectangular beam analysis.

If the neutral axis falls below the bottom of the flange, the determination of the magnitude of C in terms of f_c and the fixing of the location of C are no longer possible by simple inspection. In this connection, the student will probably find it helpful to think in terms of the wedge of stress. For a rectangular beam, this wedge of stress is a simple triangular wedge (Fig. 4.6a). The volume of the wedge gives the magnitude of C and the centroid of the wedge marks the location of the resultant C. When this concept is applied to the T-beam, as in Fig. 4.6b, neither the volume nor the centroid can be determined except by a summation process, such as that

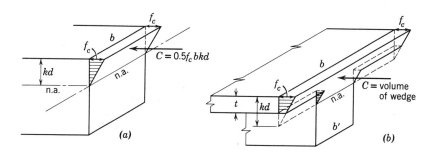

Fig. 4.6. Wedge of stress for (a) rectangular beam and (b) T-beam.

used in the following examples. The first example is calculated by the so-called "exact" analysis; the second example uses the approximate method which neglects the web area between neutral axis and flange. The approximate method fits much easier into a solution by formulas, charts, or curves, but shows very little advantage for a basic analysis such as is used here.

(b) Exact analysis

Find f_c and f_s for the T-beam shown in Fig. 4.7a under a moment of 150 k-ft, assuming $f_c' = 2500$ psi and structural grade steel.

SOLUTION

The ACI Building Code, Art. 305, shows that $n = 12$ for $f_c' = 2500$ psi. The transformed area of steel equals $12 \times 5 = 60$ in.^{2}

Try area moments about the bottom of flange to see whether the neutral axis lies higher (and a "rectangular" beam exists) or lower, and thus indicates a true T-beam.

       REINFORCED CONCRETE FUNDAMENTALS

Moment of compression area $= 40 \times 4 \times 2 = 320$ in.^{3}

Moment of tension area $\quad = 60(20 - 4) \quad = 960$ in.^{3}

∴ neutral axis falls below flange

Area moments about n.a. (Fig. 4.7b):

$$(10kd)kd/2 + (40 - 10)4(kd - 2) = 60(20 - kd)$$
$$(kd)^2 + 36kd + 18^2 = 288 + 18^2 = 612$$
$$kd = 24.7 - 18 = 6.7 \text{ in.}$$

At the bottom of the flange $f_{c1} = (2.7/6.7)f_c = 0.403f_c$.

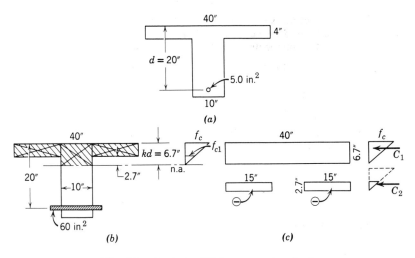

(a)

(b)   *(c)*

Fig. 4.7. Analysis of T-beam, exact method.

The total compression can be calculated by subdividing the areas, and if necessary the stresses, into pieces that can be visualized simply (Fig. 4.7c). In this case, the simplest pieces are C_1 on a rectangle 40 in. wide and extending all the way to the neutral axis and a negative C_2 deducting the surplus below the flanges. Sketches, as in Fig. 4.7c, and a tabular form are desirable. To locate the resultant C, moments are taken about some convenient axis, by custom about the top of beam.

	C	Arm abt. Top	Moment m abt. Top
$C_1 = (40 \times 6.7)f_c/2$	$= \quad 134.0f_c$	$6.7/3 = 2.23$ in.	$299f_c$
$C_2 = -(30 \times 2.7)0.403f_c/2$	$= - \quad 16.3f_c$	$4 + 2.7/3 = 4.90$	$- \quad 80f_c$
$C =$	$117.7f_c$	$m =$	$219f_c$

$$z = m/C = 219f_c/117.7f_c = 1.85 \text{ in.}$$
$$jd = 20 - z = 20 - 1.85 = 18.15 \text{ in.}$$

$$f_s = \frac{T}{A_s} = \frac{M}{A_s jd} = \frac{150,000 \times 12}{5.0 \times 18.15} = 19,800 \text{ psi vs. } 18,000 \text{ psi allowable} \qquad \text{N.G.}$$

$C = M/jd = 150,000 \times 12/18.15 = 99,200 \text{ lb} = 117.7 f_c$ (from above)

$f_c = 840 \text{ psi vs. } 0.45 \times 2500 = 1125 \text{ psi allowable} \qquad \text{O.K.}$

(c) Approximate analysis

Same beam as in (b), Fig. 4.8a.

SOLUTION

As before, the neutral axis falls below the flange. The approximate method neglects the small compressive area (and small unit stress) below the flange, Fig. 4.8b. Then area moments about the neutral axis give:

$$(40 \times 4)(kd - 2) = 60(20 - kd)$$

$$220kd = 1520$$

$$kd = 6.90 \text{ in.}$$

At the bottom of the flange, $f_{c1} = f_c \times 2.90/6.90 = 0.420 f_c$.
The areas and stresses shown in Fig. 4.8c lead to:

	C	Arm abt. Top	Moment m abt. Top
$C_1 = (40 \times 6.9)f_c/2$	$= 138.0 f_c$	$6.9/3 = 2.30$ in.	$317 f_c$
$C_2 = -(40 \times 2.9)0.420 f_c/2 =$	$- 24.3 f_c$	$4 + 2.9/3 = 4.97$	$-120.8 f_c$
	$C = 113.7 f_c$		$m = 196 f_c$

$$z = 196 f_c/113.7 f_c = 1.73 \text{ in.}$$

$$jd = 20 - 1.73 = 18.27 \text{ in.}$$

The student should see clearly that there are many different patterns for C_1 and C_2 which lead to identical values of C and m. For example, based on Fig. 4.8d:

	C	Arm abt. Top	Moment m abt. Top
$C_1 = (40 \times 4)f_c/2$	$= 80.0 f_c$	$\frac{4}{3} = 1.33$ in.	$106.7 f_c$
$C_2 = (40 \times 4)0.420 f_c/2 =$	$33.6 f_c$	$4 \times \frac{2}{3} = 2.67$	$89.5 f_c$
	$C = 113.6 f_c$		$m = 196.2 f_c$

Here the unit stress picture has been subdivided rather than the area. It could have been subdivided into a rectangle and triangle of stress or the trapezoid could have been used undivided, provided its centroid was calculated as the location of C. The subdivisions to be used are a matter of convenience, but it should be noted that in the exact solution in (b) no other subdivision leads as directly to the desired result.

$$f_s = \frac{M}{A_s jd} = \frac{150,000 \times 12}{5.0 \times 18.27} = 19,700 \text{ psi vs. } 18,000 \text{ psi} \qquad \text{N.G.}$$

$$C = M/jd = 150,000 \times 12/18.27 = 98,700 \text{ lb} = 113.6 f_c$$

$$f_c = 870 \text{ psi vs. } 1125 \text{ psi} \qquad \text{O.K.}$$

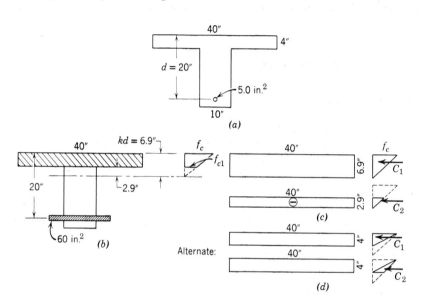

Fig. 4.8. Analysis of T-beam, approximate method.

(d) Allowable moment

Find the allowable moment on the T-beam of (b), Fig. 4.7a.

SOLUTION

An exact solution requires the location of the neutral axis ($kd = 6.7$ in.) and the determination of $jd = 18.15$ in. exactly as in (b). Without calculating the unit stresses of (b), f_s at its allowable of 18,000 psi can be shown to control the allowable moment, on the basis of similar stress triangles:

$$\text{If } f_s = 18,000 \text{ psi}, f_c = \frac{18,000}{12} \times \frac{6.7}{20 - 6.7} = 755 \text{ psi} \qquad \text{O.K.}$$

Allowable $M = A_s f_s jd = 5.0 \times 18,000 \times 18.15/12,000 = 136.2 \text{ k-ft}$

Since f_c almost never controls for a T-beam, one can *estimate* the allowable M without calculating either kd or jd. It is always possible to estimate jd

rather closely, within a few per cent. In Sec. 5.5 it is suggested that jd for a T-beam may be estimated as the larger of $0.9d$ or $d - t/2$ (where t is the flange thickness).

$$0.9d = 18 \text{ in.}, \qquad d - t/2 = 18 \text{ in.}, \qquad \text{approx. } jd = 18 \text{ in.}$$

Approx. allowable $M = A_s f_s jd = 5.0 \times 18,000 \times 18/12,000 = 135$ k-ft

This is probably closer to the accurate value of 136.2 k-ft (found above) than could normally be expected, but accuracy within 3% or better can be obtained easily.

4.8. COMPRESSION STEEL

(a) Elastic analysis

The elastic analysis of beams in which compression steel $A_s{}'$ is replaced by $(n - 1)A_s{}'$ units of transformed area has little validity* except for *changes* in stress due to live load alone, as discussed in Sec. 4.1. Shrinkage stresses and creep under dead load increase the compressive steel stress, much as in columns (Sec. 2.2). The actual distribution of compressive stresses between concrete and steel depends upon the entire history of the beam, and these shrinkage and creep effects are too complex for accurate analysis. Thus ultimate strength analysis is even more clearly indicated as desirable than for other types of beams.

(b) Semielastic analysis

The ACI Code provides a reasonable substitute method (Sec. 5.4) based on working stresses. This method, designated by the author as the semi-elastic method, considers the compressive steel stress as $2n$ times the concrete stress f_{cs}, at that same level, that is, $f_s{}' = 2nf_{cs}{}'$. The *effective* compressive steel stress (after considering displaced concrete) then becomes $f_s{}'' = (2n - 1)f_{cs}{}'$ and the transformed area $(2n - 1)A_s{}'$. The value of $f_s{}'$ must not, however, be taken larger than the allowable steel stress in tension.

The same stress assumption may be used in establishing the allowable moment on a given beam, but the process can be more involved in this case than in design, as illustrated in (c).

The transformed area of $(2n - 1)A_s{}'$ is also often used for evaluating the working stresses under a given moment. In this procedure the

* The only place in the Code which still uses the elastic analysis with compression steel is in Art. 1109a, b on eccentrically loaded columns where f_b is based on a transformed area which uses $(n - 1)A_s$ for the steel.

engineer should note that Code Art. 706*b* begins with the words "to approximate the effect." Since the distribution of compression between concrete and steel cannot actually be calculated, even a strict adherence to the Code provisions does not eliminate the crudeness of the basic approximation.

The author considers this method as reasonable for design and as fairly satisfactory for establishing an allowable moment, but in the calculation of stresses caused by a given moment the concepts get less and less significant. Only nominal compressive stresses can be found by this method. The following example illustrates the procedure and some of its complications.

(c) Analysis under ACI Code

Assume 2.0 in.^{2} of compression steel is added at 2 in. below the top of the rectangular beam of Sec. 4.5*a* and Fig. 4.3*a*, with $f_c' = 4000$ psi, $n = 7.5$, rail steel. Find stresses for $M = 100$ k-ft. Also find the allowable moment.

SOLUTION

The transformed area is shown in Fig. 4.9*b*, using $(2n - 1)A_s'$ for the compression steel as indicated by Art. 706*b*.

Area moments about neutral axis:

$$(13kd)kd/2 + 28(kd - 2) = 60(20 - kd)$$

$$(kd)^2 + 13.54kd + 6.77^2 = 193.2 + 6.77^2 = 239.2$$

$$kd = 15.47 - 6.77 = 8.70 \text{ in.}$$

Based on Fig. 4.9*c*:

$$f_{cs'} = f_c \times 6.70/8.70 = 0.770f_c$$

	C	Arm abt. Top	Moment m abt. Top
$C_1 = (13 \times 8.70)f_c/2 = 56.5f_c$		$8.70/3 = 2.90$ in.	$164.0f_c$
$C_2 = 28.0 \times 0.770f_c = 21.6f_c$		$d' = 2.00$	$43.2f_c$
$C = 78.1f_c$			$m = 207.2f_c$

$$z = 207.2f_c/78.1f_c = 2.65 \text{ in.}$$

$$jd = 20 - 2.65 = 17.35 \text{ in.}$$

$$f_s = \frac{M}{A_s jd} = \frac{100,000 \times 12}{8.0 \times 17.35} = 8650 \text{ psi vs. } 20,000 \text{ psi allowable} \qquad \text{O.K.}$$

$$C = M/jd = 100,000 \times 12/17.35 = 69,000 \text{ lb} = 78.1f_c \text{ (from above)}$$

$$f_c = 885 \text{ psi vs. } 0.45 \times 4000 = 1800 \text{ psi} \qquad \text{O.K.}$$

Check: $f_c = \dfrac{8650}{7.5} \times \dfrac{8.70}{11.30} = 888$ psi

$$f_s' = 2nf_{cs'} = 2 \times 7.5 \times 0.770 \times 885$$

$$= 10,230 \text{ psi vs. } 20,000 \text{ psi allowable} \qquad \text{O.K.}$$

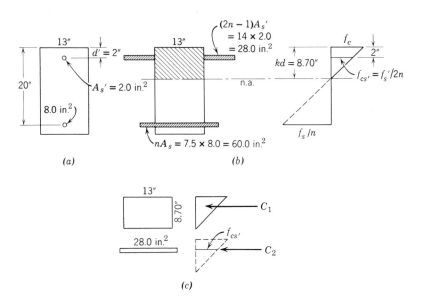

Fig. 4.9. Analysis of double-reinforced beam, semielastic method.

For allowable moment: If $f_c = 1800$ psi, similar stress triangles give:

$$f_s = nf_c \frac{20 - 8.70}{8.70} = 7.5 \times 1800 \times 11.30/8.70$$

$$= 17,500 \text{ psi vs. } 20,000 \text{ psi} \qquad \text{O.K.}$$

$$f_s' = 2nf_{cs'} = 2 \times 7.5 \times 0.770 \times 1800$$

$$= 20,800 \text{ psi vs. } 20,000 \text{ psi} \qquad \text{N.G.}$$

This value of f_s' is excessive, but it does not require that the allowable f_c must be lowered, as would be the case if f_s were excessive. What it does mean (under the ACI Code) is that the compression steel cannot be counted upon as contributing more than 20,000 psi; and this upsets the initial assumption that f_s' is $2nf_{cs'}$ and the effective transformed area is $(2n - 1)A_s'$. The effective compression area is something less, roughly 4% less; but not exactly this, because a change in this area would shift the neutral axis. Hence an "exact"

REINFORCED CONCRETE FUNDAMENTALS

theoretical solution requires a new beginning* with $f_s' = 20,000$ psi, that is, with f_s' no longer a function of f_c. It is shown in Sec. 5.4d that a balanced beam with $f_c = 0.45f_c'$ and $f_s = 20,000$ psi will also have $f_s' = 20,000$ psi when the cover $d' = 0.104d$. This fact is helpful in indicating that an f_s' of 20,000 psi will usually control when d' is less than 0.104d. The corresponding value for $f_s = 18,000$ psi is $d' = 0.134d$.

Since f_s (at 17,500 psi) is too low to become governing due to any small shift in neutral axis, a practical solution in this case can be based on maintaining the original (now erroneous) neutral axis. The moment can be evaluated as the sum of two couples, one based on $C_1 = 56.5f_c$ as before and the other on a revised C_2.

$$f_c = 1800 \text{ psi}, \qquad C_1 = 56.5 \times 1800 = 101,500 \text{ lb}$$

$$M_1 = 101,500(20 - 2.90)/12,000 = 145.0 \text{ k-ft}$$

$$f_{cs'} = 0.770f_c = 1386 \text{ psi}$$

Effective $f_s'' = 20,000 - f_{cs'} = 20,000 - 1386 = 18,610$ psi

$$C_2 = 2.0 \times 18,610 = 37,200 \text{ lb}, \qquad M_2 = 37,200(20 - 2)/12,000 = 55.8 \text{ k-ft}$$

Allowable $M = M_1 + M_2 = 200.8$ k-ft

(d) Actual stresses depend on more than moment

In the light of the allowable moment complications just discussed, a further look should be taken at the original analysis in (c) for stresses under a given moment. If the given moment had been 200 k-ft instead of 100 k-ft, all calculated stresses would have been doubled, f_c to 1776 psi, f_s to 17,300 psi, and f_s' to 20,460 psi. Although this value of f_s' exceeds the permissible value in the Code, the allowable moment calculation in (c) has proved that the beam under this 200 k-ft moment does satisfy the Code. The slight excess of f_s' is offset by an extra margin in f_c (allowable of 1800 psi). The reader should recognize that modifications in the above calculations can be directed toward satisfying the Code, but that such calculations may not give any better values of the actual stresses in the beam.

* A theoretical solution is scarcely worthwhile, but it is not difficult. One must substitute the fundamental relationship $C = T$ for the derived idea that the neutral axis is at the centroid. In this case $f_c = 1800$ psi, $f_s' = 20,000$ psi, and f_s must be expressed in terms of f_c derived from the similar stress triangles.

$$f_s = nf_c(d - kd)/kd = 7.5 \times 1800(20 - kd)/kd$$

Effective $f_s'' = 20,000 - f_{cs'}$ where $f_{cs'} = 1800(kd - 2)/kd$

$$C = 13kd \times \frac{1800}{2} + 2.0\left(20,000 - 1800\frac{kd - 2}{kd}\right) = T = 8.0 \times 7.5 \times 1800\frac{20 - kd}{kd}$$

This gives $kd = 8.74$ in. and leads to an allowable $M = 201.5$ k-ft.

Actual compressive stresses in a beam with compression steel, just as in a column, depend upon the entire history of the beam and *cannot be calculated* on the basis of load alone. In such stress calculations, refinements in the procedure mean very little.

4.9. IRREGULAR SHAPED BEAMS

Beams of irregular shape are often used for special purposes, such as curved-top or triangular-top shapes for railings, curbs over exterior bridge girders, beams with continuous side brackets, or beams with recesses for supporting a future slab or masonry. Where the shape is entirely bounded by vertical and horizontal surfaces, the location of the resultant C, as for T-beams and double-reinforced beams, is a practical procedure. Where sloping faces or curved surfaces occur, the use of the moment of inertia and $Mc = fI$ is generally simpler.

It should be noted that many irregular shaped beams are not symmetrical and are not loaded along their principal axes. Fortunately, most of these are restrained against lateral deflection by a monolithic slab. In such cases, lack of symmetry can be ignored and the bending axis will be essentially horizontal.

4.10. FORMULAS

(a) Advantages of formulas

Several advantages accrue from the development of formulas. In the author's opinion, their chief advantage lies in the possibility of constructing curves and other design aids which can shorten design calculations. Others might say that formulas constitute the most direct approach to everyday design. Finally, formulas may indicate the real variables more clearly than numerical calculations. For instance, a person who had always used area moments to locate the neutral axis, instead of the formula developed in (*b*), might not suspect that k depends on p rather than on the absolute value of A_s.

(b) Rectangular beam formulas

The transformed area concept, as shown in Fig. 4.10, will be used, with A_s replaced by pbd. The formula for k comes from an area moment equation about the neutral axis.

$$(bkd)kd/2 = npbd(d - kd)$$

When bd^2 is eliminated, the resulting quadratic in k leads to

$$k = \sqrt{2pn + (pn)^2} - pn$$

$$\quad \rho = \frac{A_s}{bd}$$

$$jd = d - kd/3, \quad \text{or } j = 1 - k/3$$

By inspection,

$$T = A_s f_s \qquad C = 0.5 f_c bkd \qquad n = \frac{E_s}{E_c}$$

$$M = Tjd = A_s f_s jd \qquad M = Cjd = 0.5 f_c kjbd^2$$

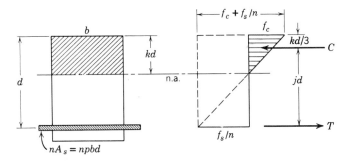

Fig. 4.10. Symbols for formulas—rectangular beams.

These equations for M can be rewritten:

$$M = A_s f_s jd = pbdf_s jd = Rbd^2$$

$$M = 0.5 f_c kjbd^2 = Rbd^2$$

where $R = pf_s j = 0.5 f_c kj$.

Based on the similar stress triangles,

$$\frac{kd}{f_c} = \frac{d}{f_c + f_s/n}, \qquad k = \frac{f_c}{f_c + f_s/n} = \frac{1}{1 + f_s/nf_c}$$

(c) T-beam formulas

The so-called approximate method of analysis, which neglects the bending stress between the neutral axis and the bottom of the flange as indicated in Fig. 4.11, will be used. It should be noted that A_s is replaced by pbd; even though bd is not a real concrete area, this definition of p leads to the simplest formulas. When the neutral axis is below the flange, area moments about the neutral axis establish k.

$$bt(kd - t/2) = nA_s(d - kd) = npbd(d - kd)$$

$$k = \frac{np + \frac{1}{2}(t/d)^2}{np + (t/d)}$$

Since the trapezoid of stress acts on a uniform width b, the resultant C acts at the centroid of the trapezoid, at a distance z from the top of the beam:

$$z = \frac{t}{3} \times \frac{3k - 2t/d}{2k - t/d}$$

$$jd = d - z, \qquad j = 1 - z/d$$

The substitution of the above values of z and k gives

$$j = \frac{1 - (t/d) + \frac{1}{3}(t/d)^2 + (t/d)^3/(12pn)}{1 - \frac{1}{2}(t/d)}$$

In terms of tension, $M = A_s f_s jd$.

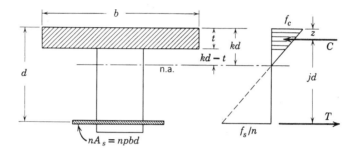

Fig. 4.11. Symbols for formulas—approximate method for T-beams.

The total compression is

$$\frac{1}{2}\left[f_c + f_c\left(\frac{kd - t}{kd}\right)\right] bt = f_c bt\left(1 - \frac{t}{2kd}\right)$$

which leads to

$$M = Cjd = f_c bt\left(1 - \frac{t}{2kd}\right) jd$$

These two equations for moments can be written in terms of coefficients as follows:

$$M = A_s f_s jd = pbdf_s jd = pjn\frac{f_s}{n} bd^2 = C_s \frac{f_s}{n} bd^2 = M_s$$

$$M = f_c bt\left(1 - \frac{t}{2kd}\right) jd = f_c \frac{t}{d}\left(1 - \frac{t}{2kd}\right) jbd^2 = C_c f_c bd^2 = M_c$$

where

$$C_s = pjn \qquad \text{and} \qquad C_c = \left(1 - \frac{t}{2kd}\right) \frac{t}{d} j$$

REINFORCED CONCRETE FUNDAMENTALS

As in the rectangular beam or any other beam, the similar stress triangles lead also to

$$k = \frac{1}{1 + f_s/nf_c}$$

(d) Double-reinforced beam formulas

Under the present ACI Code, formulas for double-reinforced beams are only partially satisfactory. For the semielastic analysis where f_s' is taken as $2nf_{cs'}$ there is no difficulty. However, Sec. 5.4d points out that for a balanced beam with $f_c = 0.45f_c'$ and $f_s = 20,000$ psi, the f_s' stress will be

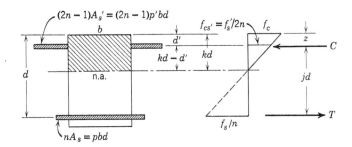

Fig. 4.12. Symbols for formulas—semielastic method for double-reinforced beams.

controlled by the 20,000-psi limit whenever $d' \lesssim 0.104d$. The author calls the 20,000-psi case the nonelastic case because f_s' is then not a function of elastic deformations. When the general case, not balanced, is considered, the boundary between semielastic and nonelastic cannot be defined simply. For the nonelastic case the location of the neutral axis is not fixed by the beam cross section alone but is a function of the absolute value of the moment.

For maximum f_s' limited to 20,000 psi, the semielastic analysis seems to be roughly limited to $d' \gtrsim 0.1d$, although it also applies to smaller d' values when the moment is much less than the allowable.

The semielastic analysis assumes the cross section of Fig. 4.12, when the concrete displaced by A_s' is considered. Area moments about the neutral axis can again be used to establish k.

$$(bkd)kd/2 + (2n - 1)p'bd(kd - d') = npbd(d - kd)$$

$$k = \sqrt{2(2n-1)p'\frac{d'}{d} + 2pn + n^2(2p' + p - p'/n)^2} - n(2p' + p - p'/n)*$$

Moments of the compressive forces about the top of the beam establish the distance z down to the resultant C.

$$z = \frac{(d/6)k^2 + p'(2n-1)(1 - d'/kd)d'}{k/2 + p'(2n-1)(1 - d'/kd)}$$

$$j = 1 - z/d$$

$$M = A_s f_s jd = f_s pjbd^2$$

Since $f_s/nf_c = (1 - k)/k$,

$$f_s = nf_c(1 - k)/k \qquad \text{and} \qquad M = \frac{f_c(1 - k)pnj}{k} bd^2$$

The elastic analysis is of little direct practical value, but curves based on this analysis may be of some value for rough estimates. Hence the basic equations, neglecting concrete displaced by A_s', are listed:

$$k = \sqrt{2n\left(p'\frac{d'}{d} + p\right) + n^2(p' + p)^2} - n(p + p')$$

$$z = \frac{(d/6)k^2 + p'nd'(1 - d'/kd)}{k/2 + p'n(1 - d'/kd)}$$

The relations for j and M are the same as for the semielastic case, although k and j represent different values.

$$M = f_c \left(\frac{1 - k}{k}\right) pnjbd^2 = Rf_c bd^2$$

where $R = pnj(1 - k)/k$.

4.11. CURVES AND CHARTS

(a) Rectangular beams

In Appendix E curves for k and j of rectangular beams are shown in Fig. E.2. In Figs. E.3 and E.4 coefficients of resistance to moment are shown for various values of n.

* When the displaced concrete is ignored this simplifies to

$$k = \sqrt{4p'n\frac{d'}{d} + 2pn + n^2(2p' + p)^2} - n(2p' + p)$$

REINFORCED CONCRETE FUNDAMENTALS

The example of Sec. 4.5a and Fig. 4.3 falls outside the chart limits. Consider this same beam with $A_s = 3.00$ in.^{2} and $M = 100$ k-ft, $n = 7.5$, and find the unit stresses.

$$n = E_s/E_c = 30 \times 10^6 \div (4 \times 10^6) = 7.5$$

$$p = A_s/bd = 3.00/(13 \times 20) = 0.0115$$

$$\text{Actual } R = M/bd^2 = 100 \times 12{,}000/(13 \times 20^2) = 231$$

Since no chart is available for $n = 7.5$, Fig. E.3 for $n = 8$ will be used. The results, without any correction, will be found at the intersection of 1.15% of steel on the abscissa and an R of 231 on the ordinate. At this intersection the stresses read $f_c = 1510$ psi and $f_s = 23{,}000$ psi. A slightly better value of f_c (but not of f_s) could be found by using a percentage of steel corrected to maintain the proper product of $pn = 0.0115 \times 7.5 = 0.0861 = p_c \times 8$. This gives the equivalent steel at $n = 8$ as $p_c = 0.0108$, which leads to $f_c = 1550$ psi.

Assume the allowable moment on the slab of Fig. 4.5 is desired for $d = 4$ in., $n = 10$, and allowable stresses of $f_c = 1350$ psi and $f_s = 20{,}000$ psi. Then $p = 0.465/(12 \times 4) = 0.0097$. In Fig. E.3 one can move vertically at this p value to read $R = 210$ at $f_c = 1350$ psi, but this corresponds to an $f_s = 24{,}000$ psi which is too much. The permissible R is at $f_s = 20{,}000$ psi, where f_c is low and $R = 174$. Allowable $M = Rbd^2 = 174 \times 12 \times 4^2/12{,}000 = 2.78$ k-ft on a 1-ft strip.

(b) T-beams

Figure E.5 of Appendix E shows k and j values for T-beams. The dashed line marked "Limit for T-Beams" corresponds to k values which put the neutral axis exactly at the bottom of the flange. If the given values of pn and t/d intersect in the blank area beyond this line, the proper solution will be found on the rectangular beam chart, Fig. E.2. Figure E.6 establishes C_s which permits f_s to be determined from M, or the reverse. Figure E.7 is a similar chart for C_c, which is a coefficient relating f_c to M.

For example, consider the T-beam of Sec. 4.7c and Fig. 4.8.

$$t/d = 4/20 = 0.20, \qquad p = 5/(40 \times 20) = 0.0063,$$

$$n = 12, \qquad pn = 0.0756$$

From Fig. E.6,

$$C_s = 0.069, \qquad M_s = C_s \frac{f_s}{n} bd^2$$

$$150 \times 12{,}000 = 0.069 f_s \times 40 \times 20^2/12$$

$$f_s = 19{,}550 \text{ psi, compared to } 19{,}700 \text{ psi in Sec. } 4.7_c$$

From Fig. E.7,

$$C_c = 0.129, \qquad M_c = C_c f_c b d^2$$

$$150 \times 12,000 = 0.129 f_c \times 40 \times 20^2$$

$f_c = 874$ psi, compared to 870 psi in Sec. 4.7c

If one is interested in k and j, they are obtained from Fig. E.5:

$$k = 0.343, \qquad kd = 6.86 \text{ in. (6.90 in. in Sec. 4.7}c)$$

$$j = 0.914, \qquad jd = 18.28 \text{ in. (18.27 in. in Sec. 4.7}c)$$

(c) Double-reinforced beams

Included in Appendix E are Figs. E.8, E.9, and E.10 for double-reinforced rectangular beams based on an elastic analysis, that is, for the effective $f_s'' = nf_{cs'}$, which neglects displaced concrete. Although elastic calculations with A_s' have little place in design under the ACI Code, approximate values for the semielastic case ($f_s' = 2nf_{cs'}$) can be obtained from these charts by inserting twice the actual p' values.

As an example, the beam of Sec. 4.8b and Fig. 4.9 will be analyzed.

$$M = 100 \text{ k-ft}, \qquad n = 7.5$$

$$pn = 7.5 \times 8.0/(13 \times 20) = 0.231$$

$$p'n = 7.5 \times 2.0/(13 \times 20) = 0.0578 \qquad \text{USE } p'n = 2 \times 0.0578 = 0.1156$$

$$d'/d = 2/20 = 0.10$$

Figure E.9, with $p'n = 0.1156$, gives $R = 0.265$ for use in $M = Rf_c bd^2$.

$$100 \times 12,000 = 0.265 f_c \times 13 \times 20^2$$

$$f_c = 870 \text{ psi}$$

The center of Fig. E.9 shows $k = 0.432$ and $f_s/nf_c = 1.32$.

$$f_s = 1.32 \times 7.5 \times 870 = 8620 \text{ psi}$$

$$kd = 0.432 \times 20 = 8.64 \text{ in.}$$

$$f_s' = 2nf_{cs'} = 2 \times 7.5 \left(\frac{8.64 - 2}{8.64} \right) 870 = 10,020 \text{ psi}$$

The better values in Sec. 4.8b are:

$$f_c = 885 \text{ psi}, \qquad f_s = 8650 \text{ psi}, \qquad kd = 8.70 \text{ in.}, \qquad f_s = 10,230 \text{ psi}$$

Part of the difference lies in the fact that Sec. 4.8b took account of the concrete displaced by A_s' whereas the curves do not.

In the semielastic analysis it is very important that f_s' be calculated. If f_s' exceeds 20,000 psi, the method is invalid and the neutral axis location becomes a function of M as well as of the beam cross section. In this connection the student might review the comments in Sec. 4.8c.

SELECTED REFERENCES

1. *Standard Specifications for Highway Bridges*, AASHO, Washington, 6th ed., 1953.
2. *Principles of Reinforced Concrete Construction*, F. E. Turneaure and E. R. Maurer, John Wiley & Sons, New York, 4th ed., 1935.

PROBLEMS

Note: Code Arts. 305 and 306 give allowable stresses and values of n. When actual stresses are calculated, always compare each with its allowable value.

Prob. 4.1.

(*a*) For the rectangular beam of Fig. 4.13, $f_c' = 3000$ psi, intermediate grade of steel, calculate f_c and f_s from the internal couple when $M = 125$ k-ft.

(*b*) Calculate f_c and f_s from $Mc = fI$.

(*c*) What is allowable (working) moment on this beam under the ACI Code?

Prob. 4.2. Same as Prob. 4.1 except A_s is 4–#10 bars of rail steel.

Prob. 4.3. Same as Prob. 4.1 except A_s is 4–#10 bars and A_s' of 2–#7 bars has been added centered 2.5 in. below the top.

Prob. 4.4.

(*a*) For the T-beam of Fig. 4.14, $f_c' = 3750$ psi, A_s of 3–#9 bars, intermediate grade steel, calculate f_c and f_s from the internal couple when $M = 100$ k-ft. Use the approximate method (Sec. 4.7c).

(*b*) Calculate f_c and f_s from $Mc = fI$.

(*c*) What is the allowable moment?

Prob. 4.5. Repeat Prob. 4.4 except change A_s to 4–#10 bars and use the exact method of analysis.

Prob. 4.6. Find the allowable moment on the joist of Fig. 4.15 if $f_c' = 3000$ psi and A_s is 2–#8 bars of rail steel. Use the exact method of analysis.

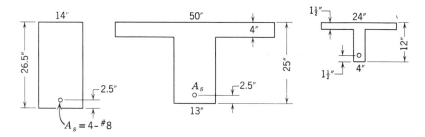

Fig. 4.13. Beam for Prob. 4.1. **Fig. 4.14.** T-beam for Prob. 4.4. **Fig. 4.15.** Joist for Prob. 4.6.

Prob. 4.7. Find the allowable moment on a 1-ft strip of the slab of Fig. 4.5 if the bars are made #7 at 7 in. on centers and $d = 6$ in., $f_c' = 3000$ psi, hard grade steel.

Prob. 4.8. Find f_c, f_s, and f_s' for the beam of Fig. 4.16 if $f_c' = 5000$ psi and hard grade steel is used. (Note Code Art. 706b.) Ignore the lack of symmetry.
(a) Use the internal couple. $M = 120$ k-ft.
(b) Use $Mc = fI$. $M = 120$ k-ft.

Prob. 4.9. If $f_c' = 3000$ psi and steel is intermediate grade, find the allowable moment on the beam of Fig. 4.17. (Note Code Art. 706b.)

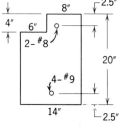

Fig. 4.16. Irregular beam for Prob. 4.8.

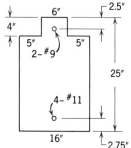

Fig. 4.17. Irregular beam for Prob. 4.9.

Prob. 4.10. Find the allowable moment about the horizontal axis of the regular hexagonal pile of Fig. 4.18 in the position shown, if $f_c' = 4000$ psi and steel is hard grade. (Suggestion: Use $Mc = fI$.)

Prob. 4.11. If the hexagonal pile of Fig. 4.18 and Prob. 4.10 is rotated 90°, find the allowable moment.

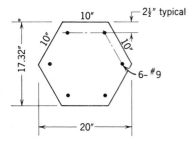

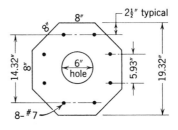

Fig. 4.18. Hexagonal pile for Probs. 4.10 and 4.11.

Fig. 4.19. Hollow octagonal pile for Prob. 4.12.

Prob. 4.12. Find the allowable moment about the horizontal axis of the regular octagonal pile shown in Fig. 4.19 if bars are rail steel and $f_c' = 5000$ psi. (Suggestion: Use $Mc = fI$.)

Prob. 4.13. Neglecting the lack of symmetry (because the flange is part of a continuing slab), find f_c and f_s in the beam of Fig. 4.20 if $f_c' = 3000$ psi and $A_s = 2-\#9$ bars of intermediate grade steel. $M = 60$ k-ft.

Prob. 4.14. Find the allowable moment on the handrail of Fig. 4.21 for intermediate grade steel and $f_c' = 3000$ psi, vertical loads.

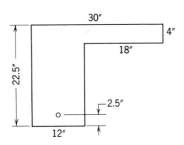

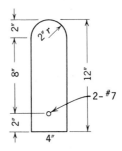

Fig. 4.20. Spandrel T-beam for Prob. 4.13.

Fig. 4.21. Handrail for Prob. 4.14.

Beams— Design for Moment

5.1. DESIGN VERSUS ANALYSIS

In analysis, whether for actual stresses or for allowable moments, the engineer deals with given beams, known both as to dimensions and steel. He has no control over the location of the neutral axis, which lies at the centroid of the transformed area.

In design, loads and allowable stresses are known and some or all of the dimensions remain to be fixed. In this case the designer has some control over the location of the neutral axis. He can shift it where he wants it, to the extent that his change in dimensions can shift the centroid of the transformed area.

The student should understand clearly this fundamental difference between design and analysis problems.

5.2. GENERAL PROCEDURES

After loads are known and the layout of the structure or structural element has been established,* the maximum bending moment can be determined. The member design for moment involves three separate steps:

1. Choice of beam cross section.
2. Choice of reinforcing steel at point or points of maximum moment.
3. Determination of points where bars are no longer needed for moment, that is, points for bending or stopping bars.

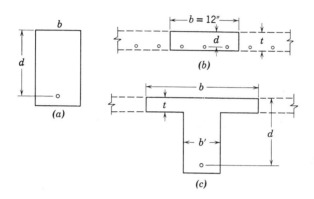

Fig. 5.1. Typical reinforced concrete beams. (*a*) Rectangular. (*b*) Slab. (*c*) T-beam.

Often other factors than moment determine the choice of the beam cross section, such as shear (Chap. 6). Such interrelationships will be discussed later.

In rectangular beams (Fig. 5.1*a*) both width *b* and depth *d* to steel are to be chosen. In slabs (Fig. 5.1*b*) the strip width *b* is fixed and only the depth *d* or the over-all thickness *t* can be selected. In T-beams (Fig. 5.1*c*) the flange thickness *t* and flange width *b* are determined, usually by a slab already designed, and this leaves the stem width *b'* and the depth *d* to the steel to be selected. The choice of *b'* and *d* is not usually determined directly by the moment alone.

* The choice of proper design loads and the layout of a structure to support these loads efficiently is a major part of the design. The choice of loads and the general problem of framing layout are not covered in this text. Chapter 8 has a brief discussion of beam-and-girder framing and the proper arrangement of loading for maximum moment on continuous one-way slabs and beams. Various types of slab construction are discussed in Chaps. 9 and 11.

In double-reinforced beams the compression steel is required because b and d have been chosen smaller than the normal requirements. However, when compression steel in limited amounts is specified, the size of double-reinforced beams can be based on moment requirements.

The design of steel, once the moment and beam size are known, is dependent upon a proper choice of the arm jd. In rectangular beams (and slabs) and in double-reinforced beams, the analytical solution for jd is feasible and commonly used. In T-beams the cut-and-try approach is customary, that is, the value of jd is first estimated, the corresponding approximate A_s is calculated, and from this A_s a better value of jd is established; in turn this jd leads to a better and usually satisfactory value of A_s. This cut-and-try solution for steel is possible for any type beam, but is not advantageous for rectangular beams and slabs.

The bending or stopping of bars is determined by the maximum moments to be resisted at various points along the beam. Bending of bars will be discussed separately from choice of beam and steel (Sec. 5.6).

5.3. RECTANGULAR BEAMS—MOMENT DESIGN

(a) The balanced beam in design

A beam which reaches its allowable f_c and its allowable f_s under the same working moment is called a balanced beam.* Such a beam will often constitute the most economical construction; and it usually represents the smallest desirable beam.

Although a balanced beam is frequently the design objective, the balanced depth will only occasionally be a practical dimension. Usually, over-all beam depths are specified in full or half inches. If the balanced depth (in decimals of an inch) is adjusted to a more practical dimension, the beam will no longer be exactly balanced for the given moment. Hence practical design is concerned with the balanced beam only as an approach to practical beam dimensions. The design of the reinforcing steel should be based on the actual dimensions used.

Slightly deeper beams are in the direction of economy. Since less steel is required with the larger jd, such a beam is termed an underreinforced beam. On the other hand, slightly shallower beams are also practical, but these require a considerable increase in steel area. Such over-reinforced beams are somewhat more expensive and become impractical

---

* The student should note that a beam thus balanced for allowable working stresses will not be balanced at failure—as Whitney defines a balanced beam. The balance at failure calls for a much larger A_s.

REINFORCED CONCRETE FUNDAMENTALS

when the depth is reduced more than 5% or 10%. For larger reductions in depth compression steel is indicated.

(b) Balanced beam design

The design procedure for a beam exactly balanced at working load will be illustrated by the design of a rectangular beam for $M = 100$ k-ft, $f_c' = 3000$ psi, hard grade steel.

SOLUTION

Since the steel is still to be selected, the neutral axis can be made to fall at any convenient location. That location corresponding to balanced stresses is desired. In this example, the ACI Code, Secs. 305 and 306, establishes: allowable $f_c = 0.45 \times 3000 = 1350$ psi, $n = 10$, allowable $f_s = 20,000$ psi.

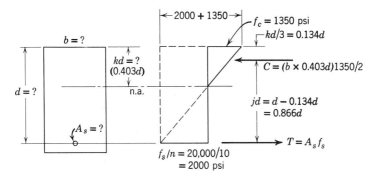

Fig. 5.2. Design of a balanced rectangular beam.

The beam, with dimensions still as symbols, can be sketched as in Fig. 5.2 along with the unit stress triangles which must accompany a straight-line distribution of stress. When simultaneous values of allowable f_c and f_s are assigned to the maximum stress values, the similar triangles locate the proportionate depth kd to the desired neutral axis. It is convenient to consider the large dashed triangle of height d and horizontal dimension $2000 + 1350$ as one of the similar triangles.

$$\frac{kd}{d} = \frac{1350}{2000 + 1350} = 0.403, \qquad kd = 0.403d$$

$$jd = d - kd/3 = d - 0.403d/3 = 0.866d$$

The resultant compression C can now be sketched in its proper location and evaluated in terms of b and kd.

$$C = (b \times 0.403d)1350/2$$

$$M = Cjd = (b \times 0.403d \times 1350/2)0.866d = 236bd^2 = Rbd^2$$

The constant, 236, is a function of the unit stresses and not of the loading. Hence every balanced rectangular beam designed for these materials (or these unit stresses) will be concerned with this constant. One calculates it once on a given job and then uses it for many designs. It is usually designated by the symbol R and will be found tabulated in all handbooks.

The size of the beam can be found by equating the maximum bending moment to this resisting moment, noting that units must be consistent, usually inches and pounds.

$$M = 100,000 \times 12 = Rbd^2 = 236bd^2$$

Reqd. $bd^2 = 5080$ in.^{3}

This requirement can be met by a wide range of sizes, for example:

If $b = 7.5$ in., $d = \sqrt{678} = 26.0$ in. $b = 11$ in., $d = \sqrt{462} = 21.5$ in.

$b = 8$, $d = \sqrt{635} = 25.2$ $b = 11.5$, $d = \sqrt{442} = 21.0$

$b = 9$, $d = \sqrt{565} = 23.7$ $b = 12$, $d = \sqrt{423} = 20.5$

$b = 9.5$, $d = \sqrt{535} = 23.1$ $b = 13$, $d = \sqrt{391} = 19.8$

$b = 10$, $d = \sqrt{508} = 22.5$ $b = 14$, $d = \sqrt{362} = 19.0$

The 7.5-in., 9.5-in., and 11.5-in. widths are listed because these are convenient widths for form lumber and forms are one of the most costly items in reinforced concrete construction. The narrowest beam shown may be too narrow to accommodate the reinforcing steel, it uses up the most headroom, and requires the greatest area of forms; but it uses the smallest volume of concrete and steel. A d/b ratio from 1.0 or 1.5 to 2.5 or 3.0 is usually considered in the desirable range, with the larger ratios for the bigger beams. Since deep beams often require increased story heights, more wall and partition height, and thus other costs than the cost of the beam, there is no simple textbook answer to the *best* depth. There are a number of satisfactory choices possible.

USE $b = 9.5$ in., $d = 23.1$ in.

The depth of 23.1 in. is probably not entirely practical; it is not a dimension one would turn over to a carpenter or steel worker. But either more or less depth than 23.1 in., with this width, would *not* give a balanced beam. This theoretical solution will be used here and possible modifications will be considered in succeeding paragraphs.

Reqd. $A_s = \dfrac{T}{f_s} = \dfrac{M}{f_s jd} = \dfrac{100,000 \times 12}{20,000 \times 0.866 \times 23.1} = 3.00$ in.^{2}

Choice of bars will be discussed in a later chapter.

(c) Beams deeper than a balanced section

When dimensions must be modified to get practical sizes, the usual procedure is to use the next larger practical dimension. Beams are also made deeper because such a size may be required for shear or to match the ceiling level established by heavier loaded beams.

Redesign the beam of (*b*) for $b = 9.5$ in., $d = 24$ in.

SOLUTION

The steel area is the only element left to design. Since the beam is larger than the balanced section, f_c tends to be less than allowable and f_s would also be less than allowable if the 3.00-in.^{2} steel area calculated above for the balanced beam were used. For economy, reduce A_s until f_s is the full allowable. The unit stress diagram in Fig. 5.3 is thus shown with $f_s = 20,000$ psi and with f_c unknown, but known (assumed) to be less than allowable. From similar triangles, the

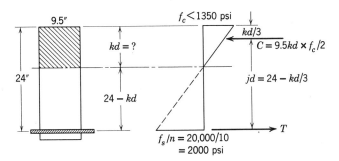

Fig. 5.3. Stress triangles for beam deeper than a balanced beam.

unknown f_c can be expressed in terms of the known f_s and unknown kd. Then C and M can be calculated in terms of kd.

$$f_c = 2000 \frac{kd}{24 - kd}$$

$$C = 9.5kd \times \frac{2000}{2} \times \frac{kd}{24 - kd}$$

$$M = 100,000 \times 12 = Cjd = 9.5kd \times \frac{2000}{2} \times \frac{kd}{24 - kd} \left(24 - \frac{kd}{3} \right)$$

$$1,200,000 = 9500 \frac{(kd)^2}{24 - kd} \left(24 - \frac{kd}{3} \right)$$

$$\frac{(kd)^2}{24 - kd} \left(24 - \frac{kd}{3} \right) = 126.5$$

This is a cubic equation which can be solved by trial from the present form about as easily as if it were simplified. The value of kd will be slightly less than the balanced beam value of $0.403 \times 24 = 9.67$ in. Try

$$kd = 9.5 \text{ in.}, \quad \frac{9.5^2}{14.5} (24 - 3.17) = 129.3 > 126.5$$

$$kd = 9.3, \quad \frac{9.3^2}{14.7} (24 - 3.10) = 123 < 126.5$$

$$kd = 9.4, \quad \frac{9.4^2}{14.6} (24 - 3.13) = 126.2 < 126.5$$

USE $kd = 9.41$ in.

$jd = 24 - 9.41/3 = 20.86$ in.

$$\text{Reqd. } A_s = \frac{M}{f_s jd} = \frac{100{,}000 \times 12}{20{,}000 \times 20.86} = 2.87 \text{ in.}^2 \longleftarrow$$

Check by area moments about the neutral axis:

$$9.5 \times 9.41 \times 9.41/2 = 10A_s(24 - 9.41)$$

$$A_s = 2.88 \text{ in.}^2$$

Verify f_c by similar triangles:

$$f_c = \frac{20{,}000}{10} \times \frac{9.41}{14.59} = 1290 \text{ psi} < 1350 \qquad \text{O.K.}$$

Since the cubic equation is awkward, an empirical approximation is usually substituted in the calculation for A_s, that is, the use of jd as the balanced j times the increased d. The balanced j was found in Sec. 5.3b to be 0.866.

$$\text{Reqd. } A_s = \frac{100{,}000 \times 12}{20{,}000 \times 0.866 \times 24} = 2.89 \text{ in.}^2$$

Since less steel is used than would be required for a balanced beam, the neutral axis is higher and the real j value is always greater than the balanced j. Thus this approximation for A_s is always on the safe side. For small increases in d it is not wasteful and is recommended. When d is 20% to 50% greater than the balanced d, some steel can be saved by using a more exact j.

(d) Beams shallower than a balanced section

It is rarely feasible to reduce d below the balanced depth by more than possibly 10%, unless compression steel is used. A reduction in depth greatly increases the required steel and makes this type of construction uneconomical except for very small deficiencies in d.

Redesign the beam of Sec. 5.3b for $b = 9.5$ in., $d = 22$ in.

SOLUTION

In this case, the reduced depth tends to cause increased f_c and f_s. A reasonable addition to A_s would bring f_s within the allowable, but would leave f_c too large. The only way to remedy the overstress in compression (other than with compression steel) is to increase the compression area by lowering the neutral axis. Extra A_s will lower the neutral axis, but a large amount is required; this operation tends to be inefficient and the steel has to work at a low unit stress. The unit stress diagram in Fig. 5.4 is thus shown with f_c at the allowable and f_s below the allowable.

$$C = 9.5kd \times 1350/2$$

$$M = 100,000 \times 12 = Cjd = 9.5kd \times \frac{1350}{2} \left(22 - \frac{kd}{3} \right)$$

$$(kd)^2 - 66kd + 33.0^2 = -561 + 33.0^2 = 528$$

$$kd = \pm \sqrt{528} + 33.0 = \pm 22.98 + 33.0 = 10.0 \text{ in.}$$

$$jd = 22 - 10.0/3 = 18.67 \text{ in.}$$

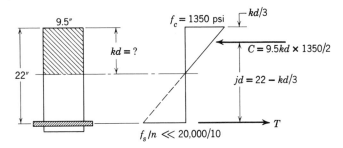

Fig. 5.4. Stress triangles for beam shallower than a balanced beam.

By similar triangles,

$$f_s/n = 1350 \times \frac{22 - 10.0}{10.0} = 1620$$

Allow. $f_s = 10 \times 1620 = 16,200$ psi (to protect against overstress in f_c)

Reqd. $A_s = \dfrac{M}{f_s jd} = \dfrac{100,000 \times 12}{16,200 \times 18.67} = 3.97$ in.^{2} ←

Check by area moments about the neutral axis:

$$9.5 \times 10.0 \times 10.0/2 = 10A_s(22 - 10.0)$$

$$\text{Reqd. } A_s = 3.97 \text{ in.}^2$$

Note that a 4.8 % reduction in d has required a 32 % increase in A_s compared to the balanced condition in Sec. 5.3b. There is no acceptable approximate solution for this case.

(e) Reinforcing steel for beam of given size

Design procedures for rectangular beams can be summarized as indicated in Table 5.1.

The first step after the beam size is known or has been established is to identify the beam as underreinforced, balanced, or overreinforced. As noted under "Identification," the actual moment may be compared to the balanced moment $M = Rbd^2$. An alternate equivalent calculation is to compare the actual $R = $ actual M/bd^2 with the balanced value of R. The

BEAMS—DESIGN FOR MOMENT

TABLE 5.1. Rectangular Beams

Identification:

Underreinforced	Balanced	Overreinforced
Actual $M <$ (bal. R)bd^2	Actual $M =$ (bal. R)$bd^2 =$ bal. M	Actual $M >$ (bal. R)bd^2
Actual $R = M/bd^2 <$ bal. R	Actual $R = M/bd^2 =$ bal. R	Actual $R = M/bd^2 >$ bal. R
Actual $d > \sqrt{M/(\text{bal. } R)b}$	$d = \sqrt{M/(\text{bal. } R)b} =$ bal. d	Actual $d < \sqrt{M/(\text{bal. } R)b}$

Designation:

Underreinforced	Balanced	Overreinforced

Design:

Underreinforced	Balanced	Overreinforced
$f_c = \dfrac{f_s}{n}\dfrac{kd}{d-kd}$	kd from similar triangles	kd from $M = Cjd$ (quadratic eq. in kd)
kd from $M = Cjd$ (cubic eq. in kd)	$M = Rbd^2$	Reduced $f_s = nf_c \dfrac{d-kd}{kd} \ll$ allow. f_s
$A_s = \dfrac{M}{(\text{allow.})f_s \times j \text{ (from above)} \times d}$	$A_s = \dfrac{M}{f_s jd}$	$A_s = \dfrac{M}{(\text{reduced})f_s \times jd}$ (requires exact j or jd)
Approx. $A_s = \dfrac{M}{(\text{allow.})f_s \times (\text{bal.}) j \times d}$ (deeper than bal. d)		

Alternate for any of the three types:

Find A_s by area moments about n.a. after kd is established: $nA_s(d - kd) = b(kd)^2/2$

REINFORCED CONCRETE FUNDAMENTALS

comparison can also be made between the actual d and the balanced $d = \sqrt{\text{actual } M/Rb}$.

If the actual d is less than 90% to 95% of the balanced d, it is more economical to design as a double-reinforced beam, as in the following section.

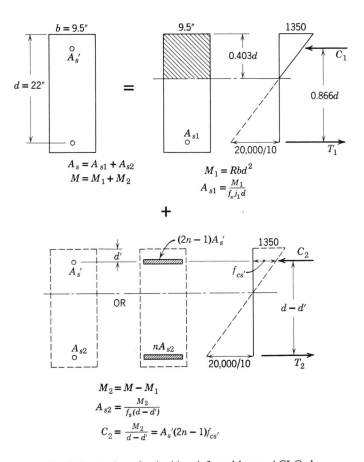

$A_s = A_{s1} + A_{s2}$
$M = M_1 + M_2$

$M_1 = Rbd^2$
$A_{s1} = \dfrac{M_1}{f_s j_1 d}$

$M_2 = M - M_1$
$A_{s2} = \dfrac{M_2}{f_s(d - d')}$
$C_2 = \dfrac{M_2}{d - d'} = A_s'(2n - 1)f_{cs'}$

Fig. 5.5. Design of a double-reinforced beam, ACI Code.

5.4. BEAMS WITH COMPRESSION STEEL—MOMENT DESIGN

(a) General

Although concrete is cheaper for carrying compression than is steel, economy is often served by using compression steel over a short critical length. Compression steel increases the toughness of a beam, reducing the possibility of a sudden type of failure. It also reduces the creep and creep deflection of a beam.

Design procedures are simple and are best shown by examples. In all cases the total design moment is subdivided into two parts, M_1 which is the allowable moment on the balanced beam without compression steel ($M_1 = Rbd^2$), and M_2 which is the surplus moment to be resisted with compression steel and extra tension steel (Fig. 5.5). The ACI Code uses a semielastic basis for the calculation of A_s' required by M_2. The older elastic method may now be considered as obsolete.

(b) ACI Code—semielastic case

Redesign the steel for the beam of Sec. 5.3d, using the ACI Code with cover $d' = 2.5$ in.

SOLUTION

The ACI Code, Art. 706b, permits the compression steel to be valued at twice the stress an elastic analysis would indicate, provided this does not exceed the allowable tension, 20,000 psi for hard grade steel. The requirement for ties around the compression steel must not be overlooked.

The procedure sketched in Fig. 5.5 will be followed. As a balanced beam the moment capacity is $M_1 = Rbd^2$. In Sec. 5.3b, for $f_c = 1350$ psi, $f_s = 20,000$ psi, $n = 10$, R has been established as 236, $kd = 0.403d$, $jd = 0.866d$.

$$M_1 = Rbd^2 = 236 \times 9.5 \times 22^2/12,000 = 90.4 \text{ k-ft}$$

$$A_{s1} = \frac{M_1}{f_s j_1 d} = \frac{90,400 \times 12}{20,000 \times 0.866 \times 22} = 2.85 \text{ in.}^2$$

$$M_2 = M - M_1 = 100 - 90.4 = 9.6 \text{ k-ft}$$

$$A_{s2} = \frac{M_2}{f_s(d - d')} = \frac{9600 \times 12}{20,000 (22 - 2.5)} = 0.30 \text{ in.}^2$$

Total $A_s = A_{s1} + A_{s2} = 2.85 + 0.30 = 3.15 \text{ in.}^2$

$$C_2 = M_2/(d - d') = 9600 \times 12/19.5 = 5900 \text{ lb} = A_s'(2n - 1)f_{cs'}$$

$$kd = 0.403d = 0.403 \times 22 = 8.87 \text{ in.}$$

$$f_{cs'} = \frac{kd - 2.5}{kd}f_c = \frac{6.37}{8.87} \times 1350 = 970 \text{ psi}$$

$$f_s' = 2nf_{cs'} = 2 \times 10 \times 970 = 19,400 \text{ psi} < 20,000 \text{ psi} \quad \text{O.K.}$$

Effective $f_s'' = (2n - 1)f_{cs'} = (20 - 1)970 = 18,430 \text{ psi}$

$$A_s' = C_2/18,430 = 5900/18,430 = 0.32 \text{ in.}^2$$

This theory is identical with the semielastic analysis of Sec. 4.8b. Check A_s' by area moments about the neutral axis with the effective transformed areas nA_{s2} and $(2n - 1)A_s'$:

$$10 \times 0.30(22 - 8.87) = (2 \times 10 - 1)A_s'(8.87 - 2.5)$$
$$A_s' = 0.33 \text{ in.}^2$$

It might be noted that the total steel used in tension and compression is 3.47 in.^{2} compared to 3.97 in.^{2} when tension steel alone was used (Sec. 5.3d). A double-reinforced beam is usually cheaper than the use of tension steel alone when the beam must be smaller than a balanced beam.

(c) ACI Code design—nonelastic value of f_s'

Redesign the steel for the beam of (b) above, using $d' = 2$ in.

SOLUTION

The values of M_1, M_2, A_{s1}, and kd can be taken unchanged from (b) above:

$$A_{s2} = \frac{M_2}{f_s(d - d')} = \frac{9600 \times 12}{20,000 \,(22 - 2)} = 0.29 \text{ in.}^2$$

Total $A_s = A_{s1} + A_{s2} = 2.85 + 0.29 = 3.14$ in.^{2}

$C_2 = 9600 \times 12/(22 - 2) = 5760$ lb $= A_s'(2n - 1)f_{cs'}$

$$f_{cs'} = \frac{8.87 - 2}{8.87} \times 1350 = 1045 \text{ psi}$$

$f_s' = 2nf_{cs'} = 2 \times 10 \times 1045 = 20,900$ psi $> 20,000$

USE $f_s' = 20,000$ psi

Effective $f_s'' = 20,000 - f_{cs'} = 20,000 - 1045 = 18,960$ psi

$A_s' = C_2/18,960 = 5760/18,960 = 0.30$ in.^{2}

In this case the 20,000-psi limit on f_s' has no relation to the elastic properties of the materials. Since total $T = $ total C, there is no reason to shift the original neutral axis, but it no longer falls at the centroid of the usual transformed areas. Hence, the check on A_s' based upon area moments about the neutral axis as used in (b) is invalid here.

This design is definitely in the direction of ultimate strength design, but it may be noted that the true ultimate strength design of Sec. 3.8b is somewhat simpler.

(d) Transition point between semielastic and nonelastic analysis

The demarkation line between the semielastic and the nonelastic procedures can be established algebraically. The stress triangles of Fig. 5.6 lead to the following expression for f_s':

$$f_s' = 2nf_{cs'} = 2nf_c \frac{kd - d'}{kd} = 2nf_c \frac{k - d'/d}{k} = \text{allowable } f_s$$

The ACI Code specifies $n = 30{,}000/f_c'$, $f_c = 0.45f_c'$. For $f_s = 20{,}000$ psi,

$$k = \frac{kd}{d} = \frac{f_c}{f_c + f_s/n} = \frac{0.45f_c'}{0.45f_c' + 20{,}000f_c'/30{,}000} = \frac{0.45}{0.45 + 0.667} = 0.403$$

$$f_s' = 2nf_c \frac{k - d'/d}{k} = 2 \times \frac{30{,}000}{f_c'} \times 0.45f_c' \frac{0.403 - d'/d}{0.403} = f_s = 20{,}000$$

$$27{,}000 - 67{,}000d'/d = 20{,}000$$

$$d' = 7000d/67{,}000 = 0.104d$$

For this or smaller values of d', f_s' is governed by the 20,000-psi value. With $f_s = 18{,}000$ psi, f_s' is 18,000 psi for $d' = 0.134d$ or less.

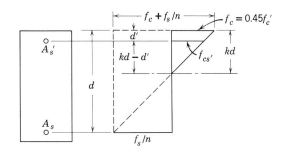

Fig. 5.6. Stress triangles for double-reinforced beam.

(e) Size of beam for desired compression steel

By a variation in the amount of compression (and corresponding tension) steel, many different beam sizes could serve as balanced sections for a given moment. The optimum size may depend upon many factors, but one frequent control used by designers is a decision as to the portion of the total moment to be assigned to the compression steel couple. This portion may be defined as a percentage of the total moment, or as a portion that can be carried by a specific percentage of compression steel, or as the portion corresponding to a specific ratio of compression to tension steel.

For any such design assumption a precise value of R' can be established, where $R' = M/bd^2$. However, the value of R' is rather sensitive to variations in d'/d and this ratio cannot be known until the size of the beam is fixed, and not exactly known until the number of layers of compression steel has been established. Fortunately it is rarely necessary that a particular design assumption be exactly fulfilled. In many cases it is

REINFORCED CONCRETE FUNDAMENTALS

sufficient to know simply that values of R' from 350 to 450 will give a reasonable amount of compression steel when $f_c' = 3000$ psi, $f_s = 20,000$ psi, and f_s' is governed by the ACI Code.

The procedure for obtaining an exact R' will be illustrated by several examples, using the unit stresses just mentioned above.

(1) R' when one-third of the total moment M is resisted by the compression steel couple.

SOLUTION

$$M = M_1 + M_2 \qquad M_1 = 236bd^2 \qquad M_2 = 0.333M$$
$$M = 236bd^2 + 0.333M$$
$$M = 353bd^2, \qquad R' = 353$$

(2) R' when compression steel is limited to $p' = 0.01$.

SOLUTION

The M_2 couple must first be evaluated. Assume $d' = 0.10d$. From Fig. 5.6, f_s' can be established from $f_{cs'}$ since the balanced beam has $kd = 0.403d$.

$$f_{cs'} = (0.303d/0.403d)0.45f_c' = 0.338 \times 3000 = 1014 \text{ psi}$$
$$2nf_{cs'} = 2 \times 10 \times 1014 = 20,280 \text{ psi} > 20,000 \text{ psi}$$

USE $f_s' = 20,000$ psi

Effective $f_s'' = 20,000 - 1014 = 18,990$ psi

$$M_2 = A_s' \times 18,990(d - d') = 0.01bd \times 18,990 \times 0.9d = 171bd^2$$
$$M = M_1 + M_2 = 236bd^2 + 171bd^2 = 407bd^2 = R'bd^2$$
$$R' = 407$$

(3) R' when compression steel is equal to one-third of tension steel.

SOLUTION

As in the above case, for $d' = 0.1d$, $f_s' = 20,000$ psi, and effective $f_s'' = 18,990$ psi.

$$M_2 = A_s' \times 18,990 \times 0.9d$$
$$A_{s2} = \frac{M_2}{f_s(d - d')} = \frac{A_s' \times 18,990 \times 0.9d}{20,000 \times 0.9d} = 0.95A_s'$$

Since $A_s' = A_s/3$, $A_{s2} = 0.95A_s/3 = 0.317A_s$.

$$A_{s1} = \frac{M_1}{f_s jd} = \frac{236bd^2}{20,000 \times 0.866d} = 0.0136bd$$
$$A_s = A_{s1} + A_{s2} = 0.0136bd + 0.317A_s$$
$$A_s = 0.0136bd/0.683 = 0.0199bd$$
$$A_s' = A_s/3 = 0.0066bd$$
$$M = 236bd^2 + 0.0066bd \times 18,990 \times 0.9d = 349bd^2 = R'bd^2$$
$$R' = 349$$

(4) Algebraic relations can be developed defining R' in terms of either p or p'. With a balanced beam, p is a direct linear function of p'.

SOLUTION

In (d) above it was established that $f_s' = 20,000$ psi controls when $d' \lesssim 0.104d$, assuming allowable $f_c = 1350$ psi and $f_s = 20,000$ psi. With the balanced $k = 0.403$,

$$f_s'' = 20,000 - \frac{0.403 - d'/d}{0.403} f_c = 18,650 + 3350d'/d$$

$$M = M_1 + M_2 = Rbd^2 + p'bdf_s''(d - d')$$

$$= 236bd^2 + p'(18,650 + 3350d'/d)bd^2(1 - d'/d)$$

$$R' = 236 + p'(18,650 + 3350d'/d)(1 - d'/d)$$

The M_2 couple establishes that $p_2 = p'f_s''/f_s$, where f_s'' is the effective compressive stress.

$$p = p_1 + p_2 = 0.0136 + p'f_s''/f_s = 0.0136 + \frac{18,650 + 3350d'/d}{20,000} p'$$

For $d'/d = 0.05$,

$$R' = 236 + p'(18,650 + 167)0.95 = 236 + 17,900p'$$

$$p = 0.0136 + \frac{18,650 + 167}{20,000} p' = 0.0136 + 0.942p'$$

or $$p' = (p - 0.0136)/0.942$$

$$R' = 236 + 17,900(p - 0.0136)/0.942, \qquad R' = 19,000p - 22.$$

For $d'/d = 0.10$, similarly,

$$R' = 236 + 17,080p'$$

$$p = 0.0136 + 0.950p'$$

or $$p' = (p - 0.0136)/0.950$$

$$R' = 17,900p - 8$$

These equations for R' have been plotted in Fig. E.11 in Appendix E. The specific p accompanying any value of p' is determined by moving horizontally from the given p' value to the d'/d curve which establishes R', thence vertically to the d'/d curve which establishes p at the left.

For $d' > 0.104d$,

$$f_s'' = (2n - 1)f_{cs'} = 19 \left(\frac{0.403 - d'/d}{0.403} \right) 1350 = 25,650 - 63,500d'/d$$

The same procedure as above then leads to the following:

For $d'/d = 0.15$,

$$R' = 236 + 13,700p', \qquad R' = 4 + 17,000p$$

For $d'/d = 0.20$,

$$R' = 236 + 10,350p', \qquad R' = 19 + 15,950p$$

5.5. T-BEAMS—MOMENT DESIGN

The T-beam flange is usually determined by the slab design, and the web size (b' and d) is often determined by shear or requirements other than moment. To some extent b', the stem width, is influenced by the number of reinforcing bars used for A_s but the student probably lacks the experience at this stage to estimate this need in advance. In this section it is assumed that design for moment consists of only two elements, the choice of the area of steel A_s and a check on the compressive stress f_c.

The flange ordinarily provides enough compression area to keep f_c low, and the check on this can be postponed until one of the last steps. The design for A_s is thus assumed to be for a beam much deeper than a balanced section. For a T-beam the algebraic approach used in Sec. 5.3b for a similar rectangular beam becomes too involved for practical use. Instead, a cut-and-try procedure is recommended, based on the fact that the value of jd can be estimated quite closely.

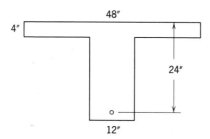

Fig. 5.7. T-beam for calculation of A_s.

Find the required area of structural grade steel for the T-beam of Fig. 5.7 if $f_c' = 2500$ psi and $M = 150$ k-ft.

SOLUTION

Both the shape of the compression area and the high neutral axis resulting from a low f_c tend to locate the resultant C high in the beam. On this basis, a good average value of jd could be taken as $0.9d$. If the small amount of compression in the web below the flange is neglected, the trapezoidal stress distribution locates the resultant C higher than the middle of the flange. This means that jd is greater than $d - t/2$, where t is the flange thickness. For the initial approximation, it is recommended that jd be taken as the larger of $0.9d$ or $d - t/2$, this giving a value probably within 1% to 3% of the exact one.

$0.9d = 0.9 \times 24 = 21.6$ in.

$d - t/2 = 24 - 2 = 22.0$ in.   USE for trial jd

Allowable $f_s = 18,000$ psi for structural grade steel

$$\text{Approx. } A_s = \frac{M}{f_s jd} = \frac{150,000 \times 12}{18,000 \times 22.0} = 4.55 \text{ in.}^2$$

This approximate A_s will be used to establish kd and a better (almost exact) value of jd. The "exact" method for T-beams, Sec. 4.7b, will be used (an arbitrary choice), as indicated in Fig. 5.8a.

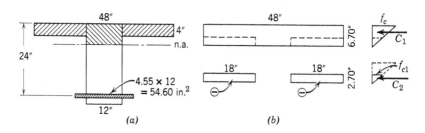

Fig. 5.8. Areas used in T-beam calculations. (a) For location of neutral axis. (b) For location of C.

Area moments about the neutral axis:

$$(12kd)kd/2 + 36 \times 4(kd - 2) = 4.55 \times 12(24 - kd)$$

$$6kd^2 + 144kd - 288 = 1312 - 54.6kd$$

$$kd^2 + 33.1kd + 16.55^2 = 267 + 16.55^2 = 542$$

$$kd = 23.25 - 16.55 = 6.70 \text{ in.}$$

f_{c1} at bottom of flange $= (2.70/6.70)f_c = 0.403f_c$

Forces shown in Fig. 5.8b:

		Arm abt. Top	m
$C_1 = (48 \times 6.70)f_c/2$	$= 160.8f_c$	$6.70/3 = 2.23$ in.	$358f_c$
$C_2 = -(36 \times 2.70)0.403f_c/2 =$	$- 19.6f_c$	$4 + 2.70/3 = 4.90$ in.	$- 96.2f_c$
$C = 141.2f_c$		$m =$	$262f_c$

$$z = \frac{262f_c}{141.2f_c} = 1.85 \text{ in.}$$

$$jd = 24 - 1.85 = 22.15 \text{ in.}$$

$$A_s = \frac{150,000 \times 12}{18,000 \times 22.15} = 4.50 \text{ in.}^2$$

The calculation of z above used $C = 141.2f_c$:

$$f_c = \frac{C}{141.2} = \frac{M}{141.2jd} = \frac{150{,}000 \times 12}{141.2 \times 22.15} = 575 \text{ psi} \ll 0.45 \times 2500 \qquad \text{O.K.}$$

An estimate of f_c based on approximate theory requires less preliminary calculation and is often adequate. A trapezoidal stress on the flange gives:

$$f_c < 2 \times \text{aver.} \, f_c, \text{ since aver. } f_c > f_c/2$$

$$f_c < 2M/(btjd)$$

$$f_c < 2\,\frac{150{,}000 \times 12}{48 \times 4 \times 22.15} = 845 \text{ psi}$$

$$f_c < 845 \text{ psi} < 0.45 \times 2500 \qquad \text{O.K.}$$

The weakness of this check lies in the fact that twice the average f_c might exceed the allowable and still be satisfactory. Such a condition calls for the more exact calculation procedure.

5.6. BENDING OF BARS—FOR MOMENT

(a) Maximum moment curves

The maximum required A_s for a beam is needed only where the moment is maximum. This steel may be reduced at points along the beam where smaller moments always exist. Hence a study of where bars can be stopped, or bent away from the tension zone, must start with a study of the maximum moments which are possible at all points along the beam.

In some simple cases, the maximum moment diagram is simply the moment diagram for full load. In other cases, as for wheel loads (Fig. 5.9a), the determination of the maximum moment diagram requires the calculation of maximum moments at many points; the maximum moment diagram is then the envelope of the maximum moment values from several loads, as in Fig. 5.9b for a single wheel load W. Each dashed triangle corresponds to a particular position of the load, the maximum moment at any point being given with the wheel at that point. The envelope in this case happens to be a parabola. With several wheels the curve approximates two half parabolas separated by a section of constant moment, as in Fig. 5.9c.

Only fixed loadings are illustrated in the remainder of this chapter. Continuous beams will be discussed in Chap. 8.

(b) Theoretical bend point or cutoff point

When a variable depth member is considered, the required A_s curve must be established by calculating the required A_s at representative points from the basic relation

$$A_s = \text{Max. } M \div (f_s jd)$$

This procedure is illustrated in Sec. 7.5k.

With constant depth beams, the denominator becomes essentially a constant, the small variations in j being of little significance. Hence A_s varies directly with the maximum moment, and the shape of the required

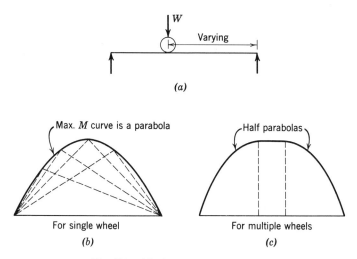

(a)

For single wheel
(b)

For multiple wheels
(c)

Fig. 5.9. Maximum moment curves.

A_s curve is identical with that of the maximum moment curve. This permits the maximum moment curve to be used as the required A_s curve, simply by changing the scale. The maximum ordinate corresponds to the maximum required A_s and this establishes the necessary correlation.

Bars can theoretically be stopped or bent wherever they are no longer needed for moment. The solution can be either graphical (for complex maximum moment diagrams), semigraphical for typical cases, or analytical where desired. The semigraphical process is illustrated in (d) for common cases.

(c) Arbitrary requirements for extending bars

The ACI Code (Art. 902a) requires that each bar be extended 12 bar diameters beyond the point where it is theoretically needed for moment.

This prohibits the cutting off of a bar at the theoretical minimum point, but can be interpreted as permitting bars to be bent at that minimum point. Three sound reasons can be advanced for this arbitrary extension.

First, when a bar is simply cut off (not bent away from the main steel), there is a large transfer of stress from this bar to those remaining. This stress concentration will cause a moment crack in the concrete at the end of the bar if the beam is carrying its working load. Bending the bar spreads out this concentration; extending the bar, without bending, removes the concentration from a point of maximum steel stress to a point of lower steel stress. (It should be noted that if a bar is cut off at the theoretical minimum point, the remaining bars necessarily work at maximum stress.)

The author gives greater weight to a second reason, which was well stated by an introductory statement in the now obsolete 1940 Joint Committee Specification (Art. 829):

> To provide for contingencies arising from unanticipated loads, yielding of supports, shifting of points of inflection, or other lack of agreement with assumed conditions governing the design of elastic structures, it is recommended that the reinforcement be extended at supports and at other points between supports as indicated. . . .

Thus interpreted, the arbitrary extension of the bar is the result of an envisioned possible extension of the maximum moment diagram. It would follow that bars must not be bent until this extra length has been provided. This is a more severe requirement than many engineers observe, but the author recommends it in the absence of test data in this area.

The third reason has developed out of diagonal tension tests. In Sec. 6.8, from consideration of the free body of Fig. 6.7b, it is pointed out that a diagonal crack leads to larger values of bar tension than would be predicted from moment alone. The larger tension is as serious as an excess of moment at the section. Such a condition argues against cutting off bars on the basis of the moment alone and points to the need for some extension beyond the theoretical bar cutoff point.

(d) Other considerations than moment

Bars are sometimes bent at points that permit them to be used as inclined stirrups, that is, for web reinforcement against diagonal tension (Chap. 6). In the United States the strength thus available is ordinarily neglected and simply left as an extra factor of safety.

Sometimes bond stresses (Chap. 6) determine whether bars can be bent or how many bars can be bent. Bond stresses are also closely related to development length, the minimum length of bar required to develop a given steel stress, discussed in Sec. 6.6.

The ACI Code requires that at least one-third of the positive moment steel extend into the support in the case of simple spans and one-fourth in the case of continuous beams. Custom usually increases these minimums.

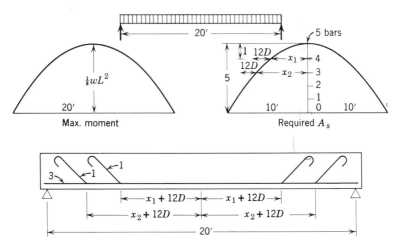

Fig. 5.10. Bending bars for uniformly loaded beam.

(e) Nomenclature

It is common to refer to the first bar bent, second bar bent, and so forth; the first bar bent means the one bent nearest the point of maximum moment.

Bars are often bent by pairs instead of singly. The first pair can be bent where the second bar is no longer required.

(f) Examples involving no excess steel

(1) A uniformly loaded beam of 20-ft simple span requires 5–#9 bars. Where can the first bar be cut off? The second bar?

SOLUTION

The maximum moment diagram is simply the full load moment diagram and this parabola can be used as the required A_s diagram as in Fig. 5.10. The maximum ordinate becomes 5 bars. Steel areas could be used as ordinates, but the number of bars provides a more convenient unit when all bars are of the same size.

REINFORCED CONCRETE FUNDAMENTALS

The first bar can theoretically be bent up at x_1 where only 4 bars are required. Since offsets to the center tangent vary as the square of the distances from the center,

$$x_1^2/10^2 = \tfrac{1}{5}, \qquad x_1 = 10\sqrt{\tfrac{1}{5}} = 4.47 \text{ ft}$$

The minimum distance from the center line of the span to the first bar bend point is $4.47 + 12D = 4.47 + 12 \times 1.13/12 = 5.60$ ft.

For the second bar bent,

$$x_2^2/10^2 = \tfrac{2}{5}, \qquad x_2 = 10\sqrt{\tfrac{2}{5}} = 6.33 \text{ ft}$$

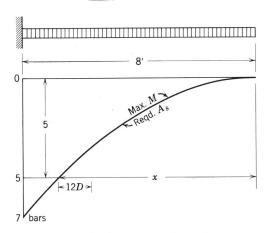

Fig. 5.11. Bending bars for cantilever beam.

The minimum distance from the center to the second bar bend point is $6.33 + 1.13 = 7.46$ ft.

(2) A uniformly loaded cantilever beam 8 ft long requires 7–#7 bars. Where can the first pair of bars be bent down?

SOLUTION

The maximum moment diagram is a half parabola, the maximum ordinate corresponding to 7 bars of required A_s (Fig. 5.11). The first pair of bars can be bent where only 5 bars are required.

$$x^2/8^2 = \tfrac{5}{7}, \qquad x = 8\sqrt{\tfrac{5}{7}} = 6.74 \text{ ft}$$

The minimum distance from the support to the bend point for the first pair is $8 - 6.74 + 12D = 1.26 + 0.88 = 2.14$ ft.

BEAMS—DESIGN FOR MOMENT

(g) Examples involving excess steel

(1) An 18-ft simple span beam with a fixed concentrated load at mid-span (negligible uniform load) requires 4.50 in.^{2} of steel but uses 5–#9 bars = 5.00 in.^{2} Where can the first pair of bars be stopped?

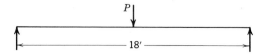

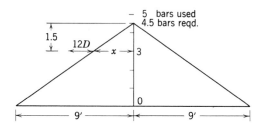

Fig. 5.12. Bending bars, excess steel.

SOLUTION

Figure 5.12 shows the maximum moment diagram used as a required A_s curve with the maximum ordinate marked as 4.50 in.^{2} = 4.50 bars required. The first pair of bars can be stopped where only 3 bars are required.

$$x/9 = 1.5/4.5, \qquad x = 3.0 \text{ ft}$$

The minimum distance from mid-span to the bend point for the first pair is $3.0 + 12D = 3.00 + 1.13 = 4.13$ ft.

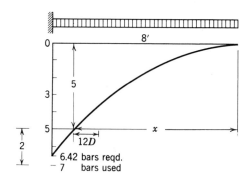

Fig. 5.13. Bending bars, excess steel, cantilever beam.

REINFORCED CONCRETE FUNDAMENTALS

(2) A uniformly loaded cantilever beam 8 ft long requires 3.85 in.^{2} and uses 7–#7 bars. Where can the first pair of bars be bent down?

SOLUTION

The maximum ordinate of the maximum moment diagram is designated as 3.85 in.^{2} = 3.85/0.60 = 6.42 bars required (Fig. 5.13). The desired point is where 5 bars are needed.

$$x^2/8^2 = 5/6.42 \qquad x = 8\sqrt{5/6.42} = 7.05 \text{ ft}$$

The minimum distance from the support to the bend point for the first pair is 8 − 7.05 + 12D = 0.95 + 0.88 = 1.83 ft.

5.7. USE OF CHARTS IN DESIGN

(a) Rectangular beams

Figures E.3 and E.4 in Appendix E determine the balanced values of R, k, and j quite satisfactorily. Values of balanced p are also available to a fair accuracy, although the author prefers to read j and calculate $A_s = M/(f_s jd)$.

The beam of Sec. 5.3c is deeper than a balanced section. For the given dimensions the actual $R = M/bd^2 = 100,000 \times 12/(9.5 \times 24^2) = 219$. For $n = 10$ and $R = 219$, Fig. E.3 shows that the permissible stresses become $f_s = 20,000$ psi and $f_c = 1290$ psi, corresponding to $p = 0.0126$ and $A_s = pbd = 0.0126 \times 9.5 \times 24 = 2.87$ in.^{2} The value of j from Fig. E.2 for this value of p is 0.870, leading to $A_s = M/f_s jd = (100,000 \times 12)/(20,000 \times 0.870 \times 24) = 2.88$ in.^{2} Either method is usually satisfactory, the latter one always being less subject to reading errors.

The same procedure is available for beams shallower than the balanced section, for example, the beam of Sec. 5.3d. The actual $R = M/bd^2 = 100,000 \times 12/(9.5 \times 22^2) = 261$. The permissible stresses are $f_c = 1350$ psi and $f_s = 16,200$ psi, corresponding to $p = 0.0192$ and $j = 0.847$.

$$A_s = 0.0192 \times 9.5 \times 22 = 4.01 \text{ in.}^2$$

$$A_s = 100,000 \times 12/(16,200 \times 0.847 \times 22) = 3.97 \text{ in.}^2$$

The algebraic solution gave 3.97 in.^{2}

(b) Double-reinforced beams

Figure E.11 is very helpful in design and is so simple any engineer can prepare similar charts for other unit stresses in which he may be interested, based on the method of Sec. 5.4e(4). From this chart reasonable values of

R' can be chosen to use directly in determining the required $bd^2 = M/R'$. For a given beam size, the actual R' leads directly to p and p'. For example, the beam of Sec. 5.4b has actual $R' = M/bd^2 = 100,000 \times 12/(9.5 \times 22^2) = 261$ and $d'/d = 2.5/22 = 0.113$. On Fig. E.11, directly above $R' = 261$, one can read $p' = 0.0015$ and $p = 0.0149$. Then $A_s' = 0.0015 \times 9.5 \times 22 = 0.31$ in.^{2} and $A_s = 0.0149 \times 9.5 \times 22 = 3.12$ in.^{2} The earlier calculations showed $A_s' = 0.33$ in.^{2} and $A_s = 3.15$ in.^{2}

The nonelastic case of Sec. 5.4c can be solved in precisely the same manner. The chart has been plotted for the method applying to the particular d'/d represented. The nonelastic case applies for $d'/d < 0.104$, so close to $d'/d = 0.10$ that no separate line for $d'/d = 0.104$ seems to be needed.

(c) T-beams

Figure E.5 assists in establishing k and j values as used in the design of T-beams. In Sec. 5.5, for example, the first approximate value of A_s is 4.55 in.^{2}, giving $pn = 12 \times 4.55/(48 \times 24) = 0.0475$ and $t/d = 4/24 = 0.167$. For these values the chart shows $j = 0.928$, or $jd = 0.928 \times 24 = 22.2$ in. The calculations gave 22.15 in.

Figure E.6 can be used to establish the required steel directly. From the relation $M = C_s(f_s/n)bd^2$,

$$C_s = Mn/(f_s bd^2) = 150 \times 12,000 \times 12/(18,000 \times 48 \times 24^2) = 0.0433$$
$$t/d = 4/24 = 0.167$$

C_s and t/d determine a point on the chart at $pn = 0.047$, giving $A_s = 0.047bd/n = 0.047 \times 48 \times 24/12 = 4.51$ in.^{2} The value of f_c can be checked by using Fig. E.5 where these values of pn and t/d give $f_s/nf_c = 2.55$ or $f_c = f_s/2.55n = 18,000/(2.55 \times 12) = 590$ psi.

PROBLEMS

Note: Designs in this series of problems are to be partial designs, for flexure alone; bond, shear, and bar spacings are not a part of these problems.

When the actual moment exceeds the balanced beam moment, the student should decide whether excess tension steel or compression steel is preferable.

Prob. 5.1.

(a) Design a rectangular beam exactly balanced for a total $M = 200$ k-ft using $f_c' = 3750$ psi, intermediate grade steel. After the required bd^2 has been established, use $b = 14$ in.

(b) Redesign steel if d is made 26 in. and b is maintained at 14 in.

(c) Redesign steel if d is made 23 in. and b is maintained at 14 in.

Prob. 5.2. A rectangular beam 13 in. wide by 20 in. deep to center of steel must carry a total moment of 108 k-ft with $f_c' = 3000$ psi and intermediate grade steel. Find the required steel.

Prob. 5.3. A slab having $d = 4$ in. must carry a total moment of 3.9 k-ft per ft width. Find the required A_s per ft if $f_c' = 3000$ psi and steel is hard grade.

Prob. 5.4. A slab 7.5 in. thick with 1.5-in. cover to center of steel must carry a total moment of 7.5 k-ft per ft width. Find the required A_s per ft if $f_c' = 3000$ psi and steel is rail steel.

Prob. 5.5. A rectangular beam 14 in. wide by 25 in. deep over-all with 3-in. cover to center of steel must carry a total moment of 220 k-ft. Find the necessary steel if $f_c' = 3750$ psi and steel is intermediate grade.

Prob. 5.6. Design a double-reinforced beam 13 in. wide for a total $M = 250$ k-ft using $f_c' = 3000$ psi, intermediate grade steel, cover 3 in. to center of steel, and basing the beam size on an approximate R' of 400.

Prob. 5.7. Find the value of R' for $f_c' = 3750$ psi, hard grade steel, $d'/d = 0.12$, $p' = 0.01$.

Prob. 5.8. From basic principles establish the value of the balanced steel ratio p for a rectangular beam with $f_c' = 3750$ psi and $f_s = 20,000$ psi.

Prob. 5.9. If the joist of Fig. 4.15 and Prob. 4.6 must care for a total moment of 13 k-ft, calculate the required A_s. Is the compression stress then satisfactory?

Prob. 5.10. A simple span beam carrying uniform load over a 19-ft span requires 3.40 in.² of steel and uses 6–#7 bars.

(a) Where can the first pair be bent up? The second pair?

(b) If the excess steel were neglected, where would these bends be permitted?

Prob. 5.11. A 20-ft simple span beam carries a large fixed concentrated load at 7 ft from the left end and requires $A_s = 3.30$ in.² The steel used is 5–#8. If the beam weight is disregarded, where can the first bar be bent up (each side of the load)? The third bar?

Prob. 5.12. A 10-ft cantilever beam carries a large concentrated load at its end, uniform load negligible. Required $A_s = 3.50$ in.²; 4–#9 used. Where can one pair of bars be stopped or bent down?

Prob. 5.13. A 9-ft cantilever beam carries only uniform load and requires $A_s = 3.50$ in.² If 4–#9 are used, where can half of the bars be bent down?

BEAMS—DESIGN FOR MOMENT

Prob. 5.14. The beam of Fig. 5.14 is subject to a fixed dead load of 1000 plf and a movable live load of 2000 plf. The required positive moment steel is 6.24 in.^{2} and the required negative moment steel is 3.67 in.^{2} If the positive moment steel used is 4–#11, where can the first pair of positive steel bars be stopped? If the negative moment steel is 4–#9 bars, where can this be reduced to 2 bars? (Note that distances on each side of the support or reaction are needed.)

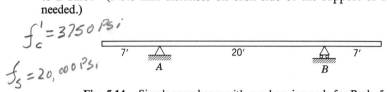

$f_c' = 3750 \text{ psi}$

$f_s = 20,000 \text{ psi}$

7' A 20' B 7'

Fig. 5.14. Simple span beam with overhanging ends for Prob. 5.14.

Design the beam & show the arrangement of the steel

REINFORCED CONCRETE FUNDAMENTALS

6

Shear Stresses— Bond and Diagonal Tension

6.1. THE NATURE OF BOND

For concrete and steel to work together in a beam it is necessary that stresses be transferred between the two materials. The term "bond" is used to describe the means by which slip between concrete and steel is prevented or minimized. Wherever the tensile or compressive stresses in a bar change, bond stresses must act along the surface of the bar to produce the change. Bond stresses are in effect longitudinal shearing stresses acting on the surface between the steel and concrete. They are normally evaluated in terms of pounds per square inch of bar surface.

In the case of smooth bars, the bond strength is largely dependent upon adhesion between the bar and concrete, but even after adhesion is broken friction between the materials continues to provide a considerable bond resistance. Friction resistance is low for a smooth bar surface, such as that of cold-rolled steel, and is higher for rougher surfaces.

Deformed bars (Sec. 1.9) satisfying ASTM Spec. A 305[1] give a higher bond resistance by providing an interlock between the steel and concrete. In this case the bond strength is primarily dependent upon the bearing (compressive) strength of the concrete against the lugs and the shear strength of the concrete between the lugs. Adhesion and friction become minor elements in this case. Longitudinal splitting of the concrete covering the bar can be the limiting strength factor when the cover is thin.

In this chapter particularly the author expresses opinions, based upon research studies, which have not yet been fully accepted by the profession. He has attempted to indicate clearly those portions which indicate only his personal opinion.

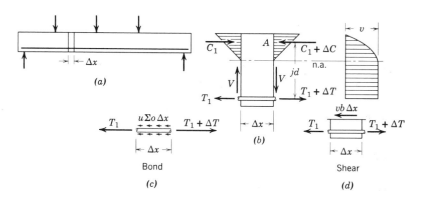

Fig. 6.1. Shear and bond stress.

6.2. CONVENTIONAL BOND FORMULA

(a) Tension steel

Consider a short length Δx of the beam in Fig. 6.1a subject to a constant shear V and moments M_1 and $M_2 = M_1 + \Delta M$. These moments will produce the bending stresses shown in Fig. 6.1b. Summation of moments about A gives:

$$\Sigma M_A = V \Delta x - \Delta T jd = 0$$
$$\Delta T = V \Delta x / jd$$

In Fig. 6.1c the Δx length of bar is taken as the free body and the bond stresses on the surface of the bar are indicated. If the average unit bond stress is called u and the perimeter of the bar (or bars) Σo,

$$\Delta T = u \Sigma o \Delta x$$

REINFORCED CONCRETE FUNDAMENTALS

Equating these two values of ΔT gives the conventional unit bond stress formula:

$$\Delta T = u \, \Sigma o \, \Delta x = V \, \Delta x / jd$$
$$u = V / (\Sigma o \, jd)$$

The same relation results for a beam carrying a uniform load w if the shear V is taken as that at the center of the Δx element. Although this is an exact formula for the assumed conditions, Sec. 6.8 indicates very different actual bond conditions in an actual beam. Since the formula is only an approximate relationship, the author considers the use of $\frac{7}{8}$ for j fully justified in all practical calculations, to give:

$$u = \frac{V}{\Sigma o \frac{7}{8} d}$$

Strictly interpreted, this formula gives the average bond stress and this average is the critical bond stress only when all bars have the same diameter.

(b) Mixed bar sizes

When n_1 bars of D_1 diameter are used together with n_2 bars of D_2 diameter, the bond stresses u_1 and u_2 are different. Since Δf_s for a Δx length is the same for each bar, it follows that for individual bars:

$$\Delta T_1 / n_1 = \Delta f_s \, \pi D_1^2 / 4 = u_1 \, \Sigma o_1 \, \Delta x = u_1 \, \pi D_1 \, \Delta x$$
$$\Delta T_2 / n_2 = \Delta f_s \, \pi D_2^2 / 4 = u_2 \, \Sigma o_2 \, \Delta x = u_2 \, \pi D_2 \, \Delta x$$

The ratio between these two relations shows that $D_1 / D_2 = u_1 / u_2$, or that the unit bond stress varies as the bar diameter. The total shear V can be subdivided into V_1 and V_2 parts in the ratio of the moments carried by the two groups of bars, that is, in the ratio of $\Delta T_1 / \Delta T_2$ or A_{s1} / A_{s2}:

$$V_1 = V A_{s1} / A_s \qquad V_2 = V A_{s2} / A_s$$

$$u_1 = \frac{V_1}{\Sigma o_1 \, jd} = \frac{V A_{s1} / A_s}{\Sigma o_1 \, jd} = \frac{V}{(A_s / A_{s1}) \Sigma o_1 \, jd}$$

But $(A_s / A_{s1}) \Sigma o_1$ is simply the perimeter that would be obtained if the entire A_s were made from bars of diameter D_1. If this is designated as $\Sigma o_1{}'$

$$u_1 = \frac{V}{\Sigma o_1{}' \, jd}$$

Similarly,

$$u_2 = \frac{V}{\Sigma o_2{}' \, jd}$$

(c) Compression steel

The 1956 Code specifically mentions bond stress on compression steel (Art. 901b). If A_s' is made of the same diameter bars as A_s, the bond stress u' on A_s' will be the bond stress u on A_s multiplied by the ratio f_s'/f_s. Since this ratio is usually less than unity, the bond stress u' will usually be low. The Code suggests a calculation equivalent to

$$u' = \frac{V'}{\Sigma o'\, jd}$$

where $\Sigma o'$ is the perimeter of compression steel and

$$V' = V\,\frac{A_s'f_s'}{\text{total comp.}} = V\,\frac{A_s'f_s'}{A_s'f_s'' + 0.5f_c bkd}$$

If A_s' has been calculated from a separate part of the moment, that is, from M_2 as in the example of Sec. 5.4b, it will be convenient and sufficiently accurate to use $V' = VM_2/M$. Several methods of calculation are compared in Sec. 8.18.

6.3. BOND PULLOUT TESTS

Permissible bond stresses have been established largely from pullout tests with some beam tests as confirmation. In the pullout test a bar is embedded in a cylinder or rectangular block of concrete and the force required to pull it out or make it slip excessively is measured. Figure 6.2 shows such a test schematically, omitting details such as hemispherical bearing plates. Slip of the bar relative to the concrete is measured at the bottom (loaded end) and top (free end). The bond stress distribution in such a specimen is very nonuniform. Even a very small load causes some slip and high bond stress near the loaded end, but leaves the upper part of the bar totally unstressed, as shown in Fig. 6.2. As more load is applied, the slip at the loaded end increases, and both the high bond stress and slip extend deeper into the specimen. With plain bars the bond stress will decrease to the friction or drag value wherever adhesion has been broken by slip; such slip is indicated by the heavy line in the right-hand sketches of Fig. 6.2. The maximum bond is somewhat idealized in these sketches; its distribution depends on the type of bar and probably varies along the bar more than shown.

When the slip first reaches the unloaded end, the maximum resistance has nearly been reached. Failure will usually occur (1) by longitudinal splitting of the concrete in the case of deformed bars, or (2) by pulling the bar through the concrete in the case of a very smooth bar, or (3) by breaking the bar, if the embedment is long enough.

The average bond resistance is always calculated just as though it were uniform over the bar embedment length. Actually, the bond stress varies greatly as slip develops and at any load the average is an average of values quite dissimilar, an average between ultimates and smaller values. The very first slip of the loaded end of the bar represents essentially an ultimate bond stress over a short length of the bar, although the calculated average

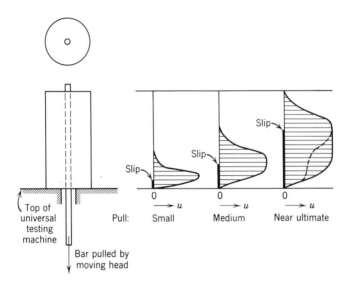

Fig. 6.2. Bond pullout test, with bond stress distribution.

bond stress may be quite low. Attention is called to the fact that this test procedure cannot measure maximum unit bond resistance unless an extremely short specimen is used (and such is not the customary test).

6.4. WEAKNESS OF ORDINARY PULLOUT TESTS AS A STANDARD—AUTHOR'S OPINION

Since the pullout test develops maximum local bond stresses always in excess of the average calculated from the tests, one might erroneously conclude that the pullout test is a conservative procedure for establishing bond strength. However, analysis indicates it is defective in several ways. First, bond stress in a beam is usually critical in a tension zone, whereas

SHEAR STRESSES—BOND AND DIAGONAL TENSION 127

the usual pullout specimen has the surrounding concrete in compression. Second, shearing stresses in a beam complicate the failure, whereas the pullout specimen carries no external shear. Third, in many pullout tests the specimens have been reinforced with spiral wire reinforcement to prevent a splitting failure. In spite of the fact that some beam tests seem to corroborate ordinary pullout tests, other types of beams do not. Bond strength needs further study.* To the author it appears that the ultimate bond strength with deformed bars may be considerably lower than pullout tests have indicated, possibly 25% to 50% lower in some practical cases.

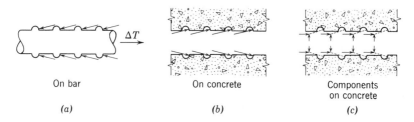

On bar	On concrete	Components on concrete
(a)	(b)	(c)

Fig. 6.3. The forces between a deformed bar and concrete which may cause splitting.

6.5. SPLITTING AROUND DEFORMED BARS—
AUTHOR'S ANALYSIS

The chief reason for lowered bond strengths seems to be premature failure by longitudinal splitting of the concrete around the deformed bars. Bond on a deformed bar is principally a matter of concrete bearing on the lugs, as shown in Fig. 6.3a. The pressure on the concrete necessarily has an outward component (Fig. 6.3b, c) which, like water pressure in a pipe, produces ring tension and leads to splitting on weak planes along the bar. The cover or reinforcing necessary to prevent splitting is a matter that needs further study. It can be a serious matter, as indicated by tests on splices discussed in the following section.

6.6. ANCHORAGE OR DEVELOPMENT LENGTH

Experiment shows that if a bar has enough embedment in a pullout specimen, it cannot be pulled out. After slip at the loaded end has progressed far enough to develop bond over a considerable length, such a bar

* The author has proposed a different type of bond test.[2]

reaches its yield strength and fails in tension. A bar can thus be fully anchored in concrete. The length of embedment necessary to provide an adequate factor of safety against pullout failure is called the anchorage length.

Consider a bar embedded in a mass of concrete as in Fig. 6.4. The actual bond stress will be distributed quite like that of the pullout test, a maximum near the surface and probably zero at the embedded end. If the average bond stress is limited to an allowable determined from comparable pullout tests, safe results should be obtained. Then

$$A_s f_s = u L'' \Sigma o$$

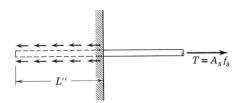

$T = A_s f_s$

L''

Fig. 6.4. Anchorage of a bar.

For round bars of diameter D, $A_s = \pi D^2/4$ and $\Sigma o = \pi D$, giving

$$\pi D^2 f_s/4 = L'' \pi D u$$

$$L'' = \frac{f_s}{4u} D$$

This L'' is the minimum permissible anchorage length. Unless splitting of the concrete around the bar is prevented (by the mass of the concrete or by reinforcement), the author advocates that a lowered value of u be used, as illustrated in the case of the splice tests discussed below.

Caution: This relation for L'' gives a safe anchorage length based on an allowable *average* bond. It cannot be used to calculate the maximum bond stress for given f_s and L''. In such a case the real bond stress varies from ultimate to zero, the factor of safety lying in the length of bar only lightly stressed, not in the size of the maximum stress.

The author also calls L'' the development length. Stress cannot be put into a bar in a length shorter than that necessary to take it out. The author finds the concept of minimum development length one of the best checks possible on bond in complex cases. The concept is widely used in the case of bar splices. For an adequate splice, bars should be lapped a distance L'', as shown in Fig. 6.5. Splices at points of maximum stress are not desirable but sometimes cannot be avoided. Strength seems very little affected by whether the spliced bars are in contact or separated.

Tests[3] show splitting of concrete seriously lowers the strength of a splice, especially when minimum cover and spacing are used without any stirrups. The 1956 ACI Code (Art. 506a) recognizes this condition by setting a minimum splice length of $24D$ or at least 12 in. The author would go further where small cover is used and, pending conclusive tests, limit the average bond in splices to approximately 50% of the usual allowable. Where large bars ($\#9$, $\#10$, or $\#11$) at *minimum* spacing accompany the small cover, this allowable bond should probably be reduced to 40%.

For $f_c' = 3000$ psi, the ACI Code (Art. 305) allows up to 300 psi in bond as discussed in the next section. With $f_s = 20,000$ psi, the nominal lap

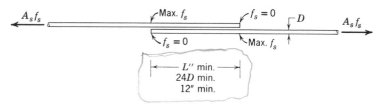

Fig. 6.5. A bar lap splice.

based on stress would be $L'' = f_s D \div 4u = 20,000D \div (4 \times 300) = 16.7D$ and this requirement is less than the $24D$ specification, which thus controls. Instead of this, the author's recommendations where small cover is used would call for $33D$ laps in most cases and $42D$ laps in extreme cases.

Reinforcement against splitting, in the form of ties, is probably a good way to gain higher bond resistance, but the necessary amount of this reinforcement still has not yet been established.*

6.7. ALLOWABLE BOND STRESSES

On the basis of tests, the ACI Code, Art. 305, shows allowable bond stresses for deformed bars up to $0.10f_c'$. The lower value of $0.07f_c'$ is specified for top steel because tests have shown that excess water and air rise in concrete as it sets and tend to accumulate under the bars. Such conditions result in seriously lowered bond strengths when horizontal bars

* To develop a yield-point stress of 65 ksi, one test with $\#5$ bars lapped $24D$ required $\#3$ ties at 2-in. spacing.

are rigidly supported. Horizontal bars are classified as top steel when they have more than 12 in. of concrete below them. Vertical bars carry no such reduction in allowable bond.

For two-way steel in column footings, the allowable bond is reduced to $0.08f_c'$, this reduction being due to the danger of moment cracks parallel to the steel.

Since bond strength increases very slowly with increased f_c' above 3000 psi, the Code places an upper limit on maximum bond stress for all types of bars at the values associated with $f_c' = 3500$ psi.

For plain bars, the Code allowable bond stress is $0.045f_c'$ for bottom steel, $0.03f_c'$ for top steel, and $0.036f_c'$ for two-way footings, with the further requirement that all tension bars have hooked ends.

The author recommends bond stresses lower than the Code values for deformed bars wherever small cover is used and splitting is not positively

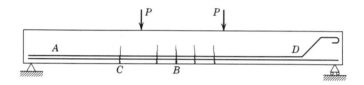

Fig. 6.6. Points where bond stresses differ from conventional calculations.

prevented by external forces or special reinforcement. His recommendation is $0.05f_c'$ for ordinary cover and spacings, without ties or stirrups, with a further reduction to $0.04f_c'$ for large bars (#9, #10, #11) at *minimum* spacing.

6.8. LIMITATIONS OF CONVENTIONAL BOND FORMULA

Bond stress distribution is actually much more complex than the conventional relationship $u = V \div (\Sigma o \frac{7}{8} d)$ suggests. Since this formula is frequently used without understanding, some of the limitations will be mentioned here.

At points where the concrete has not cracked, as at A in Fig. 6.6, the concrete carries much of the tension. The formula assumes all tension is carried by the steel and hence gives bond stresses much too high for the uncracked section.

In a constant moment section, as at B, V is zero and the bond formula would give zero bond stress. In contrast, the following analysis indicates that nearly ultimate bond stresses must exist adjacent to any moment crack. At the crack the steel carries most of the tension; but between cracks, tension in the concrete shares significantly. Thus the bond stress condition on each side of a crack is almost identical with that at the loaded end of a pullout specimen. Near ultimate values of bond stress exist adjacent to the crack instead of zero bond stresses. At a moment crack in a section carrying shear, as at C, the bond stresses due to the crack are superimposed on the average bond stresses indicated by the formula. Some readjustment in bond stress distribution probably results near such a point. It might be noted that all the reduction in bond stress along the uncracked length from A to C must be marshaled just to the left of the crack at C in order to develop the calculated f_s at this point.

The conventional bond formula applies only to beams of constant depth and constant A_s. Bond stresses near a bar bend point, as at D of Fig. 6.6,

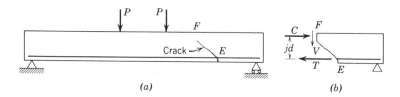

Fig. 6.7. Stress condition at a diagonal crack.

are much disturbed by the transfer of stress out of the bent bar into the straight bar. Very large bond stresses always occur at such a point. To cut off such a bar without bending it up would make the stress transfer more abrupt and the bond conditions even more severe.

At a diagonal tension crack, as at E in Fig. 6.7a, a very serious bond situation is created. Such diagonal tension cracking is discussed in Sec. 6.11. Consider the free body in Fig. 6.7b. If no web reinforcement exists, the shear is carried largely by the compressive area at F. The tension at E and the compression at F make up the couple which balances the bending moment at F. In other words, the steel stress at E is the larger stress normally associated with the larger moment at F. Hence the bond stresses to the right of E are greatly increased when a diagonal crack opens there. In test beams such stress concentration often leads to bond failure once the diagonal crack forms.

The author concludes that most bond stress calculations with the conventional formula are not very realistic. He prefers to emphasize the necessity of having the full development length between every maximum stress point and the end of the bar so stressed. Article 902a states: "The

REINFORCED CONCRETE FUNDAMENTALS

tension in any bar at any section must be properly developed on each side of the section by hook, lap, or embedment." Primary emphasis on this viewpoint has not yet been widely accepted, but the author deduces from a study of experiments and theory that high local bond stress can rarely be critical where anchorage or development length is carefully provided. Where splitting is possible, the development length should be calculated from reduced allowable bond stresses, as outlined for tension splices in Sec. 6.6.

Despite these criticisms there is merit in the conventional bond formula in that it emphasizes the desirability of small bars from the standpoint of bond. The greater total perimeter, when small bars are used, tends to minimize the effects of the above complications.

6.9. DIAGONAL TENSION BEFORE CRACKS FORM

In homogeneous beams diagonal stress can be analyzed by well-established relationships. Reinforced concrete beams, prior to the formation of cracks, probably have stresses quite similar to those of a homogeneous beam. In reinforced concrete the diagonal tension stresses are the ones which can give trouble.

In the beam of Fig. 6.8a a small element at the neutral axis at A would be subject to a shearing stress v, but no bending stress. Figure 6.8b shows that such an element will develop unit diagonal tensile and compressive stresses of magnitude v. An element at B in Fig. 6.8a will have a compressive stress f_c in addition to shear. Such a stress produces diagonal compression, as shown in Fig. 6.8c. When Fig. 6.8c is combined with a shear effect similar to that in Fig. 6.8b, to obtain the total stress, the diagonal tension on section a-a is reduced and the diagonal compression on section b-b is increased. Likewise, an element at C in Fig. 6.8a will carry a tension stress as well as a shear, leading to the added stresses shown in Fig. 6.8d. These combine to increase diagonal tension on section a-a and reduce diagonal compression on section b-b. The combined diagonal stresses are not maximum on sections a-a and b-b, tension being maximum on a steeper plane than a-a when the (horizontal) direct stress is tension, or on a flatter plane when the (horizontal) direct stress is compression. The relation developed in mechanics for maximum diagonal tension, adjusted to the notation used here is:

$$t = \frac{f}{2} + \sqrt{\left(\frac{f}{2}\right)^2 + v^2}$$

In this relation t is the unit diagonal tension, f is the unit direct stress, taken as positive when it is tension, and v is the unit shear. The direction of the maximum diagonal tension is given by the relation:

$$\tan 2\theta = 2v/f$$

where θ is the angle t makes with the stress f, in this case with the horizontal.

Figure 6.8e illustrates the approximate trajectory of maximum tensile stresses in a homogeneous rectangular beam under uniform loading. In a reinforced concrete beam the pattern will be very similar until cracks open, either vertical cracks due to moment or inclined cracks due to diagonal tension. Diagonal tension cracks would be roughly perpendicular to the trajectories shown in Fig. 6.8e for a beam uniformly loaded. Diagonal tension cracks usually open at approximately 45° with the axis of the beam and in short spans frequently start near the neutral axis.

6.10. CONVENTIONAL SHEAR STRESS FORMULA

Since the diagonal tensile stress at the neutral axis is equal to the unit shear, the unit shear stress is used as a measure of the diagonal tension. The unit shear used is itself a nominal or average stress, based on the assumption that the concrete carries no tensile bending stress. It ignores the complications at the moment cracks where the shear concentrates above the crack. The assumed distribution of unit shear stress is shown in Fig. 6.1d.

On this nominal basis, the shear stress can be found from the conditions of Sec. 6.2a and Fig. 6.1 which established the relation

$$\Delta T = V \, \Delta x/jd$$

Figure 6.1d shows that ΔT must be balanced by an average unit shear v over a horizontal area $b \, \Delta x$, or

$$\Delta T = vb \, \Delta x = V \, \Delta x/jd$$

$$v = \frac{V}{bjd} = \frac{V}{b\frac{7}{8}d} \quad \text{(closely enough)}$$

Since ΔT also determines the bond stress, an interesting relationship exists between the average bond stress u and the nominal shear stress v:

$$\Delta T = u \, \Sigma o \, \Delta x = vb \, \Delta x$$

$$u \, \Sigma o = vb$$

6.11. DIAGONAL TENSION FAILURES—WITHOUT WEB REINFORCEMENT

(a) Beams

It should first be noted that continuous or restrained beams or frames which do not have a slab so cast as to provide T-beam action are required

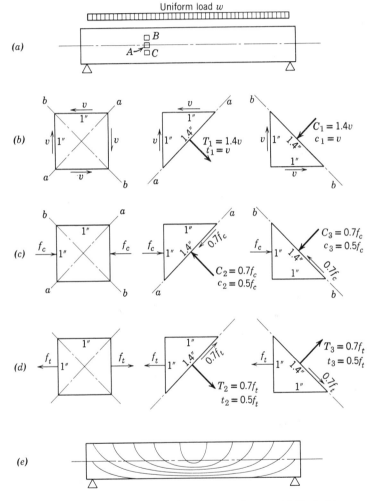

Fig. 6.8. Diagonal stresses in a homogeneous beam. (*a*) Typical beam under uniform load. (*b*) Analysis of stresses at *A*. (*c*) Analysis of stresses at *B*. (*d*) Analysis of stresses at *C*. (*e*) Tension stress trajectories.

to have web reinforcement in accordance with Code Art. 801*e*, regardless of the magnitude of the shear stress. The present section thus concerns only slabs and T-beams and statically determined rectangular beams. Allowable stresses are given in Art. 305 of the Code and are discussed in Sec. 6.12.

Since the Joint ASCE-ACI Committee on Shear and Diagonal Tension has made no recent report at the time of this writing, the following paragraphs have been based on the author's interpretation[4] of current research data.

A diagonal tension failure appears to be least complicated when it occurs away from concentrated loads and reactions. In short spans, when the shear becomes large enough, the diagonal tension near the neutral axis leads to the formation of a crack at approximately a 45° slope. This crack crowds the shear resistance into a smaller depth and by thus increasing the stresses tends to be self-propagating. In longer spans the diagonal crack is more apt to develop as a growth or extension of a vertical moment crack which turns into an inclined crack in the neighborhood of the neutral axis.

In neither case does such a diagonal crack usually proceed immediately to failure. Instead, it encounters resistance as it moves up into the zone of compression, becomes flatter, and stops at some point such as that marked 1 in Fig. 6.9a. With further load, the tension crack extends at a very flat slope until finally sudden failure occurs as indicated at point 2. If the diagonal crack forms initially from the moment crack, as shown by the vertical dashed line, it will always crack back down to point 3 before reaching the failure point at 2. Figure 6.9b illustrates such a failure with the start of the crack nearer the end than usual, this location resulting because two tension bars were cut off at the crack point.

At the same time that cracking is developing in the compression zone, a serious bond situation develops at point 3 as explained in Sec. 6.8 in connection with Fig. 6.7b. This large bond stress leads to a large unit shear stress just above the steel which is one factor leading to the localized diagonal cracking as indicated at point 4 in Fig. 6.9a. This cracking is undoubtedly accentuated by some vertical load carried across the crack by the bars acting as dowels. Such cracking around the bars leads to bond failures in some tests. It appears that such a bond failure has also been prominent in some diagonal tension failures near the point of inflection of continuous beams.

In many cases the development of the diagonal crack described above is stopped by the presence of a nearby load, as indicated in Fig. 6.10. In such cases, the vertical compressive stresses under the load reduce the possibility of further tension cracking and the vertical compression stresses over the reaction likewise limit the bond splitting and diagonal cracking along the steel.   Under greater load (often much greater) a compression failure occurs in the zone adjacent to the load.   This type of failure has

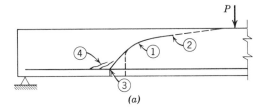

(a)

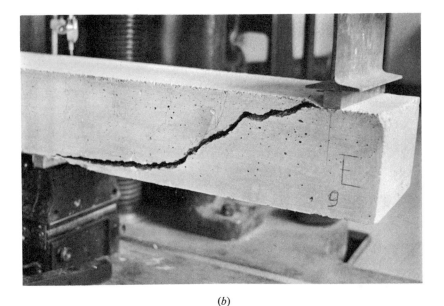

(b)

Fig. 6.9.   Development of a diagonal tension crack when loads and reactions are far apart.   (*a*) Diagram showing sequence in crack formation.   (*b*) Failure of beam tested as a balanced cantilever.   The failure developed from a moment crack extending downward from the top (tension) face and intercepting and joining the final diagonal about mid-depth.

been designated as a shear-compression failure; it can be expected to occur when the shear span *a*, as indicated in Fig. 6.10, is less than four times the beam depth.   When the shear span is small, the increased shear strength may be significant, the ultimate shear being about twice as much for $a = 1.5d$ as for $a = 3.0d$.

As a result of this shear span effect, the worst position (on the basis of diagonal tension failure) for a concentrated load on the usual simple span test beam is not adjacent to the reaction but at some distance out on the span. This is not recognized in specifications, pending further study.

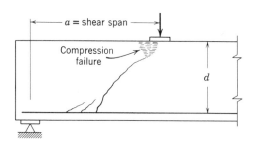

Fig. 6.10. Diagonal tension failure when shear span is small. Shear strength is increased.

Other tests[4] have shown that if the loads are applied as shear loads on the side of the beam, as in Fig. 6.11*a*, or if the reaction is picked up in shear (as when a beam frames into the side of a girder, as in Fig. 6.11*b*), not much increase in shear resistance is obtained with small shear spans.

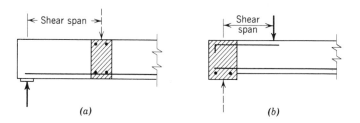

Fig. 6.11. Cases where small shear span does not increase shear strength. (*a*) Girder loaded by shear from beam. (*b*) Beam supported by girder.

Apparently most of the extra resistance is created by the vertical compressive stress under the load and over the reaction; loads or reactions applied as shears create very little vertical compression.

Tests, at present unpublished, have also shown that on simulated continuous beams diagonal tension strength is a minimum where moment cracks have opened rather than nearer the point of inflection where no moment cracks have formed.

REINFORCED CONCRETE FUNDAMENTALS

(b) Footings

Tests on column footings have shown that diagonal tension failure occurs by the formation of diagonal cracks at approximately a 45° slope around the column, as illustrated in Fig. 14.1b. The column thus punches out a truncated pyramid of concrete, the concrete within the pyramid being

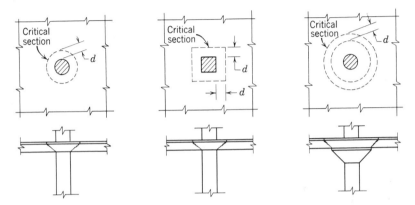

Fig. 6.12. Critical diagonal tension sections in slabs supported directly on columns.

protected from diagonal tension by the heavy vertical compression stresses under the column. Footing tests are discussed in more detail in Sec. 14.2.

(c) Flat slabs and plates

Slabs supported directly on columns, with or without enlarged column heads, act essentially like inverted footings, although some tests seem to show flatter failure angles. The critical section is taken as the section circumscribing the column at a distance d outside the column head, as indicated in Fig. 6.12.

6.12. DIAGONAL TENSION WITHOUT STIRRUPS— ALLOWABLE STRESSES

The allowable shear stress (as a measure of diagonal tension) is $0.03f_c'$ on beams* and one-way slabs, but not more than 90 psi, when no stirrups

* Note that Code Art. 801e permits no continuous *rectangular* beams without stirrups.

are used.   As in the case of bond, diagonal tension strength goes up slowly with increased f_c' above 3000 psi and this accounts for the upper limit.

On two-way column footings, the allowable bond stress is the same $0.03f_c'$ except that the upper limit is placed at 75 psi.

In flat slabs the allowable varies from $0.025f_c'$ to $0.03f_c'$ [Art. 1002c(2)] with an upper limit of 100 psi.

The variation in the upper v limit for different cases appears to reflect the unsettled status of diagonal tension analysis.   At the time of the 1956 Code several series of investigations had recently been completed and still others were in progress.   A satisfactory and comprehensive analysis of all those results, and one which could form the basis for a sound design specification, has not yet emerged.

Some recent failures indicate that designers must not ignore the effect of longitudinal tension induced in members of long frames by shrinkage and temperature changes.

6.13. WEB REINFORCEMENT

Whenever the shear stress exceeds the values shown in Sec. 6.12, web reinforcement is required.   It is also required in *all* isolated continuous rectangular beams and frames, that is, wherever a slab is not cast so as to provide T-beam action (Art. 801e).

The most common web reinforcement consists of vertical stirrups, usually in U-shape but occasionally in W-shape, as shown in Fig. 6.13. Unfortunately, the vertical stirrup carries no significant stress until after a diagonal crack forms.   It has little, if any, effect upon the shear at which such cracks form.   Once a diagonal crack opens, vertical stirrups act in tension to carry load from one side of the crack to the other.   A common analogy considers the stirrups acting as tension verticals in a truss, with the concrete acting as compression diagonals, as shown in Fig. 6.13c. Tests show that the beam cannot fail by further opening of the diagonal crack until the stirrup stress passes the yield-point value.   Even up to failure a portion of the shear is still carried by the concrete, apparently by the compression concrete above the crack.

Diagonal or inclined stirrups (Fig. 6.13d) are aligned more nearly with the principal tension stresses in the beam.   They share in carrying this tension and slightly delay the formation of diagonal tension cracks.   The ACI Code does not consider anchorage of inclined stirrups at the longitudinal steel adequate unless they are welded.   Because of the awkwardness of field welding, inclined stirrups are rarely used.   Inclined stirrups would be a preferred type where preassembled cages of steel are used, as in some precast construction. The truss analogy is still applicable, with stirrups acting as tension diagonals which alternate with concrete compression diagonals, as in a Warren type of truss (Fig. 6.13e).

Longitudinal bars are often bent up where no longer needed for moment. Such bent bars act also as inclined stirrups. Although many designs use bent-up longitudinal bars, only a few designers in the United States take the trouble to calculate their value as stirrups. One reason is that usually

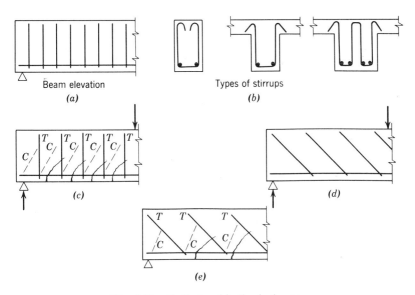

Beam elevation
(a)

Types of stirrups
(b)

(c)

(d)

(e)

Fig. 6.13. Vertical and inclined stirrups.

only a few bars are bent and these may not be conveniently spaced for use as web reinforcement.

Bent-up bars are normally bent at a 45° angle, but in some members, usually light joists, a flatter angle is used to secure some effect as diagonal tension reinforcement over a greater length.

6.14. SPACING RELATIONS FOR STIRRUPS

(a) Vertical stirrups

Although a general formula for spacing of stirrups inclined at any angle is derived in Sec. 6.14c, the special case of vertical stirrups will be presented first. The beam of Fig. 6.14 shows a stirrup intercepting a typical 45°

diagonal tension crack. The stirrup is assumed to carry the vertical component of the diagonal tensile stresses originally acting across the crack over the horizontal length s. The unit tension on the crack is taken as v' and the area contributing stress to the stirrup is $1.414sb'$, where b' is the web thickness. The vertical component of concrete stress is $0.707(1.414sb'v') = sb'v'$, which is equal to the vertical component of stirrup stress $= A_v f_v$.

$$sb'v' = A_v f_v, \qquad s = \frac{A_v f_v}{b'v'}$$

The area of the stirrup includes two bar areas for a U-type stirrup. The allowable stirrup stress is the same as for longitudinal steel, under the

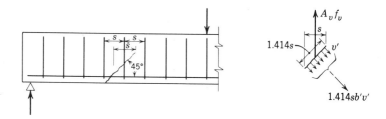

Fig. 6.14. Basis for calculation of vertical stirrups.

ACI Code. The width b' for a T-beam becomes b when a rectangular beam is considered. The shear v' is not the total shear on the beam since tests have shown some shear is carried by the concrete. No stirrups are required until v exceeds $0.03f_c'$ or 90 psi, whichever is smaller.* When v is larger, the v' used for stirrup design is the excess shear above $0.03f_c'$ or 90 psi.*

The stirrup spacing formula can be written in terms of V' where $V' = v'b'jd$. The substitution of $V'/(b'jd)$ for v' in the above formula gives

$$s = \frac{A_v f_v jd}{V'}$$

Stirrup spacing for stress varies inversely with v' or V', with the stirrup located in the middle of the length s it serves. The first stirrup should thus be placed at $s/2$ from the support, as in Fig. 6.15.

Stirrups must be spaced such that every 45° line representing a potential crack will be crossed in the tension side of the beam by at least one stirrup,

---

* But note the special requirements for continuous *rectangular* beams and frames (Art. 801e) which include stirrups to carry two-thirds of the total shear and the use of stirrups wherever there is negative moment steel.

as shown in Fig. 6.15a. This requirement limits the maximum s to $d/2$. The Code (Art. 806) goes further to require that every such potential crack must intercept two stirrups whenever v exceeds $0.06f_c'$, which is equivalent to a maximum spacing of $d/4$.

Whenever v exceeds $0.08f_c'$, the Code requires that both vertical stirrups *and* bent bars be used together. The author considers this high a shear stress undesirable and generally to be avoided. The Code permits the use of v as large as $0.12f_c'$.

Maximum stress on a stirrup is assumed to exist at mid-depth of the beam and the anchorage requirements of Art. 904 may limit either the size

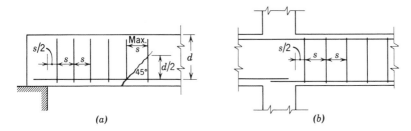

Fig. 6.15. Arrangement of vertical stirrups.

of stirrup bar that may be used or the stress f_v which may be utilized on still larger bars.

When only light stirrups are needed, the minimum area of web steel specified in Art. 807 may govern.

When web reinforcement is used it must be provided beyond the point where it theoretically might be discontinued, the extra length being the depth of the beam (Art. 801d).

(b) Inclined stirrups at 45°

For the 45° bent bars most frequently used, the spacing can be derived much as for vertical stirrups, that is, for the vertical component of the bent bar stress to resist the vertical component of the diagonal tensile stresses which existed where the crack forms. The forces are shown in Fig. 6.16a.

Vertical component of concrete stress $= 0.707(v'b's \times 0.707) = 0.5v'b's$

Vertical component of bar stress $= 0.707A_v f_v$

$$0.5v'b's = 0.707A_v f_v$$

$$s = \frac{1.414A_v f_v}{v'b'} = \frac{1.414A_v f_v jd}{V'}$$

The spacing can thus be larger by some 41 % than for vertical stirrups, but it must also be noted that the inclined legs are longer in about the same proportion.

In considering the length of beam reinforced by a bent bar, the distance s is usually measured as $s/2$ each way from the bar at mid-depth of the beam. If bent bars are used over part of the length of the beam and vertical stirrups elsewhere, the spacings should be laid out together at

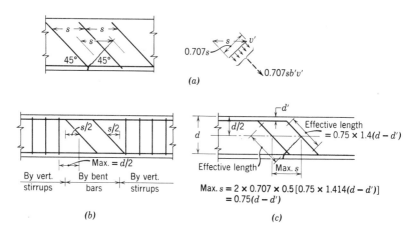

Fig. 6.16. Inclined stirrups at 45°. (*a*) Basis for calculation. (*b*) Arrangement in combination with vertical stirrups. (*c*) Maximum spacing to intercept cracks.

mid-depth as in Fig. 6.16*b*. Care must be taken to intercept all cracks as required by Art. 806.

Only the center three-fourths of the inclined bar is to be considered effective for web reinforcement (Art. 804*a*). When considering the maximum spacing rule of Art. 806, every inclined crack must intersect a bar within this effective length, as shown in Fig. 6.16*c*. This makes the maximum spacing 0.75 of the offset distance of bent bars, that is, $0.75(d - d')$ when v is not over $0.06f_c'$, or half this when v exceeds $0.06f_c'$.

(c) Inclined stirrups at more or less than 45°

The general spacing formula is derived on the same basis for the more general geometry of Fig. 6.17. The tension resisted acts over the distance y.

$$y = \frac{s \sin \alpha}{\sin (135 - \alpha)} = \frac{s \sin \alpha}{\sin (45° + \alpha)} = \frac{s \sin \alpha}{\sin 45 \cos \alpha + \cos 45 \sin \alpha}$$

$$= \frac{s \sin \alpha}{0.707(\cos \alpha + \sin \alpha)}$$

$$\text{Vertical component of stress} = 0.707v'b'y = \frac{v'b's \sin \alpha}{\cos \alpha + \sin \alpha}$$

$$\text{Vertical component of bar stress} = A_v f_v \sin \alpha$$

$$\frac{v'b's \sin \alpha}{\cos \alpha + \sin \alpha} = A_v f_v \sin \alpha$$

$$s = \frac{A_v f_v (\cos \alpha + \sin \alpha)}{v'b'} = \frac{A_v f_v jd(\cos \alpha + \sin \alpha)}{V'}$$

This formula yields the special relations above for vertical and 45° stirrups if $\alpha = 90°$ and $\alpha = 45°$, respectively. Article 804d of the Code limits the use of this relation to a series of bars bent up at different points.

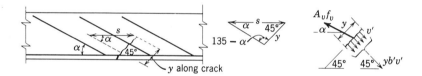

Fig. 6.17. General case of inclined stirrups.

When only a single bar is bent up or when all bars are bent at the same point, the value for diagonal tension is discounted to

$$V' = A_v f_v \sin \alpha$$

This is equivalent to saying that the vertical component of the bar stress carries the shear V'. Such a bar is considered effective over the center three-fourths of its inclined length.

6.15. DESIGN OF VERTICAL STIRRUPS

The practical problem of designing stirrups requires:

1. Determination of maximum shears and the length over which stirrups are needed.

SHEAR STRESSES—BOND AND DIAGONAL TENSION

2. Choice of desirable size of stirrup bar.
3. Selection of a series of practical spacings.

The maximum shear diagram may involve partial as well as full span loads.

Stirrup bar sizes are almost never mixed in a given beam. Hence, with uniform loads, close spacings are required at points of maximum shear; whereas at points of lesser shear the spacing may be limited by the so-called maximum spacing, that is, the interception of all potential cracks. The stirrup size must be large enough to give a minimum spacing adequate to pass the aggregate readily and, for practical reasons, rarely as small as 2 in., usually 3 in. or more. Larger bars and spacings are economical if they do not involve too many spaces fixed by crack interception instead of by stress capacity.

For a member with a constant shear the stirrup spacing would be constant and preferably near the maximum permissible. When the shear

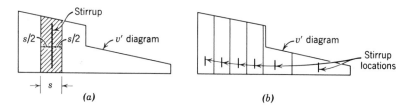

Fig. 6.18. Stirrup spacing related to area of v' diagram.

varies, as is more usual, a sound general method is to calculate the required stirrup spacing at enough points to establish a stirrup spacing curve, including thereon the specification limits on maximum spacing. From this curve the practical spacings can be worked out. A detailed design of stirrups for a continuous T-beam span is given in Secs. 6.18c and 8.19.

The theoretical number of stirrups required for stress is often useful. For any v' diagram (not total v diagram), such as Fig. 6.18a, the area under the diagram is a direct measure of the number of stirrups theoretically required. Since $s = A_v f_v \div b'v'$,

$$A_v f_v = sb'v' = b' \text{ (area of } v' \text{ diagram for length } s)$$

Each stirrup thus cares for an equal area under the v' diagram and the total number of stirrups needed is

$$N = \frac{b' \text{ (total area of } v' \text{ diagram)}}{A_v f_v}$$

This is a theoretical number. Spacings used will be stated in practical units, usually full inches (except for small dimensions, say, under 5 in.), and will thus average less than the theoretical spacings. There also will usually be some spaces kept smaller than the theoretical in order to intercept potential cracks. At least two extra stirrups will always be required beyond the theoretical in the extension called for by Art. 801d. The practical number of stirrups in a carefully designed section will usually be from three to six more than the theoretical number.

6.16. SPACING STIRRUPS FROM THE AREA OF THE SHEAR DIAGRAM

The above discussion indicates another possible method of spacing stirrups especially adaptable for irregular v' diagrams. The area under

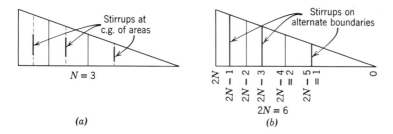

Fig. 6.19. Location of stirrups for triangular v' diagram.

the v' diagram cared for by one stirrup is calculated first. The total area can then be subdivided into areas of this same size, as in Fig. 6.18b, with a stirrup placed at the centroid of each, except where maximum spacing controls.

The v' diagram is frequently a triangle, which is an area easy to subdivide into equal pieces. If there are N stirrups to be located at the centroid of N areas, the placement of the stirrups would be such as to subdivide each area into two equal parts, thereby creating $2N$ half areas, as in Fig. 6.19a. The simplest procedure is based on subdividing the triangle directly into $2N$ parts, as in Fig. 6.19b, placing the stirrups on alternate subdivisions.

Consider $2N$ equal areas from the triangle of Fig. 6.20, with boundaries at $2N$, $2N - 1$, $2N - 2$, . . ., 3, 2, 1, located at distances from 0 equal to

$z_{2N}, z_{2N-1}, z_{2N-2}, \ldots, z_3, z_2, z_1$. Since the total area of a triangle of base z, from the origin at 0, varies as z^2, the following ratios exist:

$$\frac{z_{2N-1}^2}{z_{2N}^2} = \frac{(2N-1)\ \text{areas}}{(2N)\ \text{areas}} = \frac{2N-1}{2N}$$

$$\frac{z_{2N-3}^2}{z_{2N}^2} = \frac{2N-3}{2N}$$

$$\cdot \qquad \cdot$$
$$\cdot \qquad \cdot$$
$$\cdot \qquad \cdot$$

$$\frac{z_1^2}{z_{2N}^2} = \frac{1}{2N}$$

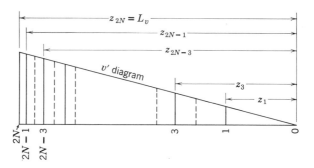

Fig. 6.20. Notation for slide-rule method of spacing stirrups.

In the denominators, $z_{2N} = L_v$ and the only unknowns in the equations are $z_{2N-1}, z_{2N-3}, z_{2N-5}, \ldots, z_1$. The above ratios can be rewritten in the form:

$$\frac{\sqrt{2N}}{L_v} = \frac{\sqrt{2N}}{z_{2N}} = \frac{\sqrt{2N-1}}{z_{2N-1}} = \frac{\sqrt{2N-3}}{z_{2N-3}} = \cdots \frac{\sqrt{3}}{z_3} = \frac{1}{z_1}$$

which can very easily be set as a constant ratio on the slide rule, as shown in Fig. 6.21.

L_v is set on the C scale opposite $2N$ on the A scale. The rider is moved to $2N - 1$ on the A scale to indicate z_{2N-1} on the C scale, and so forth. Obviously, the B and D scales could be used just as readily.

Since stirrups are to be located only at alternate boundaries, only the z distances to these boundaries need be calculated.

REINFORCED CONCRETE FUNDAMENTALS

6.17. MEMBERS OF VARYING DEPTH

Attention is called to the fact that the relations for shear, bond, and even moment resistance must be modified for members in which the depth is varying, that is, members in which the bottom and top surfaces are not parallel. The moment effect is not large unless the angle between the faces is at least 10° or 15°, but shear for diagonal tension and bond may be

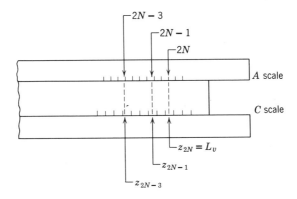

Fig. 6.21. Slide-rule setting for stirrup locations.

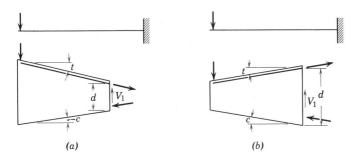

Fig. 6.22. Shear in beams of varying depth.

modified as much as 30% by 10° slopes. The 1940 Joint Committee Specification gave the following formula for the effective total shear V_1 to be used in the usual relations for v and u:

$$V_1 = V \pm \frac{M}{d} (\tan c + \tan t)$$

where V and M are the external shear and moment to be resisted, d is the depth to tension steel, and t and c are the slope angles of the top and bottom of the beam as shown in Fig. 6.22. The plus sign is used when the beam depth decreases as the moment increases, as in Fig. 6.22a, and the minus sign is used for the more usual case of increasing depth with increasing moment, as in Fig. 6.22b. When the sum of the angles becomes as much as 30°, such a formula becomes very inexact.

6.18. EXAMPLES OF SHEAR AND BOND CALCULATIONS

(a) The beam of Fig. 6.23 will be checked for shear and bond, assuming $f_c' = 3000$ psi, $f_s = 20,000$ psi, deformed bars.

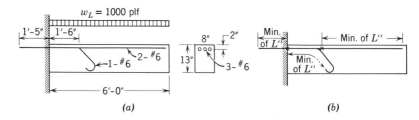

(a)   (b)

Fig. 6.23. Beam of Sec. 6.18a.

SOLUTION

$$\text{Beam weight} = (8 \times 13/144)150 = 108 \text{ plf}$$
$$d = 13 - 2 = 11 \text{ in.}$$

At support:

$V = (1000 + 108)6 = 6650 \text{ lb}$

$v = V/(b \tfrac{7}{8}d) = 6650/(8 \times \tfrac{7}{8} \times 11) = 86.6 \text{ psi} < 0.03 f_c' = 90 \text{ psi}$ O.K.

$\Sigma o = 3 \times 2.36 = 7.08 \text{ in.}$

$u = V/(\Sigma o \tfrac{7}{8}d) = 6650/(7.08 \times \tfrac{7}{8} \times 11) = 97.5 \text{ psi}$

The concrete under the bars is less than 12 in., leaving the allowable $u = 0.10 f_c'$ $= 300$ psi. (Without stirrups the author would prefer to use an allowable u of $0.05 f_c' = 150$ psi, but this is also greater than the actual u.)   O.K.

According to the ACI Code, Art. 901a, the perimeter of the bar bent down can be included in Σo until it is more than $d/3$ distant from the straight bars, that is, out to $1.50 + 0.33 \times 11/12 = 1.80$ ft from the face of support. Beyond this point $\Sigma o = 2 \times 2.36 = 4.72$ in.

$V_{1\cdot 80} = (1000 + 108)4.20 = 4650 \text{ lb}$

$u_{1\cdot 80} = 4650/(4.72 \times \tfrac{7}{8} \times 11) = 103 \text{ psi} < 0.10 \times 3000 = 300 \text{ psi}$ O.K.

Assuming the 1-ft 5-in. anchorage into the support qualifies as top steel, that is, has more than 12 in. of concrete below it, the allowable $u = 0.07 \times 3000 = 210$ psi. For a bar stress of 20,000 psi, the total tension on each bar is $A_s f_s = L'' \Sigma o\, u$.

$$20,000 \times 0.44 = L'' \times 2.36 \times 210$$

$$\text{Reqd. } L'' = 17.8 \text{ in.} > 1 \text{ ft 5 in.}$$

This is not satisfactory unless the actual $f_s < 20,000$ psi.

$$\text{Actual } f_s = \frac{M}{A_s jd} = \frac{(1108 \times 6 \times 3)12}{(3 \times 0.44) \times 0.866 \times 11} = 19,100 \text{ psi}$$

$$\text{Min. } L'' = (19,100/20,000)17.8 = 17.0 \text{ in. vs. 1 ft 5 in.} \qquad \text{O.K.}$$

Within the beam as noted in Fig. 6.23b, the bar bent down has a length of more than L'' available in which to develop its full f_s. Since this single bent bar is probably in the middle of the beam width, the bent portion is well encased in concrete and this justifies the use of the Code value of $u = 300$ psi in the calculation of L''. The other two bars also obviously project more than L'' beyond their full f_s at the bend down point. Although under the Code this L'' could also be based on $u = 300$ psi, these two bars are close to the surface and a splitting failure must be considered possible. Accordingly, the author recommends an allowable u of $0.05f_c' = 150$ psi for cases like these two bars.

After the bond stress has been checked at $x = 1.80$ ft, the check on L'' for the bars that continue to the end is actually unnecessary, because these two calculations in a way duplicate each other. However, for bars bent down or simply stopped *short* of the end, bond stress calculations alone are not adequate because they do not certify that the necessary L'' length exists beyond each maximum stress point.

(b) Determine the stirrups for the beam of Fig. 6.24a, using intermediate grade steel and $f_c' = 3000$ psi.

SOLUTION

Beam wt. $= (9 \times 22/144) \times 150 = 207$ plf

$V_0 = 20,000 + 207 \times 6 = 21,200$ lb

$v_0 = 21,200/(9 \times \frac{7}{8} \times 19) = 142$ psi $> 0.03f_c' = 90$ psi

$\qquad\qquad\qquad\qquad\qquad\qquad < 0.08f_c' = 240$ psi   O.K. with stirrups

$V_{3ft} = 20,000 + 207 \times 3 = 20,600$ lb

$v_3 = 20,600/(9 \times \frac{7}{8} \times 19) = 138$ psi

Stirrups should be designed for $v' = v - 0.03f_c'$ over the 3-ft length, the shear between loads being so small that no stirrups are needed there.

Try #2 U-stirrups, $A_v = 2 \times 0.05 = 0.10$ in.²

$$s_0 = A_v f_v/v'b = \frac{0.10 \times 20,000}{(142 - 90)9} = 4.27 \text{ in.}$$

Since $v < 0.06f_c'$, max. $s = d/2 = 19/2 = 9.5$ in.

Try #3 U-stirrups, $A_v = 2 \times 0.11 = 0.22$ in.²

SHEAR STRESSES—BOND AND DIAGONAL TENSION

$$s_0 = 0.22 \times 20,000/(52 \times 9) = 9.40 \text{ in.} < 9.5 \text{ in.}$$

USE #3 U-stirrups.

The length of stirrup above mid-depth should be checked against the anchorage (or development) length required. With the minimum standard hook [Art. 906a(1) of Code] and 1.5-in. clear cover, Fig. 6.24c shows that the length of the straight part of the bar to mid-depth is $9.5 - 1.5 - 1.31 = 6.69$ in., which is sufficient to develop a stress of $L''\Sigma o\, u/A_s = 6.69 \times 1.18 \times 300/0.11 = 21,500$ psi. Since Art. 904a(1) indicates that the hook alone may be counted as developing 10,000 psi, the straight section has more than twice the necessary length.

A formal stirrup spacing curve could be prepared as in Fig. 6.26, but it scarcely seems necessary for this short length and this simple pattern of v' values. The stirrup size chosen does not permit the use of a wider spacing nearer the load but the theoretical spacing will be calculated at $x = 3$ ft to be sure that the spacing used will not be unduly wasteful.

$$s_{3\text{ft}} = \frac{0.22 \times 20,000}{48 \times 9} = 10.0 \text{ in.} > 9.5 \qquad \text{N.G.} \qquad \text{USE 9 in.}$$

USE 5–#3 U at 4 in., 4 at 9 in., at each end. This arrangement is sketched in Fig. 6.24d, which shows the last stirrup 4 in. beyond the load. Although the last stirrup might stop $s/2$ short of the load, the author prefers to get a stirrup near the last load. On the other hand, this arrangement completely ignores the last sentence of Art. 801d which requires that stirrups be extended a distance equal to the depth of the member beyond the point theoretically required. With a gradually varying v' diagram, as in the case of uniform load, this is a desirable extra safety factor. In this case, with the shear in the center 6 ft almost negligible, and assuming that the loads cannot shift in location or amount enough to make this center shear significant, there seems to be no point to adding more stirrups at a maximum spacing of $d/2$ to fill out this extra length.

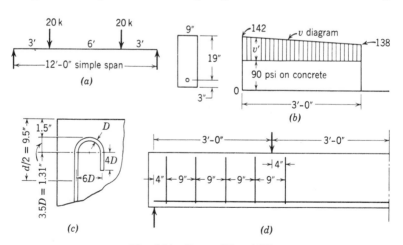

Fig. 6.24. Beam of Sec. 6.18b.

The minimum area of web reinforcement required by Art. 807 is not less than 0.15% of the area measured by the beam width and horizontal stirrup spacing. For #3 U at 9 in., in a beam 9 in. wide,

$$0.0015 \times 9 \times 9 = 0.121 \text{ in.}^2 \text{ required vs. } 2 \times 0.11 = 0.22 \text{ in.}^2 \text{ used} \qquad \text{O.K.}$$

(c) A continuous T-beam* with $b' = 11.5$ in., $d = 20.5$ in., $f_c' = 3000$ psi, intermediate grade steel, must provide for the unit shears shown in Fig. 6.25. (These shears are calculated in Sec. 8.19.) Design and space the necessary stirrups.

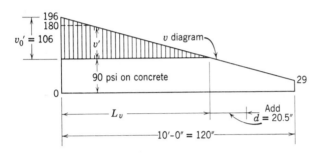

Fig. 6.25. v' diagram for beam of Sec. 6.18c.

SOLUTION

Stirrups are needed for a distance L_v, out to the point where $v = 0.03f_c' = 90$ psi, the allowable without stirrups, plus an extra distance $d = 20.5$ in. (Art. 801d).

$$\frac{L_v}{120} = \frac{196 - 90}{196 - 29} = \frac{106}{167}, \qquad L_v = 75.3 \text{ in.}$$

$$\text{Add } d \text{ of 20.5 in., total} = 95.8 \text{ in.}$$

Within this L_v length the stirrups must be designed for $v' = v - 90$, as indicated by the shaded area in Fig. 6.25.

For vertical stirrups, the maximum spacing permitted by Art. 806a is $d/2 = 10.25$ in. for zones where v is $0.06f_c' = 180$ psi or less. Near the support v is larger, reducing the maximum spacing to $0.25d = 5.12$ in. For #3 U-stirrups

$$s_0 = A_v f_v / v'b = 2 \times 0.11 \times 20,000/(106 \times 11.5) = 3.62 \text{ in.}$$

For #4 U-stirrups

$$s_0 = 2 \times 0.20 \times 20,000/(106 \times 11.5) = 6.55 \text{ in.}$$

Next to the column this must be reduced to the maximum spacing limit of 5.12 in. Since the theoretical spacing increases to infinity at $L_v = 75.3$ in., the

* Note Code Art. 801e and Sec. 8.21 in Chap. 8 for the quite different requirements for a continuous *rectangular* beam or frame.

#4 stirrups will have an excessive number of spaces determined by the maximum spacing of 10.25 in. This would be wasteful of steel. On the other hand, the initial spacing for #3 stirrups is quite satisfactory. The #3 stirrups will next be investigated at the practical maximum spacing of 10 in. with respect to the 0.15% minimum specified in Art. 807.

$$\text{Min. } A_v = 0.0015bs = 0.0015 \times 11.5 \times 10 = 0.172 \text{ in.}^2 < 2 \times 0.11$$

Any stirrups must be of small enough diameter to develop full anchorage above mid-depth of the beam. Figure 6.24c shows the upper part of a typical stirrup. The hook with $3D$ radius for $180°$ plus a $4D$ straight extension beyond the hook is accepted by the Code, Art. 906a, b, as developing 10,000 psi on the bar. This leaves 10,000 psi to be developed between mid-depth and the start of the hook, a distance of $d/2 - 1.5$-in. cover $- 0.5D - 3.0D = 10.25 - 1.50 - 3.5 \times 0.375 = 7.44$ in. $= 19.8D$. The required distance is $[10,000/(4 \times 300)]D = 8.3D \leqslant 19.8D$.

The detailed stirrup spacing curve will be developed for establishing the final spacings graphically. Theoretical spacings will be calculated at several points by noting that $s \propto 1/v'$, this being simpler than numerical calculation of v' values.

$0.75L_v = 56.5$ in. $\qquad v' = v_0'/4 \qquad s = 4s_0 = 4 \times 3.62 = 14.48$ in.

$0.50L_v = 37.6$ in. $\qquad v' = v_0'/2 \qquad s = 2s_0 = 2 \times 3.62 = 7.24$ in.

$0.25L_v = 18.8$ in. $\qquad v' = 0.75v_0' \qquad s = (1/0.75)s_0 = 1.33 \times 3.62 = 4.83$ in.

These values are plotted in Fig. 6.26 and a theoretical curve sketched through the points. The maximum spacings are also drawn in, both for $v > 0.06f_c'$ and for $v < 0.06f_c'$, only the latter being found to govern. Stirrups are needed over the distance L_v plus a distance d according to Art. 801d.

The practical spacings are established graphically in the following fashion. Spacings equal to or just less than the theoretical are laid out horizontally, each stirrup indicated by a vertical line. A stair-step curve of the spacings actually used is also plotted at the same time, step by step. The vertical lines keep track of the actual stirrup locations and the stair-step curve indicates how these compare with the allowable curve values.

The first space is necessarily a half (theoretical) space to put the stirrup in the center of the horizontal area it serves. The next space could as well have been 3.5 in. It may appear that the 4-in. spacing was introduced prematurely. Careful analysis will show, however, that the criterion is not that the spacings used stay *under* the theoretical values at all points but that the area under the practical curve served by a single stirrup (that is, $s/2$ each side of the stirrup) must not exceed the area under the theoretical curve. On this basis the 4-in. spacing is amply safe.

The next to last stirrup falls 3.3 in. from the end of the zone to be covered. Since this is less than one-half space, such a stopping point would be entirely in order on the basis of stress. However, Art. 801d seems to call for a stirrup at the end of the distance d beyond L_v. Since it does not appear possible to stretch the spacings by 3.3 in., the last stirrup was added. With this surplus on the length covered, the spacings could be simplified as indicated with dashed lines and the alternate spacing shown with a dimension line. USE 16–#3 U at 1.5 in., 3 in., 4 at 4 in., 2 at 5 in., 3 at 6 in., 5 at 10 in., each end of beam.

An alternate procedure for spacing stirrups, less accurate but still satisfactory in the hands of one skilled at it, consists of (1) calculating the theoretical total number of stirrups required, (2) calculating the spacing at a few points, and (3) simply writing down a series of spacings which satisfy (2) and at the same

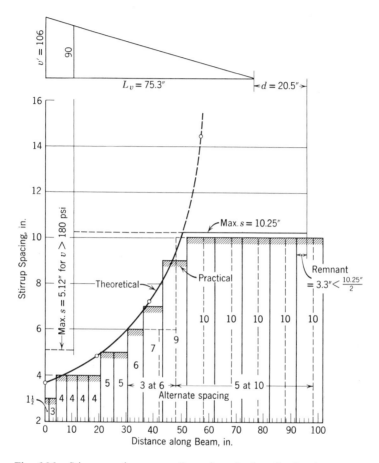

Fig. 6.26. Stirrup spacing curve. Record results thus, for the alternate solution: USE 16–#3 U at 1.5, 3, 4 at 4, 2 at 5, 3 at 6, 5 at 10, each end.

time provide enough extra stirrups to account for the lengths that are governed by maximum spacing instead of stress. Extra stirrups are always necessary as illustrated by the design just completed with 15 stirrups compared to a theoretical

$$N = \frac{b'(\text{area } v' \text{ diag.})}{A_v f_v} = \frac{11.5 \times 0.5 \times 106 \times 75.3}{2 \times 0.11 \times 20,000} = 10.4 \text{ stirrups}$$

SHEAR STRESSES—BOND AND DIAGONAL TENSION   155

(d) Given a simple span beam 11 in. wide and 18 in. depth to steel, $f_c' = 2500$ psi, for which the v' diagram is the triangle shown in Fig. 6.27, choose and space stirrups using intermediate grade steel.

SOLUTION

The idea developed at the end of Sec. 6.16, that of subdividing the v' diagram into equal areas, will be used as an alternate to the formal stirrup spacing curve. This method is sometimes called the slide-rule method.

Try #3 U-stirrups

$$s_0 = A_v f_v / v' b = 2 \times 0.11 \times 20{,}000/(76 \times 11) = 5.26 \text{ in.}$$
$$\text{Max. } s = d/2 = 9 \text{ in.}$$

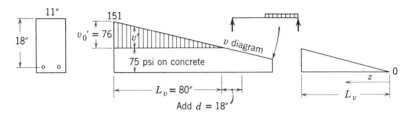

Fig. 6.27. v' diagram for Sec. 6.18d.

This maximum spacing would govern for over half of the length, since a calculated s of 9 in. results from v' of about 45 psi. A simple layout would result, but it would be wasteful of steel.

Try #2 U-stirrups

$$s_0 = 2 \times 0.05 \times 20{,}000/(76 \times 11) = 2.39 \text{ in.}$$

This spacing is very close, nearly the minimum used and below the more desirable minimum of 2.5 to 3 in. There is little to choose between these two stirrup sizes.

USE #3 U-stirrups.

$$\text{Theoretical number of stirrups} = N = \frac{b(\text{area of } v' \text{ diag.})}{A_v f_v}$$

$$N = \frac{11(0.5 \times 76 \times 80)}{2 \times 0.11 \times 20{,}000} = 7.60$$

The v' diagram will be subdivided into 7.60* equal areas, or, as pointed out in Sec. 6.16, with greater efficiency into $2N = 15.2$ equal areas. The slide-rule ratio is set up by lining up $z_{2N} = L_v = 80$ in. on the C scale opposite $2N = 15.2$ on the A scale, as in Fig. 6.21. The rider is moved to $2N - 1 = 14.2$ on the A scale, to read $z_{2N-1} = 77.5$ in. on the C scale; then to $2N - 3 = 12.2$ on the

---

* 7.60 equal areas sounds highly theoretical compared to simply using 8 areas. However, with the triangular v' diagram, the theoretical spacing approaches infinity as v' approaches zero, causing the maximum spacing of $d/2$ to control. Hence this last area might as well be 0.6 of a full area; it is an unused area either way one proceeds.

A scale, and so forth. It is suggested that z be read only as accurately as the stirrup spacing is to be stated, that is, to the nearest full inch if the designer wishes to avoid half-inch spacings. When tabulated as in Table 6.1, the calculations are completed by recording s as the difference between successive z values. The theoretical s given by $z_{4\cdot2} - z_{2\cdot2}$ exceeds the maximum of $d/2 = 9$ in. Hence this last 42 in. ($z_{4\cdot2}$) plus the 18 in. additional required by Art. 801d, a total of 60 in., must be completed at 9-in. spacing, requiring $60/9 = 7$ more stirrups.

USE 13–#3 U-stirrups at 2.5 in., 2 at 6 in., 7 in., 7.5 in., 8 at 9 in., each end.

TABLE 6.1.   Stirrup Spacing from Slide-Rule Calculation
(Sec. 6.18d)

Subdivision Points		z	s
$2N$	$= 15.2$	$L_v = 80$ in.	
			2.5 in.
$2N - 1$	$= 14.2$	77.5	
			6
$2N - 3$	$= 12.2$	71.5	
			6
$2N - 5$	$= 10.2$	65.5	
			7
$2N - 7$	$= 8.2$	58.5	
			7.5
$2N - 9$	$= 6.2$	51.0	
			9
$2N - 11$	$= 4.2$	42.0	
			11.5 > max. $s = d/2 = 9$ in.
$2N - 13$	$= 2.2$	30.5	
			9-in. spacing for 42.0 + 18 in. = 60/9 = 7 spaces
$2N - 15$	$= 0.2$	9.0	
By specification continue stirrups 18 in. beyond L_v			

6.19. TORSION

Torsion in a beam results from a twisting moment around the axis of the beam. Most frequently this is a secondary effect, as when a floor slab frames into a spandrel or wall beam and the deflection of the slab twists the beam. It becomes a primary effect in the case of an isolated beam which is curved in plan, such as the curved beams which follow the rounded corner of a building.

Torsion causes shearing stresses, which are maximum around the face of the beam, somewhat as in a circular shaft. However, in the case of practical beam shapes the cross sections warp under torsion and the unit shears are not proportional to their distance from the center of rotation. For example, in a rectangular beam the largest shearing stress is at the middle of the larger face, which is the face closest to the center of rotation.

Since torsion increases the shear on one side of the beam (and reduces it on the opposite side), it increases the diagonal tension stresses on that side. This increase leads to earlier diagonal tension cracking on the one side under the combined stress. Extra stirrups, or, better, extra ties as in a column, can provide additional resistance against the increased diagonal tension which exists on this one side; also against the diagonal tension due

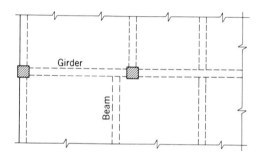

Fig. 6.28. This beam framing produces severe torsional stresses in girder adjacent to column.

to the torsion alone on the tension face of the beam. Diagonal tension on the far side is reduced by the torsion and the torsion effect on the compression face of the beam is not important.

The elastic analysis for torsion is well presented elsewhere* and is not repeated here for several reasons. (1) Its validity when applied to sections already cracked from moment stress is questionable. (2) Tests on simple span T-beams[7] have indicated an enormous reserve in ultimate strength over that which elastic analysis would indicate and even some reserve over that given by plastic analysis. (3) In most practical beam problems involving torsion the beam is monolithic with a slab which modifies the center of rotation and at the same time probably actively assists in caring for the torsion.

Primary torsion loading should be avoided wherever possible. However, in the author's experience in testing beams for diagonal tension and

* Peabody,[5] pp. 174–184, 412–420. Sutherland and Reese,[6] pp. 289–294.

REINFORCED CONCRETE FUNDAMENTALS

torsion, he has observed that beams with f_c' under 4000 psi have a considerable tolerance for torsion with small loss in over-all strength. He therefore believes that most of the situations where a slab creates only a secondary torsion in the supporting beam can be ignored. Likewise, he is very distrustful as to the magnitude of negative slab moments which the torsional stiffness of a spandrel beam can develop.

Secondary torsional stresses may be quite high and serious in a girder where a beam frames into one side close to a column joint which does not rotate in the same direction as the beam. In a case such as shown in Fig. 6.28 the connection of the beam to the column is too rigid to give much relief, through the twist of the girder. The torsion in such a girder approaches the full negative moment in the beam.

6.20. ULTIMATE STRENGTH DESIGN

Until such time as the committees restudying the general problem of shear strength of beams and slabs formulate their reports, there is no advantage in calculating bond and shear stresses on an ultimate strength basis. The Report of the ASCE-ACI Joint Committee on Ultimate Strength Design made no recommendation on bond and shear, on the assumption that this part of design would continue on a working stress basis for the present.

SELECTED REFERENCES

1. "Tentative Specifications for Minimum Requirements for the Deformations of Deformed Steel Bars for Concrete Reinforcement," *ASTM Spec. A 305–53T*, ASTM, Philadelphia, 1953.

2. Phil M. Ferguson, Robert D. Turpin, and J. Neils Thompson, "Minimum Bar Spacing as a Function of Bond and Shear Strength," *ACI Jour.*, **25**, June 1954; *Proc.*, **50**, p. 869.

3. James Chinn, Phil M. Ferguson, and J. Neils Thompson, "Lapped Splices in Reinforced Concrete Beams," *ACI Jour.*, **27**, Oct. 1955; *Proc.*, **52**, p. 201.

4. Phil M. Ferguson, "Some Implications of Recent Diagonal Tension Tests," *ACI Jour.*, **28**, Aug. 1956, June 1957; *Proc.*, **53**, pp. 157, 1190.

5. Dean Peabody, Jr., *The Design of Reinforced Concrete Structures*, John Wiley & Sons, New York, 2nd ed., 1946.

6. Hale Sutherland and R. C. Reese, *Introduction to Reinforced Concrete Design*, John Wiley & Sons, New York, 2nd ed., 1943.

7. Earl I. Brown, II, "Strength of Reinforced Concrete T-beams under Combined Direct Shear and Torsion," *ACI Proc.*, **26**, May 1955; *Proc.*, **51**, p. 889.

8. Arthur P. Clark, "Comparative Bond Efficiency of Deformed Concrete Reinforcing Bars," *ACI Jour.*, **18**, Dec. 1946; *Proc.*, **43**, p. 381.

9. Arthur P. Clark, "Bond of Concrete Reinforcing Bars," *ACI Jour.*, **21**, Nov. 1949; *Proc.*, **46**, p. 161.

10. Herbert J. Gilkey, Stephen J. Chamberlin, and Robert W. Beal, "Bond Between Concrete and Steel," Iowa Eng. Exp. Sta. *Bull. No. 147*, Iowa State College, 1940.

11. David Watstein, "Bond Stress in Concrete Pull-Out Specimens," *ACI Jour.*, **13**, Sept. 1941; *Proc.*, **38**, p. 37.

12. T. D. Mylrea, "Bond and Anchorage," *ACI Jour.*, **19**, Mar. 1948; *Proc.*, **44**, p. 521.

13. S. J. Chamberlin, "Spacing of Reinforcement in Beams," *ACI Jour.*, **28**, July 1956; *Proc.*, **28**, p. 113.

14. Armas Laupa, Chester P. Siess, and Nathan M. Newmark, "Strength in Shear of Reinforced Concrete Beams," Univ. of Ill. Eng. Exp. Sta. *Bull. No. 428*, 1955.

15. K. G. Moody, I. M. Viest, R. C. Elstner, and E. Hognestad, "Shear Strength of Reinforced Concrete Beams, Parts 1, 2, 3, and 4," *ACI Jour.*, **26**, Dec. 1954, Jan., Feb., Mar., 1955; *Proc.*, **51**, pp. 317, 417, 525, 697.

16. Richard C. Elstner and Eivind Hognestad, "Shear Strength of Reinforced Concrete Slabs," *ACI Jour.*, **28**, July 1956; *Proc.*, **28**, p. 29.

17. Paul Andersen, "Rectangular Concrete Sections Under Torsion," *ACI Jour.*, **9**, Sept.-Oct. 1937; *Proc.*, **34**, p. 1.

18. Chas. S. Whitney, "Ultimate Shear Strength of Reinforced Concrete Flat Slabs, Footings, and Frame Members Without Shear Reinforcement," *ACI Jour.*, **29**, Oct. 1957; *Proc.*, **54**, p. 265.

19. JoDean Morrow and I. M. Viest, "Shear Strength of Reinforced Concrete Frame Members Without Web Reinforcement," *ACI Jour.*, **28**, Mar. 1957; *Proc.*, **53**, p. 833.

20. Boyd G. Anderson, "Rigid Frame Failures," *ACI Jour.*, **28**, Jan. 1957; *Proc.*, **53**, p. 617.

21. Richard C. Elstner and Eivind Hognestad, "Laboratory Investigation of Rigid Frame Failure," *ACI Jour.*, **28**, Jan. 1957; *Proc.*, **53**, p. 637.

PROBLEMS

Note: The problems in this group relate only to bond and shear stress; flexural considerations are not included, unless specifically stated. Whenever actual stresses are called for, these should be compared with the specified allowables of Art. 305*a*.

Prob. 6.1.

(*a*) Calculate the maximum bond stress on the beam of Fig. 6.29 for a uniform load of 3000 plf (plus weight of beam), $f_c' = 3000$ psi.

(*b*) Are stirrups required?

(*c*) Repeat calculations in (*a*) assuming the total steel is changed to 2–#8 with one of these bent up.

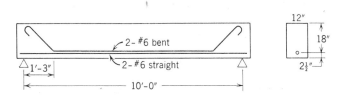

Fig. 6.29. Simple span beam for Prob. 6.1.

Prob. 6.2.

(*a*) Calculate the maximum bond stress on the beam of Fig. 6.30, $f_c' = 3000$ psi, intermediate grade steel.

(*b*) Calculate the required anchorage length L''.

(*c*) Are stirrups required? If so, what size and spacing of vertical stirrups?

Prob. 6.3. If the load on the beam of Fig. 6.30 is changed to 6000 plf (including the beam weight), recalculate as indicated in Prob. 6.2.

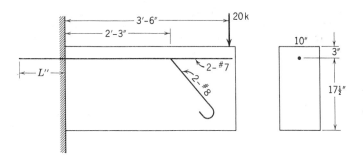

Fig. 6.30. Cantilever beam for Probs. 6.2 and 6.3.

Prob. 6.4. For the beam of Fig. 6.31, $f_c' = 3000$, intermediate grade steel, beam weight neglected, calculate the depth d required for these items individually:

(*a*) Diagonal tension without stirrups.

(*b*) Bond stress.

(*c*) Stress on the steel.

(*d*) Balanced stresses in flexure.

Prob. 6.5. Design and space vertical stirrups for an 18-ft simple span rectangular beam, $b = 11$ in., $d = 28$ in., $f_c' = 2500$ psi, intermediate grade steel, w_D (including beam weight) = 800 plf, and $w_L = 2500$ plf.

(*a*) Use stirrup spacing curve.

(*b*) Use slide-rule method.

SHEAR STRESSES—BOND AND DIAGONAL TENSION   161

Prob. 6.6. Calculate the allowable shear V on the beam of Fig. 4.14 with $f_c' = 3750$ psi:

(a) If no stirrups were used.

(b) If adequate stirrups are used.

(c) What Σo would be required at the support for the shear found in case (b)?

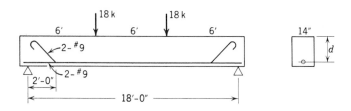

Fig. 6.31. Simple span beam for Prob. 6.4.

Prob. 6.7. Answer the questions of Prob. 6.6 for the beam of Fig. 4.15 where $f_c' = 3000$ psi.

Prob. 6.8. Answer the questions of Prob. 6.6 for the beam of Fig. 4.16 where $f_c' = 5000$ psi.

Prob. 6.9. The loads shown in Fig. 6.32 are at fixed points, not moving loads. Each load consists of 3000 lb of dead load and a possible 4500 lb of live load. Establish the maximum shear curve and design and space the necessary stirrups for $f_c' = 2500$ psi and intermediate grade steel. Consider uniform load negligible.

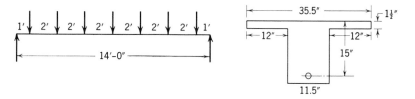

Fig. 6.32. Simple span beam for Prob. 6.9.

Prob. 6.10. If no stirrups were used, what would be the allowable V on the pile of Fig. 4.18 which has $f_c' = 5000$ psi. (Consider the analysis shown in Fig. 6.1 which was based on uniform beam width and modify as required. Actually, the necessary ties surrounding the bars would act as light stirrups.)

Prob. 6.11. If no stirrups are considered in the pile of Fig. 4.19 with $f_c' = 4000$ psi, establish the governing width for use in calculating the allowable shear.

CHAPTER

7

Cantilever
Retaining
Wall Design

7.1. TYPES OF RETAINING WALLS

Retaining walls provide soil stability at a change in ground elevation. Dead weight in such a wall is a major requirement, both to resist overturning from the lateral earth pressures and to resist horizontal sliding from the same forces. (The curved-plane sliding of soil on soil well below the retaining wall constitutes the most common kind of sliding failure,* but this is strictly a matter of soil mechanics, not of reinforced concrete.)

A *gravity* retaining wall (Fig. 7.1a) depends entirely upon its own weight to provide the necessary stability. Plain concrete or even stone masonry constitutes an adequate material. Design is then concerned chiefly with keeping the thrust line within the middle third of the cross section.

The *cantilever* retaining wall (Figs. 7.1c and 7.2) is a reinforced concrete wall that utilizes the weight of the soil itself to provide the desired weight.

* See Fig. 24–2 of Ref. 1.

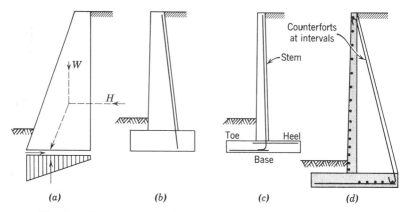

Fig. 7.1. Common types of retaining walls. (*a*) Gravity. (*b*) Semigravity. (*c*) Cantilever. (*d*) Counterfort.

Fig. 7.2. Cantilever retaining wall. (Courtesy Texas Highway Department.)

Stem, toe, and heel are each designed as cantilever slabs, as indicated in Fig. 7.8.

The *semigravity* type of wall uses very light reinforcement and is intermediate between the cantilever and gravity types (Fig. 7.1*b*).

The *counterfort* retaining wall looks something like a cantilever wall and likewise uses the weight of the soil for stability. The wall and base are tied together at intervals by counterforts or bracing walls (Figs. 7.1*d* and

(a)   *(b)*

Fig. 7.3. Counterfort retaining wall. (Courtesy Texas Highway Department.) *(a)* Under construction. *(b)* Before backfilling.

7.3). These act as tension ties and totally change the supports for stem and heel slabs. The stem becomes a slab spanning horizontally between counterforts and the heel becomes a slab supported on three sides. This type of wall becomes more economical than the cantilever type somewhere in the 20 to 25-ft height range.

A *buttressed* wall is similar to the counterfort wall except that the bracing members are on the opposite side of the wall and act in compression.

Crib-type retaining walls may be made of precast concrete, timber, or metal. The face pieces are supported by anchor pieces extending back into the soil for anchorage.

7.2. ACTIVE SOIL PRESSURE

For the purpose of this text only a general idea of the soil mechanics theory of soil pressure is needed. Only the case of cohesionless soil will be considered, that is, essentially a dry sand. Cohesion in the soil theoretically reduces the demands upon a retaining wall but cohesion generally goes with other adverse factors, such as reduced friction and expansive-type soils, which increase the total effect. An expansive type of soil, such as many clays, can introduce problems of such magnitude as to be beyond economic solution. This type of soil is totally unsuited for a backfill material behind a wall.

Dry sand left unbraced will not stand steeper than a certain slope which depends upon its internal friction. When confined behind a wall, such a sand tends to slide. Closely enough, the sliding can be considered as taking place on plane surfaces, with the slope to be established.

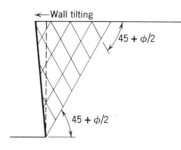

Fig. 7.4. Rankine's plastic equilibrium for active soil pressure.

Rankine in 1857 analyzed this condition of active soil pressure on a smooth wall as one of plastic equilibrium in the soil. In such a case sliding occurs on two sets of planes in a wedge behind the wall, as sketched in Fig. 7.4. For a smooth (frictionless) wall these planes make an angle of $45 + \phi/2$ with the horizontal, where ϕ is the friction angle for soil on soil. Slip on these planes gives the maximum pressure which can follow through against a wall. (For a wall which does not deflect at all, larger pressures can exist.) The plastic equilibrium idea of sliding planes is a fundamental of soil mechanics. However, for all conditions except that of a vertical frictionless wall and a horizontal fill, Coulomb's theory presented in 1773 gives a better result than that of Rankine's; and since for this special case the two theories give the same result, only Coulomb's will be developed.

Coulomb considered possible sliding planes at different slopes and found the one which demanded the greatest holding force on the part of the wall. When friction on the wall is neglected, the holding force is perpendicular to the wall, that is, horizontal for a vertical wall face. Neglect of wall friction is on the safe side for active pressure (but not for the passive pressures of Sec. 7.4).

Consider a wall at AB in Fig. 7.5a. The sand behind will tend to slide on some plane such as BC_1. If the wedge of sand ABC_1 is taken as a free body, it will be in equilibrium under three forces: (1) W_1, the weight of the soil; (2) R_1, the reaction from the soil below BC_1, which may be considered as a normal reaction N_1 and a friction force F_1 resisting sliding; (3) H_1,

REINFORCED CONCRETE FUNDAMENTALS

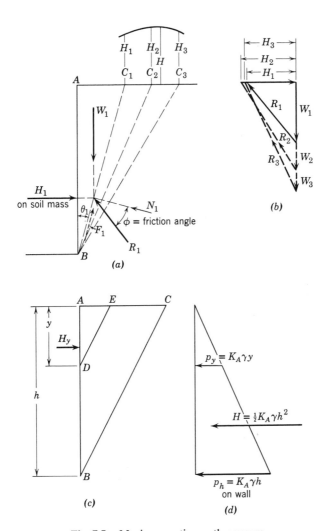

Fig. 7.5. Maximum active earth pressure.

the holding force from the wall. For any given slope angle, θ_1, the force H_1 (and R_1 if desired) can be found from the force triangle as shown in Fig. 7.5b. Similar force triangles can be constructed for other potential sliding planes such as BC_2, BC_3, and so on, leading to other necessary holding forces H_2, H_3, and so forth. A number of trials will lead to the determination in Fig. 7.5b of the maximum possible value of H. A helpful procedure for visualization is to plot an ordinate H_1 over C_1, H_2 over C_2, and so on, and sketch a curve through the points so located. Enough ordinates can be determined to evaluate the peak value H and to locate its sliding plane, say BC in Fig. 7.5c.

A similar analysis of the soil above point D would lead to a critical sliding plane through D parallel to BC. The holding force for the depth AD will be proportional to the weight of sand in the wedge ADE, that is, proportional to y^2 and the unit weight of soil γ. If the constant of proportionality is indicated as $K_A/2$,

$$H_y = K_A \gamma y^2/2$$

The coefficient K_A is called the coefficient of active earth pressure and is usually in the order of 0.27 to 0.34, depending upon the sliding friction angle ϕ. It can be shown mathematically that for this simple case

$$K_A = \frac{1 - \sqrt{1 - \cos^2 \phi}}{1 + \sqrt{1 - \cos^2 \phi}} = \frac{1 - \sin \phi}{1 + \sin \phi} = \tan^2 \left(45° - \frac{\phi}{2} \right)$$

Rankine's formula for the more general case of a surface at a slope:

$$K_A = \cos \theta \left(\frac{\cos \theta - \sqrt{\cos^2 \theta - \cos^2 \phi}}{\cos \theta + \sqrt{\cos^2 \theta - \cos^2 \phi}} \right)$$

where θ is the surface slope measured from the horizontal and ϕ is the friction angle for soil on soil.

A total pressure increasing with the square of the depth corresponds to a unit pressure increasing directly with the depth, that is,

$$p_y = K_A \gamma y$$

Thus the pressure on the wall is as shown in Fig. 7.5d.

Since the pressure on the wall is like that from a fluid, that is, one weighing somewhat less than water, many designers have used the term *equivalent fluid weight* or *equivalent fluid* for the term $K_A \gamma$. Call this fluid weight w_f. Then

$$p_y = w_f y \qquad H_y = w_f y^2/2$$

Equivalent fluid weight is often assumed without an adequate knowledge of the factors which enter into a calculated value of K_A.

These pressures are called active soil pressures because they can continue to act on a wall after it deflects or slides. Pressures in a confined soil may be higher, because the active earth pressure has been calculated on the favorable basis of a considerable holding force developed by friction. Some small movement on plane BC in Fig. 7.5c is necessary to develop this

REINFORCED CONCRETE FUNDAMENTALS

friction; without it H will be larger. For the triangular pressure distribution to be possible, there must be some sliding on all parallel planes, such as DE, above BC. Hence the wall must deflect more at the top than at the base, by approximately 0.001 times its height, this necessary theoretical deflection corresponding to a rotation of the wall about the base at B.

It should be noted that many practical constructions fail to satisfy this deflection requirement, for example, basement walls when supported at or near the ground level by the first floor framing. Another case is the usual braced trench construction, where excavation starts with a brace placed near the top of the trench. In both these cases, the total pressure is roughly the same (say 10% more, for the ideal cohesionless soil, than

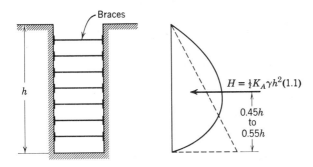

Fig. 7.6. Earth pressure in a braced trench.

discussed above, or in extreme cases on an individual strut in loose sand possibly as much as 45%), but it acts nearer mid-depth than at the lower third point. The distribution may vary considerably but it may be thought of as somewhat parabolic as shown in Fig. 7.6. It might be emphasized that this entire discussion has related to cohesionless soils and has ignored the complications brought about by cohesion and swelling action. Materials which expand under increasing moisture content should not be used as backfill behind retaining walls.

7.3. SURCHARGE

Loads on the surface of the ground over a possible sliding plane, as in Fig. 7.7, increase the horizontal pressure by adding to the ordinary soil weight W in Fig. 7.5a. Uniform surcharge over the entire area adds the same effect as an additional height of soil. Such a surcharge is often evaluated in terms of an equivalent height of earth, this height being given by the unit surcharge weight divided by the unit weight of soil. Such a surcharge adds a uniform pressure to the triangular soil pressure already discussed, as shown in Fig. 7.7a.

Surcharge far enough removed from the wall causes no pressure on the wall. The presence of a surcharge well to the right of C in Fig. 7.5c cannot influence the sliding plane BC or the pressure H. A load just to the right of C would influence the sliding on a slightly flatter plane and might make such a plane critical.

Engineers commonly assume that a surcharge cannot influence the pressure above the point where a line sloping downward from the load

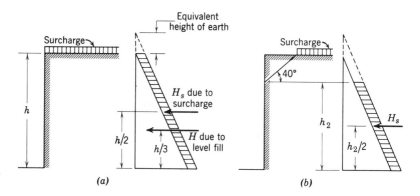

Fig. 7.7. Effect of surcharge on earth pressure.

intersects the wall, as shown in Fig. 7.7b. A slope of 40° is suggested by Terzaghi and Peck* for this line. The AREA Committee on Masonry formerly used a 45° line, but now suggests the wedge calculation. The actual pressure does not change as abruptly as shown in Fig. 7.7b, but this assumption is reasonable and indicates a greatly reduced overturning effect compared to Fig. 7.7a.

7.4. PASSIVE EARTH PRESSURE

If the wall is pushed against the soil, the resistance is very much higher than the active pressure because in this case the soil friction resists the wall movement. In this case the sliding plane is much flatter $(45 - \phi/2$ according to Rankine) and an analysis similar to that of Fig. 7.5 involves a greatly increased W. The mathematical solution leads to

$$H = \tfrac{1}{2}K_p\gamma h^2$$

* Ref. 2, p. 317.

where $K_p = \cos \theta \left(\dfrac{\cos \theta + \sqrt{\cos^2 \theta - \cos^2 \phi}}{\cos \theta - \sqrt{\cos^2 \theta - \cos^2 \phi}} \right)$,   according to Rankine

θ = surface slope measured from the horizontal

ϕ = friction angle for soil on soil.

Unfortunately, the wall friction is an important element in this case, the true failure is on a curved plane, and the actual H developed is significantly less than this solution indicates. Nevertheless, passive resistance is several times as large as active pressure.

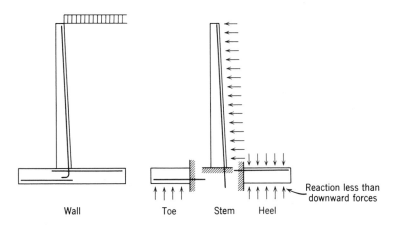

Fig. 7.8. Design parts of cantilever retaining wall.

7.5. DESIGN OF CANTILEVER RETAINING WALL

(a) Data

Over-all height = 18 ft 0 in.

Level fill, 400 psf surcharge, soil weight of 100 pcf.

Horizontal pressure based on equivalent fluid of 31 pcf.

$f_c' = 3000$ psi, intermediate grade steel, ACI Building Code.

Allowable soil pressure under toe = 3500 psf.

(b) Design sequence

The design of a cantilever wall involves the choice of heel and toe lengths and the separate design of stem, heel, and toe slabs. Each of these three slabs acts as a cantilever, as shown in Fig. 7.8.

Foundation conditions determine the location of the bottom of the base and thus the over-all height. The thickness of base must be estimated in order to establish a design height for the stem. A tentative stem thickness can then be calculated. The necessary length of heel and toe for stability can next be established. Heel and toe can then be completely designed and the stem design can be completed on the basis of the actual base thickness chosen. The design solution of this wall follows, with discussion somewhat interspersed.

(c) Stem design

The base thickness will be roughly 7% to 10% of the over-all height with a minimum of about 12 in. Assume a 16-in. base, giving a stem height of $18.0 - 1.33 = 16.67$ ft as shown in Fig. 7.9. The 400-psf surcharge weighs the same as a 4-ft height of earth and creates a uniform lateral pressure of $4 \times 31 = 124$ psf. This adds to the triangular soil pressure varying from zero at the top to $16.67 \times 31 = 517$ psf at the bottom. The resultant horizontal forces are calculated in Fig. 7.9.

Maximum moment and maximum shear occur at the bottom of the stem and the initial design will be at this section, for a 1-ft length of wall. Stem dead load creates no moment in the stem and the small direct compression it causes, less than 18 psi, is generally neglected.

$$M = 2070 \times 8.33 + 4310 \times 5.56 = 41,200 \text{ ft-lb}$$

Allowable $f_c = 0.45 \times 3000 = 1350$ psi

Allowable $f_s = 20,000$ psi

Balanced R (Fig. E.3) $= 236$

$$M = Rbd^2$$

$$41,200 \times 12 = 236 \times 12d^2$$

$$d = \sqrt{174} = 13.20 + 2\text{-in. cover (Art. 507}a) + 0.5 \text{ bar diam.}$$
$$(\text{say } 1.0/2) = 15.70 \text{ in.}$$

USE $t = 16$ in., $d = 13.5$ in. (Revised below to 13.36 in.)

The design would normally proceed to the choice of base length at this stage, but, at the risk of necessary revision later, stem design will be carried further here in order to show it as a complete unit of design.

$$A_s = \frac{M}{f_s jd} = \frac{41,200 \times 12}{20,000 \times 0.866 \times \substack{13.5 \\ 13.36}} = \substack{2.11 \\ 2.13} \text{ in.}^2/\text{ft} = \substack{0.176 \\ 0.178} \text{ in.}^2/\text{in.}$$

For #7, spcg. $= 0.60/0.176 = 3.40$ in.

#8, $\qquad 0.79/0.176 = 4.48$

#9, $\qquad 1.00/0.176 = 5.67$

#10, $\qquad 1.27/0.176 = 7.18$

#11, $\qquad 1.56/0.176 = 8.80$

USE #10 at 7 in. $(A_s = 1.27 \times 12/7 = 2.17 \text{ in.}^2/\text{ft.})$

It is noted that this bar has $D = 1.27$ in., greater than the assumed D. Corrected $d = 16 - 2.0 - 1.27/2 = 13.36$ in. Corrected $A_s = 2.11 \times 13.5/13.36 = 2.13$ in.²/ft vs. 2.17 in.² actual. O.K. This revision would normally be made as indicated on the original A_s calculation above.

Max. $V = 2070 + 4310 = 6380$ lb

$$v = \frac{V}{bjd} = \frac{6380}{12 \times \frac{7}{8} \times 13.36} = 46 \text{ psi} < 0.03f_c' = 90 \text{ psi} \qquad \text{O.K.}$$

$$u = \frac{V}{\Sigma ojd} = \frac{6380}{3.99 \times \frac{12}{7} \times \frac{7}{8} \times 13.36} = 80 \text{ psi} < 0.10f_c' = 300^* \text{ psi} \qquad \text{O.K.}$$

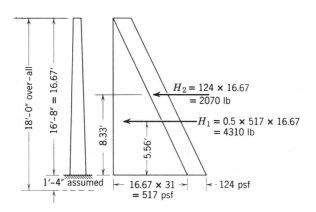

Fig. 7.9.   Earth pressure on stem.

The use of the more exact j is scarcely warranted by the general accuracy of these formulas.

(d) Choice of base length

The minimum length of base results when the resultant force R strikes the ground immediately below the front face of the stem.   The heel should be made just long enough to bring the resultant to this position (Fig. 7.10a).   The necessary length of toe is then a matter of the required soil pressure distribution under the base.   If a triangular reaction pressure will not result in too high a toe pressure or too much tilting of the wall due to differential settlement, the base need extend only one-third of its total length beyond the point where the resultant cuts the bottom of the base (Fig. 7.10b).   A longer toe will give a trapezoidal soil reaction and smaller toe pressures as shown in Fig. 7.10c.   If the toe is extended until the

* The author's recommended allowable u is lower for this situation, namely, $0.05f_c' = 150$ psi. See Sec. 6.7.

resultant is in the middle of the base, a uniform soil pressure results as in Fig. 7.10d. The student should note that the straight-line variation in reaction pressure is the design assumption commonly made. The actual pressure will probably follow some curved line, but the shape will necessarily vary with the location of the resultant R.

A fairly accurate determination of the required heel length can be made very simply by neglecting the extra weight of stem and base above that of the displaced soil and by neglecting entirely the weight of the toe concrete. In the free body shown in Fig. 7.10a one can ignore the shaded toe concrete and take

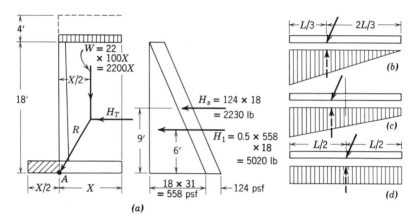

Fig. 7.10. Stability of entire retaining wall against overturning.

the load W as that of soil 18 ft deep, 1 ft thick, and X feet wide, plus the weight of X square feet of surcharge.

$$M_A = 2200X(X/2) - 2230 \times 9 - 5020 \times 6 = 0$$
$$1100X^2 = 50{,}200$$
$$X = \sqrt{45.7} = 6.75 \text{ ft}$$

The minimum base length for triangular pressure is $1.5X = 10.13$ ft. A solution properly including the concrete weight would change X only slightly, reducing it by less than 1 in. The maximum soil pressure will be twice the average, but in this calculation it is not adequate to neglect the extra concrete weight.

$$\text{Max. } p > \frac{2200 \times 6.75}{10.13} \times 2 = 2930 \text{ psf}$$

The student will note that the minimum length of base thus chosen will have a nominal factor of safety of two against overturning since the total H would have to be doubled to put the resultant through the extreme toe.

(e) Reaction soil pressure

For this problem, to obtain the more usual trapezoidal pressure, USE $X = 6.75$ ft $= 6$ ft 9 in., toe projection $= 4.5$ ft $= 4$ ft 6 in. The toe chosen is an arbitrary one in the absence of more specific soil limitations.

The unit soil pressures can be determined by considering the resultant as an eccentric load on a rectangular section. The resultant will be located and evaluated more accurately for this purpose, by taking the summation of moments about A in Fig. 7.11, using the entire wall as a free body. W_3 will be taken as the extra 50 pcf weight of concrete as compared to soil, since this same volume is included in W_2 as though it were soil.

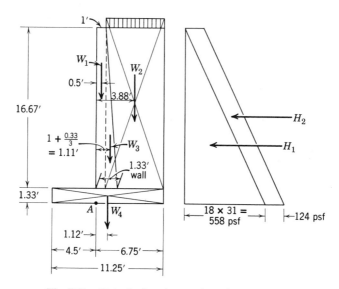

Fig. 7.11. Data for locating resultant base pressure.

			Arm	M_A
$W_1 = 1 \times 16.67 \times 150$	$= 2,500$ lb		0.50 ft	$+1,250$ ft-lb
$W_2 = 5.75(16.67 + 4)100$	$= 11,880$		3.88	46,200
$W_3 = 0.5 \times 0.33 \times 16.67 \times 50 =$	137		1.11	150
$W_4 = 11.25 \times 1.33 \times 150$	$= 2,250$		1.12	2,520
	$\Sigma W = 16,770$			$+50,100$
$H_1 = 0.5 \times 558 \times 18$	$= 5,020$		6.00	$-30,100$
$H_2 = 124 \times 18$	$= 2,230$		9.00	$-20,100$
	$\Sigma H = 7,250$			$-50,200$
			$\Sigma M_A =$	-100 ft-lb

$$x_R = -\frac{100}{16,770} = -0.01 \text{ ft (to left of } A)$$

$$= 4.49 \text{ ft to right of toe}$$

Reqd. coef. of friction $= \Sigma H \div \Sigma W = 7250/16,770 = 0.432$ plus at least 50% as a factor of safety. If this friction requirement is difficult to satisfy, some relief can be obtained by means of a key into the soil below the base to lock the two together, as shown in Fig. 7.15d.

The soil pressure distribution under the base is ordinarily assumed to be linear. Since the resultant R falls within the middle third of the base, the pressure distribution is trapezoidal. The toe and heel pressures can be found from statics (Fig. 7.12). The upward pressure can be considered as two triangles of

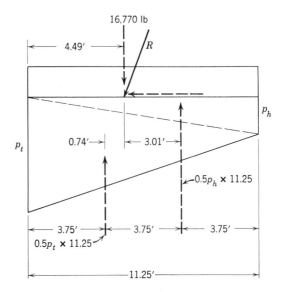

Fig. 7.12. Calculation of soil reaction.

pressure with individual resultants at their third points. Moments about the smaller resultant (on the right in Fig. 7.12) give:

$$(0.5p_t \times 11.25)3.75 - 3.01 \times 16,770 = 0$$

$$p_t = 2390 \text{ psf}$$

Similarly,

$$(0.5p_h \times 11.25)3.75 - 0.74 \times 16,770 = 0$$

$$p_h = 590 \text{ psf}$$

The pressures can also be calculated considering ΣW applied as an eccentric load on a rectangular section 11.25 ft by 1.0 ft. The eccentricity is 1.13 ft from the center of the base. The moment of inertia of this section is $1 \times 11.25^3/12 = 118.6 \text{ ft}^4$.

$$p_t = \frac{P}{A} + \frac{Pec}{I} = \frac{16{,}770}{11.25} + \frac{16{,}770 \times 1.13 \times 5.62}{118.6} = 1490 + 898 = 2388 \text{ psf}$$

$$p_h = \frac{P}{A} - \frac{Pec}{I} = 1490 - 898 = 592 \text{ psf}$$

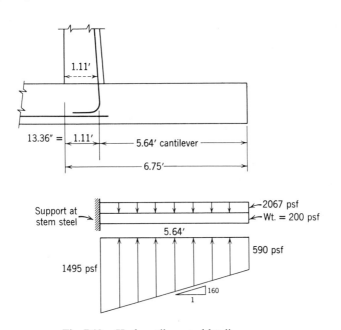

Fig. 7.13. Heel cantilever and loading.

(f) Design of heel

The load on the heel is predominantly a downward load. The supporting upward reaction comes from the tension in the stem steel. Hence the effective cantilever length is 6.75 ft less the effective depth of stem = 6.75 − 13.36/12 = 5.64 ft as shown in Fig. 7.13.

The heel illustrates a loading condition which should be given special attention. The maximum moment and shear result from the difference between rather large loadings in opposite directions. Such design is automatically safe only if the opposed loadings always maintain the same relative size. In this case, if the horizontal loading were increased, the resultant loading would shift forward and the reaction under the heel would be reduced. The AASHO specification[3] requires that the retaining wall heel be designed considering the upward reaction as zero. This is quite severe. The author prefers the 1940 Joint Committee Specification and the present AREA specification[4] which require that the design unit stresses not be exceeded by more than 50% when the upward reaction is omitted. This is equivalent to saying that such moments or shears should govern design only when they are in excess of 150% of full load values. This specification will be followed here.

Full loading:

$$M_1 = -2267 \times 5.64^2/2 + 0.5 \times 590 \times 5.64 \times 3.76 + 0.5 \times 1495 \times$$
$$5.64 \times 1.88$$
$$= -36,000 + 6250 + 7920 = -36,000 + 14,170 = -21,830 \text{ ft-lb}$$
$$V_1 = +2267 \times 5.64 - 0.5(590 + 1495)5.64 = +12,800 - 5870 =$$
$$+6930 \text{ lb}$$

Without upward reaction:

$$M_2 = -36,000 \text{ ft-lb} \qquad\qquad V_2 = +12,800 \text{ lb}$$
$$M_2 \times \tfrac{2}{3} = -24,000 \text{ ft-lb} > M_1 \qquad V_2 \times \tfrac{2}{3} = +8530 \text{ lb} > V_1$$
$$\therefore M_2 \text{ governs} \qquad\qquad \therefore V_2 \text{ governs}$$

Instead of designing for M_2 and V_2 at unit stresses 150% of the usual values, the design will be made for the equivalent expressed as $\tfrac{2}{3}M_2$ and $\tfrac{2}{3}V_2$ at the usual stresses, that is, $M = -24,000$ ft-lb and $V = 8530$ lb.

$$d = \sqrt{\frac{M}{Rb}} = \sqrt{\frac{24,000 \times 12}{236 \times 12}} = \sqrt{101.5} = 10.07 + 2.0\text{-in. cover} + D/2$$
$$= 12.57 \text{ in. for } D = 1 \text{ in.}$$

The unit shear relation $v = V \div bjd$ can be rewritten to give:

$$d_v = \frac{V}{v\tfrac{7}{8}b} = \frac{8530}{90 \times 0.875 \times 12} = 9.02 \text{ in.} < 10.07 \text{ in. for } M$$

USE $t = 14$ in., $d = 10.5$ in. for $D = 1$ in. (Error: $t = 13$ in. better)

This changes the stem height slightly. The weight of heel and earth is reduced by 2 in. at 50 pcf (difference between concrete and soil weight) but the 8-psf difference is negligible.

$$A_s = \frac{M}{f_s jd} = \frac{24,000 \times 12}{20,000 \times 0.866 \times 10.5} = 1.58 \text{ in.}^2/\text{ft} = 0.132 \text{ in.}^2/\text{in.}$$

The unit bond relation $u = V \div \Sigma ojd$ can be rewritten to give:

$$\Sigma o = \frac{V}{u\tfrac{7}{8}d} = \frac{8530}{300 \times 0.875 \times 10.5} = 3.10 \text{ in./ft} = 0.258 \text{ in./in.}$$

$$\text{Spcg. for } A_s = \frac{\text{area of bar}}{0.132} \qquad \text{Spcg. for } \Sigma o = \frac{\text{perimeter of bar}}{0.258}$$

Try #8 $0.79/0.132 = 5.99$ in., say 6 in. $3.14/0.258 = 12.1$ in.

This is satisfactory without further trials and the assumed D and d are unchanged.

USE #8 at 6 in.

(g) Design of toe

Toe design is similar to that of heel design but the problem of large opposing loads does not exist here. Also, the diagonal tension situation on the toe is like that of a wall footing, critical at a distance d from the face of the wall, according to Code Art. 1205a. This matter is discussed in detail in Sec. 14.2. Earth fill over the toe has been neglected thus far since it may not always be present. Such fill adds also to the toe reaction, but this reaction and fill weight cause little change in M and V on the toe.

The maximum moment on the toe occurs where the shear changes sign. Since the large compression from the stem causes this shear reversal to

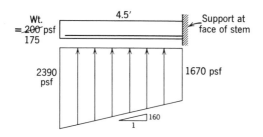

Fig. 7.14. Toe cantilever and loading.

occur just inside the face of the stem, the case is usually simplified by considering the cantilever support *at* the face of stem (Fig. 7.14).

The toe weight is assumed to be 200 psf.

$$M = -200 \times 4.5^2/2 + 0.5 \times 2390 \times 4.5 \times 3.0 + 0.5 \times 1670 \times 4.5 \times 1.5$$

$$= -2025 + 16{,}150 + 5650 = +19{,}780 \text{ ft-lb}$$

$$d_M = \sqrt{\frac{19{,}780 \times 12}{236 \times 12}} = \sqrt{84.0} = 9.18 \text{ in.} + 3 \text{ in.} + D/2 \quad (\text{Art. } 507a)$$

$$t = 12.68 \text{ in. for } D = 1 \text{ in.}$$

If $d = 9.5$ in., the critical plane for diagonal tension shear is $4.50 - 0.79 = 3.71$ ft from the toe. At this plane the reaction pressure is $2390 - 3.71 \times 160 = 1796$ psf.

$$V_v = (2390 + 1796) \times 0.5 \times 3.71 = 7750 \text{ lb}$$

Code Arts. 305 and 809a limit v for footings to $0.03f_c'$ but not to exceed 75 psi.

$$d_v = \frac{7750}{75 \times 0.875 \times 12} = 9.85 \text{ in.}$$

If $d = 10$ in.,

$$V_v \text{ (closely enough)} = 7750 - 1796 \times 0.5/12 = 7670 \text{ lb}$$

$$d_v = \frac{7670}{75 \times 0.875 \times 12} = 9.77 \text{ in.} \quad \text{O.K.}$$

$$t = 9.77 + 3.00 + D/2 = 13.27 \text{ in. for } D = 1 \text{ in.}$$

A thickness of 13.5 in. could be used but this is so close to the heel thickness of 14 in. that this value will be used for the entire base for the sake of simplicity.

USE $t = 14$ in., $d = 10.5$ in. for $D = 1$ in.

Wt. $= 150 \times 14/12 = 175$ psf vs. 200 assumed

Inspection indicates no need to revise calculations for d and t. Moment will be larger by $25 \times 4.5^2/2 = 253$ ft-lb.

Revised $M = 19{,}780 + 253 = 20{,}000$ ft-lb

$$A_s = \frac{M}{f_s jd} = \frac{20{,}000 \times 12}{20{,}000 \times 0.866 \times 10.5} = 1.32 \text{ in.}^2/\text{ft} = 0.110 \text{ in.}^2/\text{in.}$$

$$V_u = (2390 + 1670) \times 0.5 \times 4.5 - 175 \times 4.5 = 8360 \text{ lb}$$

$$\Sigma o = \frac{V}{ujd} = \frac{8360}{300 \times 0.875 \times 10.5} = 3.03 \text{ in./ft} = 0.252 \text{ in./in.}$$

	Spcg. for A_s	Spcg. for Σo
Try #8	$0.79/0.110 = 7.18$ in.	$3.14/0.252 = 12.5$ in.
#9	$1.00/0.110 = 9.09$	$3.54/0.252 = 14.1$
#10	$1.27/0.110 = 11.5$	$3.99/0.252 = 15.9$

USE #9 at 9 in. as a convenient spacing.

(h) Revision of stem

Both the toe and heel have been made 14 in. thick, which is 2 in. less than the amount assumed in designing the stem. The stem height is thereby increased 2 in. Shear on the stem was far from critical in design. Since the added 2-in. height of horizontal load will change the moment very little, the increased moment on the stem will be, closely enough,

New M = old $M + V \times 0.17$ ft

$$= 41{,}200 + 6380 \times 0.17 = 42{,}300 \text{ ft-lb}$$

$$d = \sqrt{\frac{42{,}300 \times 12}{236 \times 12}} = \sqrt{179} = 13.37 \text{ in. vs. } 13.36 \text{ in. used}$$

$$A_s = \frac{42{,}300 \times 12}{20{,}000 \times 0.866 \times 13.36} = 2.19 \text{ in.}^2/\text{ft} \text{ vs. } 2.17 \text{ provided}$$

Both d and A_s are a trifle on the unsafe side, but not enough to require a change. Say O.K.

(i) Junction of stem, heel, and toe

Joining of stem, heel, and toe involves provision of a key to carry the shear from stem to base and the arrangement of reinforcing steel at the junction.

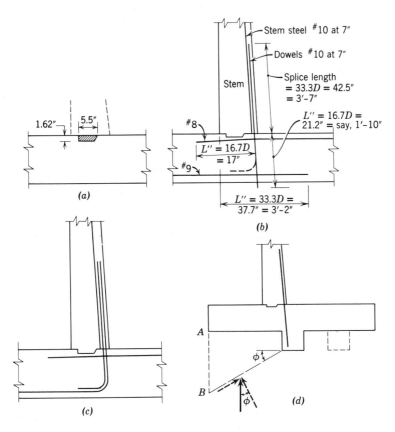

Fig. 7.15. Details at junction of stem and base.

The key is usually made by embedding a beveled 2-in. by 4-in. or 2-in. by 6-in. timber in the top of the footing as shown in Fig. 7.15a.* When the timber is removed and the stem is cast in place, the 1.62-in. vertical face provides an allowable bearing of $12 \times 1.62 \times 0.25 \times 3000 = 14,600$ lb per ft of wall compared to the approximately 6400-lb horizontal

* Some designers prefer that the key be cast as a projection on top of the base which extends up into the stem.

force on the stem. The distribution of shear force on the horizontal section of the key at the top of footing is uncertain. If it is taken as parabolic, as for a homogeneous rectangular beam, the maximum unit shear is $1.5 \times 6400 \div (12 \times 5.5) = 145$ psi. The allowable shear in this case is not too definite. Some designers might prefer to limit it to $0.03f_c' = 90$ psi. The author considers $0.06f_c' = 180$ psi a very conservative value.* As a practical matter, the bending moment on the stem gives $C = T = 2.19 \times 20,000 = 43,800$ lb of compression pressing down on top of the base, and friction alone should be adequate to resist the 6400-lb sliding force.

Since the stem steel cannot be supported in position while the base concrete is placed, it is customary to provide dowels (or stub bars) in the base equal to the stem steel. These must project a full anchorage length into the base and a full splice length (Sec. 6.6) above the base, as shown in Fig. 7.15b. The anchorage length into the base is then

$$L'' = f_s D/4u = 20,000D/(4 \times 300)$$

$$= 16.7D = 21.2 \text{ in. for } \#10 \text{ bars, which may be}$$
either straight or bent, as shown dashed

The stem splice, where the cover is small, should be very conservatively calculated, say, for $u = 150$ psi (Sec. 6.6).

$$L'' = f_s D/4u = 20,000D \div (4 \times 150) = 33.3D = 42.5 \text{ in. for } \#10 \text{ bars}$$

The toe and heel steel must also be anchored beyond their critical design sections. The same $33.3D$ seems appropriate for the toe steel with its limited cover. The heel steel might also be anchored $33.3D$ but it is noted that the compression from bending in the stem effectively prevents splitting around the heel steel anchorage. Hence the $16.7D$ anchorage is considered adequate (Fig. 7.15b).

It should be obvious, as a matter of detailing, that some of the stem dowel steel might be replaced by toe steel bent up as shown in Fig. 7.15c and this would probably save some steel. Figure 7.18 shows such a design. The detailing then is facilitated by using the same spacings for toe and stem steel.

(j) Key against sliding

Resistance against sliding can be changed from friction between concrete and soil to the shear strength of the soil by including a key of concrete

---

* Based on some of his tests of column brackets where shears of over $0.20f_c'$ were developed before failure.

into the soil as shown in Fig. 7.15d. The key is usually placed somewhat below the stem in order to use it for anchorage of the stem dowels, but it may be more effective when somewhat more to the rear. The value of such a key has frequently been overestimated. In a cohesionless soil its maximum effect cannot be more than to mobilize the passive resistance of the soil over the depth AB in Fig. 7.15d, where ϕ is the friction angle for soil on soil.

(k) Stopping bars in stem

Some of the bars in the stem may be stopped at part height. The method of Sec. 5.6, which simply substituted the moment diagram for the required A_s curve, must be modified to take the variable depth into account. In Fig. 7.16 the required A_s curve has been plotted accurately for a graphical solution. The upper sketches show the effective depth d and the soil pressures at various depths. From these the moment and steel requirements have been determined and are tabulated in Table 7.1. These data are the basis for the plotted curve in Fig. 7.16.

TABLE 7.1. Calculations for Required A_s Curve

Distance y from Top, ft	Bending Moment, ft-lb	Slab Depth d, in.	Required A_s, in.^{2}
0	0	9.36	0
5	2,200	10.55	0.145
9	8,800	11.50	0.527
12	17,900	12.21	1.020
15	31,500	12.93	1.69
16.83	42,300	13.36	2.19

The cutoff points have been indicated for one-third and two-thirds of the stem steel, considering the stem steel alone. From this solution it is evident that the 3 ft 7 in. splice length is nearly equal to the 4-ft height needed for one-third of the steel, after allowing 12 diameters beyond the theoretical cutoff point. Accordingly, the dowels are lengthened to the 4 ft 0 in. necessary to eliminate one-third of the separate stem bars. (Actually, two-thirds of the dowels could be stopped at 3 ft 7 in. if one were willing to use two different lengths.) The second third of the main bars can be stopped at 6.5 ft plus 12 diameters extension or 7 ft 9 in. from top of base. The other one-third runs the full height.

It should be noted that the stopping of some bars causes peak or near maximum stresses in those bars continued. Hence in Fig. 7.16 three different points are marked as stress peaks and the detailer should be

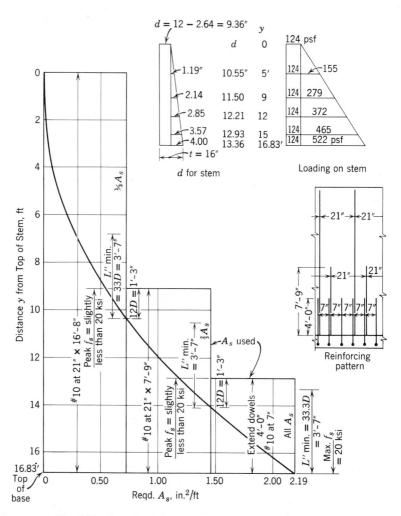

Fig. 7.16. Stopping of stem steel, based on required A_s curve.

careful to provide the full development length on bars that continue. This may safely be measured from the theoretical cutoff points as indicated in the figure.

An alternate procedure for moment length which is preferred by many is to plot design moment and resisting moments as in Fig. 7.17. At the base, allowable moments are proportional to A_s (neglecting change in j) and at the top they are reduced in the ratio of reduced effective depth.

REINFORCED CONCRETE FUNDAMENTALS

The L'' lengths must be considered here as in Fig. 7.16 and the bar lengths should be identical by the two procedures.

Figure 7.18 shows a design made with special reference to economy in detailing. The stem steel has been redesigned to match the toe steel, using #9 at 9 in. plus #7 at 6 in. The toe steel is utilized as dowels for the #9 bars with an extension of $33.3D$ or 3 ft 2 in. into the stem. The #7 bars

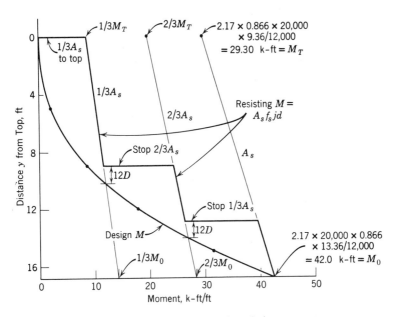

Fig. 7.17. Stopping of stem steel, based on design moment curve.

need extend only 3.33 ft for moment (plus an extra 12 diameters), since this is more than the development length of $33D = 29$ in. $= 2$ ft 5 in. Bars this height do not require separate dowels. The #7 bars must be anchored $16.7D = 14.6$ in. $= 1$ ft 3 in. into the base and may either be bent or extended toward the soil key shown in Fig. 7.15d. The #9 toe steel must project $33.3D = 38$ in. $= 3$ ft 2 in. into the stem. Figure 7.18c shows the pattern for the stem steel.

(l) Longitudinal steel

Longitudinal bars are used to space the moment bars and to provide for shrinkage and temperature stresses. The wall should be placed in short lengths to reduce shrinkage stresses. The old Joint Committee

CANTILEVER RETAINING WALL DESIGN   185

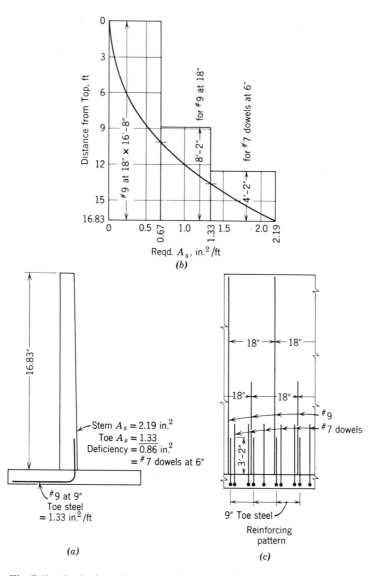

Fig. 7.18. Revised steel layout to utilize toe steel as dowels for stem steel.

REINFORCED CONCRETE FUNDAMENTALS

specification calls for "not less than 0.50 sq in. area per ft of height with a maximum spacing of bars of 12 in. center to center" near the exposed face. The ACI Code (Art. 1111h) calls for $0.0025bt$ horizontally and $0.0015bt$ vertically on walls (presumably *exposed* walls) which would be:

	$0.0025bt$	$0.0015bt$
$b = 12$ in., $t = 12$ in.,	0.36 in.²	0.22 in.²
16 in.,	0.48 in.²	0.29 in.²

Fig. 7.19. Reinforcing in wall stem with the front form being lifted into place. Frequently the rear or front face form is first erected and the reinforcement is next placed. (Courtesy Texas Highway Department.)

The steel used is thus in part a matter of judgment. The following is chosen:

Stem: exposed face, horizontal #5 at $7\frac{1}{2}$ in. = 0.495 in.²/ft

exposed face, vertical #4 at 12 in. = 0.20 in.²/ft

rear face, horizontal #5 at 15 in. = 0.248 in.²/ft

Toe: longitudinal spacers in bottom, #5 at 18 in. = 0.207 in.²/ft

Heel: longitudinal spacers in top, #5 at 18 in. = 0.207 in.²/ft

Such steel is shown in Fig. 7.19, the exposed face steel being in the foreground, as can be seen most clearly at the bottom of the illustration, adjacent to the form panel which is being lifted into place.

(m) Drainage

Since walls are usually not designed for water pressure, one must provide complete drainage of backfill by French drains, drains through the wall, or the like.   A porous backfill, such as gravel, should be provided directly behind the wall to allow the water to reach these drains.

SELECTED REFERENCES

1. Whitney Clark Huntington, *Earth Pressures and Retaining Walls*, John Wiley & Sons, New York, 1957.
2. Karl Terzaghi and Ralph B. Peck, *Soil Mechanics in Engineering Practice*, John Wiley & Sons, New York, 1948.
3. *Standard Specifications for Highway Bridges*, AASHO, Washington, 6th ed., 1953.
4. "Retaining Walls and Abutments," *AREA Manual*, Vol. 1, Chap. 8, Part 5, Chicago, 1953.

PROBLEMS

Prob. 7.1.   Investigate the stability, sliding resistance, and foundation soil pressure of the wall of Fig. 7.20.   Surcharge = 200 psf, soil weight = 100 pcf, equivalent fluid for horizontal pressure = 30 psf, concrete weight (including reinforcing) = 150 pcf, coefficient of friction of concrete on soil = 0.40, allowable soil pressure = 3000 psf.

Prob. 7.2.   Design the stem, heel, and toe for the wall of Fig. 7.20 assuming the foundation soil pressure and sliding resistance found in Prob. 7.1 are satisfactory.

Prob. 7.3.   Redesign the retaining wall of Sec. 7.5 for horizontal pressure based on an equivalent fluid of 27 pcf, $f_c' = 3750$ psi, allowable foundation soil pressure = 4000 psf, and a *minimum* base length.
(a) Stem design.
(b) Minimum base length and resulting soil pressure under base.
(c) Heel design based on AREA specification[4] (Sec. 7.5f).

(*d*) Toe design with thickness based on stresses, but not less than thickness of heel.

(*e*) Is a key into the soil needed if the coefficient of friction for concrete on soil is 0.40?

(*f*) Sketch the detail of the joint where the stem, heel, and toe come together.

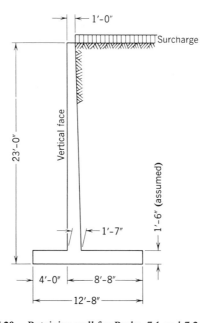

Fig. 7.20. Retaining wall for Probs. 7.1 and 7.2.

Prob. 7.4. Redesign the retaining wall of Sec. 7.5 changing only the following data from those originally used:

Omit surcharge.

Limit foundation soil pressure to 4000 psf.

Use minimum length base.

Coefficient of friction of concrete on soil = 0.40.

Prob. 7.5. Redesign the retaining wall of Sec. 7.5 on the assumption that the foundation soil pressure must not exceed 2000 psf, all other data remaining unchanged.

Prob. 7.6. Redesign the heel of the wall of Sec. 7.5*f* on the assumption that the upward soil reaction under the heel is totally neglected (AASHO specification[3]) without any increase in allowable unit stresses.

Prob. 7.7. Assume that the retaining wall of Sec. 7.5 is to be made without any toe projection, that is, as an L-shaped wall. What length of heel will be necessary to keep the resultant at the third point of the base? What will then be the maximum foundation pressure (ignoring the change in heel thickness which will probably be necessary)?

Prob. 7.8. Would it be feasible to design the retaining wall of Sec. 7.5 without any heel slab, that is, as an ⌐-shaped wall? (Two reasons.)

Prob. 7.9. It is possible in Fig. 7.16 to stop all #10 bars at the same height and splice them with #8 bars which continue upward. Where can such a splice be made and what is the length of bars to be used, assuming half of the #8 bars are stopped as soon as the stresses permit?

Prob. 7.10. It is possible in the steel arrangement of Fig. 7.16 to stop the longest #10 bars somewhat shorter than full height and splice on smaller bars, say #7 bars. Sketch the bar arrangement and specify the bar lengths. Does this save steel?

Prob. 7.11. Assume that the #9 bars at 9-in. spacing shown in the stem in Fig. 7.18 are to be made into three equal groups and cut off at three different levels, instead of two as shown. Sketch the reinforcing pattern and establish the length of each group of bars. (For this problem overlook the wide top spacing which results.)

CHAPTER

8

Continuous Beams and One-Way Slabs

8.1. TYPES OF CONSTRUCTION

Most reinforced concrete members are statically indeterminate because they are parts of monolithic structures.

The most usual form of building construction consists of a slab cast monolithically with a beam-and-girder floor framing which carries the floor load to the columns. The plan view of such a floor in Fig. 8.1a indicates that such slabs are supported on all four sides and should properly be designed with two-way steel by the methods of Chap. 9.

When the slab is more than twice as long as it is wide, it is usually designed as a one-way slab continuous over the beams, but with special negative moment steel added across the girders.* When such a slab is designed for a uniform load the supporting beams are also designed for a

---

* Because they find the one-way steel arrangement simpler, many engineers actually design one-way slabs for all panels except those that are nearly square.

uniform load, this process in effect ignoring the portion of the slab load which goes directly to the girder from the end of the panel. For the beams, the uniform load assumption is on the safe side since it overestimates the beam load. For the girders, the corresponding assumption is to place the beam reactions on the girder as concentrated loads and to add the uniform load situated directly over the girder. This assumption is not on the safe side for the girder design, particularly for maximum shear. More realistic tributary loading areas are shown in Fig. 9.11b. The student might investigate the difference in maximum girder shear between the two loadings in the case of a girder simply supported.

Sometimes, for long spans, closely spaced beams with a very thin slab are used. This so-called joist construction (Fig. 8.1b) is facilitated by the availability of removable metal pans which are used as forms between the joists.

When no beams are used except those between columns, as in Fig. 8.1c, the slabs are definitely supported on all four sides and both beams and slabs should be designed as discussed in Chap. 9.

In light construction the beams at times are run in only one direction, as shown in Fig. 8.1d and e. In this case true one-way slabs result, except at the end walls. The slab band construction of Sec. 11.16 is really this same type of construction utilizing wide shallow beams.

Particularly for heavy loads, and sometimes even for light loads, slab-type floors without any interior beams are economical, for instance, the flat slab and flat plate floors of Chap. 11. For such floors beams are used only at outside walls and around openings through the slabs.

8.2. INTERACTION BETWEEN PARTS OF THE STRUCTURE

In all the various types of construction the designer is faced with a highly indeterminate type of structure, a structure in three dimensions which cannot be precisely analyzed as a planar structure.[1-3] More specifically, the intermediate beams of Fig. 8.1a cannot be analyzed exactly without considering the vertical deflection and torsional stiffness of the girders as well as the stiffness of the columns. Likewise, the beams framing into the columns have moments which are influenced by the column joint rotations and hence by any torsion present in the girders. These aspects may often be ignored, but the designer should realize that he then has only an approximate analysis.

A designer commonly utilizes approximate methods of analysis, but he becomes a better designer when he understands the nature of his approximations and how exact or how crude these may be. This chapter assumes

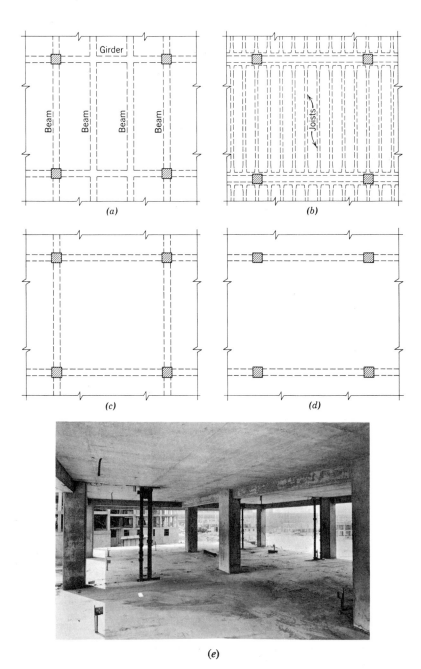

Fig. 8.1. Typical floor beam framing. (*a*) Beam-and-girder layout. (*b*) Joist construction. (*c*) Two-way slab and beams. (*d*) One-way slab and beams. (*e*) One-way construction. (Courtesy Portland Cement Assn.)

CONTINUOUS BEAMS AND ONE-WAY SLABS 193

that the reader is familiar with ordinary moment distribution procedures (Appendix B) and the plotting of continuous member moment and shear diagrams (Sec. A.10 in Appendix A).

The ordinary conventional assumption is that analysis in two dimensions is adequate for most designs. This assumption fits in better with structures designed for uniform floor loads than for those with moving concentrated or wheel loads. It may be reasonably assumed that, in carrying a uniformly distributed load, any one beam gets little help from its neighbor, because this neighboring beam is probably also fully loaded.* Likewise,

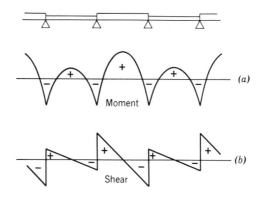

Fig. 8.2. Typical M and V diagrams for a continuous beam.

in a one-way slab each strip may be assumed to carry the load directly above it when the entire slab is loaded.

When moving concentrated loads are involved, each slab strip may carry a different moment and the load on a single beam may depend greatly upon the stiffness of the slab and the adjoining beams. The problem of moving concentrated loads is discussed in Chap. 12.

Moment diagrams for continuous beams normally show negative moments over supports and positive moments near mid-span, as indicated in Fig. 8.2a. The presence of columns changes the picture only slightly. The moment diagram in any span may be considered as the sum of two parts, one the simple beam moment diagram for that span, and the other

* This statement is not strictly true, of course. In Fig. 8.1a, with equal spacing of beams, the beam framing directly into the column is stiffer because its end joints are stiffer, whereas the girder provides only a yielding support for the neighboring beam. The beam framing into the column thus tends to carry the greater load and to some extent relieves the intermediate beam. It might be noted, however, that at the ultimate or collapse load, for beams of equal size, each beam would probably be carrying almost exactly the same load, since the load distribution changes after some yielding takes place.

the moments across the span due to the negative support moments, as outlined in Sec. A.10. Since these negative moments at supports are influenced by loads on *any* span, it follows that the moment at each point is influenced by every load on every span. Loading patterns for maximum moment are thus a major consideration.

The typical shear diagram (Fig. 8.2b) differs only slightly from that for a series of simple spans. In any span the shear diagram for a given loading consists of the simple beam shear plus a constant correction which will be designated as the continuity shear V_c. The continuity shear is usually relatively small except in end spans.

8.3. THE GENERAL DESIGN PROBLEM FOR CONTINUOUS MEMBERS

Each span of a continuous beam or slab requires a separate design for negative and positive moment conditions, even though practice in the United States usually uses a constant depth member for any given span, often for all spans. Figure 8.3 shows the design conditions for continuous slabs, rectangular beams, and T-beams, in diagrammatic fashion. To indicate clearly that at this stage no consideration is being given to the arrangement of steel, the reinforcement is indicated only in the vicinity of maximum moment zones. Moment at A is assumed to be the governing (maximum) negative moment in all cases. The letter t designates the tension face.

In the thinner slabs compression steel is not desirable because it would lie so close to the neutral axis that a slight displacement would make it ineffective. Hence Fig. 8.3a shows the maximum negative moment at A determining the balanced slab depth, with underreinforced sections elsewhere. Thick slabs can be designed with compression steel, similar to rectangular beams, if desired.

Rectangular beams may be designed with compression steel at supports, as in Fig. 8.3b, or without it. In the latter case the design is similar to that shown for slabs.

T-beams become, in effect, inverted rectangular beams at the supports with only the web width b' effective in compression, as indicated in Fig. 8.3c. This restricted compression zone is improved by using a double-reinforced section; and such is recommended for ordinary use.

Shear (diagonal tension) rarely governs in ordinary one-way slab design, in spite of the fact that the allowable v is only $0.03f_c'$. Stirrups in slabs would be awkward even if needed. Continuous rectangular beams and T-beams normally require stirrups. If the allowable v with stirrups is

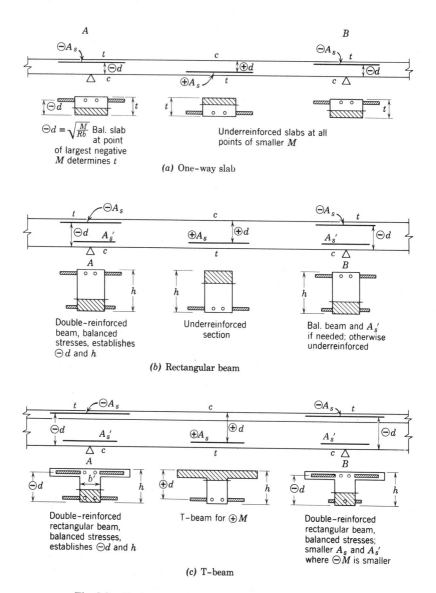

$\ominus d = \sqrt{\dfrac{M}{Rb}}$ Bal. slab at point of largest negative M determines t

Underreinforced slabs at all points of smaller M

(a) One-way slab

Double-reinforced beam, balanced stresses, establishes $\ominus d$ and h

Underreinforced section

Bal. beam and A_s' if needed; otherwise underreinforced

(b) Rectangular beam

Double-reinforced rectangular beam, balanced stresses, establishes $\ominus d$ and h

T-beam for $\oplus M$

Double-reinforced rectangular beam, balanced stresses; smaller A_s and A_s' where $\ominus M$ is smaller

(c) T-beam

Fig. 8.3. Design procedures for continuous slabs and beams.

kept as low as $0.06f_c'$, the web size for the continuous T-beam may occasionally be governed by shear instead of moment, but with the shear at $0.08f_c'$ the moment usually governs the design.

8.4. LOADING PATTERNS FOR MAXIMUM MOMENTS

(a) Maximum positive moment

Influence lines might be used to determine the loading arrangement, but the critical patterns are easy to deduce from a single load-deflection sketch, such as that in Fig. 8.4a in which deflections are greatly exaggerated. The usual carry-over moment idea leads directly to the moment diagram in Fig. 8.4b. It is observed that this loading produces positive moment near

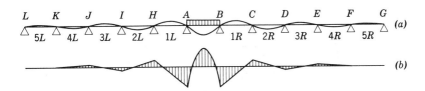

Fig. 8.4. The influence of a single panel load on a continuous beam.

mid-span in all even-numbered spans. One concludes that if all even-numbered spans were loaded, each such load would increase the positive moments in the other loaded spans. This loading pattern is usually stated as follows:

> For maximum positive moment near the middle of a span, load that span and alternate spans on each side, as shown in Fig. 8.5a.

The dead load always acts and is included on the moment diagrams shown. This one loading arrangement gives the maximum positive moments on all the loaded spans. The maximum positive moment on all other spans is given by loading only those spans, as in Fig. 8.5b, taking off the live loads shown in Fig. 8.5a. Thus all maximum positive moments on all spans are determined by two load arrangements and two moment distributions. Extended to a multistory frame, these patterns become checkerboard arrangements of loading (Fig. 8.5c), with only two patterns still needed for the complete analysis.

CONTINUOUS BEAMS AND ONE-WAY SLABS 197

(b) Minimum positive moment (or maximum negative moment) near mid-span

Since the minimum positive moment is simply the opposite extreme of loading from that for maximum positive moment on beam AB, all the live loads in Fig. 8.5a must be removed and live loads must be placed on the

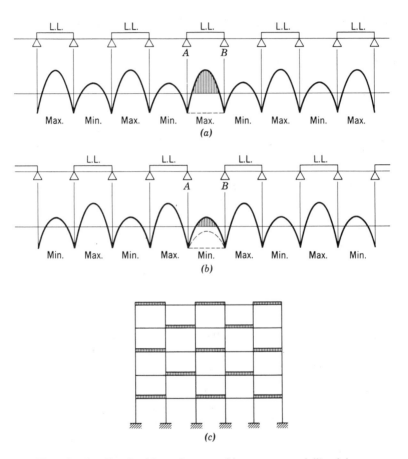

Fig. 8.5. Loading for (a) maximum positive moment and (b) minimum positive moment at mid-span. (c) Checkerboard loading for multiple stories.

other spans as in Fig. 8.5b. It should be noted that the two loadings already discussed for maximum positive moment, Fig. 8.5a and b, give all the necessary minimum positive moments or maximum negative moments near mid-span. The loading criterion is:

Omit live load on span considered; load adjacent spans and alternate spans beyond.

With smaller dead load moment, the mid-span moment in AB could be negative, as indicated by the dashed curve in Fig. 8.5b.

(c) Maximum negative moment at left support

The single panel loading of Fig. 8.4 shows that negative M is produced at

B by loading adjacent span to left

D by loading third span to left

F by loading fifth span to left

A by loading adjacent span to right

I by loading third span to right

K by loading fifth span to right

This can be summarized by the criterion:

For maximum negative moment at a given support, load adjacent spans on each side and alternate spans beyond.

Applied to maximum moment at the left support A, this criterion results in the loading and moment diagram shown in Fig. 8.6a.   Only the resulting moments adjacent to A are significant, since no others are either maximum or minimum moments.   These moments are critical at the face of support, as will be discussed in Sec. 8.4g.

(d) Maximum negative moment at right support

The same criterion applies to this maximum moment as in the case above.   The loadings are placed on spans adjacent to B, and alternate spans beyond, as shown in Fig. 8.6b.   Unfortunately, the loading gives maximums only near the one support at B.

(e) Partial span loadings

It should be noted that both maximum positive and maximum negative moment conditions call for full load on the span under consideration. Maximum negative moment occurs with a very unsymmetrical moment diagram in the span involved.   On the other hand, maximum positive moment results in a moment diagram nearly symmetrical about the middle of the span.   Minimum positive moment at mid-span (or maximum negative there when dead load is small) also gives a moment diagram nearly symmetrical, in this case a moment diagram based on dead load alone on the span in question.

In building frame design it is not customary to deal with partial span loads since they do not increase the principal design moments. In highway structures partial span loads would have a considerable influence on

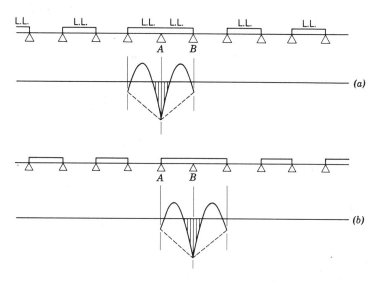

Fig. 8.6. Loadings for maximum negative moment; (*a*) at left support *A*; (*b*) at right support *B*.

detailing the steel. Partial span loads are mentioned briefly in Sec. 8.6 in connection with maximum moment diagrams.

(f) Permissible simplifications

The ACI Code encourages the use of a reduced or simplified frame in the analysis of buildings [Art. 702*a*(1)]. One floor may be analyzed at a time with the far ends of columns taken as fixed. In calculating maximum negative moments the live load may be applied on only the two adjacent spans. This permits the use of simplified moment distribution procedures such as the 2-cycle procedure given in Ref. 1. These methods, in the author's opinion, are quite reasonable for ordinary structures, except that they give beam and column moments at the exterior columns which tend to be considerably too small.

REINFORCED CONCRETE FUNDAMENTALS

(g) Moment at face of support

Moment distribution generally implies moments calculated on the basis of spans taken center to center of supports. Since such calculations treat the support reaction as though it were concentrated at a point, the resulting moment diagram within the support width is entirely imaginary. This is of no concern since both theory and tests show that the critical moment is at the *face* of the support [Art. 702b(2)].

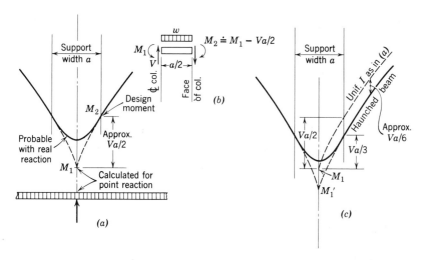

Fig. 8.7. Moment at face of support. (*a*) Without correction for increased stiffness at support. (*b*) Free-body diagram establishing procedure in (*a*). (*c*) Recommended procedure recognizing increased stiffness at support.

Many engineers establish the design moment at the face of support from the calculated moment at the center line of support, simply by deducting $Va/2$, where V is the shear and a is the column width, as illustrated in Fig. 8.7a. This is almost the same as scaling the moment value from the moment diagram, because the small length of uniform load within the column width (Fig. 8.7b) would cause little change in moment.

The author prefers the more conservative correction recommended by the old Joint Committee Specification, namely, a reduction taken as $Va/3$. The reasoning behind this value is as follows. The support stiffens the end of the beam much as would a haunch. A calculation considering this increased end stiffness would lead to an increased negative moment at the center of the column, as indicated by M_1' in Fig. 8.7c. Instead of

CONTINUOUS BEAMS AND ONE-WAY SLABS 201

calculating M_1' (which might be roughly $Va/6$ larger than M_1), an approximate equivalent is obtained by applying a smaller correction, $Va/3$, to the original M_1 value. The design moment is then $M_1 - Va/3$, as in Fig. 8.7c.

The extra stiffness at the support also leads to smaller positive moments. However, the correction would be only about $Va/6$. Most engineers consider this correction less certain than that to the face of the column and use the original positive moments without any correction.

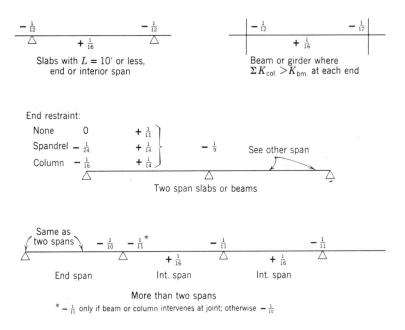

Fig. 8.8. ACI Code moment coefficients for nearly equal spans.

8.5. MOMENT COEFFICIENTS

Any given moment can be expressed as a moment coefficient times wL'^2, where w is the total load per foot and L' is the clear span. The maximum moment coefficients will be largest when the ratio of live load to dead load is large and when the column or other joint restraint is relatively small. Negative moment coefficients may also be large when adjacent spans are longer or more heavily loaded than the span in question.

Based on uniform live loads not greater than three times the dead load and upon span lengths "approximately equal (the larger of two adjacent spans not exceeding the shorter by more than 20 per cent)," the ACI

REINFORCED CONCRETE FUNDAMENTALS

Building Code Committee has established by analysis certain reasonable moment coefficients to use for maximum moment calculations. Article 701c tabulates these coefficients and Fig. 8.8 presents them in diagrammatic fashion.

When the ratio of dead to live load is particularly large, some economy can be achieved by calculating the moments by more accurate methods.

The use of moment coefficients should be restricted to rather standard conditions unless one uses general tables such as those in the Appendix of the ACI *Reinforced Concrete Design Handbook*.[4]

For ultimate strength design, the comments in Sec. 8.23 should be noted.

8.6. MAXIMUM MOMENT DIAGRAMS

In order to determine the best arrangement of the reinforcing it is necessary for the designer to have in mind a clear picture of the extreme range of moments all along the beam or slab. The major part of such a diagram can be assembled from the several moment diagrams for critical maximum moments already illustrated in Figs. 8.5, 8.6, and 8.7. For a typical interior span with equal spans and equal live loads, these moment curves are drawn to larger scale in Fig. 8.9a–d and grouped together in Fig. 8.9e.

By loadings exactly opposite to those for maximum negative moment, some small positive moment can often be obtained over supports as suggested by the dashed lines. Some partial span loadings may also increase the negative moments slightly, as indicated by dashed lines, but these are not very significant changes.

A very significant fact about the maximum moment diagrams is that either positive or negative moment may exist over a considerable portion of the beam. Hence the designer must provide tension steel in both top and bottom over this zone.

Definite locations for some of the inflection points on Fig. 8.9 are calculated in connection with the bending of bars in Sec. 8.14.

8.7. MAXIMUM SHEARS

The loading for maximum shear at a support is the same as for maximum negative moment there. Hence the end shear can always exceed the simple beam shear by an amount equal to the continuity shear V_c. On interior spans the value of V_c will be in the order of 3% to 9% of the simple beam shear, with 5% a fair average value. On end spans it can run as large as 20% or more of the simple beam shear. This large V_c on

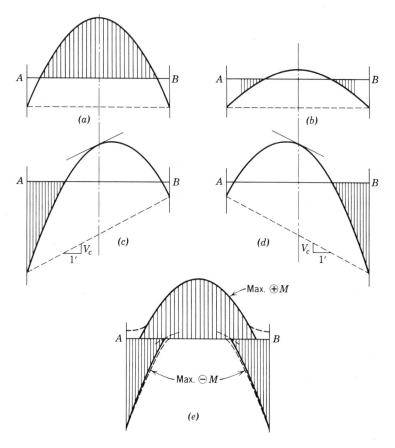

Fig. 8.9. Moment diagrams for maximum moment. (*a*) Positive moment at mid-span. (*b*) Negative moment near mid-span. (*c*) Negative moment at left support. (*d*) Negative moment at right support. (*e*) Composite maximum moment diagrams.

the end span is additive only on the half beam adjacent to the first interior support. For nearly equal spans, the Code in Art. 701*c* suggests 15% extra shear in end members at the first interior support and no addition elsewhere. The author prefers to make a nominal addition in interior spans as well as the substantial addition in the end span.

8.8. DESIGN OF CONTINUOUS ONE-WAY SLAB

Design a continuous one-way slab supported on beams at 12 ft 0 in. on centers, ACI Code moment coefficients (Art. 701c), dead load of 25 psf (plus slab weight), live load of 200 psf, $f_c' = 3000$ psi, intermediate grade steel. Assume the beam stem is 12 in. wide.

SOLUTION

The moment coefficients shown in Fig. 8.8 indicate that the negative moment at the first interior support is the maximum, at $0.10wL'^2$. The slab at this point will be designed as a balanced section, since slabs are generally too thin for satisfactory placement of compression steel.

$$w_L \qquad = 200 \text{ psf} \qquad\qquad \text{Bal. } R = 236$$

$$w_D \qquad = 25 \qquad\qquad\qquad \text{Bal. } j = 0.866$$

$$\text{Slab wt.} = \cancel{75} \quad 63 \text{ (assumed)}$$

$$w_T = \cancel{300} \quad 288 \text{ psf}$$

$L' = 12.0 - 1.0 = 11.0$ ft clear span

$M = -0.10 \times 300 \times 11^2 = 3630$ ft-lb/ft width of slab

$d = \sqrt{M/Rb} = \sqrt{3630 \times 12/(236 \times 12)} = \sqrt{15.37} = 3.92$ in.

Article 507b specifies 0.75-in. clear cover.

$t = d + D/2 + 0.75 = 3.92 + 0.25 + 0.75 = 4.92$ in. for #4 bars, say 5 in.

Slab wt. $= 150 \times \frac{5}{12} = 63$ psf

The change from the 75 psf assumed is only 4% of the total load, indicating a 4% reduction in M and approximately 2% in the required d, an amount insufficient to permit a practical reduction in t, as verified below. The revised weight is shown above and used for a revised M.

$M = -0.10 \times 288 \times 11^2 = -0.10 \times 34{,}900 = 3490$ ft-lb/ft

$d = \sqrt{3490 \times 12/(236 \times 12)} = 3.84$ in.

For #4 bars, $t = 3.84 + 0.25 + 0.75 = 4.84$ in., say 5 in., as estimated.

USE $t = 5$ in., $d = 5 - 0.25 - 0.75 = 4.00$ in. for #4 bars

All other sections have less moment and will be designed as members deeper than a balanced section by the approximate method of Sec. 5.3c.

$$A_s/\text{ft} = \frac{M/\text{ft}}{f_s jd} = \frac{(M \text{ in ft-lb/ft})12}{20{,}000 \times 0.866 \times 4.00} = \frac{M \text{ in ft-lb/ft}}{5790}$$

It is convenient to tabulate A_s per in. width if the bar spacing is to be determined without the use of tables.

$$A_s/\text{in.} = \frac{M \text{ in ft-lb/ft}}{5790 \times 12} = \frac{M \text{ in ft-lb/ft}}{69{,}300}$$

TABLE 8.1. Calculation of Slab Steel

	Exterior Span		1st Int. Sup.	Typical Interior	
	Ext. End	Middle		Middle	Support
M coef. C	$-1/24$	$+1/14$	$-1/10$	$+1/16$	$-1/11$
$M = C \times 34{,}900$	-1450 ft-lb/ft	$+2490$	-3490	$+2180$	-3170
A_s/ft $= M/5790$	0.250 in.²/ft	0.430	0.602	0.377	0.548
A_s/in. $= M/69{,}300$	0.0209 in.²/in.	0.0358	0.0503	0.0315	0.0457
Min. $A_s = 0.0025bd$	0.010 in.²/in.	—	—	—	—
Spcg. #4 bars	9.60 in.	5.60	3.98	6.36	4.40
USE #4 at	9 in.	5.5	4	6	4

The required areas and the spacing of #4 bars are given in Table 8.1 as though top and bottom steel were to be totally separate as they are in Fig. 8.10a. The bottom steel in the end panel would be simpler if the bottom bars from other spans (#4 at 6 in. = 0.40 in.²/ft) were also used there supplemented by additional #2 bars at 18 in. to make the total 0.433 in.²/ft, about that required.

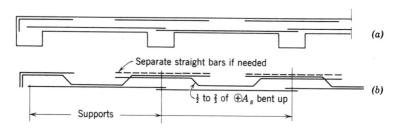

Fig. 8.10. Arrangement of slab steel. (*a*) Straight bars alone. (*b*) Some bars bent.

The designer would not be too happy with this particular design. The typical interior span steel is somewhat excessive, averaging some 8 % more than needed for the given moments, which indicates that a slightly larger spacing of beams would require no more steel. If there were numerous interior spans, it might be desirable to reduce the depth of these slabs more nearly to that of a balanced section. The resulting greater depth of end span would call for entirely separate end span bottom steel; or the designer might choose to try the same reduced depth for the end span, designing it as a section shallower than a balanced slab, as in Sec. 5.3*c*. When there is much duplication of typical members, alternate designs as well as alternate layouts are often the mark of the good designer.

Many designers prefer to use some bent-up bars, feeling that this positions the top steel more exactly. The arrangement of Fig. 8.10*b* is

REINFORCED CONCRETE FUNDAMENTALS

the most common bending pattern. The top bars are actually all in one layer and the bottom bars in one layer, but they are sketched separately to indicate the patterns more clearly.

The bend points and stop points for bars in slabs involve almost exactly the same considerations as for any other continuous member. These considerations are discussed in considerable detail in Secs. 8.13 through 8.16 in connection with the design of a continuous T-beam. Out of such analyses rules for uncomplicated cases have been developed. In the *CRSI Design Handbook*[5] are tabulations of many slab designs in which alternate bottom bars are bent up in the pattern of Fig. 8.10*b* to form the negative moment steel. Their suggested bend points are specified for simple spans, end spans, and interior spans respectively in Figs. E.12, E.13, and E.14 in Appendix E.

Bond stresses may be critical at the face of support, at points of inflection where the tension steel starts to develop stress, and at all points where tension steel has been stopped or bent. The details of such calculations are shown for a T-beam in Secs. 8.17 and 8.18. Slabs are slightly simpler in that slab bars are usually bent at only one point in each half span.

The student should note that temperature or spacing steel is required parallel to the beams, at least in the amount specified in Art. 707 of the Code. Also, bar supports or chairs should be provided to hold the steel at proper levels.

Slab shear stresses could easily have been computed, but they do not control on one-way slabs of ordinary span.

The design of rectangular beams will be discussed in Sec. 8.21.

8.9. CONTINUOUS T-BEAM DESIGN—GENERAL

The principles of design for a continuous T-beam can be discussed most easily in terms of a numerical example. Much of the remainder of this chapter (through Sec. 8.20) is devoted to various aspects of such design in terms of a typical interior span, as follows: A typical interior panel of a continuous T-beam of 20 ft clear span with 15-in. square columns is to be designed to carry the slab designed in Sec. 8.8. Beams are 12 ft 0 in. on centers, $t = 5$ in., $w_L = 200$ psf, $w_D = 88$ psf (including slab weight but excluding stem weight), $f_c' = 3000$ psi, intermediate grade steel, ACI Code, maximum moment coefficients of -0.091 and $+0.072$ based on clear span.

The controlling element on the choice of web size will be the requirements for negative moment as a double-reinforced rectangular beam. Shear must also be considered.

The given moment coefficients indicate that positive moment steel will be approximately 75% to 80% of the negative moment tension steel, since *jd* will not be greatly different for positive and negative moment. If half of the positive moment steel is bent up in the fashion indicated in Fig. 8.12b, the other half will continue in the bottom part of the beam into the column and thereby almost automatically provide compression steel in the amount $A_s' = 0.5 \times 0.8A_s = 0.4A_s$, where A_s is the negative moment tension steel. By lapping this compression steel from two adjacent spans as in Fig. 8.13e A_s' becomes approximately $0.8A_s$.

The designer has considerable freedom in selecting the approximate A_s' to use, and estimates such as the above are necessarily approximate at this stage. (For example, the positive moment steel may work out to be five bars, which means either 40% or 60% bent up, instead of half.) For this design the value $A_s' = 0.4A_s$ is chosen, but the student should not take this as a general rule, or even as a wise decision. The choice can only be evaluated after the design is further advanced.

A scratch paper calculation for $A_s' = 0.4A_s$ and $d' = 0.1d$, as in Sec. 5.4e(3), gives R' as 385. If d' becomes $0.15d$, the value of R' drops to 357. About as good a start as any for this type of beam is to choose arbitrarily an R' of something near 400. An R' of 385 will be used in this design.

8.10. CONTINUOUS T-BEAM DESIGN— NEGATIVE MOMENT SECTION

Size will first be established for moment as a double-reinforced rectangular beam.

$$LL = 200 \times 12 \qquad = 2400 \text{ plf}$$
$$\text{Slab} + DL = 88 \times 12 = 1056$$
$$\overline{3456}$$
$$\text{Estimated stem wt.} \quad = \cancel{300} \quad 215$$
$$\overline{}$$
$$w_T = \cancel{3760} \quad 3670 \text{ plf}$$
$$M = -0.091 \times 3760 \times 20^2 = 136{,}800 \text{ ft-lb}$$
$$\text{Reqd. } b'd^2 = M/R' = 136{,}800 \times 12/385 = 4270$$

If $b' = 11.5$ in., $d = \sqrt{4270/11.5} = \sqrt{372} = 19.30$ in.

Add 1.5-in. cover + 0.5-in. stirrup
+ 0.5-in. (= D/2) + 1 in. (to c.g. of two
layers of steel)   = 3.5
                                        $\overline{}$
                                say, over-all = 23 in.

REINFORCED CONCRETE FUNDAMENTALS

For shear on interior spans Code Art. 701c suggests $V = wL'/2$, but the author prefers to add 5% as an allowance for the continuity shear which is present under maximum negative moment loading. (More generally, to fix the stem size, the 1.15$wL'/2$ end span shear would be used, to permit uniformity in size.)

$$V = 1.05 \times 3760 \times 20/2 = 39,500 \text{ lb}$$

The maximum practical v is $0.08f_c'$; the $0.12f_c'$ value should be reserved for emergencies (and experts).

$$\text{Reqd. } b'd = \frac{V}{vj} = \frac{39,500}{(0.08 \times 3000)\frac{7}{8}} = 188 \text{ in.}^2$$

If $b' = 11.5$ in., $d = 16.3$ in. $< d$ for M

This is a typical situation in that moment usually controls. Under older specifications which limited v to $0.06f_c'$, the beam size was sometimes established by the shear requirements.

Stem wt. (Fig. 8.11b), $w_s = 11.5(23 - 5) \times 150/144 = 215$ plf

Revised $w_T = 3670$ plf

The 2% drop in w_T would reduce the depth required for M by about 1% and possibly permit the use of $d = 19$ in. and an over-all depth of 22.5 in. However, considering the approximate nature of the assumed R',

USE over-all depth = 23 in., $b' = 11.5$ in.

Negative $d = 23 - 3.5 = 19.5$ in., as sketched in Fig. 8.11a.

The 11.5-in. width fits nicely with form lumber dimensions and the ratio of height to width looks reasonable. A ratio as low as 1:1 will sometimes be used for small beams, a ratio as much as 3:1 for heavy beams.

The steel required is calculated as in Sec. 5.4b.

$$M = -0.091 \times 3670 \times 20^2 = 134,000 \text{ ft-lb}$$

$$M_1 = Rbd^2 = 236 \times 11.5 \times 19.5^2/12 = 86,000 \text{ ft-lb}$$

$$A_{s1} = \frac{M_1}{f_s jd} = \frac{86,000 \times 12}{20,000 \times 0.866 \times 19.5} = 3.06 \text{ in.}^2$$

$$M_2 = M - M_1 = 134,000 - 86,000 = 48,000 \text{ ft-lb}$$

Assuming $d' = 2.5$ in.,

$$A_{s2} = \frac{M_2}{f_s(d - d')} = \frac{48,000 \times 12}{20,000(19.5 - 2.5)} = 1.69 \text{ in.}^2$$

Total negative $A_s = A_{s1} + A_{s2} = 3.06 + 1.69 = 4.75 \text{ in.}^2$

This A_s steel might go into one layer instead of the two assumed, with a 1-in. reduction in the over-all beam depth. However, the design will be continued on the two-layer basis. Based on Fig. 8.11c,

$f_{cs'} = 1350 \times 5.35/7.85 = 920$ psi

$f_s' = 2nf_{cs'} = 2 \times 10 \times 920 = 18,400$ psi $< 20,000$ O.K.

Effective $f_s'' = (2n - 1)f_{cs'} = 19 \times 920 = 17,480$ psi

$$A_s' = \frac{M_2}{f_s''(d - d')} = \frac{48,000 \times 12}{17,480(19.5 - 2.5)} = 1.94 \text{ in.}^2 \quad \text{O.K. for one layer}$$

8.11. CONTINUOUS T-BEAM DESIGN—
POSITIVE MOMENT DESIGN

The over-all depth of 23 in. already chosen for negative moment fixes the effective depth at mid-span. For one layer of steel (Fig. 8.11d),

Positive d = 23 in. − 1.5-in. cover − 0.5-in. stirrup − 0.5 in. (for $D/2$)

$$= 20.5 \text{ in.}$$

Trial jd = 20.5 − $t/2$ = 18 in., or $0.9d$ = 18.45 in.   Use larger value.

M = +0.072 × 3670 × 20² = 106,000 ft-lb

$$\text{Trial } A_s = \frac{M}{f_s jd} = \frac{106,000 \times 12}{20,000 \times 18.45} = 3.45 \text{ in.}^2$$

The use of curves to establish a better value of jd saves much calculation: p = 3.45/(60 × 20.5) = 0.00280, pn = 0.0280, t/d = 5/20.5 = 0.243. Figure E.5 shows an intersection off of the curves, indicating a neutral axis in the flange and action as a rectangular beam. Figure E.2 for rectangular beams shows j = 0.93.

Calculations independent of curves would be as follows, neglecting the web area below the flange. Area moments about neutral axis:

$60 \times 5(kd - 2.5)$ = $10 \times 3.45(20.5 - kd)$

$334.5kd$ = 1457

kd = 4.37 < t. Equation not valid; rectangular beam.

$60(kd)^2/2 = 10 \times 3.45(20.5 - kd)$

$(kd)^2 + 1.15kd + 0.575^2$ = 23.6 + 0.575² = 23.9

kd = 4.88 − 0.575 = 4.30 in.

jd = 20.5 − 4.30/3 = 19.07 in.

$$\text{Positive } A_s = \frac{106,000 \times 12}{20,000 \times 19.07} = 3.34 \text{ in.}^2$$

The more exact theoretical solution based on the cubic equation for kd (beam deeper than a balanced section, Sec. 5.3b) would have given kd = 4.25 in., jd = 19.08 in., A_s = 3.33 in.² This A_s may fit into the assumed one layer of steel, but it still depends upon the bar size selected.

f_c is O.K. by inspection because kd < bal. kd of $0.403d$ = 8.27 in.

8.12. CONTINUOUS T-BEAM DESIGN—CHOICE OF BARS

Bond stress can be important in fixing a proper bar size. Bond is most apt to be critical on the positive moment steel at the point of inflection. This point of inflection can be calculated from Fig. 8.11e.

$0.125wL_0^2 = 0.072wL'^2 = 0.072w \times 20^2$

$L_0 = 20\sqrt{8 \times 0.072}$ = 15.12 ft

$V_{P.I.}$ = 3670 × 15.12/2 = 27,700 lb

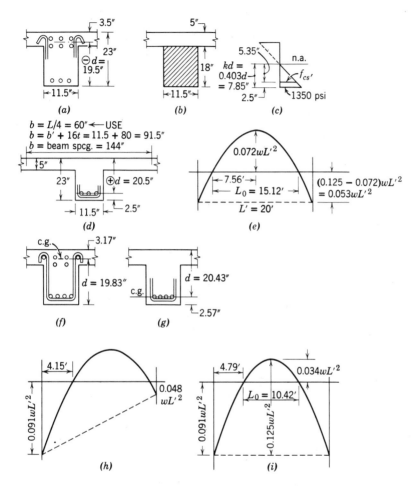

Fig. 8.11. Design sketches for continuous T-beam design. (a) Assumed depth for negative moment. (b) Estimated weight, shaded area. (c) Stress triangle for f_s' calculation. (d) Assumed depth for positive moment. (e) Location of P.I. with maximum positive M. (f) Actual depth to top steel as selected. (g) Actual depth to bottom steel as selected. (h) "Exact" location of P.I. with maximum negative M. (i) Approximate location of P.I. with maximum negative M.

For bottom steel, where stirrups will be present to control splitting, the allowable bond stress is $0.10f_c'$ or 300 psi.

$$\text{Reqd. } \Sigma o = 27{,}700/(300 \times \tfrac{7}{8} \times 20.5) = 5.15 \text{ in.}$$

This is probably too small to govern. (The 2–#9 used below give $\Sigma o = 7.08$ in.)

	$-A_s$	A_s'	$+A_s$
Reqd., in.²	4.75	1.94	3.34
USE	4–#8 bent = 3.16 in.²	2–#9	2–#8 bent = 1.58 in.²
	2–#8 straight = 1.58	= 2.00 in.²	2–#9 straight = 2.00
	4.74 in.²		3.58 in.²

A study of Fig. 8.11*f* indicates that negative moment steel could have been detailed in one rather crowded layer. The two-layer arrangement selected raises the originally assumed centroid of steel by 0.33 in. and would permit a slight reduction in A_s and A_s' or a slight reduction in the over-all depth. For positive moment steel, the use of two #9 bars raises the assumed centroid of steel by 0.07 in. (Fig. 8.11*g*). Some recalculation and even some juggling of b' and d might be profitable on a very special design, but the remaining errors are small, none appears to encroach on safety, and the steel arrangement is simple and apparently economical.

The schematic bending arrangement of the steel selected is the same as that shown for the slab in Fig. 8.10.

8.13. CONTINUOUS T-BEAM DESIGN—GENERAL REQUIREMENTS FOR BENDING BARS

The fabricator must detail each bar, but the designer can be satisfied to locate bend points and cutoff points reasonably accurately. Many offices use rules such as "bend up half the bottom steel at the quarter point of clear span," but more exact procedures are presented here to indicate more adaptable methods needed in many cases. Figures E.15, E.16, and E.17 in Appendix E show bending charts used for designs tabulated in the *CRSI Design Handbook*.

The author recommends a very conservative attitude towards bar detailing. There has been much ineffective detailing of what would otherwise have been good designs. The final member is no better than its details.

Bend points may be governed by:

1. Moment requirements.
2. Development lengths.

3. "Arbitrary" requirements of Code, Art. 902.
4. Bond requirements.
5. Use of bent bars as stirrups.

Several "arbitrary" specification requirements will be noted. Article 902a requires that at least one-third of the total reinforcement for negative moment be extended beyond the extreme location of the point of inflection by the greater of: (1) half of the development length; (2) $L'/16$; (3) beam depth. Article 902b requires that at least one-fourth of the positive reinforcement in continuous beams shall extend 6 in. into the support. Both of these, in the words of the old Joint Committee Specification, are "to provide for contingencies arising from unanticipated distribution of loads, yielding of supports, shifting of points of inflection, or other lack of agreement with assumed conditions governing the design of elastic structures."

Article 902a also requires that every bar, whether required for positive or negative reinforcement, shall be extended 12 diameters beyond the point at which it is no longer needed for stress. The Code would seem to permit this 12 diameters to be in a bent portion of the bar. The author prefers to consider it as another requirement for a shifting moment diagram, as shown dashed in Fig. 8.12a. This means he uses it as a required straight length before stopping *or bending*. This rather severe usage is followed in the next article.

Arrangements satisfying moment requirements, development lengths, and Art. 902 may sometimes be varied slightly to help out in bond or in web reinforcement. For example, if bond on the bottom steel at the point of inflection is excessive, it may be possible to shift the bend-up points towards the column and keep more steel available for bond; or the spacing of bend points may be shifted to make the bent bars more useful for web steel.

8.14. CONTINUOUS T-BEAM DESIGN—MOMENT DIAGRAMS GOVERNING BAR BENDS

The positive moment diagram has already been established from Fig. 8.11e.

For maximum negative moment the actual moment diagram is unsymmetrical and the maximum moment calculation alone does not provide sufficient data for the entire diagram. The diagram can be reasonably approximated by using a negative moment at the far end as slightly less than that accompanying the maximum positive moment, in this case say

$-0.048wL'^2$ instead of the $-0.053wL'^2$ value shown in Fig. 8.11e. Figure 8.11h would be almost exact insofar as the location of P.I. (point of inflection) on the left is concerned. The method of Sec. A.10 can then be used to locate the P.I. at 4.15 ft from the face of column.

More commonly the approximate P.I. is calculated for the assumed symmetrical diagram of Fig. 8.11i, which will be used here.

$$\tfrac{1}{8}wL_0^2 = 0.034w \times 20^2$$
$$L_0 = 20\sqrt{0.272} = 10.42 \text{ ft}$$

Hence the P.I. is 4.79 ft from the column. The further approximation of using a triangle for the section of the parabola is reasonable when the P.I. is not too near mid-span, say, is outside the middle third of the span.

The maximum moment diagrams are assembled in Fig. 8.12a. It is here assumed that the minimum positive moment near mid-span does not become negative and hence does not control the design at all.

8.15. CONTINUOUS T-BEAM DESIGN—BENDS AND STOP POINTS FOR TENSION BARS

Although most designers would probably bend the two #8 bars at a single point, they will be bent singly in this case to illustrate better the calculation procedure. A sketch such as Fig. 8.12b is recommended to the student for tabulation of the calculated values, although the repetition of bar labels would prove confusing on a design drawing. Since the first bar bent is defined as the bar bent closest to the point of maximum moment, it will be noted that the first bar bent down is the same as the second bar bent up.

The positive moment diagram determines the minimum distances x_1 and x_2 from the center line of span for the first and second bars bent up, as dimensioned in Fig. 8.12b. These dimensions also establish the maximum distances from the column. In like fashion the negative moment diagram fixes minimum bend-down distances from the support. If the small difference between the two upper layers is ignored, the distance between the positive and negative steel is 17 in. or 1.42 ft. This is called the offset distance and, with the usual 45° bends, is equal to the horizontal distance or run used in making the offset. The minimum bend-down distances plus this run establish the minimum distances to the bend-up point. The designer thus has some freedom of choice, between 4.02 and 5.45 ft out to the first bend-up point and between 3.22 and 3.98 ft to the second.

Thus far only moment requirements have been considered, but development length also has to be watched. For top steel the allowable bond

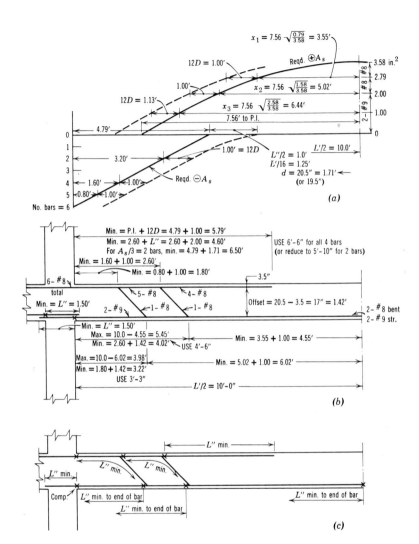

Fig. 8.12. Calculation of stop and bend points for bars. (*a*) Use of maximum moment diagrams for required A_s calculations. (*b*) Arrangement of data related to arrangement of bars. (*c*) The development length requirements separated for clarity.

stress is $0.07f_c'$ or 210 psi, it being assumed that stirrups prevent splitting difficulties.

$$L'' = \frac{f_s}{4u} D = \frac{20,000}{4 \times 210} \times 1.00 = 23.8 \text{ in.} = \text{say, } 2.0 \text{ ft}$$

In Fig. 8.12c the crosses indicate the points of maximum steel stress and the places beyond which L'' lengths are needed. For the bottom steel, as usual, the bars continue far enough to provide much more than the needed L'' (by inspection, even without calculating the distance for #9 bars with $u = 300$ psi). For the top steel which is bent down, it seems desirable that the bars go horizontally at least $L''/2$ before being bent down. The minimum distance for the first bend-down point in Fig. 8.12b is already more than $L''/2$. For the second bar bent down, the minimum bend-down point is only 0.80 ft beyond the first bar minimum. For this reason the distance to the second bend-down point was increased above the minimum, as indicated by the dimensioned bend-up points. The arbitrary choice of 4 ft 6 in. could as well have been 4 ft 3 in., or as much as 5 ft 5 in.

For the top steel not bent down, the minimum length for development becomes $2.60 + L'' = 4.60$ ft, which does not control. It should be noted that it is on the safe side to measure L'' from the theoretical bend-down point rather than from the bend-down point actually used. (Theoretically, the requirement is an L'' beyond the actual bend point but calculated for the actual reduced f_s.) Article 902a requires that one-third of the negative A_s go farther, that is, to a minimum of 6.50 ft.

Two alternative bar patterns will be considered to emphasize a few points. In Fig. 8.13a the two #8 bars are bent as a single pair. Strictly interpreted, the maximum and minimum distances indicate this is impossible, but the small difference can be overlooked when one considers the strict interpretation placed on the extra $12D$ length and the safe approximations made in defining the maximum negative moment diagram. A comparison of Fig. 8.13a with Fig. 8.12b indicates two differences: (1) The leeway in selecting bend points is reduced when bars are bent in pairs. (2) There are fewer development length distances to watch, there being three instead of five points of maximum tension bar stress.

As a second alternate, Fig. 8.13b shows the four top bars which are not bent down stopped by pairs. The top dimension in each case is the minimum for moment, the second line the minimum for development length. It should be noted that development length becomes more of a control in this case. If one started to stop the first two unbent bars singly, the development length would prevent stopping of either at less than 4 ft 8 in.; hence this arrangement would be impractical.

The author prefers the separate stopping points of Fig. 8.13b to the

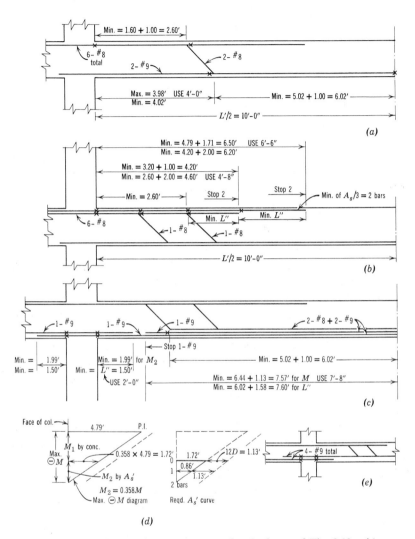

Fig. 8.13. Alternate bar arrangements for the beam of Fig. 8.12. (*a*) Two bars bent up together. (*b*) Straight top bars stopped in two groups. (*c*) One bottom bar stopped short of support (minimum number of bars continuing into column). (*d*) Development of required A_s' diagram from maximum negative moment curve. (*e*) Arrangement of bottom bars for larger A_s'.

"sudden" stopping of all bars as shown in Fig. 8.12b, although he would consider the layout of Fig. 8.13b still better if the two intermediate bars were carried out close to the point of inflection at 4 ft 10 in. There is evidence that the stopping of bars in a tension zone contributes to weakness in diagonal tension.

8.16. CONTINUOUS T-BEAM DESIGN—STOP POINTS FOR COMPRESSION STEEL

For this design the development length of the compression steel fixes the length of bottom straight bars. The design of A_s' in Sec. 8.10 was based on $f_s' = 18,400$ psi and this requires

$$L'' = \frac{f_s'}{4u} D = \frac{18,400}{4 \times 300} \times 1.13 = 17.3 \text{ in.} = \text{say, } 1.50 \text{ ft}$$

Thus the bottom steel should extend into the column 1.50 ft, which actually means 3 in. beyond the far face of the column. The design on the far side of the column needs no help from this 3 in. of steel because the bottom steel from that span completely provides for A_s' there. An alternate way of analyzing this would be to consider the bars from adjacent spans spliced by lapping $L'' = 1.50$ ft. This would require the bars to extend only 1.5 in. beyond the far face of the column. In neither case does the length for moment enter into these calculations, because the two #9 bars for A_s' are *not* cut off within the span. But the student should compare the following layout which shows that moment length can enter into such calculations.

Consider the layout in Fig. 8.13c where nearly the minimum 25% of the bottom steel continues into the support. The bars have been drawn separately, but they are all in the same layer. For tension, $L'' = [20,000/(4 \times 300)] \times 1.13 = 18.8$ in. = say, 19 in. = 1.58 ft; and in compression, $L'' = 1.50$ ft as already calculated. The stopping point of the #9 tension bar is governed by development length rather than moment.

The compression steel must extend at least 1.50 ft beyond the column to care for development length. For moment, a diagram of required A_s' must be established. The maximum negative moment diagram can be used. By referring to the design of A_s' in Sec. 8.10, it will be noted that the negative moment diagram in Fig. 8.13d can be subdivided into $M_1 = Rbd^2$ on the concrete and M_2 for the compression steel couple. The total negative moment is 134,000 ft-lb, M_1 is 86,000 ft-lb, and M_2 is 48,000 ft-lb or 0.358M. All A_s' could be stopped at $1.72 + 12D$, but this is not desired. Half of A_s' can be stopped at $0.86 + 12D = 0.86 + 1.13 = 1.99$ ft from the column. This arrangement saves a little steel, but is slightly more complex and could involve bond trouble on the bottom steel. However, the lapping of bottom steel to furnish A_s' on both faces of the column is frequently the best detail, for example, for a beam which might require A_s' of four #9 bars, as shown in Fig. 8.13e.

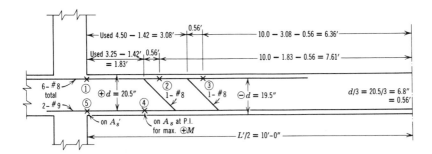

Fig. 8.14. Locations where bond must be checked.

8.17. CONTINUOUS T-BEAM DESIGN—
BOND ON TENSION STEEL

The points of maximum bond stress are marked in Fig. 8.14. Attention is called to Art. 901a which states that bent bars not more than $d/3$ from the longitudinal steel may be counted in the perimeter. Hence critical bond stresses on top steel will be calculated at a distance $d/3$ beyond the bend points. Although the Code does not require it on interior spans, the author will continue to use the simple beam shear increased by $0.05wL'/2 = 1840$ lb, to represent the shear due to continuity, when dealing with steel determined by negative moment.

At point 1

$$V_1 = 1.05wL'/2 = 1.05 \times 3670 \times 20/2 = 38,500 \text{ lb}$$

$$u_1 = \frac{38,500}{(6 \times 3.14)\frac{7}{8} \times 19.5} = 120 \text{ psi} < 0.07f_c' = 210 \text{ psi} \quad \text{O.K.}$$

At point 2

$$V_2 = 7.61 \times 3670 + 1840 = 27,900 + 1840 = 29,700 \text{ lb}$$

$$u_2 = \frac{29,700}{(5 \times 3.14)\frac{7}{8} \times 19.5} = 111 \text{ psi} < 210 \quad \text{O.K.}$$

At point 3

$$V_3 = 6.36 \times 3670 + 1840 = 23,300 + 1840 = 25,100 \text{ lb}$$

$$u_3 = \frac{25,100}{(4 \times 3.14)\frac{7}{8} \times 19.5} = 117 \text{ psi} < 210 \qquad \text{O.K.}$$

If bond stress at points 1 and 3 are satisfactory, the designer can usually see by inspection whether the stress at intermediate bend points could be critical. For the arrangement of Fig. 8.13b, the highest bond stress is probably on the two bars remaining at 4.67 ft from the support.

The bond stress on bottom tension steel at point 4 has already been checked in Sec. 8.12 by calculating the required perimeter as 5.15 in. while $2 \times 3.54 = 7.08$ in. was provided. This is equivalent to a calculated $u = 300 \times 5.15/7.08 = 218$ psi. No shear due to continuity enters into this calculation because this location of the point of inflection goes with the symmetrical loading for maximum positive moment.

Reference may now be made to the alternate bar arrangement of Fig. 8.13c. Since a perimeter of 5.15 in. is required for bottom steel, the short straight bar is required for bond all the way to the point of inflection. This requirement has been met, although in minimum fashion. On the basis of bond the author would be inclined to extend this bar to the P.I. plus $12D$ or $7.56 + 1.13 = 8.69$ ft from the center line of span.

8.18. CONTINUOUS T-BEAM DESIGN—BOND ON COMPRESSION STEEL

On $A_s{}'$ at the face of support, the ordinary bond formula does not apply because it was derived for the full transfer of ΔT to the bars in bond. Only a portion of ΔC goes into bond on $A_s{}'$; much of it goes into increased compression on the concrete. The Code suggests that V "be reduced in the ratio of compressive force assumed in the bars to the total compressive force at the section." At least three calculation procedures appear to be available. The simplest, where the design calculations are available (Sec. 8.10), is to use the ratio as $M_2/M = 48,000/134.000 = 0.358$. Another evaluation of the ratio is in terms of compression as suggested by the Code. This is:

$$\frac{(\text{Reqd. } A_s{}')f_s{}'}{(\text{Reqd. } A_s{}')(f_s{}' - f_{cs}{}') + 0.5f_c bkd}$$

$$= \frac{1.94 \times 18,400}{1.94(18,400 - 920) + 0.5 \times 1350 \times 11.5 \times 0.403 \times 19.5}$$

$$= \frac{35,700}{94,600} = 0.377$$

Closely enough, the denominator can be approximated by M/jd with an assumed average j and the numerator with the value of A_s' actually used:

$$\frac{A_s' f_s'}{M/jd} = \frac{2.00 \times 18,400}{134,000 \times 12/(0.87 \times 19.5)} = 0.388$$

The actual bond stress is probably influenced more by detailing practice than by the variation in these values of coefficients.

$$V = 1.05 wL'/2 = 1.05 \times 3670 \times 10 = 38,500 \text{ lb}$$

$$u = \frac{38,500 \times 0.388}{(2 \times 3.54)\frac{7}{8} \times 19.5} = 124 \text{ psi} < 300 \text{ psi} \qquad \text{O.K.}$$

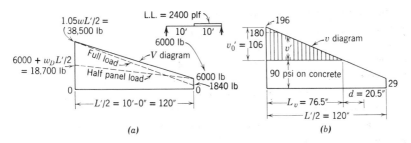

Fig. 8.15. Shear diagrams for stirrup calculations.

8.19. CONTINUOUS T-BEAM DESIGN—STIRRUPS

Under maximum moment loading the beam is subject to an end shear equal to the simple beam shear $wL'/2 = 36,700$ lb plus a continuity shear of 1840 lb (Art. 8.17) and a mid-span shear of 1840 lb as shown dashed in Fig. 8.15a. The shear at mid-span will be greater when live load is removed from the left half of the span. This loading will produce a smaller continuity shear, which will be neglected. The simple beam shear at mid-span is $2400 \times 10 \times \frac{5}{20} = 6000$ lb. The solid line in Fig. 8.15a will be used as a maximum shear diagram for stirrups design. With $b' = 11.5$ in. and $d = 19.5$ in. at the end and 20.5 in. at mid-span:

$$v_0 = \frac{38,500}{11.5 \times \frac{7}{8} \times 19.5} = 196 \text{ psi}$$

$$v_{10ft} = \frac{6000}{11.5 \times \frac{7}{8} \times 20.5} = 29 \text{ psi}$$

The unit shear curve is plotted in Fig. 8.15b. Stirrups are needed for the L_v length* where v is in excess of $0.03f_c'$; also for an additional length equal to $d = 20.5$ in. according to Art. 801d.

The design of these stirrups has already been worked out in detail in Sec. 6.18c. One very minor difference might be noted here, in the calculation of the maximum spacing as $d/4$ near the support where $v > 0.06f_c'$. In Chap. 6 the depth d was used as 20.5 in. for negative as well as for positive moment, making this maximum $s = 5.25$ in. The correct value for this T-beam is $19.5/4 = 4.88$ in.

8.20. PLACEMENT OF STIRRUPS

The proper placement of stirrups in continuous beams presents a problem. The best anchorage of stirrups would call for the hooks to be in compression concrete, which near the supports would be the bottom concrete. Since construction is simpler with the open end of the stirrup turned up, the matter of anchorage has generally been ignored. Furthering this easier placement is the requirement that the compression (bottom) steel be tied, somewhat as in columns (Art. 706a). The closed end of the stirrups will serve as ties when only two or three compression bars are used. Practice has not yet adequately solved the matter of ties for a wide layer of compression steel nor for multiple layers of compression steel. Stirrups of double-U shape or possibly auxiliary ties seem to be indicated.

A further function of stirrups, which has not yet found a place in the Code, is the prevention of splitting from high bond stresses on deformed bars. In the foregoing T-beam, bond stresses on top steel are all low, 120 psi or less as calculated in Sec. 8.17. This requires no reinforcement against splitting. Where bond stresses in excess of, say, 150 psi occur, reinforcement against splitting is needed. It appears that the use of closed ties as stirrups may be desirable in many cases. In the preceding case it may be possible to make top slab steel across the beam function to prevent splitting along the top steel, but experimental verification is needed. The bond stress on bottom steel at the point of inflection, calculated in Art. 8.17 as 218 psi, indicates that the closed side of the stirrup must be around this steel to prevent possible splitting along these bars.

* Note the quite different treatment for continuous rectangular beams required by Art. 801e and discussed in Sec. 8.21.

8.21. CONTINUOUS RECTANGULAR BEAMS

The design differences between continuous rectangular beams and continuous T-beams are all minor. The foregoing design of the T-beam can serve just as well as a model for continuous rectangular beam design. Other than the obvious difference in designing the positive moment steel for a rectangular beam, attention needs to be called to a special web steel requirement which does not apply to T-beams with monolithic slabs (Art. 801e). This requires stirrups for rectangular beams to be designed for two-thirds of the total v (rather than $v' = v - 0.03f_c'$) and requires stirrups wherever negative moment steel exists, regardless of the size of v. Such stirrups must extend stated distances beyond the extreme position of the point of inflection, if this exceeds the ordinary length for L_v based on v'. In the case of the T-beam designed above, the stirrups were extended $L_v + d = 97$ in. from the column whereas the special requirements of Art. 801e for a rectangular beam would have been:

Length of negative moment steel (Fig. 8.12b) = 6 ft 6 in. = 78 in.

Point of inflection plus $L'/16 = 4.79 + 1.25 = 6.04$ ft

Point of inflection plus $d = 4.79 + 20.5/12 = 6.50$ ft = 78 in.

Since the 97-in. length requirement also applies to rectangular beams, it is still the controlling dimension; but in beams designed for smaller v values, the special requirements for length will control. Within the 78-in. length the use of two-thirds of the shear on the stirrups increases these noticeably. The T-beam required a theoretical 10.6 #3 U stirrups within the 76.5-in. L_v length. The corresponding calculation for 76.5 in. of the rectangular beam is

$$N = \frac{11.5 \times 0.67 \times 0.5(196 + 90)76.5}{2 \times 0.11 \times 20,000} = 19.1 \text{ stirrups}$$

This special Code requirement is the result of some frame failures which occurred in the neighborhood of the point of inflection in sections without stirrups.

8.22. END SPANS AND IRREGULAR SPANS

End spans always involve negative moments smaller at the outer end and larger at the inner end, with the points of inflection and point of maximum positive moment shifted towards the outer support. Irregular

CONTINUOUS BEAMS AND ONE-WAY SLABS

spans and loads also result in maximum moment diagrams which are less symmetrical than those used in this chapter.

Proper detailing of end spans and irregular spans requires a better knowledge of unsymmetrical moment diagrams, but no additional reinforced concrete theory. Where approximations are deemed proper, the designer should be more conservative than where exact moments requirements are known.

8.23. MOMENTS FOR ULTIMATE STRENGTH DESIGN

Ultimate strength design (Chap. 3) assumes that moments will be calculated from elastic methods of frame analysis. Since the load factor used with live load is greater than that used with dead load, over-all moment coefficients will correspond to higher ratios of live load to dead load than those used with a working load analysis. This tends to increase the moment coefficients a little. However, the most significant difference which results is that the point of inflection accompanying maximum negative moment moves farther from the supports. This requires longer negative moment steel.

SELECTED REFERENCES

1. "Continuity in Concrete Building Frames," Portland Cement Association, Chicago, 3rd ed.
2. Phil M. Ferguson, "Analysis of Three-Dimensional Beam-and-Girder Framing," *ACI Jour.*, **22**, Sept. 1950; *Proc.*, **47**, p. 61.
3. R. H. Wood, "Studies in Composite Construction: Part I, The Composite Action of Brick Panel Walls Supported on Reinforced Concrete Beams; Part II, The Interaction of Floors and Beams in Multi-Storey Buildings," National Building Studies, *Research Papers No. 13* (1952) and **22** (1955), Her Majesty's Stationery Office, London.
4. ACI Committee 317, Thor Germundsson, Chairman, *Reinforced Concrete Design Handbook*, ACI, Detroit, 2nd ed., 1955.
5. Raymond C. Reese, *CRSI Design Handbook*, Concrete Reinforcing Steel Institute, Chicago, 2nd ed., 1957.
6. Raymond C. Reese, "Detailed Design of Reinforced Concrete Members," pp. 39–69 in Sec. 24 of R. W. Abbett (ed.), *American Civil Engineering Practice*, Vol. III, John Wiley & Sons, New York, 1957.
7. Phil M. Ferguson, "Analysis of Beam-and-Girder Framing With Known Column Settlements," *ACI Jour.*, **24**, Oct. 1952; *Proc.*, **49**, p. 77.

PROBLEMS

Prob. 8.1. The reduced frame of Fig. 8.16*b* should be used for the analysis of the second floor of the bent of Fig. 8.16*a* since standard coefficients are not applicable. Assume all the beams have $I = 30,000$ in.[4], the 16-in. columns

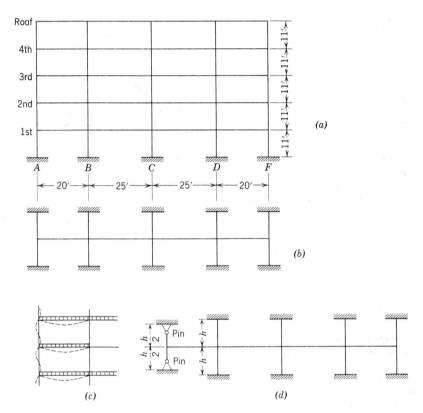

(a)

(b)

(c) *(d)*

Fig. 8.16. Analysis of building frame. *(a)* The frame considered. *(b)* Ordinary reduced frame for calculation of moments on a single floor. *(c)* Loading for maximum negative moment at exterior end of beam; also nearly maximum for exterior column moment. *(d)* Improved form of reduced frame for maximum moments at exterior joint.

below the floor have $I = 5450$ in.[4], and the 14-in. columns above the floor have $I = 3200$ in.[4] Each beam carries a dead load of 850 plf and a live load of 2150 plf.

(a) Calculate the maximum negative moment for the beam *BC* at *C* and correct this to the design moment at the face of the column. (Note that symmetry about *C* is equivalent to a fixed end for moment distribution purposes.)

(*b*) Calculate the maximum negative design moment at *B* of beam *BC*.

(*c*) Calculate the maximum positive moment for *BC*; also the minimum positive moment.

(*d*) Locate the several points of inflection that are useful in detailing steel.

(*e*) Compare the points of inflection in (*d*) with those which would be obtained if each moment diagram were assumed to be symmetrical about mid-span, as in Fig. 8.11*i*.

Prob. 8.2. In Prob. 8.1 calculate the corresponding maximum moments in span *AB* and the points of inflection needed. (For this end span the use of a symmetrical moment diagram is scarcely valid.)

Prob. 8.3. In Prob. 8.1 make the analyses for ultimate strength loads, assuming load factors of 1.2 for dead load and 2.4 for live load. In addition to parts (*a*) through (*e*), add the following:

(*f*) Compare these ultimate strength design moments to those found in Prob. 8.1 and note whether these ratios exceed the ratio of the ultimate load $1.2w_D + 2.4w_L$ to the working load $w_D + w_L$.

Prob. 8.4. In the frame of Prob. 8.1 calculate the maximum bending moment on column *B*:

(*a*) On the basis of the working loads.

(*b*) On the basis of the ultimate strength loads of Prob. 8.3.

Prob. 8.5. Repeat Prob. 8.4 for the exterior column *A*, using the reduced frame of Fig. 8.16*b*.

In addition, note that loads on successive floors as in Fig. 8.16*c* give a reverse bending condition in the exterior columns which is almost equivalent to the reduced frame of Fig. 8.16*d*. Recalculate column *A* moments and negative moment at *A* in beam *AB*:

(*c*) On the basis of working loads.

(*d*) On the basis of ultimate strength loads.

Prob. 8.6. Design an interior span of a continuous one-way slab supported on beams 15 ft 0 in. on centers using moment coefficients of Art. 701*c*, live load of 175 psf, no dead load except slab weight, $f_c' = 3000$ psi, intermediate grade steel, beam stems 11 in. wide, cover over center line of steel of 1.12 in. Carry the design through the choice and spacing of bars (same size bars for both positive and negative moment). Draw a lengthwise section of slab and sketch the bars in place, assuming no bars bent up.

Prob. 8.7. Assume the steel found in Table 8.1 for a typical interior span of the slab of Sec. 8.8 is to be arranged as shown in Fig. 8.10*b*, with half of the bottom bars bent up and extra straight top bars added over the support. Calculate all bend points and stop points (for a typical interior span).

Prob. 8.8. A continuous rectangular beam is to carry a uniform live load of 2000 plf plus its own weight over equal 20-ft spans. Supports may be considered of negligible width (knife edges). Design a typical interior span through the choice of beam size and the choice of reinforcing. Assume maximum $V = 1.05wL'/2$, $f_c' = 3750$ psi, intermediate grade steel. Show a cross section at support and at mid-span with detailed spacing of bars; also an elevation of beam showing the schematic arrangement (bending) of bars.   Exact bend points, and so forth, are not a part of this problem.

Prob. 8.9.   Design an intermediate span of one of a series of continuous T-beams spaced 10 ft 0 in. on centers to carry a 5-in. slab, live load of 200 psf, and its own weight over a 22-ft clear span, using $f_c' = 3000$ psi, intermediate grade steel, ACI moment coefficients, $V = 1.05wL'/2$.   It is suggested that the stem size be based on using $R' = 375$ at the support, and that a stem width of

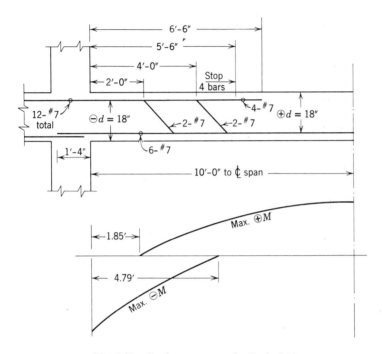

Fig. 8.17.   Steel arrangement for Prob. 8.13.

11.5 in. be first tried.   Stem weight may be assumed 250 plf without revision. Sketch the cross section at the support and at mid-span and also show the trial arrangement of longitudinal steel.

Prob. 8.10.   Assume that an interior span of a continuous beam with uniform live load has been designed for moment coefficients of -0.093 and $+0.067$, based on using the clear span of 21 ft.   The steel used is 10–#7 for negative moment, 7–#7 for positive moment, and 4–#7 for compression steel at the support.   Assume the columns are 16 in. square, $d - d' = 16.5$ in., $f_c' = 3000$ psi, $f_s = 20,000$ psi, and $f_s' = 16,000$ psi.   The M_2 couple represents 0.33 of the maximum negative moment.   Arrange the bars to be bent up, using a single bent bar nearest mid-span and then a pair of bent bars nearer the support. The offset distance between top and bottom steel may be taken as 16 in.   For

CONTINUOUS BEAMS AND ONE-WAY SLABS   227

location of points of inflection, the simplifying assumption of Fig. 8.11*i* may be used. Sketch the arrangement of steel and detail all bend and stop points. (If any bends fail to work out satisfactorily, note this fact and compromise lengths as seems best, but do not revise the bending scheme.) Show the results on a sketch similar to Fig. 8.12*b*.

Prob. 8.11. A typical interior span of a continuous beam of 20-ft clear span supported by 18-in. square columns and designed for uniform load moment coefficients of $-\frac{1}{12}$ and $+\frac{1}{16}$ (based on clear span) requires 9–#8 for negative moment, 6–#8 for positive moment, and 6–#8 for compression steel at the support. If $M_2 = 0.54$ of maximum negative moment, $f_c' = 3000$ psi, $f_s = 20,000$ psi, $f_s' = 13,000$ psi, and the offset distance between top and bottom steel is 14 in., sketch the steel arrangement and locate bend and stop points for bars. Record the results as in Fig. 8.12*b*.

Prob. 8.12. An interior 18-ft clear span of a continuous beam is loaded at its third points with concentrated loads P such that the uniform load may be neglected in establishing the shape of the moment diagram. Columns are 16 in. square. The maximum moments, including an allowance for uniform load, are $-0.25PL'$ and $+0.17PL'$. The negative moment is broken down into $M_1 = 0.42M$ and $M_2 = 0.58M$ for purposes of design. The bar offset between top and bottom steel is 15 in. The required number of #7 bars is 8 for negative moment A_s, 5 for compression steel A_s', and 5 for positive moment steel. $f_c' = 2500$ psi, $f_s = 20,000$ psi, $f_s' = 17,000$ psi. Arrange and detail the steel, attempting to bend at least two bars up from the bottom. Record the results as in Fig. 8.12*b*.

Prob. 8.13. If the bar arrangement of Fig. 8.17 is used, establish *for bond stress alone* what would be the limiting allowable uniform load *w* on the beam. Take $f_c' = 2500$ psf and maximum end $V = 1.05wL'/2$.

Two-Way Slabs
on
Beams or Walls

9.1. TYPES OF SLABS

The preceding chapter discussed one-way slabs simply as shallow beams. Actually, all one-way slabs carry cross steel to distribute temperature effects, to act as spacers for the main steel, and to act as distribution steel in the case of concentrated loads (Chap. 12). Most wide slabs designed as one-way slabs are constructed monolithically with girders along their edges and might more logically be designed as special cases of two-way slabs.

The usual two-way slab spans a square or rectangular panel, and this is the only case listed in the ACI Code. The supports on all sides are assumed relatively stiff, with deflections quite small compared to those of the slab. Article 709a suggests that slabs with fillers and two-way joist systems may be designed on the same basis. The two-way system implies that steel will be provided for calculated moments in two directions.

Triangular slabs and slabs supported on two adjacent edges are usually

229

two-way slabs, but such slabs are not mentioned in the Code. Slabs supported directly by columns without intervening beams (except at discontinuous edges) also have two-way reinforcement but are classified under the name flat slabs, flat plates, or slab band. Such slabs are discussed separately in Chap. 11.

9.2. ELASTIC ANALYSIS—MATHEMATICAL APPROACH

Two-way slabs, even single panels simply supported, require a three-dimensional approach for analysis. Such slabs are rarely statically determinate in their internal moments and shears. They are the most highly indeterminate of all ordinary structures.

Usually slabs have been analyzed as flat thin plates made of a homogeneous elastic material which has equal strength and stiffness in every direction, that is, an isotropic material. On this basis solutions for simple cases can be established from partial differential equations by the use of advanced mathematics. Westergaard[1, 2] was a pioneer in such analysis in this country.

Approximations must generally be introduced to handle practical cases. The use of difference equations has given reasonably accurate solutions for some problems. Not one of these methods even approaches a practical office procedure, but these solutions have provided theoretical boundaries of great value in assessing the merits of shorter and less accurate analyses.

9.3. TYPICAL MOMENT PATTERNS

Since the student cannot really analyze a slab except by arbitrary code provisions, it is desirable that he have a clear picture of the physical action of the slab. With a little imagination he should be able to visualize the general deflected shape taken by a uniformly loaded slab. A simply supported square slab will deflect into a saucerlike shape; and unless the corners are held down they will actually rise a little off the supports. An oblong slab will take a platterlike shape. A very long narrow slab will take a troughlike shape except near the ends. For fixed edges, there must be a transition zone around the edges in which the slope gradually turns downward from the horizontal edge tangents. If contours are roughly sketched, as in Fig. 9.1 for the simple supports, they give more than a clue to the moment pattern.

In a square slab, simply supported, a strip across the middle cuts the greatest number of contours and has the sharpest curvature and largest moment. In a long narrow slab only the short strips have significant curvature and bending over most of the panel length. The long center strip is essentially flat and without moment except near its ends.

In the continuous slab all slab strips in each direction have negative moments near the supports and positive moments near mid-span, as shown in Fig. 9.2a. The long center strip in a long narrow slab is an

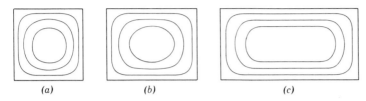

Fig. 9.1. Approximate contours for two-way slabs simply supported. (a) Square slab. (b) Oblong slab. (c) Long rectangular slab.

exception, or a special case, in that its positive moment occurs not at the center but at the point where the strip starts to curve upward; the moment over its mid-span length is small or zero (Fig. 9.2b) and the short center strips act almost exactly as one-way slabs.

Mathematical analysis shows that the negative moment on such a long strip is nearly the same regardless of the long span length. It is almost the

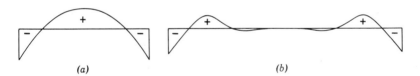

Fig. 9.2. Typical moment diagrams for continuous slabs. (a) Short span strip. (b) A very long strip, say, length three times width.

same as it would be for a square panel having the short span dimensions. Thus Method 2 of the ACI Code Art. 709 finds it most convenient to express *all* slab moments in terms of coefficients to be applied to wS^2 where S is the *short* span.

9.4. APPROXIMATE ANALYSES

Approximate analyses of slabs are usually somewhat crude, certainly so from the standpoint of the theoretical man or mathematician. Section 9.3

has indicated that the slab in each direction acts somewhat as a one-way slab. But these perpendicular slab strips of Fig. 9.3a are not independent in action. They share in carrying the load and thus each has smaller moments than a one-way slab. They must deflect the same total amount; hence their relative stiffness becomes a factor in establishing the load and the moment each must carry. With slab thickness a common factor, the longer span is the more flexible and carries the smaller moment and load.

The use of a *single* slab strip in each direction is obviously a crude analogy. The short span element across the middle of the panel deflects a much greater amount than a parallel strip alongside the edge beam; the edge strip can deflect little more than the beam. A better analysis would

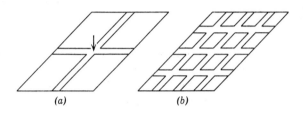

(a)   (b)

Fig. 9.3. The strip idea for two-way slabs. (a) Single intersecting strips. (b) Multiple intersecting strips.

result if the slab were considered as several strips in each direction, held to common deflections at their intersections, as in Fig. 9.3b. A still better approximation would consider torsional stiffness of these strips as well as their bending stiffness. Since three strips each way would give nine intersections, it should be noted that the labor of such an analysis increases at least with the square of the number of strips considered. Many simultaneous equations must be solved, one for each intersection, or many successive approximations must be tried for a solution. With enough strips, results closely equivalent to those obtained from the partial differential equation solution are found, but the labor is excessive.

Although elastic analyses of homogeneous isotropic plates provide much information that is helpful, they are exact solutions only for the assumed conditions. They do not recognize the fact that reinforcing steel is made lighter near the panel edges than at the center and that short span steel is heavier than long span steel. Nor do they recognize the changes in relative stiffness which result as cracked sections develop from the bending moment.

9.5. INELASTIC CONSIDERATIONS IN SLAB DESIGN

In a 1926 paper[2] Westergaard recommended moment coefficients which gave considerable weight to the nonelastic readjustments in slab moments which take place before failure. In recognition of these favorable readjustments, his recommended coefficients were established at 28% below strictly elastic values. This percentage reduction corresponds in a way to a similar reduction which had been accepted for flat slabs (Sec. 11.3), but it gives more recognition to maximum moment loadings. The ACI Code requirements fundamentally stem from Westergaard's recommendations.

Design practice and codes by no means attempt to design for the real distribution of bending moment existing across the slab under elastic conditions. This moment actually varies from element to element across a strip. If a square slab is considered as subdivided into 1-ft strips in a given direction, the center strip obviously has the sharpest curvature and largest moment. Curvature and moment on adjacent strips decrease gradually until alongside the edge beam the deflection, curvature, and moment all approach zero.

Such a slab does not collapse when the maximum moment raises the steel stress in a single narrow strip beyond its yield point. This one strip then simply becomes more flexible and leaves more of the additional load to be carried by adjacent elements less highly stressed. Before real failure can occur, all elements must be yielding in some fashion. (Chapter 10 discusses the yield-line analysis for the ultimate strength of slabs.)

This readjustment in stiffness and bending moment indicates that the steel does not have to be placed exactly in accordance with the elastic moment requirements. With its highly redundant system of supporting the load, the slab will, before failure, go far towards shifting the moments to the sections capable of resisting them. One can *almost* say that any arbitrary arrangement of steel, in sufficient quantity to carry the total load, will be developed before a slab completely fails.

At working loads, however, a poor distribution of slab steel may result in local yielding of the steel, large cracks, and increased deflection. For desirable action under working loads, steel should be placed at least roughly in accord with the moments existing at the working load; and these moments are more nearly the elastic analysis moments.

Engineering practice uses a uniform spacing of steel over the center strip (one-half the panel width in a square panel) and reduces the steel towards the edges of the panel. This uniform center strip steel is designed to take the *average* rather than the maximum moment on the center strip, as shown in Fig. 9.4 for a simply supported slab. Thus the working stress method takes considerable cognizance of modified behavior as failure approaches.

In spite of the fact that in practice approximate moments are used and the steel is actually designed for average moments rather than maximum, slabs have proved one of the most trustworthy structural elements and have stood up well under great abuse and overload.

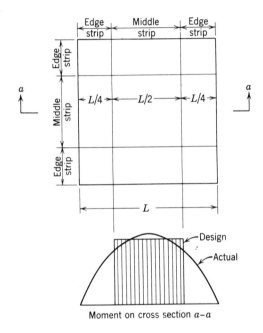

Fig. 9.4. Middle strip positive moment, slab simply supported. Comparison of actual and design moments.

9.6. SLAB DESIGN BY CODE

The ACI Code in Art. 709 presents two procedures for the design of two-way slabs for square and rectangular panels. Actually, two procedures are presented only for determining the moments and shears for such slabs and their supporting beams. When moments and shears are known, no new principles of design are necessary.

Method 1 of Art. 709 is the more detailed specification. It is a simplification of analyses originally prepared for the New York City Building Code and presented by Di Stasio and Van Buren[3] in 1936. The present simplified method by Bertin and the original authors[4] appeared in 1945.

The coefficients used agree closely with theoretical analyses. A design by this method is worked out in Secs. 9.9 and 9.10.

A simple table of moment coefficients, which originally appeared in the Joint Committee Specification of 1940, is given in Method 2. This method has been widely used in spite of the fact that it is more approximate than Method 1. It does not furnish the auxiliary information on beam bending moments and shears that is given with Method 1. Method 2 is illustrated in Secs. 9.11 and 9.12.

In studying either method, it will be noted that primary emphasis is placed on slabs having length-to-width ratios of 2 or less. When the length is twice the width, or more, the short span strip at the center acts essentially as a one-way slab and the typical two-way slab action is confined to regions nearer each short edge. It is sometimes stated that two-way slab design is only for slabs having a length-to-width ratio of 2 or less. A more correct statement would be that slabs with larger ratios may be designed as one-way slabs provided attention is also given to the negative moments over the short end beams.

9.7. STEEL PLACEMENT

The placing of two-way bottom steel over the entire slab and two-way top steel over the panel corners requires a planned sequence of placement, especially when bent bars are used. The short span bars, both for positive and negative moment, should be given the preferred positions near the slab surface in order to develop the maximum effective depth for this heavier steel (Fig. 9.5). Bars crossing each other may be placed in contact as shown. A sequence of bar placement which can be used* for two-way slabs (Fig. 9.6) is as follows:

1. Place all short span straight bottom bars.
2. Place all long span bars in the outer one-eighths of the short span. (The short span bars are usually bent up at about the one-eighth points of the span.)
3. Place all short span bent bars and accompanying straight top bars.

* Slab reinforcing bars are flexible and the projecting end of a bent bar can easily be forced into a plane one bar diameter above or below that which it occupies at the bend point. For this reason many designers feel it unnecessary to be as careful as the author about theoretical bar interference. The author's reasoning is as follows. When bars must be displaced because of interference, it requires close field inspection to see that the correct group of bars is displaced. The construction man frequently has no knowledge of the designer's desires in this respect. Proper placement is more apt to result if bars are detailed in such a way that the field man does not have to readjust the steel levels.

(The bent bars fit between the straight bars placed in step 1 and go over the top of the bent bars of step 2.)

4. Place all long span steel in the center three-quarters of the short span.

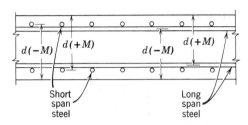

Fig. 9.5.   Steel arrangement in a two-way slab.

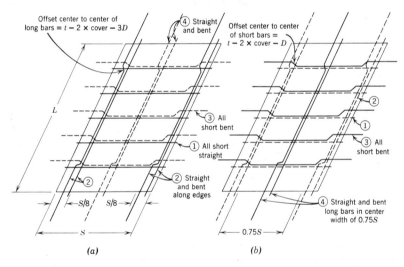

Fig. 9.6.   Skeleton placement pattern for two-way slab steel. (*a*) First two placements shown in solid lines and those to follow as dashed lines. (*b*) Last two placements shown by solid lines superimposed on earlier placements shown as dashed lines.

9.8. SLAB THICKNESS

Ordinarily the slab thickness for strength is governed by the negative moment on the short strip which gives $t_s = d_s + 0.5D +$ cover. However, another condition must be considered. Near the slab corners the foregoing placement sequence puts the long span bent-up bars *under* the

REINFORCED CONCRETE FUNDAMENTALS

short span bent-up bars. If the same height of long bent-up bars is maintained all across the slab, the other requirement for slab thickness* becomes $t_L = d_L + 1.5D + \text{cover}$. When slabs are nearly square, the required t_L will often be greater than t_s, not a very economical arrangement. In such cases the designer may choose to use an *average* value of $d = t - \text{cover} - D$, as in the case of the square slab discussed in the next paragraph; this procedure is equally logical.

A square slab has equal moments in each direction. If these moments were statically determined, instead of being highly redundant, the unequal depth to steel in the two directions would call for unequal steel areas, the less favorably placed layer being the heavier. However, tests have shown that slabs supported on four sides have a remarkable ability to carry load in the direction of strength, whether or not this strength is provided in accordance with elastic analysis. (See also the discussion of the yield-line method in Chap. 10.) Hence it is customary for designers to use the average $d = t - \text{cover} - D$ for designing both positive and negative steel in each direction for square panels.

In order to provide adequate stiffness and to avoid excessive deflection, the Code specifies the minimum slab thickness as not less than 4 in. or the perimeter of the slab divided by 180. This minimum thickness often exceeds that required for moment.

9.9. DESIGN OF TWO-WAY SLAB BY ACI CODE METHOD 1

A two-way slab (Fig. 9.7) for a typical interior panel 16 ft 0 in. by 17 ft 8 in. center to center of beams will be designed for a 12-psf finish and a 160-psf live load, using $f_c' = 3000$ psi and intermediate grade steel. Assume the beam webs are 11.5 in. wide on all sides and the columns are 14 in. square at all beam intersections. Code Method 1 will be used.

SOLUTION

By Art. 709d: Minimum $t \geqslant 4$ in.

Minimum $t \geqslant (\text{slab perimeter})/180$

---

* The most critical portion of the long span top steel is over the middle section of the short beams. At this point the top steel could easily be brought up one bar diameter closer to the top surface. Beyond each side of this section, approximately between the quarter and one-eighth points, the short span top steel could be depressed enough to put the long span top steel in this same more favorable position. The individual designer must decide whether (1) he wants to assign this readjustment to the field, (2) whether he wants to use the larger d near the center width and a smaller d near the edges, or (3) whether he wishes to follow the very conservative approach of using the smaller d for all the long span negative steel, as in this text.

Slab perimeter will be taken at the face of supporting members.

$$t \geq \frac{2(16 - 0.96) + 2(17.67 - 0.96)}{180} = 0.353 \text{ ft} = 4.24 \text{ in., say, } 4.5 \text{ in.}$$

Thickness for moment must be investigated and this makes it desirable to establish all design moments.

$$L = 15.04 \text{ ft} \qquad L_1 = 16.71 \text{ ft}$$

For the typical interior panel, Plan 6 in Fig. 1 of Code Art. 709 shows that the distances between points of inflection for only this span loaded are $gL = 0.76L$

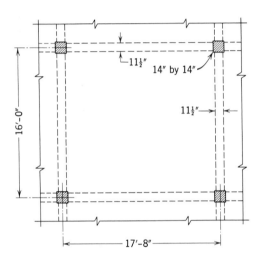

Fig. 9.7. Plan of slab designed in Sec. 9.9.

and $g_1L_1 = 0.76L_1$, thus establishing $r = gL/g_1L_1 = L/L_1 = 15.04/16.71 = 0.90$. This value of r in Table 1 gives $C = 0.40$ and $C_1 = 0.27$, indicating that moments on the short strip are to be taken as 0.40 times those for a one-way slab, and those on the long strips as 0.27 times those for one-way slabs, these one-way slab moments being based on Arts. 701 and 702. As a matter of convenience strips 1 ft wide will be used.

The moment coefficients shown in Art. 701 for interior spans are $+\frac{1}{16}$ and $-\frac{1}{11}$. Although the experienced designer could determine the one or two moments determining the slab thickness, all the design moments will be calculated here and interpreted in terms of their individual demands for slab thickness.

For a 4.5-in. slab,

$$w_s = 150 \times 4.5/12 = 56 \text{ psf}$$

$$w_T = 56 + 12 + 160 = 228 \text{ psf} = 228 \text{ plf}$$

REINFORCED CONCRETE FUNDAMENTALS

Short span: $L = 15.04$ ft

$$CWL = CwL^2 = 0.40 \times 228 \times 15.04^2 = 20{,}700 \text{ ft-lb}$$

Negative $M = -20{,}700 \times \frac{1}{11} = -1885$ ft-lb/ft

$$d_s = \sqrt{\frac{1885 \times 12}{236 \times 12}} = 2.82 \text{ in.}$$

$$t_s = 2.82 + 0.75 + 0.5D = 3.57 + 0.5D$$

If $D = 0.5$ in., $t_s = 3.57 + 0.25 = 3.82$ in. $<$ min. $t = 4.5$ in.

Positive $M = +20{,}700 \times \frac{1}{16} = +1290$ ft-lb/ft

$$d_s = \sqrt{\frac{1290 \times 12}{236 \times 12}} = 2.33 \text{ in.}$$

$$t_s = 2.33 + 0.75 + 0.5D = 3.08 + 0.5D < \text{min. } t = 4.5 \text{ in.}$$

Long span: $L_1 = 16.71$ ft

$$C_1 W_1 L_1 = C_1 w L_1{}^2 = 0.27 \times 228 \times 16.71^2 = 17{,}250 \text{ ft-lb}$$

Negative $M = -17{,}250 \times \frac{1}{11} = -1566$ ft-lb/ft

$$d_L = \sqrt{\frac{1566 \times 12}{236 \times 12}} = 2.57 \text{ in.}$$

$$t_L = 2.57 + 0.75 + 1.5D = 3.32 + 1.5D$$

If $D = 0.5$ in., $t_L = 3.32 + 0.75 = 4.07$ in. $<$ min. $t = 4.5$ in.

Positive $M = +17{,}250 \times \frac{1}{16} = +1075$ ft-lb/ft

$$d_L = \sqrt{\frac{1075 \times 12}{236 \times 12}} = 2.13 \text{ in.}$$

$$t_L = 2.13 + 0.75 + 1.5D = 2.88 + 1.5D < \text{min. } t = 4.5 \text{ in.}$$

The minimum t of 4.5 in. governs throughout.

USE $t = 4.5$ in.

If the minimum t had been smaller, the thickness would have been controlled by $t_L = 4.07$ in., based on negative moment for the long span. **Before going to** $t = 4.25$ in. or 4.50 in., the author would have recalculated t_s and t_L on the basis of using an average d, as discussed in Sec. 9.8:

$$t_s = 3.57 + D = 4.07 \text{ in. for } \#4 \text{ bars}$$
$$t_L = 3.32 + D = 3.82 \text{ in. for } \#4 \text{ bars}$$

Although this still seems to demand t greater than 4 in., comparison with the original calculations shows that intermediate values of d could be used which would approach the average d idea and leave $t = 4$ in.:

$$d_s = 4.00 - 0.75 - 0.43 = 2.82 \text{ in., which deducts } 0.86D$$
$$d_L = 4.00 - 0.75 - 0.57 = 2.68 \text{ in., which deducts } 1.14D$$

For panel shapes still further from a square, it is necessary to calculate only the thickness for the short span negative moment, since it will control, subject only to minimum thickness requirements.

TWO-WAY SLABS ON BEAMS OR WALLS

TABLE 9.1. Steel Calculation for Slab of Sec. 9.9

For $D = 0.50$ in. (#4): Short Span   Long Span

	Short Span Neg. M	Short Span Pos. M	Long Span Neg. M	Long Span Pos. M
d	3.50	3.50	3.00	3.00
M (ft-lb/ft)	1885	1290	1566	1075
$jd = 0.866d$	3.03	3.03	2.60	2.60
$A_s = \dfrac{M \times 12}{20{,}000jd}$, in.²/ft	0.372	0.255	0.362	0.248
$0.0025bd$, in.²/ft	0.105	0.105	0.090	0.090
Spcg. #4 ($3t = 13.5$ in.)	6.45	9.44	6.64	9.66
USE #4 at	9 in. (bent) = 0.267	9 in. (bend half)	9 in. (bent) = 0.267	9 in. (bend half)
plus #3 at	12 in. (str.) = 0.11		12 in. (str.) = 0.11	
	0.38		0.38	

Long $A_s >$ short $A_s/3$ O.K.
[Art. 709, Method 1c(1)]

For students there is some advantage in tabulating A_s calculations as in Table 9.1. In the illustrations in Table 9.1 bars are shown only part way across a section when these bars occur only near the corners of the panel or near the edges of the middle strips. Some engineers would prefer to tabulate the total moment in each strip and thus obtain the total number of bars per strips as in Table 11.1. Table 9.1, however, uses moment on 1-ft strips and obtains bar spacings instead of numbers of bars.

The positive moment steel may be reduced by 25% in zones alongside beams for a width of one-quarter of the shorter span, or $15.04/4 = 3.76$ ft. This will be achieved by omitting alternate straight bars in these zones.

USE: For 3 ft 9 in. strip alongside each beam, OMIT alternate straight bars.

Bend up the bent bars at the points of inflection for the one span loaded,* that is, at $0.38L$ or $0.38L_1$ from mid-span, as indicated in Fig. 9.8. At the bend point on the short strip, average $V = C_s W = (0.19 - 0.016)228 \times 15.04 = 596$ lb/ft width. Estimate maximum V per ft as 50% higher, 75% on square slabs.

$$\text{On bottom bars, } u = \frac{596 \times 1.5}{1.57 \times \frac{12}{9} \times \frac{7}{8} \times 3.5} = 151 \text{ psi}$$

On top bars not bent down the equivalent steel in terms of #4 bars (see Sec. 6.2b for mixed bar sizes) = $\frac{12}{18} + 0.11/0.20 = 1.22$ bars; $\Sigma o' = 1.22 \times 1.57 = 1.92$ in.

$$\text{On #4 bars, } u = \frac{596 \times 1.5}{1.92 \times 0.875 \times 3.5} = 153 \text{ psi}$$

* Newmark and Siess[5] suggest this point of inflection be taken as $L/6$ from the support both for short and long spans.

At the support on short span top bars:

$$\text{Average } V = 0.29W = 0.29 \times 228 \times 15.04 = 1000 \text{ lb/ft}$$

$$\Sigma o' = (\tfrac{1.2}{9} + 0.11/0.20)1.57 = 1.88 \times 1.57 = 2.95 \text{ in.}$$

$$\text{On } \#4 \text{ bars, } u = \frac{1000 \times 1.5}{2.95 \times 0.875 \times 3.5} = 165 \text{ psi}$$

A bond check on long steel is scarcely needed but will be made using the tabulated C_{s1} coefficients.

At P.I., that is, $x = 0.12L'$, $C_{s1} = (0.13 - 0.012) = 0.118$

(Note that Ref. 5 suggests $x = L/6 = 15.04/6 = 2.51 \text{ ft} = 0.151L'$.)

$$\text{Average } V = 0.118 \times 228 \times 16.71 = 450 \text{ lb/ft}$$

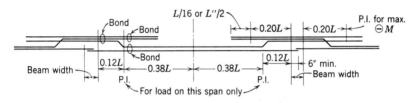

Fig. 9.8. Slab bar arrangement with points where bond could be critical.

At this point top steel is half of total bottom steel, $\#4$ at 18 in., plus $\#3$ at 12 in. Equivalent $\#4$ bars for bond stress $= \tfrac{1.2}{18} + 0.11/0.20 = 1.22$ bars.

$$u_{\text{top}} = \frac{450 \times 1.5}{1.22 \times 1.57 \times 0.875 \times 3} = 135 \text{ psi}$$

At support, $V = 0.21 \times 228 \times 16.71 = 802 \text{ lb/ft}$

Equivalent $\#4$ bars $= \tfrac{1.2}{9} + 0.11/0.20 = 1.88$ bars

$$u = \frac{802 \times 1.5}{1.88 \times 1.57 \times 0.875 \times 3} = 154 \text{ psi}$$

Shear for diagonal tension is also small. Average V (short strip) $= 1000$ lb

$$v = \frac{1000 \times 1.5}{12 \times 0.875 \times 3.5} = 40.8 \text{ lb}$$

9.10. BEAMS FOR TWO-WAY SLABS—METHOD 1

The Code in effect calls attention to the fact that the total moment in a given direction is shared by the slab and beam. In the short (L) direction, $M = (1 - C)BWL$, where B is the usual beam moment coefficient. The beam receives essentially its full part of the panel load but its span between columns is slightly less than the panel length.   The coefficient C is that used in evaluating the slab moment.

$$M = B(1 - 0.4)(228 \times 16.71 \times 15.04)(16 - 1.17) = 510,000B$$

To this must be added the moment due to the full weight of the beam plus the live load directly on it.   For the moment coefficient of $-\frac{1}{11}$, an assumed total beam weight of 150 psf, and an actual live load and finish of $172 \times 11.5/12 = 165$ plf, the total negative moment for the short beam is:

$$-510,000 \times \tfrac{1}{11} \qquad\qquad = -46,300$$
$$-\tfrac{1}{11}(150 + 165)(16 - 1.17)^2 = -\ 6,300$$

$$\text{Neg. } M = -52,600 \text{ ft-lb}$$

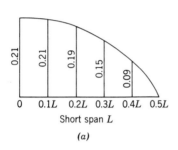

Short span L

(a)

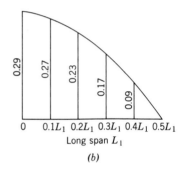

Long span L_1

(b)

Fig. 9.9.   Shear coefficients for beams supporting two-way slabs.   (a) Short span coefficients.   (b) Long span coefficients.

For a positive moment coefficient of $+\frac{1}{16}$, by proportion,

$$\text{Pos. } M = \tfrac{11}{16} \times 52,600 = 36,200 \text{ ft-lb}$$

The beam design from this point is entirely typical except for recognition of the fact that the load is not uniformly distributed along the beam; it is larger near mid-span.   Table 2 in Code Art. 709 is helpful for beam shears.   For $r = 0.90$, the shear coefficient C_b for the short span has been plotted in Fig. 9.9a.   These coefficients apply to the total panel load from the slab, that is, $V_b = C_b w L L_1$.   The shear from the beam's weight and the live load directly over the beam must be added to the shear from the slab load.   The maximum beam shear is:

$$0.21 \times 228 \times 15.04 \times 16.71 = 12,050$$
$$(150 + 165)(16 - 1.17)/2 = \ \ 2,330$$

$$V = 14,380 \times 1.05 = 15,100 \text{ lb}$$

To be consistent with the author's recommendation in Chap. 8, this shear has been increased 5% to represent the shear due to beam continuity in an interior panel.

The shape of the shear diagrams causes a more gradual increase in stirrup spacing away from the column than would be used for a beam uniformly loaded. Likewise, there results a moment diagram with a little sharper peak near mid-span, requiring slightly longer negative moment steel and permitting a small reduction in positive moment steel lengths.

The long span beam has moment and shears (Fig. 9.9b) established in similar fashion. Assume the beam weight is 200 plf.

$$M = B(1 - 0.27)(228 \times 16.71 \times 15.04)(17.67 - 1.17) = 693,000B$$

For negative moment:

Slab load $M = -693,000 \times \frac{1}{11}$ $\qquad = -63,000$

Direct load $M = -(200 + 165) \times 16.5^2/11 = -9,040$

$\qquad\qquad\qquad\qquad$ Neg. $M\ = -72,000$ ft-lb

Slab load $V = 0.29 \times 228 \times 16.71 \times 15.04 = \quad 16,700$

Direct load $V = (200 + 165) \times 16.5/2 \qquad = \quad 3,010$

$\qquad\qquad\qquad$ Max. $V = 1.05 \times 19,700 = 20,700$ lb

9.11. DESIGN OF TWO-WAY SLABS BY ACI METHOD 2

The typical interior span slab of Sec. 9.9 and Fig. 9.7 will be redesigned by Method 2.

SOLUTION

If the perimeter of the slab is defined as the clear span perimeter, the minimum thickness requirement will be unchanged from that for Method 1, namely, $t = 4.5$ in.

For design purposes, the slab is divided into middle and column strips as shown in Fig. 9.10a. (When $m = S/L < 0.5$, the middle strip is defined somewhat differently, with a width $L - S$, as shown in Fig. 9.10b.) The middle strip moments govern most of the design. The necessary moment coefficients, in terms of wS^2 for a 1-ft strip, are given in Table 3 of Art. 709 for various values of $m = S/L$. Case 1 represents the typical interior span coefficients.

By definition S and L are defined as center to center of supports or the clear span plus $2t$ if this is smaller.

$$S = 16.0 - 0.96 + 2 \times 0.375 = 15.79 \text{ ft} < 16.0$$
$$L = 17.67 - 0.96 + 2 \times 0.375 = 17.46 \text{ ft} < 17.67$$
$$m = S/L = 15.79/17.46 = 0.905, \text{ say } 0.90$$

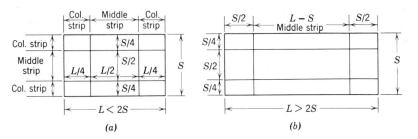

Fig. 9.10. Column and middle strips for ACI Method 2. (*a*) Long span < 2S. (*b*) Long span > 2S.

TABLE 9.2. Depth and Steel Calculation for Slab of Sec. 9.11

For $D = 0.50$ in. (#4): Short Span   Long Span

$wS^2 = 57,000$ ft-lb	Neg. M	Pos. M	Neg. M	Pos. M
Middle Strip				
M coefficient	0.040	0.030	0.033	0.025
Moment, ft-lb	2280	1710	1880	1420
Min. $d = \sqrt{M/236}$	3.12	2.70	2.82	2.46
Cover	0.75	0.75	0.75	0.75
For #4 bars	0.25	0.25	0.75*	0.75*
Min. t	4.12	3.70	4.32	3.96
Actual d for $t = 4.5$	3.50	3.50	3.00	3.00
$A_s = \dfrac{M \times 12}{20,000 \times 0.866d}$, in.²/ft	0.452	0.338	0.435	0.328
$0.0025bd$ min.	0.105	0.105	0.090	0.090
Spcg. of #4	5.33	7.10	5.53	7.33
(Max. = $3t = 13.5$ in.)				
USE #4 at:†	7 in. (bent) = 0.343	7 in. (bend half)	7 in. (bent) = 0.343	7 in. (bend half)
plus #3 at 12 in. (str.)	= 0.110		14 in. (str) = 0.095	
	0.453		0.438	
Column Strips				
Strip width, ea. side	16.71/4 = 4.18 ft		15.04/4 = 3.76 ft	
Reqd. A_s (in width above)	1.26	0.95	1.09	0.82
USE no. of #4, ea. side	4 bent 3 str. (1.40)	2 bent 3 str. (1.00)	4 bent 2 str. (1.20)	2 bent 3 str. (1.00)
Approx. max. spcg.	10.7 in.	13.5 in.	11.3 in.	13.5 in.

* This allowance could be reduced to $D/2$ for the middle strip only, not for column strips.

† Some would prefer to calculate the total A_s in the middle strip and specify the total number o bars, as in Table 11.1.

Moment coefficients:

Short span: Neg. $M = -0.040wS^2$ Pos. $M = +0.030wS^2$

Long span: Neg. $M = -0.033wS^2$ Pos. $M = +0.025wS^2$

With the 4.5-in. slab, $w_T = 160 + 12 + 56 = 228$ psf $= 228$ plf

$$wS^2 = 228 \times 15.79^2 = 57,000 \text{ ft-lb}$$

The entire calculation for the slab thickness and the required steel is given in Table 9.2. The experienced designer would find it necessary to calculate the required depth only for one or two sections. The cross sections in the table show assumed bar arrangements which are consistent with the placement sequence specified in Sec. 9.7. Where bars occur only near the edges of the middle strip or near the corners of the panel, they are shown only part way across the sketch.

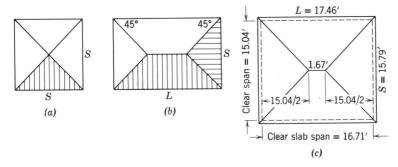

Fig. 9.11. Slab load areas to beams. (*a*) Square slab. (*b*) Oblong slab. (*c*) Load areas for beams of Sec. 9.12.

Rather than calculate steel per foot and specify the bar spacing, some prefer to calculate total steel in the middle strip and specify the total number of bars, as shown in Table 11.1 for a flat slab.

Method 2 provides that column strips, which might better be called edge strips, may be designed for two-thirds as much moment on a 1-ft strip as is used for the middle strip. The half column strip on each side will be $16.71/4 = 4.18$ ft wide for the short strips and $15.04/4 = 3.76$ ft wide for the long strips. In these strips the steel spacing could vary from the spacing of the middle strip to a maximum of three times this spacing at the edge of the panel, thus maintaining an average of two-thirds as much steel per foot. Instead, the maximum spacing of $3t$ could control here. Because of the varying spacing, the calculations for the edge strips have been based on total steel in each half column strip. The maximum spacing based on 1.50 times the average spacing has been tabulated to be careful that this stays under $3t = 13.5$ in.

Bond and shear stresses are not expected to be critical in a slab such as this one but can be calculated in much the same way as for Method 1 (Sec. 9.9). The Code suggests that the load going to each beam be calculated from the contributing areas shown in Fig. 9.11. For this slab the dimensions are shown in Fig. 9.11*c*.

TWO-WAY SLABS ON BEAMS OR WALLS   **245**

It would be conservative (possibly overly so) to take $V = wS/2$ since the clear span could be used and the shear could be averaged over at least a couple of feet and probably more. On the long strips or on a square slab this average shear would be less than $wS/2$.

$$V_s < 228 \times 15.79/2 = 1800 \text{ lb, on short strip}$$
$$v < 1800/(12 \times 0.875 \times 3.5) = 49 \text{ psi} < 90$$

It appears that bond will be maximum on the top bars just beyond the point where bars are bent down. There the top steel is #4 bars at 7 in. plus #3 at 12 in. Assume the bars are bent up at $S/6$, which is at the point of inflection suggested in Ref. 5. On the short strip, at this point of inflection (theoretically at $d/3$ beyond the bend-down point):

$$V < 228 \times 15.79 \times 0.333 = 1200 \text{ lb}$$
$$\text{Equivalent #4 bars} = \tfrac{12}{7} + 0.11/0.20 = 2.27 \text{ bars/ft}$$
$$\Sigma o = 2.27 \times 1.57 = 3.55$$
$$u < 1200/(3.55 \times 0.88 \times 3.5) = 110 \text{ psi}$$

If the point of inflection should shift closer to the support, the bond stress on the bottom steel would be based on the unbent bottom bars, that is, #4 at 14 in. having $\Sigma o = 1.57 \times \tfrac{12}{14} = 1.34$ in.

$$u < 1200/(1.34 \times 0.88 \times 3.5) = 292 \text{ psi}$$

Although this stress is less than the Code allowable of 300 psi, it is too close to this limit to leave a liberal allowance for weakness in splitting. Since this contingency is easy to avoid, bars will be bent up at $0.12S$ or $0.12L$ from the support instead of at $S/6$ as first suggested. This reduces the bond stress on bottom steel by doubling the perimeter with only a small increase in shear. The increase in the small bond stress on the top bars creates no problem.

No further bond calculations appear to be needed. The student is referred to Sec. 9.9 for a more thorough check on bond which can serve as a model for points theoretically needing investigation.

9.12. BEAMS FOR TWO-WAY SLABS—METHOD 2

Beam loads can be calculated from the contributing areas of Fig. 9.11c, interior beams picking up loads from each adjacent slab. No further information is needed for the beam design but the Code lists the equivalent *uniform* load from *each* slab to be used for moment alone:

$$\text{For short span} = \frac{wS}{3}$$

$$\text{For long span} = \frac{wS}{3}\frac{(3 - m^2)}{2}$$

The moments and end shears will be calculated for the beam supporting the slab of Sec. 9.11 to permit comparison with the Method 1 values in

Sec. 9.10. For this purpose clear spans will be used both for the slab and beams and the extra load directly over the beams will be added separately.

For the short span the beam weight will be assumed 150 plf.

Equivalent w plf for $M = 2wS/3 + 150 + 0.96(160 + 12)$

$$= 2 \times 228 \times 15.04/3 + 150 + 165 = 2600 \text{ plf}$$

Neg. $M = -\frac{1}{11} \times 2600(16 - 1.17)^2 = -51,800 \text{ ft-lb}$

Pos. $M = 51,800(\frac{1}{16})/(\frac{1}{11}) = 51,800 \times \frac{11}{16} = 35,500 \text{ ft-lb}$

$$V = 2 \times \frac{228}{2} \times \frac{15.04}{2} \times \frac{15.04}{2} + (150 + 165)\frac{14.83}{2}$$

$$= 12,900 + 2330 = 15,230 \text{ lb on simple span}$$

$V = 1.05 \times 15,230 = 15,900 \text{ lb, allowing for continuity}$

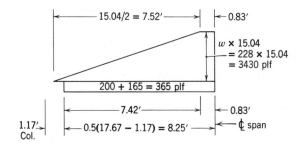

Fig. 9.12. Load on the long span beam between two slabs.

On the long span, assume the beam weight is 200 plf.

Equivalent w plf for $M = \dfrac{wS}{3}\dfrac{(3 - m^2)}{2} + 200 + 165$

$$= 2 \times \frac{228 \times 15.04}{3} \times \frac{(3 - 0.90^2)}{2} + 365 = 2860 \text{ plf}$$

Neg. $M = -\frac{1}{11} \times 2860(17.67 - 1.17)^2 = -70,800 \text{ ft-lb}$

From Fig. 9.12

$$V_s = 365 \times 8.25 + 3430 \times 0.83 + 0.5 \times 3430 \times 7.52$$

$$= 3020 + 2840 + 12,900 = 18,760 \text{ lb on simple span}$$

$V = 1.05 \times 18,760 = 19,600 \text{ lb, allowing for continuity}$

TWO-WAY SLABS ON BEAMS OR WALLS

9.13. FREELY SUPPORTED SLAB CORNERS

Two-way slabs supported on steel beams or masonry walls are designed by the same methods as those built monolithically with their supports. However, a special problem arises at the exterior corners of simply supported slabs which are not securely fastened down. Such corners rise off their supports under load and can create a horizontal crack in masonry walls in which they may be embedded. This is especially the case with roof slabs carrying parapet walls. Code Art. 709*b* calls for special reinforcement at free corners. Probably a better solution is to anchor such corners down (to a substantial mass of masonry, for example) and to provide reinforcing steel for the restraining moment thus developed.

9.14. TESTS ON TWO-WAY SLABS

Two-way slab specifications have originated from theoretical studies with some relaxation for the design moments because of test data which indicated lower steel stresses. The author is among those who question the validity of these stresses, feeling that the interpretation of the data failed to differentiate properly between average stress and maximum stress at a crack. Nevertheless, there is little question but that slabs as now designed have a large factor of safety.

Newmark and Siess[5, 6] have proposed some liberalization in the combined beam and slab design, with the stated objective of bringing the design of two-way and flat slabs into better agreement. Chapter 11 discusses flat slabs and points out that the basis for their design is considerably different, that is, apparently much less conservative. The Reinforced Concrete Research Council and others have initiated a 5-year study and test program on slabs with the objective of developing consistent design procedures for slabs of the various types. Such procedures should assure equal factors of safety for all types of slabs.

SELECTED REFERENCES

1. H. M. Westergaard and W. A. Slater, "Moments and Stresses in Slabs," *ACI Proc.*, **17,** 1921, p. 415.

2. H. M. Westergaard, "Formulas for the Design of Rectangular Floor Slabs and the Supporting Girders," *ACI Proc.*, **22,** 1926, p. 26.

3. J. Di Stasio and M. P. Van Buren, "Slabs Supported on Four Sides," *ACI Jour.*, **7**, No. 3, Jan.-Feb. 1936; *Proc.*, **32**, p. 350.

4. R. L. Bertin, Joseph Di Stasio, and M. P. Van Buren, "Slabs Supported on Four Sides," *ACI Jour.*, **16**, No. 6, June 1945; *Proc.*, **41**, p. 537.

5. N. M. Newmark and C. P. Siess, "Rational Analysis and Design for Two-Way Floor Slabs," *ACI Jour.*, **20**, No. 4, Dec. 1948; *Proc.*, **45**, p. 273.

6. N. M. Newmark and C. P. Siess, "Proposed Design Specifications for Two-Way Floor Slabs," *ACI Jour.*, **21**, No. 8, Apr. 1950; *Proc.*, **46**, p. 597.

PROBLEMS

Prob. 9.1. Explain why it is less advantageous to use a higher strength concrete in a two-way slab than in a column.

Prob. 9.2. Design an interior span of a two-way slab for a panel 18 ft by 21 ft (to centers of supporting beams), assuming beam stems are 12 in. wide, $f_c' = 3000$ psi, steel is intermediate grade, live load is 150 psf, and there is no dead load except slab weight. Use Method 1 or 2 as directed.

Prob. 9.3. Design an exterior panel (not at a corner) for the conditions of Prob. 9.2.

Prob. 9.4. Design a corner slab for the conditions for Prob. 9.2.

Prob. 9.5.

(*a*) As though in preparation for a moment distribution analysis, calculate the fixed end moment for a beam supporting the 21-ft side of adjacent two-way slabs exactly as in Prob. 9.2 except that the *total* slab load ($D + L$) is 225 psf. Assume the beam stem below the slab weighs 150 plf and that columns 15 in. square exist at each beam intersection. Use the beam loading specified for Method 2 and shown in Fig. 9.11. (Area moment solution is suggested instead of the use of the equivalent uniform load stated in the Code.)

(*b*) Compare with (*a*) the fixed end beam moment developed by one-way slabs of 18-ft span on the same fixed end beam, neglecting any change in the slab weight.

(*c*) Compare also the positive moments for the fixed end beams in (*a*) and (*b*).

(*d*) What is the ratio of the moment specified under Method 1, for beams carrying two-way slabs, to the moment specified for beams carrying one-way slabs? Compare this ratio with those found in (*b*) and (*c*).

Prob. 9.6.

(*a*) Design the interior panel of the 21-ft span beam between the two-way slabs of Prob. 9.2, taking the *total* slab load as 225 psf (unless a better value has been established) and assuming 15-in. columns. Use Method 1 or 2 as instructed.

(*b*) Establish the stirrup spacing curve for this beam.

Prob. 9.7. Repeat Prob. 9.6 for the 18-ft beams.

Prob. 9.8. Design a 21-ft square interior panel of a two-way slab, assuming beam stems are 12 in. wide, $f_c' = 3000$ psi, intermediate grade steel, live load of 200 psf. Use Method 1 or 2 as directed.

Prob. 9.9. Design the corner panel of the slab of Prob. 9.8.

Yield-Line Theory for Slabs

10.1. YIELD-LINE THEORY AS A DESIGN GUIDE

Although the yield-line theory for slabs has been well developed and well verified by tests, the large bulk of this material is not available in English. Most of Johansen's work[1,2] is in Danish. Ingerslev's paper[3] on rectangular slabs in 1923, Johansen's brief paper[4] in 1948, a short outline by Craemer[5] in 1950, and his paper[6] on rectangular slabs in 1952 represent the literature available in English prior to 1953; none had appeared in American publications. In 1953 Hognestad summarized[7] some of Johansen's work and this paper has constituted the chief source material for this discussion.

Although the yield-line theory is not recognized by the ACI Code and is little known to engineers in this country, this chapter is entirely devoted to this one subject. The reason for such emphasis is a practical one. The student and the usual structural designer, in connection with two-way

251

slabs and irregular slabs, find in the codes only a few rules and coefficients for regular panel conditions. The exact elastic analysis of such slabs is beyond their ability and irregular cases are too difficult even for the expert. In comparison, the yield-line method is straightforward, reasonably simple, and emphasizes the lines of highest stress. It is adaptable to irregular cases. In short, it is a method the ordinary engineer can use.

Yield-line analysis is an ultimate strength method. The designer must assume a liberal load factor so long as he has no code to guide him. He must keep in mind that slab deflection is quite large before failure. It is possible that when the method is written into codes in this country, some of the ultimate slab strength will be discounted because of large deflections, just as engineers discount that portion of structural steel strength which lies between the yield point and the ultimate. This is equivalent to saying that larger load factors may be specified for such slab design. The yield-line analysis deals with moment alone; it does not assure adequate strength in diagonal tension.

Tests in Europe have closely verified the yield-line analysis. Hognestad reports that the calculated ultimate load underestimates the actual test results, being usually only 80% to 90% of the true capacity. Unfortunately, not much of this test material is printed in English. Nevertheless, it appears that engineers may use the yield-line method with confidence; it gives a conservative estimate of strength in moment.

The real concern of the designer using this method will be to establish that his slabs will be entirely satisfactory at working loads. The Danish code has for some time permitted a form of ultimate strength design for slabs. It is the author's understanding that design for ultimate strength alone does not necessarily lead to acceptable slabs. The deflection and stiffness of such slabs may not be satisfactory. Evidently these specific matters must be investigated or limited by establishing maximum L/t ratios.

Ultimate strength design based on the readjustment of moments after yielding has thus far not been recognized in the ACI Code. However, there has been some indirect recognition of similar readjustments that take place in other structural elements. Two-way isolated column footing tests have definitely shown that steel under the column must yield considerably before all the steel across the footing takes its share of the stress. In spite of this, such footings are designed for uniform distribution of steel. As a second example, the design of slab steel in two-way slabs and flat slabs does not attempt to distribute steel in exact proportion to the elastic moment. Rather, the steel is uniformly distributed over half the slab width and its amount is based on average rather than maximum moments.

The author expects ultimate strength design of slabs to be recognized specifically in codes in the not too distant future.

10.2. BASIC IDEAS OF YIELD-LINE THEORY

(a) Angle changes at yielding

The yield-line theory, like limit design (Appendix C), is an ultimate strength theory. Slabs are normally underreinforced, with much less steel than a balanced section (at failure). As a result, on progressive loading the steel reaches its yield-point stress before the slab reaches its ultimate strength. As the steel yields, the center of compression on the cross section moves nearer the face of the slab until finally a secondary failure in compression takes place, at a moment only slightly greater than the yield-point moment.

For a one-way simple span slab, the increase in moment after the steel starts to yield is not large, in the order of 5% to 10%, but the further angle change ϕ occurring at the point of maximum moment is quite large in comparison with the "elastic" angle change. Relative values can be shown as an M-ϕ curve, as in Fig. A.10 of Appendix A.

In a statically indeterminate slab these extra angle changes permit (or cause) significant modifications of the resisting moments and shears. Yielding at one point in such a slab marks the gradual beginning of larger deflections but by no means marks the end of reliable load capacity.

(b) Yield lines as axes of rotation

Yielding under increasing load progresses to form lines of yielding. Until yield lines are formed in sufficient numbers to break up the slab into segments which can form a collapse mechanism, additional load can be supported. To act as hinges for a collapse mechanism, yield lines must usually be straight lines. (Actually, it would be more accurate to say that yielding zones develop on the tension face over narrow bands as in Fig. 10.1a and the yield line is an idealization in which all of the angle change is considered on a line at the center of the yielding bands, as in Fig. 10.1b.) Yield lines are axes of rotation for the movements of the several parts of the final mechanism. Yield lines form at lines of maximum moment, but this action is not restricted to those maximum moment lines originally developed under initial "elastic" conditions.

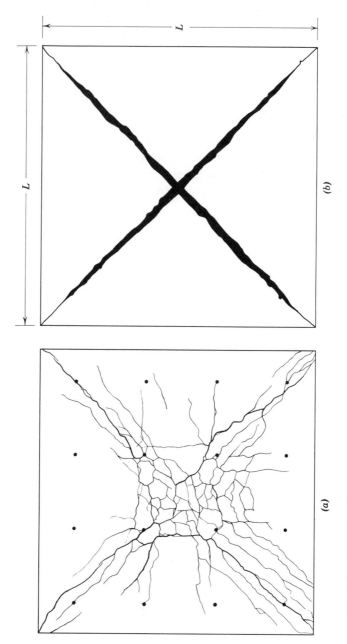

(a)   *(b)*

Fig. 10.1. Yield lines in a square slab on stiff beams. (*a*) Actual cracking at failure. (*b*) Assumed "yield lines" or "fracture lines." (These figures are copied by permission from *Reinforced Concrete Review.*[8])

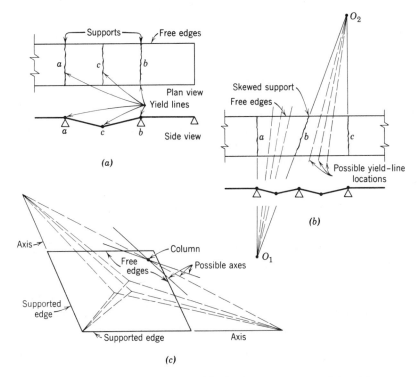

Fig. 10.2. Yield-line patterns. (*a*) Continuous one-way slab, right supports at *a* and *b*. (*b*) Continuous slab with a skewed support at *b*. (*c*) Slab supported on two adjacent edges and a column.

(c) Interrelationships between axes of rotation

The supports of a slab determine some of the axes of rotation of the several slab segments. In general, each support line constitutes an axis of rotation and each separate column support constitutes a pivot point, that is, a point on an axis of rotation. For example, a one-way continuous slab in a given span must fail by the development of yield lines at each support acting together with an intermediate yield line which is dependent upon the loading, as indicated in Fig. 10.2*a*. (This might be compared to the local collapse mechanism of Fig. C.3 in the limit design discussion in Appendix C. The yield-line analysis is a limit design procedure as applied to slabs.)

Consider a continuous slab with a skewed support *b* as shown in Fig. 10.2*b*. With a yield line over two adjacent supports such as *a* and *b*, one segment rotates about *a* and one about *b*; and the common yield line between the segments joins material rotating about both these axes.

YIELD-LINE THEORY FOR SLABS   255

Hence the common yield line must lie on an axis through O_1 at the intersection point of a and b extended. Which of the possible dashed axes through O_1 will develop depends upon the reinforcement and type of loading on the span. Likewise, for collapse in span bc, the third yield line must pass through O_2.

In Fig. 10.2c a slab is shown supported on two adjacent sides and a column. The general pattern of failure will be as indicated, but the axis through the column is at an unknown angle and the yield-line intersection point in the slab depends upon the loading and upon whether the supported edges are simple supports or are lines of negative moment resistance.

(d) Segments as free bodies to verify yield-line locations

The free body represented by each collapsing segment must be in equilibrium under (1) its applied loads, (2) the yield moments on each yield line, and (3) the reaction or shear on support lines. Since the intermediate yield lines form at lines of maximum moment, neither shear nor torsion can be present along these lines. The yield-line moments establish the load the segments can support, as indicated in Fig. 10.3. For a uniformly loaded slab, the location of the intermediate yield lines must subdivide the slab into segments each of which support the same uniform ultimate load w_u.

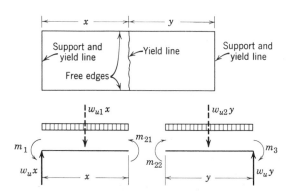

Fig. 10.3. Free body diagrams for verification of yield-line location.

If, for given values of yield moments m_1, m_2, and m_3 and a given trial location of the yield line, the calculated w_u values for the separate segments differ, the yield line must lie in a different position. The real location must be such as to reduce the segment size where the calculated w_u is smaller and to increase segment size where the calculated w_u is larger. The correct location is a unique location for a given loading.

REINFORCED CONCRETE FUNDAMENTALS

For design purposes, it may be convenient to take as the known quantity the load times the desired load factor. Then, with the segments as the free bodies, the required yield moments may be calculated. At a given yield line the moment thus found for one segment must match that from the adjoining segment, that is, m_{21} must be the same as m_{22}; otherwise the yield line is incorrectly located.

When only one yield line remains to be located, an algebraic equation can be solved for a governing dimension, but in more complex cases this may not be as simple as a cut-and-try procedure.

(e) Virtual work or energy-mechanism criterion

If a slab has been reduced to a mechanism by yield lines acting as hinges, a known additional deflection of any specific point in the mechanism (by geometry) establishes the additional deflections at all points, along with the additional angle changes at the yield lines or hinges. For such a slab deflection, the loads also deflect and thereby contribute energy to the mechanism, while the hinges resist movement and absorb energy from the system. Thus, for a given mechanism, a given loading imparts enough energy to develop specific yield moments in the hinges. No smaller yield moment will be adequate to resist these loads. Some other mechanism may represent a more probable failure pattern; if so, it demands a larger yield moment to balance the given load. Thus the worst mechanism, and the real mechanism which actually forms, is the one which requires the largest resisting yield moment. Any trial mechanism or yield-line pattern establishes a lower bound or lower limit on the required yield moment.

The same procedure can be used with given yield moments to establish the ultimate load. Any given mechanism establishes an upper bound or upper limit on the collapse load. The real collapse load is the smallest that can be found from all possible mechanisms.

The energy calculations and the segment equilibrium conditions are alternative procedures. One can be used to check the other and each has some advantage under particular situations. The energy-mechanism approach indicates that the solution is not very sensitive to small changes in the yield-line pattern.

(f) Yield moment on axes not perpendicular to reinforcing

When the yield moments in two perpendicular directions are equal, the yield moments in all directions are equal. This condition of isotropic reinforcement simplifies the problem very considerably.

Hognestad has shown (following Johansen's demonstration) that, when the reinforcement in one direction differs from that in the perpendicular direction by some constant ratio, the slab dimensions can be modified to permit analysis as an isotropic slab. Such cases will not be considered here.

If m_x represents the yield moment about the x-axis and m_y about the y-axis, the yield moment about an axis at angle α with the x-axis (Fig. 10.4) will be

$$m_\alpha = m_x \cos^2 \alpha + m_y \cos^2 (90 - \alpha) = m_x \cos^2 \alpha + m_y \sin^2 \alpha$$

(g) Correction forces where the yield line intersects a free edge

Yield-line moments are maximum moments and therefore segmental sections formed by yield lines do not have torsional moments on these yielding edges.

At a free or simply supported edge the maximum moment, and hence the yield line, must be perpendicular to the edge. However, this necessary condition applies only quite close to the edge. For computation purposes Johansen suggests that the straight intermediate yield line be used as in Figs. 10.2b and 10.5, rather than the curved dashed lines of Fig. 10.5. The use of the straight line requires the use of a correction which, for a positive moment, can be represented by a vertical downward shear load* in the acute angle and an equal vertical upward shear load on the adjoining segment at the obtuse angle. This shear force is in magnitude $m_t = m \cot \alpha$, where α is the acute angle.

When an entire slab is considered, this downward shear on one segment

---

* A torsional moment of $m_t = m \cot \alpha$ on the free face is needed to balance the maximum moment applied at the false "straight-line" angle. The substitution of "corner shears" for torsion is a device borrowed from the theory of elasticity which likewise has some difficulties with boundary conditions. The following and Fig. 10.6 are taken directly from Hognestad's ACI paper[7] in substantiation of the magnitude of m_t.

"The magnitude of m_t may be established by considering the equilibrium of the infinitesimal triangle AOB shown in Fig. 10.6 in which AO is a finite length and AB is infinitesimal. Neglecting differentials of higher order, the moment in the section OB must equal the moment m in the yield line OA as m is a maximum value. Since the bending moment is zero along $AB = ds$, the total moment acting on the triangle AOB is found by vector addition

$$m(\overline{AO} + \overline{OB}) = m\overline{AB} = m\overline{ds}$$

Equilibrium of moments about OB then gives

$$m \, ds \cos \alpha = m_t \, ds \sin \alpha, \qquad \text{or } m_t = m \cot \alpha$$

differentials of higher order again being neglected. It should be noted that m_t acts down in the acute corner. These boundary conditions were first introduced into the yield-line theory by Johansen in 1931."

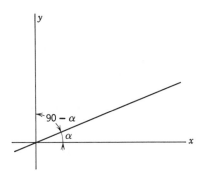

Fig. 10.4 (above). Moment axes.

Fig. 10.5 (right). The curved yield line at a free boundary.

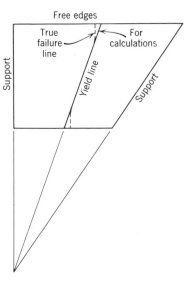

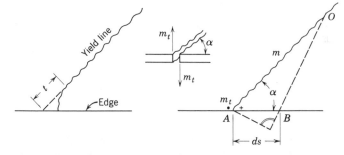

Fig. 10.6. The shear load m_t at boundary when straight yield lines are used. (Reprinted from *ACI Journal*.[7])

and the upward shear on the adjacent segment are internal and mutually offsetting forces, and hence do not show in the over-all energy equation.

(h) Corner pivots and corner yield lines

Corners introduce the problem of what might be called localized yield-line patterns, as in Fig. 10.12. Hognestad[7] reports: "According to Johansen it is most expedient in practical design to disregard the corner levers and then later apply corrections, for which he has developed general equations and tabulated the most common cases." In this brief treatment of the subject, corner patterns will be evaluated as any other regular pattern. Such discussion will be deferred until an example not needing this corner analysis has been considered.

10.3. ONE-WAY SLAB EXAMPLE

In Fig. 10.7a consider that the yield moment at a is $m_a = -4000$ ft-lb/ft width, at b is $m_b = -5000$ ft-lb/ft, and for positive moment is $m_c = +3000$ ft-lb/ft. By the yield-line method, calculate the ultimate uniform load the slab will support on a 12-ft span.

SOLUTION

The slab capacity is independent of adjacent panel conditions except as these are reflected in the values of m_a and m_b. The one-way slab can be very simply solved by limit design procedures, with identical results, but the object here is to introduce yield-line procedures.

An algebraic solution is simple, based on the free body diagrams of Fig. 10.7b.

$$\Sigma M_A = -4000 - 3000 + wx^2/2 = 0, \qquad w_A = 7000 \times 2/x^2 = 14,000/x^2$$

$$\Sigma M_B = +3000 + 5000 - w(12 - x)^2/2 = 0, \quad w_B = 8000 \times 2/(12 - x)^2$$

Since w_A is to be equal to w_B,

$$14,000/x^2 = 16,000/(12 - x)^2$$

The quadratic could be solved algebraically, but a solution more typical of the general possibilities of this method would be by trial.

$$\text{If } x = 6 \text{ ft}, \quad 388 < 444$$
$$x = 5.5 \quad 463 > 378$$
$$x = 5.8 \quad 415 \doteq 417, \text{ say } 416$$
$$\text{Ultimate } w = 416 \text{ psf}$$

The virtual work or energy-mechanism solution is also entirely feasible, using Fig. 10.7a. For a 1-ft strip the energy input for a unit deflection at the center yield line is

$$0.5wx + 0.5w(12 - x)$$

The work done on the slab at the yield lines or hinges is $m\theta$, where θ is the angle of rotation. At the center yield line the total angle change depends upon the combined rotation of A and B. However, the most convenient treatment is to calculate the work there as the separate amounts due to A and B respectively. The work at the yield lines is then:

$$\text{Due to rotation of } A: \quad (4000 + 3000)(1/x)$$
$$\text{Due to rotation of } B: \quad (3000 + 5000)[1/(12 - x)]$$

Equating energy input to energy consumption,

$$0.5wx + 0.5w(12 - x) = 7000/x + 8000/(12 - x)$$
$$6w = 7000/x + 8000/(12 - x)$$

For the needed minimum w, $dw/dx = 0$

$$6(dw/dx) = -7000/x^2 - 8000(-1)/(12 - x)^2 = 0$$

This is the same algebraic equation solved in the other approach, which gave $x = 5.8$ ft. If this value is substituted in the energy equation,

$$6w = 7000/5.8 + 8000/6.2 = 2498$$

$$w = 416 \text{ psf}$$

For the more usual slab with a more complex yield-line pattern, a group of partial derivatives would replace dw/dx. This type of solution might not be

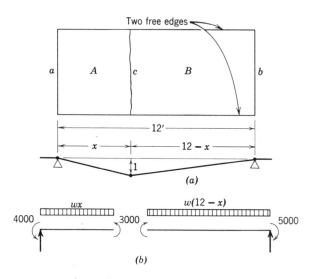

Fig. 10.7. One-way slab example. (*a*) Free body diagrams. (*b*) Failure mechanism.

practical. However, it is practical to try different patterns, in this case different x values, in the energy equation: $6w = 7000/x + 8000/(12 - x)$.

$$\text{Try } x = 6, \quad w = 1167/6 + 1333/6 = 417 \text{ psf}$$
$$x = 5, \quad w = 1167/5 + 1333/7 = 424 \text{ psf}$$
$$x = 5.5, \quad w = 1167/5.5 + 1333/6.5 = 417 \text{ psf}$$
$$x = 5.7, \quad w = 1167/5.7 + 1333/6.3 = 417 \text{ psf}$$
$$x = 5.85, \quad w = 1167/5.85 + 1333/6.15 = 416 \text{ psf}$$

This solution indicates, as is usually the case, that the calculated w by the virtual work or energy approach is not too sensitive to the exact yield-line location. A cut-and-try approach to the problem is thus feasible. The calculation of w for the several segments is more sensitive, but it has the advantage of indicating more definitely the needed shift in assumed yield-line location. The shifts with the energy method are more in the nature of groping one's way towards the correct solution rather than clearly observing the needed change.

YIELD-LINE THEORY FOR SLABS   261

10.4. TWO-WAY SLAB ON NONPARALLEL SUPPORTS

The slab of Fig. 10.2b illustrates two further points of procedure and brings up a possible practical complication. In addition, it serves to emphasize that moments are vector quantities and as such may need to be resolved into components. The ultimate uniform load will be calculated on the basis of the dimensions of Fig. 10.8a, $m_a = -4000$ ft-lb/ft, $m_b = -5000$ ft-lb/ft, and $m_c = 3000$ ft-lb/ft both longitudinally and transversely.

SOLUTION

Since yield lines for negative moment will occur over each support, the corresponding axes of rotation intersect at O. The intermediate positive moment yield line (extended) must also pass through O and can be defined in terms of an unknown angle at O or by the dimension x, the length of one side of the A segment.

This solution requires the yield moment m_c along the inclined yield line between A and B. With equal m_c values longitudinally and transversely, m_c is the same for all orientations. This follows from the equation of Sec. 10.2f:

$$m_\alpha = m_x \cos^2 \alpha + m_y \sin^2 \alpha = m_c(\cos^2 \alpha + \sin^2 \alpha) = m_c$$

If the transverse reinforcement were lighter, as would often be the case, the yield moment would have a specific m_α value for each assumed slope of yield line. The variable m_x would constitute an extra complication* in the solution, which would make general equations rather difficult. However, successive trials for different values of x would be feasible. Solution by trial may constitute the simpler approach even for the given isotropic case because of the somewhat involved geometry for moment arms and angles.

The second new procedure arises from the fact that the middle yield line crosses two free edges at other than a 90° angle. This requires a correction (Sec. 10.2g) in the form of a downward shear m_t at the acute angles and an upward shear m_t at the obtuse angles.

$$m_t = m \cot \alpha = m(x/18) = mx/18$$

These are marked on the plan view in Fig. 10.8a by an x for a downward force and by a dot within a small circle for an upward force. These shear forces influence an analysis by segments but not an energy equation. The first trial will be made with segments.

* Hognestad presents Johansen's proof showing that the slab dimensions can be modified to give a solution based on the simpler isotropic case. Assume the reinforcement in the transverse direction leads to a value of μm across longitudinal sections compared to m for the longitudinal strips. The simpler isotropic case ($m_x = m_y = m$) can be used if the length in the transverse direction and the size of any concentrated loads are first divided by $\sqrt{\mu}$, any uniform load w remaining unchanged. This provides a relatively simple solution for the problem but it appears that in a general case the ratio μ would have to be the same for both positive and negative moments in a given direction.

Assume $x = 4.2$ ft, giving the dimensions in Fig. 10.8b. The moment about aa' of the yield moments acting along cc' is

$m_c(\text{length } cc')\cos \gamma = m \times 12$

$m_t = m_c x/18 = 3000 \times 4.2/18 = 700$

$\Sigma M_{aa'} = -4000 \times 12 - 3000 \times 12 - 700 \times 4.2 + 700 \times 7$
$\qquad + 0.5 \times 12w \times 4.2 \times 1.4 + 0.5 \times 12w \times 7.0 \times 3.73 = 0$

$-48{,}000 - 36{,}000 - 2940 + 4900 + 35.3w + 156.6w = 0$

$w_A = 82{,}040/191.9 = 427$ psf

The yield moment along $cc' = m(\text{length } cc')$, which gives a moment about axis $bb' = m(\text{length } cc')\cos \beta$. The angle β in triangle $c'Ob'$ is

$\beta = \tan^{-1} 9/18 - \tan^{-1} 4.2/18 = 26°34' - 13°08' = 13°26'$

$\cos \beta = 0.973 \qquad \cos (\gamma + \beta) = 0.895$

An alternate procedure would be to obtain the moments for cc' as components about the x- and y-axes and then to take the components of these about bb'.

The slab load on segment B will be subdivided into triangular areas of load as in Fig. 10.8b, c. Triangle $bb'c$ has an area $8 \times \frac{12}{2} = 48$ ft^2 which indicates an altitude perpendicular to bb' of $48 \times 2/13.42 = 7.15$ ft. For triangle $cc'b'$, the centroid will be on the median at 8.27 ft to the left of b. Thus the horizontal distance between the centroid and bb' is 4.27 ft. The arm about $bb' = 4.27 \cos (\gamma + \beta) = 4.27 \times 12/13.42 = 4.27 \times 0.895 = 3.82$ ft.

$M_{bb'} = 3000 \times 12.33 \times 0.973 + 5000 \times 13.42 - 700 \times 4.8 \times 0.895$
$\qquad + 700 \times 8.0 \times 0.895 - 48w \times 7.15/3 - 4.8 \times 12w \times 0.5 \times 3.82 = 0$

$+36{,}000 + 67{,}100 - 3000 + 5000 - 114.3w - 110w = 0$

$w_B = 105{,}100/224.3 = 470$ psf $> w_A = 427$ psf

The indication is that x was taken a little too large, but the difference between w_A and w_B is quite small and an answer of ultimate $w = 445$ psf would be quite close. Normally one would not expect results of a trial to be this near to a correct answer; this choice of x benefited from the somewhat similar analysis of the slab in Sec. 10.3. On the other hand, the individual trial calculation should not be as long as here shown. The rather involved geometry was worked out in detail; graphical determination of some of the dimensions might be preferable, especially for initial trials.

The same problem will be solved from the energy-mechanism or virtual work approach, still using Fig. 10.8. Here also the geometry and angles must be carefully determined. Use $x = 4.2$ ft as before and assume a unit vertical movement at c'. Point c then deflects $30/18 = 1.667$ units (in proportion to the distance from O). Part B rotates through an angle $1/(4.8 \times 0.895) = 0.233$, and the yield hinge at bb' absorbs energy of

$$E_1 = 5000 \times 13.42 \times 0.233 = 15{,}650$$

For the yield hinge at cc', it is convenient to work with the x- and y-components of these moments and the respective components of the rotation angle. For rotation of B:

$$E_2 = 3000 \times 12 \times 1/4.8 + 3000 \times 2.8 \times \tfrac{1}{18} = 7970$$

For the rotation of A, the energy at cc' is:
$$E_3 = 3000 \times 12 \times 1/4.2 + 3000 \times 2.8 \times \tfrac{1}{18} = 9040$$
At aa', $\quad E_4 = 4000 \times 12 \times 1/4.2 = 11,420$

The total energy absorbed is $15,650 + 7970 + 9040 + 11,420 = 44,080$.

The same load triangles will be used as before. Triangle $bb'c$ at its centroid deflects $(\tfrac{1}{3})\ 1.667 = 0.555$

$$E_5 = (12w \times 8/2)0.555 = 26.7w$$

Triangle $cc'b$, $\quad E_6 = (12w \times 4.8/2)(4.27/4.8)1.0 = 25.6w$

Triangle $aa'c$, $\quad E_7 = (12w \times 4.2/2)\tfrac{1}{3} = 8.4w$

Triangle acc', $\quad E_8 = (12w \times 7.0/2)(3.73/4.20)1.0 = 37.3w$

The total energy available from loads is $26.7w + 25.6w + 8.4w + 37.3w = 98.0w$.

$$98.0w = 44,080$$
$$w = 450 \text{ psf}$$

An ultimate load of 450 psf is a good answer, the reliability of this answer being judged more on the basis of the equilibrium calculation for parts A and B than on the energy equation. It must be kept in mind that the energy equation always gives loads at least equal to and generally greater than the true ultimate load; that is, errors are always on the unsafe side.

To indicate the effect of a small error in locating the center yield line, the energy calculation will be repeated for $x = 4.5$ ft instead of the 4.2 ft used above. (The equilibrium calculation indicated the true value was *less* than 4.2 ft.) The dimensions are shown in Fig. 10.9.

$$\cos(\gamma + \beta) = 12/13.42 = 0.895$$

Energy absorbed:

$$5000 \times 13.42 \times 1/(4.5 \times 0.895) \qquad = 16,700$$
$$3000 \times 12 \times 1/4.5 + 3000 \times 3.0 \times \tfrac{1}{18} = \ 8,500$$
$$3000 \times 12 \times 1/4.5 + 3000 \times 3.0 \times \tfrac{1}{18} = \ 8,500$$
$$4000 \times 12 \times 1/4.5 \qquad\qquad\qquad = 10,660$$
$$\overline{ 44,360}$$

Energy from loads:

$bb'c$: $\quad 0.5 \times 12w \times 7.5 \times \tfrac{1}{3} \times 1.667 \qquad = 25.0w$

$cc'b$: $\quad 0.5 \times 12w \times 4.5 \times (4/4.5) \times 1.00 = 24.0w$

$aa'c$: $\quad 0.5 \times 12w \times 4.5 \times \tfrac{1}{3} \qquad\qquad = \ 9.0w$

acc': $\quad 0.5 \times 12w \times 7.5 \times (4/4.5) \times 1.00 = 40.0w$

$$\overline{ 98.0w}$$

$$w = 44,360/98.0 = 453 \text{ psf}$$

This differs very little from the better solution above.

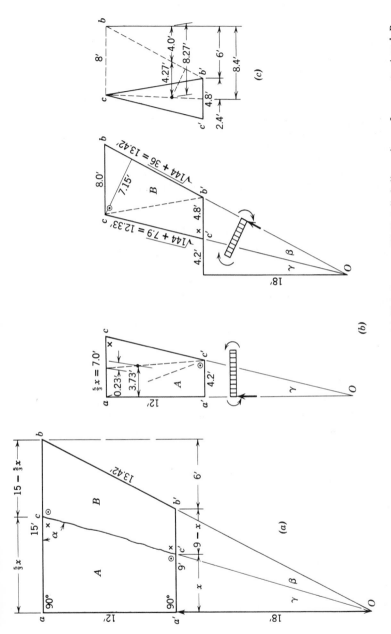

Fig. 10.8. Two-way slab on nonparallel supports. (a) Slab layout. (b) Detailed dimensions of segments A and B. (c) Subdivision of segment B.

10.5. SQUARE PANEL, IGNORING CORNER EFFECT

Find the ultimate uniform load that a continuous two-way slab 16 ft square can carry if the yield moment is 3000 ft-lb/ft for positive moment and 4000 ft-lb/ft for negative moment, equal in both directions.

SOLUTION

The yield pattern is established by symmetry in this case, with triangular segments rotating about each edge, as shown in Fig. 10.10.

When triangle *abo* is considered, each diagonal carries a positive moment of 3000 ft-lb/ft, since the slab is isotropic with equal resistance at any angle. The component about *ab* of the moments on the diagonals is equal to the moment *m* times the projected length *ab*. Hence the equilibrium equation for this segment becomes:

$$16(4000 + 3000) - 0.5 \times 16 \times 8w \times \tfrac{8}{3} = 0$$

$$w = 112,000/171 = 655 \text{ psf}$$

Except for possible corner effects (Sec. 10.6), this is an exact solution and there is no need for trial solutions. The energy equation would serve just as well. For a unit deflection at *o*:

$$16(4000 + 3000)\tfrac{1}{8} = 0.5 \times 16 \times 8w \times \tfrac{1}{3}$$

$$14,000 = 21.3w$$

$$w = 655 \text{ psf}$$

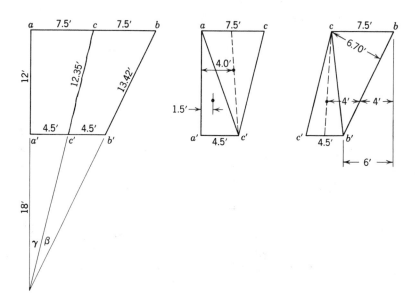

Fig. 10.9. Dimensions for another trial solution of slab of Fig. 10.8.

REINFORCED CONCRETE FUNDAMENTALS

10.6. CORNER EFFECTS

A simply supported square slab at a corner may not follow the simple yield-line pattern used in Sec. 10.5. If the corners are not fastened down,

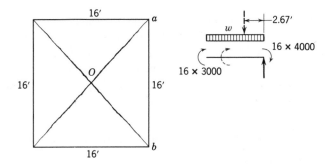

Fig. 10.10. Two-way slab supported on all four sides.

they will rise off the supports as the slab is loaded and the diagonal yield line will split or divide into two branches to form a Y, as in Fig. 10.11a. This forms an additional corner segment with yield moments on only two

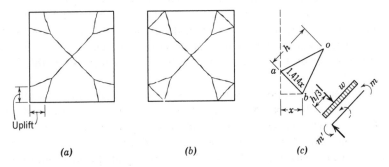

Fig. 10.11. Corner segments. (a) When corners are not fastened down. (b) When corners are held down but not reinforced for negative moment. (c) Equilibrium of corner segment.

faces and with support only on the two points where the yield lines cross the boundary. This condition is called a corner pivot, since the segment pivots about these two points.

If the corners are held down, but are not specially reinforced, similar yield lines form but in addition a corner crack opens along the pivot line as in Fig. 10.11*b*.   If the corner is specially reinforced for negative moment, this adds a yield moment m' across this boundary of the triangular segment which increases its capacity and moves the junction of the Y farther from the corner.   With a large enough m', the triangular segment fails to form and the simple diagonal yield line into the corner is correct without modification.

In continuous slabs, the corners have top steel which provides an m' for the corner segment.   Whether the Y-pattern or the straight diagonal yield line forms depends upon the amount of this reinforcement.

Consider the free body formed by one of these corner segments, as in Fig. 10.11*c*.   The positive moment m along sides *ao* and *ob* adds vectorially to give a positive moment m on the width *ab*, when m is the same in each direction.

$$\Sigma M_{ab} = -1.414xm' - 1.414xm + 0.5(1.414xhwh)/3 = 0$$

$$wh^2/6 = m + m'$$

$$h = \sqrt{6(m + m')/w}$$

The length h is thus independent of x or the width of the segment and increases with the ratio of the sum of positive and negative yield moments to w.   If, in a given slab, the moment-load ratio establishes a distance h much less than the length of the diagonal along which it lies, this corner pattern will control; that is, it does reduce the slab capacity.   If the calculated h is large enough to push the Y-intersection beyond the limits of its particular diagonal, it means that the corner segment does not form. Intermediate values of h indicate that the corner element controls but has a smaller effect on the ultimate load or required moment strength of the slab.

With a simply supported square slab of side dimension a the ultimate moment is $wa^2/24$ if no corner segment forms.   This is the true condition with the corner held down and with m' made equal to m.   With $m' = 0$, or with the corners free, the corner pivots produce corner segments which increase the ultimate moment to $wa^2/22$.   In the square panel the maximum effect of the corner segments is thus slightly less than 9%.

10.7. SQUARE PANEL, CONSIDERING CORNER EFFECTS

The effect of the slab corners upon the ultimate moment on the square slab of Sec. 10.5 will now be investigated by basic principles.*

* Reference 7 develops three simultaneous equations for the square slab case which establish the corner segment dimensions algebraically.

REINFORCED CONCRETE FUNDAMENTALS

In Sec. 10.5 w was found to be 655 psf, and this will not be seriously changed, say, not below 600 psf based on the 9% correction of Sec. 10.6. With this assumed w, summation of moments for the corner segment, as above, gives

$$m' + m = wh^2/6$$

$$4000 + 3000 = 600h^2/6$$

$$h = \sqrt{7000/100} = 8.35 \text{ ft}$$

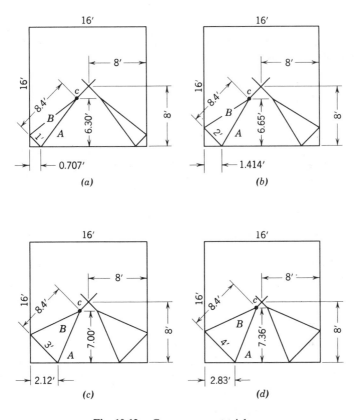

Fig. 10.12. Corner segment trials.

The full diagonal length is $1.414 \times \frac{16}{2} = 11.3$ ft. Hence it is probable that the corner segment does form. Since the edge does not have $M = 0$, corner shears are not necessary in this example.

Try the failure pattern of Fig. 10.12a, using the energy method with a center deflection of one unit. Since the pattern repeats, only one set of areas A and B will be included.

The deflection of point c is $(8.4 + 0.50)/11.3 = 0.787$. Energy input from the load is:

$$E_A = 0.5 \times 16w \times 8 \times \tfrac{1}{3} - 2 \times 0.5 \times 0.707w \times 6.30 \times 0.787/3 = 20.1w$$

$$E_B = 0.5 \times 1w \times 8.4 \times 0.787/3 = 1.10w$$

Energy absorbed in hinges:

$$E_A = (4000 + 3000)(16 - 2 \times 0.707)\tfrac{1}{8} = 12{,}950$$

$$E_B = (4000 + 3000) \times 1 \times 0.787/8.4 = 657$$

$$20.1w + 1.10w = 12{,}950 + 657$$

$$w = 13{,}610/21.2 = 643 \text{ psf} < 655 \text{ psf of Sec. } 10.5$$

This comparison proves that the corner segment does form.

A larger corner segment may drop the ultimate w lower. Try the increased segment of Fig. 10.12b. The deflection of c is $(8.4 + 1.00)/11.3 = 0.835$. As for the above trial,

$$18.7w + 2.34w = 11{,}550 + 1390$$

$$w = 12{,}940/21.04 = 615 \text{ psf} < 643$$

Since this governs over the preceding calculation, further trials were made for the conditions of Fig. 10.12c and d which gave 607 psf and 605 psf respectively.

Although all possibilities have not been exhausted, the h used was based on w quite close to the calculated w. It appears safe to say that the ultimate load is approximately the 600 psf originally estimated.

10.8. RECTANGULAR SLABS

Investigate the ultimate load capacity of a 12-ft by 20-ft slab continuous on all edges, which has a yield moment of 3000 ft-lb/ft for positive moment and 4000 ft-lb/ft for negative moment, both uniform in each direction.

SOLUTION

Symmetry dictates a yield line at the middle, parallel to the long side, which merges with corner diagonals symmetrical about unknown points O and O' as shown in Fig. 10.13a. The corner effect with the Y-form on the corner diagonals is also possible, but this will be treated as a later modification of the simple pattern.

The first trial dimensions shown in Fig. 10.13a will be considered, first in terms of the equilibrium of segments A and B.

Segment A:

$$-12(4000 + 3000) + 0.5 \times 12w \times 8 \times 2.67 = 0$$

$$w_A = 84{,}000/128 = 655 \text{ psf}$$

Segment B:

$$-20(4000 + 3000) + 4w \times 6 \times 3 + 2 \times 0.5 \times 8w \times 6 \times 2 = 0$$

$$w_B = 140{,}000/168 = 834 \text{ psf} \gg w_A$$

Try a smaller A segment as noted in Fig. 10.13a for the second trial. These dimensions lead to $w_A = 858$ psf and $w_B = 730$ psf. A third trial with point O at 7.5 ft from the end gives $w_A = 745$ psf and $w_B = 775$ psf. This is reasonably close and will be checked by the energy relationship, using half of the panel for convenience and a unit deflection along OO'.

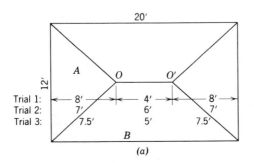

(a)

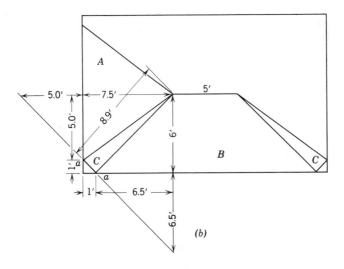

(b)

Fig. 10.13. Rectangular slab analysis. (a) Neglecting corner segments. (b) With trial corner segments.

Energy input:

$$A: 0.5 \times 12w \times 7.5 \times \tfrac{1}{3} \qquad = 15w$$
$$B: 5w \times 6 \times \tfrac{1}{2} \qquad\qquad = 15w$$
$$+2 \times 0.5 \times 7.5w \times 6 \times \tfrac{1}{3} = 15w$$
$$\overline{45w}$$

YIELD-LINE THEORY FOR SLABS

271

Energy absorbed:

$$A: 12(4000 + 3000)1/7.5 \qquad = 11,200$$
$$B: 20(4000 + 3000)\tfrac{1}{6} \qquad = 23,300$$

$$\overline{34,500}$$

$$w = 34,500/45 = 767 \text{ psf}$$

For the location of O the third trial dimensions will be assumed correct enough.

The corner segment situation will now be investigated. For equilibrium of the corner segment,

$$-4000 - 3000 + 0.5wh^2/3 = 0, \qquad h = \sqrt{42,000/w}$$

$$\text{If } w = 750 \text{ psf}, h = 7.46 \text{ ft}$$

This compares with the diagonal length of $\sqrt{7.5^2 + 6.0^2} = 9.60$ ft. It appears that there will be a significant corner segment, probably one extending most of the way to point O.

The corner segment shown in Fig. 10.13b will be analyzed by the energy approach, using the deflection at O as unity. At aa the x- and y-components of the moments and rotations are used for calculating the energy absorbed by the hinges. Only half the panel (one segment each of A, B, and two of C) will be used.

Energy input by loads:

$$B: 5w \times 6 \times \tfrac{1}{2} \qquad\qquad = 15.0w$$
$$+2 \times 0.5 \times 6.5w \times 6 \times \tfrac{1}{3} \qquad = 13.0w$$
$$A: 0.5 \times 10 \times 7.5w \times \tfrac{1}{3} \qquad = 12.5w$$
$$C: 2 \times 0.5 \times 1w \times 6.0 \quad = \quad 6.0w$$
$$+2 \times 0.5 \times 1w \times 7.5 = \quad 7.5w$$
$$-2 \times 0.5 \times 1w \times 1 \quad = -1.0w$$

$$\overline{12.5w \times \tfrac{1}{3} = \quad 4.17w}$$

$$\overline{44.67w}$$

Energy absorbed by hinges:

$$B: 18(4000 + 3000)\tfrac{1}{6} \qquad = 21,000$$
$$A: 10(4000 + 3000)1/7.5 \qquad = 9,330$$
$$C: 2 \times 1(4000 + 3000)1/12.5 \quad = 1,120$$
$$+2 \times 1(4000 + 3000)1/12.5 = 1,120$$

$$\overline{32,570}$$

$$w = 32,570/44.67 = 730 \text{ psf} < 767$$

A number of variations were computed by the energy method, partly to be certain the worst case was found, partly to study the rather minor differences in

w which resulted. The results of these calculations are shown just to the right of each illustration in Fig. 10.14. Where several values of w are shown, they come from analyses of the separate segments. It appears that an ultimate load of about 710 psf is correct.

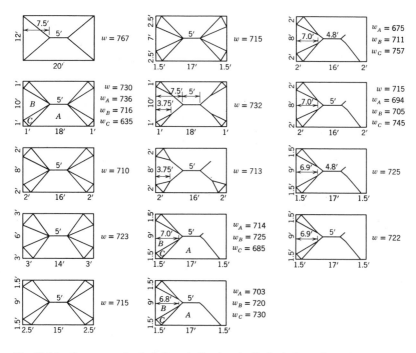

Fig. 10.14. Summary of calculations indicating the limited effect of corner segments.

10.9. OTHER YIELD-LINE ANALYSES

A few yield-line patterns for other cases may be helpful as suggestions. Figure 10.15a shows a triangular slab simply supported and carrying uniform load. Johansen[4] shows for isotropic conditions that the yield lines intersect at the center of the inscribed circle and result in $m = wr^2/6$, where r is the radius of the circle. He extends this case to show the same moment in any polygon shape which circumscribes a circle, as in Fig. 10.15b. It is assumed that any of these might need to be investigated for a possible corner pivot or segment. Johansen[4] also shows free edge slabs as shown in Fig. 10.15c, d, e.

Hognestad[7] shows the slab of Fig. 10.15f. He also analyzes a radial pattern which at times develops under concentrated loads, Fig. 10.15g.

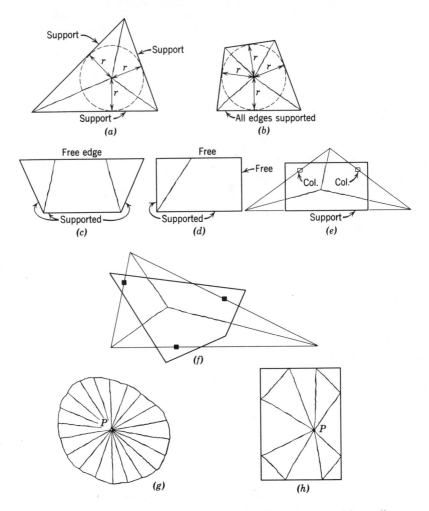

Fig. 10.15. Yield-line patterns. (*a*) Triangular slab supported on all sides. (*b*) Polygonal slab circumscribed around a circle, all edges supported. (*c*) Slab supported on three of four sides. (*d*) Slab supported only on adjacent sides. (*e*) Slab supported on one side and two columns. (*a*)–(*e*) Adapted from Ref. 4, Internat'l Assn. for Bridge and Struct. Engng. (*f*) Slab supported on three columns. (*g*) Yield pattern around a concentrated load. (*f*) and (*g*) Adapted from Ref. 7, ACI. (*h*) Yield pattern from an unsymmetrical concentrated load on a rectangular slab. Adapted from Ref. 9, Chamecki.

With a single concentrated load in a rectangular panel Chamecki[9] shows eight triangular segments radiating from the load P whether P is centered or off center from both axes as in Fig. 10.15h. He develops equations to locate all key dimensions for the simple support case when the corners are

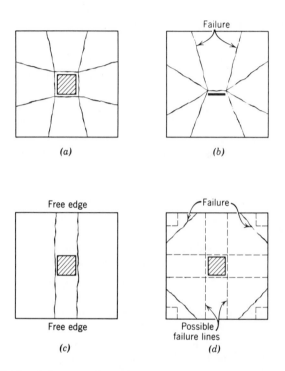

Fig. 10.16. Slabs supporting column loads (from Ref. 10, ACI). (a) Simply supported on all edges, corners free. (b) Eccentric column load treated as a line load, simply supported on all edges, corners free. (c) Simply supported on two opposite edges. (d) Supported at corners only.

anchored down and when they are free to rise. He also shows the condition necessary to eliminate the corner segments.

Elstner and Hognestad[10] show the yield patterns of Fig. 10.16 for slabs carrying a center load in the form of a column stub cast monolithically with the slab. Figure 10.16a shows a slab simply supported and corners free; Fig. 10.16b is the same except that an eccentric column load is considered as a line load. The case of simple supports on two opposite sides only is shown in Fig. 10.16c and simple support on four corners only in Fig. 10.16*d*; in the latter case the dashed lines represent an alternate yield-line pattern.

SELECTED REFERENCES

1. K. W. Johansen, *Pladeformler*, Polyteknish Forening, Copenhagen, 2nd ed., 1949.
2. K. W. Johansen, *Pladeformler; Formelsamling*, Polyteknish Forening, Copenhagen, 2nd ed., 1954.
3. A. Ingerslev, "The Strength of Rectangular Slabs," *Jour. Instn. Struct. Engrs.*, **1**, No. 1, Jan. 1923, p. 3.
4. K. W. Johansen, "The Ultimate Strength of Reinforced Concrete Slabs," Final Report, Third Congress, International Association for Bridge and Structural Engineering, Liége, Sept. 1948, p. 565.
5. H. Craemer, "Slabs Spanning in Two Directions Analyzed by Consideration of Pattern of Fractures," *Concr. Constr. Engng.*, **45**, No. 8, Aug. 1950, p. 279.
6. H. Craemer, "Rectangular Slabs Spanning in Two Directions," *Concr. Constr. Engng.*, **47**, No. 7, July 1952, p. 195.
7. Eivind Hognestad, "Yield-Line Theory for the Ultimate Flexural Strength of Reinforced Concrete Slabs," *ACI Jour.*, **24**, No. 7, Mar. 1953; *Proc.*, **49**, p. 637.
8. F. E. Thomas, "Load Factor Methods of Designing Reinforced Concrete," *Reinf. Conc. Review*, **3**, No. 8, 1955, pp. 540, 544.
9. Samuel Chamecki, *Cálculo No Regime de Ruptura, Das Lajes de Concreto Armadas em Cruz*, Curitiba, Parana, Brazil, 1948, 107 pages.
10. Richard C. Elstner and Eivind Hognestad, "Shearing Strength of Reinforced Concrete Slabs, Appendix 1," *ACI Jour.*, **28**, No. 1, July 1956; *Proc.*, **53**, p. 55.

PROBLEMS

Prob. 10.1. In Figs. 10.2*a* and 10.7 calculate the ultimate load by yield-line procedures if:

(*a*) The positive moment capacity m_c is increased to $+4000$ ft-lb/ft, m_a and m_b remaining unchanged at -4000 and -5000 ft-lb/ft respectively.

(*b*) The negative moment capacity m_a is decreased to -3000 ft-lb/ft, m_b and m_c remaining at -5000 and $+3000$ ft-lb/ft respectively.

Prob. 10.2. Recalculate the ultimate load for the slab of Sec. 10.4 and Fig. 10.8 if the right support has only a 3-ft skew, that is, if b' in Fig. 10.8*a* is moved 3 ft to the right.

Prob. 10.3. If $m = +2000$ ft-lb/ft and $m' = -2500$ ft-lb/ft, find the ultimate load which can be carried by an 18-ft square slab continuous on all sides. Consider first without corner effect and then establish effect of corner segments.

Prob. 10.4. Investigate the ultimate load capacity of a 14-ft by 20-ft slab continuous on all sides and having a yield moment of 3000 ft-lb/ft for positive moment and 4000 ft-lb/ft for negative moment. Compare results with those for the 12-ft by 20-ft slab of Sec. 10.8.

Prob. 10.5. Assume for this problem that a load factor of 2.5 would be considered adequate for a yield-line analysis. If the ultimate moments used in the analysis of Sec. 10.8 were reduced to permissible service load moments and these were equated to the maximum moments required in Code Art. 709, Method 1 (or Method 2 if so directed), what working load capacity w would be indicated for this slab? For this slab the yield-line method indicates what factor of safety over the working load method?

11

Flat Slabs
and
Related Types

11.1. INTRODUCTION

A flat slab is a concrete slab so reinforced in two (or more) directions as to bring its load directly to supporting columns, generally without the help of any beams or girders, as in Fig. 11.1. Beams are used where the slab is interrupted, as around stair walls, and at the discontinuous edges of the slab.

The supporting columns may be increased in size near the top to form a column head or column capital, as shown in Figs. 11.1 and 11.7. In addition, the slab may be thickened by a drop panel around the column, as shown in Figs. 11.1 and 11.7b, but many slabs are constructed without the drop panel.

The ACI Code also considers "slabs with recesses or pockets made by permanent or removable fillers between reinforcing bars" as flat slabs.

This includes two-way joist systems and the so-called waffle slab (Fig. 11.2a).

The flat plate floor is a flat slab having neither drop panel nor column capital, as in Fig. 11.2b.

The slab band type of floor thickens the slab into bands of greater depth, as in Fig. 11.3. Although the most usual pattern results in one-way slabs of variable depth supported on wide shallow beams or bands in the perpendicular direction, some engineers have used such thickened sections in end panels much like a drop panel around a flat slab column. Such construction partakes somewhat of the nature of flat slabs.

Fig. 11.1. Typical flat slab construction, with drop panel. (Courtesy Portland Cement Assn.)

Two-way slabs supported on all sides by wide shallow beams also involve some flat slab action. When the slab proper occupies only the middle half of the panel, the Code recognizes it as a flat slab with a recessed center panel.

Flat slabs, being thin members, are not economical of steel, but they are economical in their formwork. Since formwork represents over half the cost of reinforced concrete, economy of formwork often means over-all economy.

For heavy live loads, that is, over 100 psf, flat slabs have long been recognized as the most economical construction. In more recent years, flat plate floors have proved economical in apartment house construction in the New York City area. Reduced story height resulting from the thin floor, the smooth ceiling, and the possibility of slightly shifting column locations to fit the room arrangement all seem to be factors in the over-all economy.

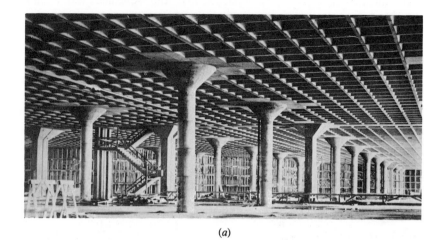

(a)

(b)

Fig. 11.2. Variations of flat slab form. (Courtesy Portland Cement Assn.) (a) Waffle slab. (b) Flat plate.

11.2. THE STATICS OF A FLAT SLAB

In 1914 J. R. Nichols[1] showed that statics required a total positive and negative moment of

$$M_0 = \frac{1}{8}\, WL \left(1 - \frac{2}{3}\frac{c}{L}\right)^2$$

Fig. 11.3. Slab band construction. (Courtesy Portland Cement Assn.)

where W is the total uniform panel load, L is the span, and c is the diameter of the column capital. This conclusion follows from an analysis of a half panel.

Consider the interior panel of Fig. 11.4a, loaded with a unit load w and surrounded with similar panels equally loaded. The straight boundaries of the slab are all lines of symmetry, indicating that they are free from shear and torsion. Hence all of the shear and torsion must be carried around the curved corner sections which follow the column capital.

Likewise, if the slab is subdivided along the middle of the panel, this line is a line of zero shear and torsion. Thus the free body of Fig. 11.4b, c is subject to a downward load W_1 acting at the centroid of the loaded area, an equal upward shear W_1 acting on the curved quadrants, the total positive moment M_1 acting on the middle section ab, and the total negative moment M_2 acting about the y-axis on section $cdef$. This assumes the bending moment around the column capital is uniformly distributed, which means no torsional moments exist there. Moments also exist about the x-axis on efa and dcb, but these do not enter into $\Sigma M_y = 0$.

$$W_1 = w(L^2/2 - \pi c^2/8) = (L^2 - \pi c^2/4)w/2$$

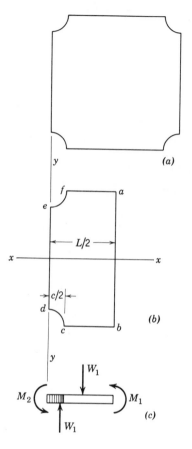

Fig. 11.4. Equilibrium conditions indicate $M_1 + M_2$ is established by statics.

The moment of this load about axis y-y is:

$$\frac{wL^2}{2} \times \frac{L}{4} - \frac{\pi c^2 w}{8} \times \frac{2c}{3\pi} = \frac{wL^3}{8} - \frac{wc^3}{12}$$

If the upward shear W_1 is considered uniformly distributed around the quadrants cd and ef, the resultant acts at a distance c/π from the y-axis. Equilibrium of moments about the y-axis then gives:

$$-M_1 - M_2 + \frac{wL^3}{8} - \frac{wc^3}{12} - \frac{w}{2}\left(L^2 - \frac{\pi c^2}{4}\right)\frac{c}{\pi} = 0$$

$$M_1 + M_2 = M_0 = \frac{wL^3}{8} - \frac{wc^3}{12} - \frac{wcL^2}{2\pi} + \frac{wc^3}{8} = \frac{wL^3}{8}\left(1 + \frac{c^3}{3L^3} - \frac{4c}{\pi L}\right)$$

REINFORCED CONCRETE FUNDAMENTALS

$$M_0 \doteq \frac{WL}{8} \left(1 - \frac{2}{3} \frac{c}{L} \right)^2$$

The value of $[1 - \frac{2}{3}(c/L)]^2$ approximates the longer parenthesis reasonably well.*

This statics solution tells nothing about how this total moment is distributed between positive or negative moment or how either varies along the slab width. The solution also neglects possible torsional moments around the column capital which will act if the tangential bending moments there are not uniform in their distribution.

When flat slab panels are not square, the long span thus produces the larger moment. The student should contrast this with the two-way slab supported on all four sides where the short slab strips carry the larger load and larger moment. In such a slab the long strips carry less load and less moment, but it should be noted that the long beams have to carry heavy slab reactions and large moments. Slab moments in both directions are reduced because the beams help to carry the moment. In the flat slab, in contrast, the full load must be carried in both directions by the slab alone.

11.3. DEVELOPMENT OF FLAT SLAB ANALYSIS FOR MOMENT

Flat slabs, although now widely used throughout the world, are distinctly an American development. Originated by C. A. P. Turner, they were built and sold long before a generally accepted theory of design was developed. Numerous flat slab structures were load-tested during the period from 1910 to 1920.† These slabs performed well under test loads, in fact so well that there is some difficulty in correlating test results with the static moments Nichols showed were required for equilibrium. This difficulty is discussed in the following paragraph.

On a number of these tests strains were measured on concrete and steel. The investigators recognized that their strain measurements did not lead directly to maximum steel stresses because their instruments measured average stress over a considerable length in a rapidly varying moment zone; they also could not separate the higher steel strain at cracks from the smaller steel strains between cracks. In spite of attempted corrections Slater[2] found an average factor of safety for beams 10% higher than the

* For $c/L = 0.1$ the error is about 0.5% low, for $c/L = 0.2$ about 0.5% high. For $c/L = 0.25$ the approximation is about 1.3% high, and for $c/L = 0.30$ about 2.0%.

† In 1947 Professor J. Neils Thompson and the author ran such a test on a flat slab constructed about 1912. Although it cracked badly, its strength was surprising.

ratio of f_y to working stress f_s; this difference became 18% for $p = 0.0049$, which was about the steel used in the slabs. Since the flat slab tests were not generally carried to failure, it was necessary by calculation to estimate the ultimate load capacity based on yielding of the steel. These calculations indicated factors of safety that Slater considered excessive. Even when the total design moment M_0 was taken as $0.09WL[1 - \frac{2}{3}(c/L)]^2$, the indicated factor of safety averaged 2.72, which he compared to a factor of safety on beams of about 2.25 for $f_y = 33,000$ psi and working $f_s = 16,000$ psi.

On the basis of such comparisons the value of $M_0 = 0.09WL[1 - \frac{2}{3}(c/L)]^2$, which had been proposed in ACI recommendations, was judged to be entirely safe and to provide a larger factor of safety than in simpler types of construction. This M_0 represents a 28% reduction from the moments which statics shows must exist. The 0.09 coefficient thus leads

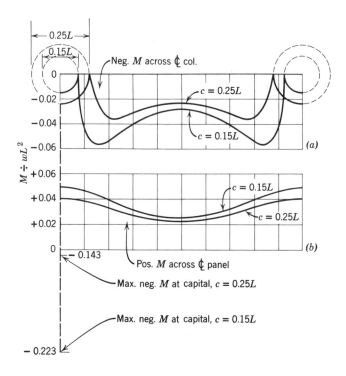

Fig. 11.5. Theoretical bending moments (Poisson's ratio zero). Adapted from Ref. 2, ACI. (*a*) Negative moments on strips crossing the center line of column and the column capital. (*b*) Positive moments on strips crossing the center line of span.

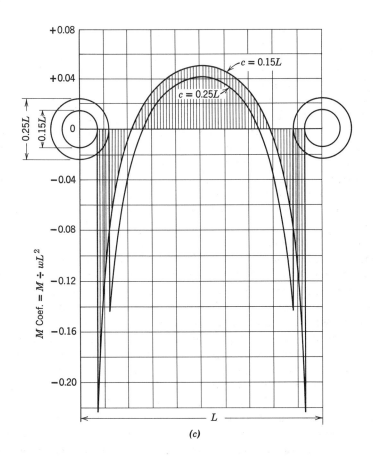

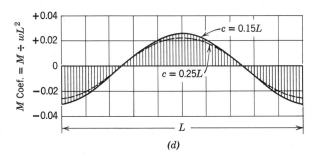

Fig. 11.5 (continued). Theoretical bending moments (Poisson's ratio zero). Adapted from Ref. 2, ACI. (c) Moment diagram for strip along center line of columns. (d) Moment diagram for strip along middle of panel.

FLAT SLABS AND RELATED TYPES

to a totally imaginary moment, but it provides a reasonable margin of safety.*

The flat slab, with its calculated strength based largely on tests and with unbalanced loadings for maximum moment very lightly considered, now has a favored position in design, a position not shared by any competitive form of concrete construction, such as two-way slabs supported on all four sides. This is one of the important reasons for the test program on various types of slabs now under way (Sec. 9.14). Possibly flat slab design specifications should be regarded as a crude application of limit or collapse load ideas. Such ideas have some real merit in connection with slabs, but the present result seems to be that the ACI Code uses a larger factor of safety for the two-way slab and even for many one-way slabs than for the flat slab.

Westergaard developed a theoretical slab analysis which accompanied Slater's test analyses. He established the distribution of positive and negative moments which would exist throughout a flat slab when it was considered as an isotropic plate. His work, roughly checked by Slater's test analyses, forms the basis for the specified subdivision of the total M_0 into positive and negative moments and for the further subdivision of these into moments on the two design strips set up in the specifications. Figure 11.5a shows his calculated distribution of negative moments on strips crossing the column center line for $c/L = 0.15$ and 0.25. Around the column capitals the moment in a radial direction is considered constant at $-0.223wL^2$ for $c/L = 0.15$ and at $-0.143wL^2$ for $c/L = 0.25$. These values are nearly four times the maximums shown between columns. The positive moments on strips crossing the middle of the span are shown in Fig. 11.5b. For a strip running along the center line between columns, the moment diagram is shown in Fig. 11.5c, and for a strip running along the middle of the panel in Fig. 11.5d. It will be noted that both these strips have a form of moment diagram very similar to that of a one-way slab, with positive moment in the middle of the span and negative moments at the ends.

11.4. DESIGN MOMENTS FOR FLAT SLABS

For design purposes a flat slab is divided into two strips in each direction, each strip one half panel in width, as shown in Fig. 11.6. Within these

---

* The author sincerely regrets this disregard of statics. He would have been better satisfied as a teacher if, for instance, the real moments had been used with higher permissible unit stresses, or if the steel calculated on the basis of real moments and ordinary allowable steel stress had been arbitrarily reduced.

strips, average moments are used for design rather than maximum moments. The column strip carries the heavier moments and in design controls the thickness of slab for moment. The middle strip carries smaller moments, which call for lighter steel.

The Code sets up two methods for establishing these design moments. The first method is to establish total negative and total positive moments in each direction from elastic frame analysis and then to separate these into moments on column and middle strip on the basis of percentages set out in the Code. The second method, limited to regular slab layouts and

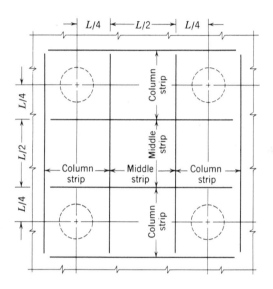

Fig. 11.6. Flat slab design strips.

a minimum of three continuous panels, tabulates directly the empirical moment coefficients to be used for each design moment.

The table of empirical moment coefficients is a method of long standing, ever since flat slab design was recognized in codes. The 1956 Code introduces a new term F as a multiplier into the equation for total moment M_0, where $F = 1.15 - c/L$ but not less than 1:

$$M_0 = 0.09 WLF \left(1 - \frac{2}{3}\frac{c}{L}\right)^2$$

When a column capital is not used, c becomes the column size, which is usually small enough to make F greater than unity. A design using the empirical design method is developed in Sec. 11.8.

The elastic analysis procedure is a more recent development and is less restricted in usage. As a preferred method it should logically be presented first. However, the author believes the methods peculiar to the elastic analysis can be most clearly presented after the general flat slab procedures have been developed in connection with the empirical moment coefficients. Hence Secs. 11.11 and 11.12 on moment distribution and its application to flat slabs have been presented after the empirical design discussion of Secs. 11.8 and 11.9.

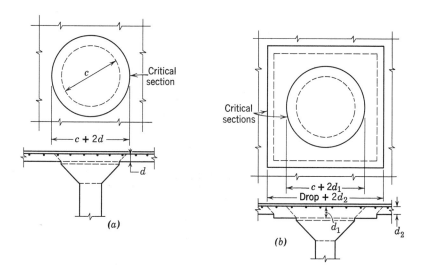

Fig. 11.7. Critical sections for diagonal tension. Flat slab (a) without drop, (b) with drop.

11.5. SHEAR AND BOND IN FLAT SLABS

Diagonal tension around the column capital may determine the depth of slab required. The critical section is taken parallel to the column capital, at a distance d beyond it, as indicated in Fig. 11.7a. (The student might compare the critical section used for isolated footings in Secs. 6.11b and 14.3d.) Since stirrups are not convenient in slabs, the allowable shear is limited to $0.03f_c'$ (but not more than 100 psi) when 50% of the column strip negative steel passes through the section, and to lower values for other conditions [Art. 1002c(2)].

In flat plate construction the lack of a column capital reduces the section which must resist shear. Often some form of reinforcement for diagonal tension would then seem to be needed in preference to additional thickness. However, the ACI Code [Art. $1002c(2)$] does not permit the use of a flat slab shear in excess of $0.03f_c'$ or 100 psi in any case, and the limit is nearer to $0.025f_c'$ for the usual flat plate; nor does it permit less than 25 % of the negative moment steel in the column strip to cross the critical shear section. Many designers ignore one or both of these restrictions (Sec. 11.14).

Diagonal tension stresses around the column frequently constitute the controlling requirement for the thickness of a flat slab or a flat plate floor. Hence openings adjacent to the columns should always receive the most careful and conservative design attention. Although the average shear around a column appears to be adequate as a design basis for slabs without holes, there is as yet no convincing test evidence that shear concentrations adjacent to an opening may safely be ignored. Possibly when openings are essential alongside a column, each face of the column should be separately considered; and as an extra safety measure the unit shear at face of column might be calculated instead of that at a section a distance d from the column. The effectiveness of web reinforcement in such cases is not well established (Sec. 11.14). Additional research on slab openings and on slab web reinforcement is seriously needed.* The general problem of holes in slabs is discussed briefly in the next chapter.

When drop panels are used, the diagonal tension must also be checked at a distance d_2 outside of this panel, as shown in Fig. 11.7b.

Bond stresses in slabs are usually not critical if care is taken to extend straight bars and bent bars well beyond the extreme range of the points of inflections and if small enough bars are used to comply with the maximum spacing provisions of Art. $1002d(1)$. The minimum bar lengths are carefully specified in Art. $1004g$ for designs based on empirical coefficients for moment. Article $1002d$ covers some general specifications for reinforcing at discontinuous edges and calls for a minimum lap of 36 bar diameters at splices.

The actual calculation of bond stresses is made a little awkward by the fact that loads are carried in two directions in a statically indeterminate fashion and thus shears are not easy to visualize. However, reasonable approximations can be easily established. For example, if the shear is desired at a distance 5 ft from the center of column, as in Fig. 11.8, one can take the total shear on four sides as one full panel load minus the load on the 10-ft square. The shear on one face of the square will be one-fourth of this.

In general, bond is usually handled indirectly. The author would

* Recently some serious slab failures have occurred when holes were placed alongside the columns.

suggest that the best security is obtained by being careful that all bars extend a full anchorage length beyond their points of maximum tension. Such points occur not only at points of maximum moment but also may occur where part of the other bars are bent up or bent down. (Compare the discussion of anchorage length in Sec. 8.15.)

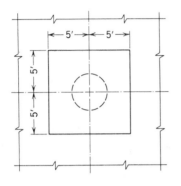

Fig. 11.8. Use of a centered square as a method of calculating shear for bond stress.

11.6. COLUMNS FOR FLAT SLABS

Columns for flat slabs necessarily carry a moment as well as axial load. When an elastic frame analysis is used, this moment is definite, as obtained from unbalanced live load for interior columns and from combined dead and live load for exterior columns.

When empirical moment coefficients are used, Art. 1004b(2) specifies a minimum moment to be divided between the columns above and below. The size of column is also specified, as discussed in the next paragraph.

The empirical moment coefficients for flat slabs are not only some 28% lower than statics would indicate, but they also correspond more nearly to full load condition than to loadings for maximum negative or positive moments. If, for example, the loading of a single panel is not to produce a larger positive moment than the design moment, infinitely stiff columns would be necessary. The Code does not require such massive columns as this standard might indicate. Instead, comparisons were made between moments calculated by frame analysis and those specified empirically. The minimum I specified for the column in Art. 1004b(1) is just enough to hold the adjusted theoretical (frame analysis) moments within a 33% overrun beyond the empirical moment values. These limitations are used in selecting a column in Sec. 11.10 for the slab of Sec. 11.9.

11.7. BAR PLACEMENT SEQUENCE AND EFFECTIVE DEPTH

As in the case of two-way slabs supported on all four sides (Sec. 9.7), a planned sequence for placing the reinforcing steel is necessary to avoid confusion in the field and to ensure agreement between actual and assumed effective depths. The following examples are based on a placing sequence

REINFORCED CONCRETE FUNDAMENTALS

quite similar to that used for the slab supported on all four sides (Fig. 9.6). This placing sequence is shown in Fig. 11.9, only a few typical bars actually being shown. The sequence is as follows:

1. Place all long span straight bottom bars.

2. Place short span bars (bent and straight) in column strips only. (Modify width placed if middle strip bars are not bent up at 0.25L from column center line.)

3. Place all bent bars and top straight bars in the long span strips.

4. Place short span bars (bent and straight) in the middle strip.

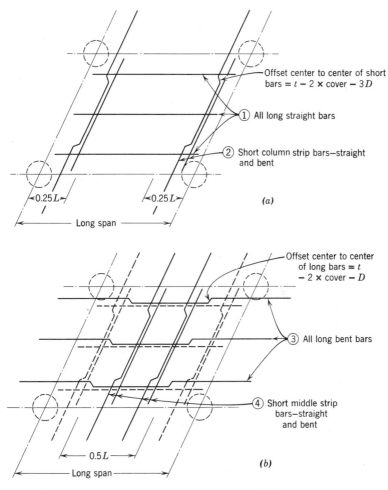

Fig. 11.9. Placement sequence for steel. (a) First two groups. (b) Remaining two groups.

This sequence avoids bar interference almost completely and permits all bars to be dropped vertically into place except for a few of the short span middle strip bars, which must be slipped sidewise under the long span top steel projecting from adjoining spans.* Furthermore, this sequence

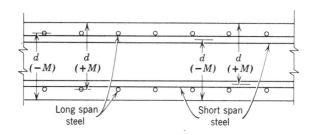

Fig. 11.10. Steel arrangement and effective depths.

places long span steel, both top and bottom, in the favorable position nearest the surface of the slab, as illustrated in Fig. 11.10. All short span steel utilizes an effective depth 1 bar diameter less than that available for the long span. (Some may prefer to offset the short span middle strip steel by 1 additional bar diameter and thus increase the effective depth for negative moment, ignoring the interference with long span top steel near the edges of the strip.)

In square slabs many designers use an average effective depth in designing column strip negative moment steel and middle strip positive moment steel. These two layers of steel are in contact and the average effective depth would be t minus the cover minus 1 bar diameter D. Although such an approach was recommended in the case of the slab supported on all four sides, the basis there was that load could be carried in either direction in such an indeterminate slab and excess strength in one direction would offset a slight deficiency in the other direction. In the flat slab such reasoning is not valid, unless supplemented by further analysis.

* The *CRSI Design Handbook*[3] suggests a slightly different sequence:

1. Place straight bottom bars in long span column strip.
2. Place all short span bars (bent and straight) in column strips only.
3. Place remaining long span steel, both straight and bent.
4. Place short span middle strip bars.

This arrangement places both long and short span column strip steel in the bottom of the slab, but seems to lead to considerable interference of bottom steel, especially when the drop panels are omitted and the bottom straight bars are therefore long. Where interference exists, close inspection is required to assure that the interference is resolved as the designer expects it to be.

REINFORCED CONCRETE FUNDAMENTALS

Although it is true that the flat slab can carry load in either direction, it must in fact carry the load in *both* directions. As indicated by Nichols' analysis in Sec. 11.2, statics requires that the sum of positive and negative moments in *each* direction meet a fixed total. A deficiency of positive moment resistance in one direction can be made up by a surplus of negative moment strength in that same direction, but excess positive moment in the perpendicular direction is not pertinent to the direction in question. Similar statements can be made about the negative moment strength over the column. Thus indeterminate action extends only to the distribution of moment between column and middle strip and between positive and negative moments, not to any possibility of assistance to strength in one direction by excess strength in the perpendicular direction.

Accordingly, the author does not recommend the use of average *d* in flat slab construction except in the calculation of shear strength around the column capital or drop panel. With square panels the smaller *d* will be used to establish the required steel. With rectangular panels the smaller *d* will be used for the short span and the larger *d* for the long span.

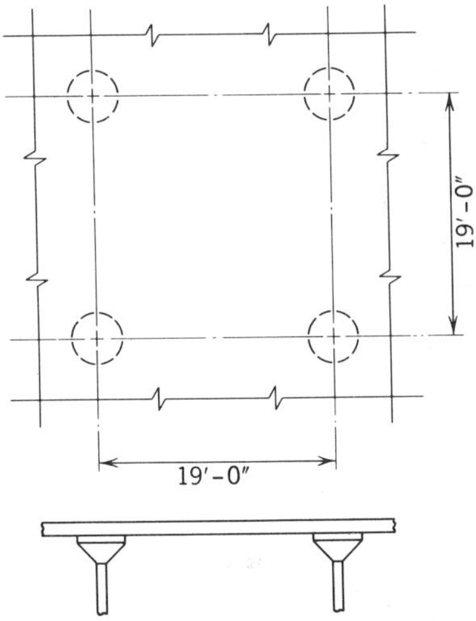

Fig. 11.11. Layout of flat slab of Sec. 11.8a.

11.8. FLAT SLAB DESIGN WITHOUT DROP PANELS USING EMPIRICAL MOMENTS

(a) Design conditions

A flat slab to carry a total dead plus live load of 200 psf, which includes its own weight, is to be designed for a 19-ft by 19-ft interior panel (Fig. 11.11), intermediate grade steel, $f_c' = 3000$ psi. The empirical method of Art. 1004 will be used.

SOLUTION

The use of this method requires that there be at least three continuous panels of nearly equal span and that the panel length-to-width ratio not exceed 1.33 (Art. 1004*a*). Under this empirical method most of the design steps are specified.

(b) Choice of slab thickness

Try a column capital of about $0.2L = 3.8$ ft, say, 3 ft 6 in. diameter. This arbitrary choice may be increased if shear stress is too large, reduced if shear stress is small. However, it should also be noted that the total moment M_0 is rather sensitive to a change in c, a large c considerably reducing M_0.

Articles 1002c(4) and 1004d(1) require the minimum slab thickness $t = L/36 = 228/36 = 6.35$, say, 6.5 in., which exceeds the absolute minimum of 5 in. Minimum t_1 by Art. 1004d(2), where c and L are in feet and t_1 is in inches, is

$$t_1 = 0.028L \left(1 - \frac{2}{3}\frac{c}{L}\right) \sqrt{\frac{w'}{f_c'/2000}} + 1.5$$

$$= 0.028 \times 19(1 - 0.123) \sqrt{\frac{200}{3000/2000}} + 1.5$$

$$= 5.38 + 1.5 = 6.88, \text{ say, } 7 \text{ in.}$$

These trial dimensions must be checked for stress conditions.

The critical section for shear [Art. 1002c(2)] lies a distance $d = 7 - 1.5 = 5.5$ in. beyond the column capital and thus has a diameter of $42 + 2 \times 5.5 = 53$ in. $= 4.42$ ft and a perimeter of $3.14 \times 53 = 166.5$ in.

$$V = 200(19^2 - 3.14 \times 4.42^2/4) = 200(361 - 15.3) = 69,100 \text{ lb}$$

The allowable v depends upon the distribution of tension steel. For a uniform steel spacing across the column strip, which is $19 \times 12/2 = 114$ in. wide, the proportion of the total column strip steel passing through the critical section is $53/114 = 0.465$.

$$\text{Allowable } v = 0.025f_c' + 0.005f_c'(0.465 - 0.25)/0.25$$

$$= 0.025f_c' + 0.0043f_c' = 0.0293f_c' = 87.9 \text{ psi}$$

$$\text{Reqd. } d_v = V/bjv = 69,100 \div (166.5 \times 0.875 \times 87.9) = 5.39 \text{ in.}$$

This average d calls for $t = 5.39 + D + 0.75 = 6.14 + D$, say, 7 in.

Because the foregoing formula for t_1 is actually a calculation of depth for a moment of $0.50M_0$, the column strip negative moment of $0.46M_0$ (Art. 1004f) should always require a smaller thickness if $F = 1.0$. This will be verified by actual calculation.

$$M_0 = 0.09WLF \left(1 - \frac{2}{3}\frac{c}{L}\right)^2$$

$$W = 200 \times 19^2 = 72,200 \text{ lb}$$

$$F = 1.15 - c/L = 1.15 - 3.5/19 = 1.15 - 0.184 = 0.966 < 1.00$$

$$M_0 = 0.09 \times 72,200 \times 19 \times 1(1 - 0.667 \times 0.184)^2 = 95,000 \text{ ft-lb}$$

The negative moment for the column strip is shown in the Code as $0.46M_0 = 0.46 \times 95,000 = 43,700$ ft-lb. The effective width for bending [Art. 1002c(1)] is $0.75 \times 19 \times 12/2 = 85.5$ in. This reduced effective width gives partial recognition to the heavy concentration of negative moment near the column.

$$d_M = \sqrt{M/Rb} = \sqrt{(43,700 \times 12) \div (236 \times 85.5)} = 5.08 \text{ in.}$$

TABLE 11.1. Steel Calculations for Flat Slab of Sec. 11.8

	Column Strip				Middle Strip			
	Negative		Positive		Negative		Positive	
	E-W	N-S	E-W	N-S	E-W	N-S	E-W	N-S
	1.69 / 5.31	1.06 / 5.94	5.31 / 1.69	5.94 / 1.06	5.31 / 1.69	1.06 / 5.94	5.31 / 1.69	5.94 / 1.06
	Use same d		Use same d		Use same d		Use same d	
M coefficient	0.46		0.22		0.16		0.16	
M, ft-lb	43,700		20,900		15,200		15,200	
d, for #5	5.31		5.31		5.31		5.31	
for #4					5.37		5.50	
$A_s = \dfrac{M \times 12}{20{,}000 \times 0.866d}$ $= M/1445d$	5.70		2.73		1.98	1.96	1.98	1.91
$0.0025bd = 0.285d$	—		—		1.52	1.53	1.52	1.57
No. of #5	19		9		7		7	
No. of #4	—		—		10		10	
USE Bent	8-#5		4-#5		10-#4		5-#4	
Straight	11-#5		5-#5		none		5-#4	

Based on #5 bars

7"

FLAT SLABS AND RELATED TYPES

To provide this d with the steel in the less favorable layer requires:

$$t = 5.08 + 1.5D + 0.75 = 5.83 + 1.5D < 7 \text{ in.}$$

USE $t = 7$ in., $c = 3$ ft 6 in.

Table 11.1 is a convenient form for assembling calculation data. The sketches assume $\#5$ bars and 0.75-in. clear cover.

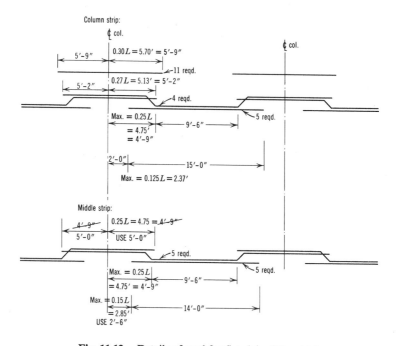

Fig. 11.12. Details of steel for flat slab of Sec. 11.8c.

(c) Choice of reinforcing bars

In working out the depths available at the several sections of critical moment, the designer must visualize the sequence* in which steel must be placed, as discussed in Sec. 11.7. In rectangular panels, the long span steel is given the more favorable position, as shown in Table 11.1. The calculations for reinforcing steel are also included in this table. The E-W and N-S strips would involve separate calculations except in the square slab.

The minimum number of bars in the middle strip for maximum spacing of $2t$ is $9.5 \times 12/(2 \times 7.0) = 9^-$. The use of $\#4$ bars in the middle strip increases d for this strip by 0.06 in. to 5.37 in. for the negative moment and by 0.19 in. to 5.50 in. for the positive moment. Although this reduces the required steel slightly, it does not change the number of bars.

The bars selected should be bent in accordance with the requirements of Code

* The designer must specify the placement sequence on the drawings.

Art. 1004g. These requirements are summarized in Fig. 1004g of the Code. The bar details are shown in Fig. 11.12. The drawings would show these as bands of steel, as in Fig. 11.13.

(d) Bond stresses—anchorage

Probably the best check on bond stresses is to see that all bars have the full development length beyond points of critical stress. Since the cover is small,

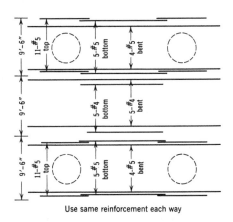

Use same reinforcement each way

Fig. 11.13. Bands of slab steel in flat slab of Sec. 11.8c.

the author will use the allowable bond stress for anchorage or development as $u = 150$ psi instead of the ACI Code value of $0.10f_c'$.

Then $L'' = (f_s/4u)D = [20{,}000/(4 \times 150)]D = 33.3D = 21$ in. for $\#5$ bars or 17 in. for $\#4$ bars. For the positive moment steel more than these lengths are provided, even beyond the bend-up points. For the negative moment steel the Code (Art. 1002b) suggests that the maximum moment (and stress) be considered at a distance A from the center line of the column. In this case $A = 0.5c + 0.5t = 21 + 3.5 = 24.5$ in. $= 2.04$ ft. There is an ample development length beyond the distance A. The point where part of the top steel is bent down can also create a peak stress in the adjacent bars which continue. Since the bend-down point is near the point of inflection, this peak stress must be relatively small and unimportant. Since cracks tend to form at the end of bars, it is better not to stop all the top steel at one point. Hence the straight portion of the top bars in the middle strip will be lengthened to 5.0 ft beyond the center line of the column. As an alternate, the bend-up point might be moved a little closer to the column.

(e) Nominal bond stresses

Some formal calculations of bond stress can be made. Consider a circular section around the column at the distance A, as in Fig. 11.14a. The diameter is then $2A = 49$ in. $= 4.08$ ft. The number of negative moment bars through this section each way is approximately $19 \times 4.08/9.50 = 8.16$, say, 8 bars. Each bar is picking up tension at two places, where it enters the section and where it leaves it. With equal bars in the perpendicular direction, $\Sigma o = 4 \times 8 \times 1.96 = 62.6$ in. The total shear is one full panel load less the load over the circular area within the section, that is,

$$V = 72,200 - 0.786 \times 4.08^2 \times 200 = 69,600 \text{ lb}$$

The average depth may be used in calculating the bond stress here.

$$u = \frac{V}{\Sigma o \times 0.875d} = \frac{69,600}{62.6 \times 0.875 \times 5.62} = 227 \text{ psi}$$

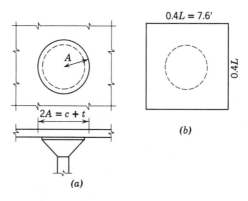

Fig. 11.14. Sections used in check on bond on flat slab of Sec. 11.8e.

This is less than the Code allowable of 300 psi but is greater than the author would permit for this small cover (150 psi) except that this bond stress drops off rapidly as larger circles are considered. On this basis the bond is considered satisfactory.

Bond might also be checked at the point of inflection around the column—for separate points of inflection for maximum negative and maximum positive moment if both were known. For example, the bond stress at sections $0.2L$ from the center of the column will be checked. If one considers the closed section of Fig. 11.14b, total $V = 72,000 - 7.6^2 \times 200 = 61,700$ lb. On this section the positive moment steel provides the smaller perimeter and hence the higher bond stress. The number of bars at one face of this section is $5 \times 7.6/9.5 = 4.0$

$$u = \frac{61,700}{(4 \times 4 \times 1.96)0.875 \times 5.31} = 424 \text{ psi}$$

This would exceed the Code allowable. The situation could be improved by: (1) substituting 8-#4 straight bars for the 5-#5, which would give u approximately 350 psi; (2) using more straight bottom bars and fewer bars bent up; (3) moving the bend-up point of the bent bars closer to the support to avoid the necessity of checking the straight bars alone. Actually, the high local bond stress does not worry the author since the development length seems to be entirely adequate in this case.

It might reasonably be argued that all bond stresses calculated on this basis should be discounted. If the static moment is to be reduced 28% from the value given by a coefficient of 0.125 to a value based on 0.09, this implies a reduced tension in the steel and along with this must go bond stresses also reduced by the same 28%.

Perhaps this discussion indicates why bond stresses in flat slabs are rarely calculated. It certainly indicates the desirability of using small bars at closer spacing rather than large bars.

11.9. FLAT SLAB DESIGN USING DROP PANELS AND EMPIRICAL MOMENTS

(a) Design conditions

A flat slab to carry a total dead plus live load of 200 psf, which includes its own weight, is to be designed for a 19-ft by 21-ft typical interior panel, intermediate grade steel, $f_c' = 3000$ psi. The empirical method of Art. 1004 will be used.

SOLUTION

As in Sec. 11.8, the use of the empirical method requires that there be at least three continuous spans and that the panel length-to-width ratio not exceed 1.33.

(b) Choice of column capital and slab thickness

Try a column capital of about $0.2L = 4.2$ ft, say 4 ft 3 in., subject to further investigation. Articles 1002c(4) and 1004d(1) require a 4-in. minimum thickness outside of the drop but not less than $t_2 = L/40 = 252/40 = 6.3$ in., say, 6.5 in., provided the drop meets two conditions. The drop must give $t_1 = 1.25t_2 = 1.25 \times 6.3 = 7.86$ in.,* or more, say, 8 in., and the drop panel must extend for at least one-third of the span in each direction [Art. 1004e(2)]. Accordingly, the drop panel will be first tried as $L/3 = 7$ ft square. (In the 19-ft direction this could have been reduced to 6 ft 4 in.)

Equation 8 in Art. 1004d(2) also gives a minimum value of t_1:

$$t_1 = 0.028L \left(1 - \frac{2}{3}\frac{c}{L}\right) \sqrt{\frac{w'}{f_c'/2000}} + 1.5$$

$$= 0.028 \times 21 \left(1 - \frac{2}{3}\frac{4.25}{21}\right) \sqrt{\frac{200}{3000/2000}} + 1.5$$

$$= 0.508 \sqrt{133.3} + 1.5 = 5.86 + 1.5 = 7.36 < 8.0 \text{ in.}.$$

* This could be interpreted to require $t_1 = 1.25t_2 = 1.25 \times 6.5 = 8.15$ in.

When the drop panel is used with $F = 1.0$, this formula will never control, since it was derived on the basis of $M = 0.50M_0$ and an effective width of 0.75 times the half panel width instead of 0.75 times the drop panel. When no drop panel is used, the formula does govern over the usual calculation based on $0.46M_0$.

The shear will next be checked around the column capital. The critical section (Fig. 11.15a) lies a distance $t_1 - 1.5 = 6.5$ in. outside of the column capital, with a perimeter of $3.14(51 + 2 \times 6.5) = 201$ in.

$$V = 200(21 \times 19 - 3.14 \times 5.33^2/4) = 200(399 - 22.3) = 75,300 \text{ lb}$$

Allowable $v = 0.03f_c' = 90$ psi since the critical section has a diameter of 5.33 ft in a 10.5-ft strip, putting over half of the negative moment steel across the section when the bars are uniformly spaced.

$$\text{Reqd. } d_v = \frac{75,300}{90 \times 0.875 \times 201} = 4.77 \ll 8.0 - 1.5 = 6.5$$

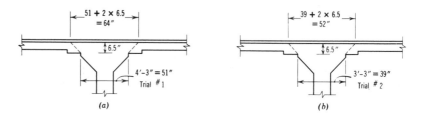

Fig. 11.15. Critical diagonal tension section for flat slab of Sec. 11.9b.

These specification minimum dimensions appear to provide an excess thickness both for shear and moment. The column capital could be reduced in size. Instead, first investigate a thinner drop panel, say 7.5 in. as required by Code Eq. 8. For this thinner drop, minimum $t_2 = L/36 = 252/36 = 7.0$ in. This suggests the possibility of using a slab without drop with a uniform $t = 7.5$ in. Such a slab would be a good design (involving slightly more dead weight) for many cases. This design, however, will be continued as an example of a slab with a drop panel, as shown in Fig. 11.15a.

$$\text{Try } t_1 = 8.0 \text{ in.,} \qquad t_2 = 6.5 \text{ in.}$$

Since the large column capital appears unnecessary, try a reduced column capital, $c = 3$ ft 3 in. The critical section for shear has a width of $39 + 2 \times 6.5 = 52$ in. and a circumference of $3.14(39 + 2 \times 6.5) = 164$ in. (Fig. 11.15b).

$$V = 200(21 \times 19 - 3.14 \times 4.33^2/4) = 76,800 \text{ lb}$$

The 52-in. diameter of the critical section is $52/126 = 0.413$ of the width of one column band and $52/114 = 0.457$ of the width of the other. Thus an average of $(0.413 + 0.457)/2 = 0.435$ parts of the column strip steel passes through this critical section.

$$\text{Allowable } v = \left(0.025 + 0.005 \frac{0.435 - 0.25}{0.25}\right) f_c'$$

$$= (0.025 + 0.0037)3000 = 86.3 \text{ psi}$$

$$d_v = 76,800 \div (86.3 \times 0.875 \times 163) = 6.25 \text{ in.} < 8.0 - 1.5 = 6.5 \quad \text{O.K.}$$

By inspection, this change in c will not increase the minimum t_1 enough for it to exceed 8.0 in.

USE $c = 3$ ft 3 in., drop = 7 ft 0 in. square

$F = 1.15 - c/L = 1.15 - 3.25/21 = 0.995.$ $F = 1.00$ governs for 21-ft strip.

$F = 1.15 - 3.25/19 = 1.15 - 0.171 = 0.979.$ $F = 1.00$ governs for 19-ft strip.

For the long strips:

$$M_0 = 0.09WLF\left(1 - \frac{2}{3}\frac{c}{L}\right)^2$$

$$= 0.09 \times 200 \times 21 \times 19 \times 21 \times 1.00 \left(1 - \frac{2}{3}\frac{3.25}{21}\right)^2 = 121,700 \text{ ft-lb}$$

Code Table 1004f [or Fig. 1004f(b)] shows moment coefficients:

Column strip, negative: 0.50   Middle strip, negative: 0.15

positive: 0.20   positive: 0.15

The column strip negative moment is $0.50 \times 121,700 = 60,800$ ft-lb. As a partial allowance for moment concentration around the column, Art. 1002c(1) permits only three-fourths of the drop panel width to be used for compression in resisting moment, that is, $b = 0.75 \times 84 = 63$ in.

$$d_M = \sqrt{\frac{60,800 \times 12}{236 \times 63}} = 7.01 \text{ in.}$$

With A_s for this moment in the top layer,

$$t_1 = 7.01 + 0.75 + D/2 = 7.76 + D/2 > 8.0$$

USE $\quad t_1 = 8.5$ in., $\quad t_2 = 6.5$ in.

Article 1004e(1) requires $t_2 \geqslant 8.5/1.5 = 5.67$ O.K.

For the short strips:

$$M_0 = 0.09 \times 200 \times 21 \times 19 \times 19 \times 1.0 \left(1 - \frac{2}{3}\frac{3.25}{19}\right)^2 = 107,000 \text{ ft-lb}$$

Column strip negative moment = $0.50M_0 = 53,500$ ft-lb

$$d_M = \sqrt{\frac{53,500 \times 12}{236 \times 63}} = 6.58 \text{ in.}$$

With A_s for this strip in the lower layer of top steel,

$$t_1 = 6.58 + 0.75 + 1.50D = 7.33 + 1.50D < 8.5 \quad \text{O.K.}$$

FLAT SLABS AND RELATED TYPES

It might be noted that the short strip requires a greater t than the long strip, because of the steel arrangement, but the 8.5-in. thickness is satisfactory for both. The final dimensions are shown in Fig. 11.16.

The critical t_2 for stresses is probably that specified in Code Eq. 9 of Art. 1004d(3), which was derived* for negative moment at the face of drop under average conditions. Consider the long strip.

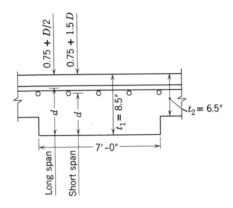

Fig. 11.16. Slab and drop section used in Sec. 11.9b.

* Mr. Joseph Di Stasio, chairman of the subcommittee which developed this chapter of the ACI Code, from a study of moment diagrams found $0.38M_0$ as an average value of the negative moment at the face of drop, giving, with $F = 1.0$,

$$M = 0.38 \times 0.09WL \left(1 - \frac{2}{3}\frac{c}{L}\right)^2 = 0.0342w\ BL^2 \left(1 - \frac{2}{3}\frac{c}{L}\right)^2$$

where B is the perpendicular span.

$$R = M/bd^2 = 0.5f_c'jk$$

For $f_c = 0.45f_c'$, $f_s = 20,000$ psi, $n = 30,000,000/1000f_c' = 30,000/f_c'$,

$nf_c = 0.45nf_c' = 0.45 \times 30,000 = 13,500$
$k = f_c \div (f_c + f_s/n) = 1 \div (1 + f_s/nf_c) = 1 \div (1 + 20,000/13,500) = 0.403$
$j = 1 - k/3 = 0.866$,
$R = 0.5 \times 0.45f_c' \times 0.866 \times 0.403 = 0.0787f_c' = 157f_c'/2000$
$b = 0.75B/2 = 0.375B$

$$d = \sqrt{\frac{M}{Rb}} = \sqrt{\frac{0.0342w'BL^2 \left(1 - \frac{2}{3}\frac{c}{L}\right)^2}{(157f_c'/2000)0.375B}} = 0.024L \left(1 - \frac{2}{3}\frac{c}{L}\right) \sqrt{\frac{w'}{f_c'/2000}}$$

To obtain t_1, 1 in. was added for cover and distance to center of crossed reinforcing steel. The 1-in. value was recognized as slightly less than average.

REINFORCED CONCRETE FUNDAMENTALS

$$t_2 = 0.024L \left(1 - \frac{2}{3}\frac{c}{L}\right) \sqrt{\frac{w'}{f_c'/2000} + 1}$$

$$= 0.024 \times 21 \left(1 - \frac{2}{3}\frac{3.25}{21}\right) \sqrt{\frac{200}{3000/2000} + 1}$$

$$= 5.24 + 1 = 6.24 < 6.5 \text{ used} \qquad \text{O.K.}$$

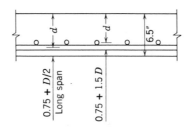

Fig. 11.17. Positive moment section used in Sec. 11.9b.

The largest moment away from the drop panel is the column strip positive moment on the long strip, which is $0.20 \times 121,700 = 24,300$ ft-lb. The width for compression [Art. 1002c(1)] is $0.75 \times 19 \times 12/2 = 85.5$ in.

$$d_M = \sqrt{\frac{24,300 \times 12}{236 \times 85.5}} = 3.82 \text{ in.}$$

For bottom layer steel (Fig. 11.17),

$$t_2 = 3.82 + 0.75 + 0.5D = 4.57 + 0.5D < 6.5 \qquad \text{O.K.}$$

The short strip steel is in upper layer, but t_2 is ample (by inspection).

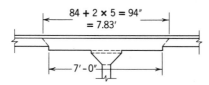

Fig. 11.18. Diagonal tension section near drop panel face.

For shear the average distance $d = 6.5 - 1.5 = 5$ in. outside the drop establishes a square $84 + 2 \times 5 = 94$ in. $= 7.83$ ft on each face, as indicated in Fig. 11.18.

$$V = 200(21 \times 19 - 7.83 \times 7.83) = 67,700 \text{ lb}$$

$$\text{Reqd. } d_v = \frac{67,700}{90 \times 0.875 \times 94 \times 4} = 2.28 \text{ in.} \ll 5 \text{ in.} \qquad \text{O.K.}$$

FLAT SLABS AND RELATED TYPES

TABLE 11.2. Steel Calculations for Flat Slab of Sec. 11.9

$M_0 = 121.7$ k ft (Long Span) $M_0 = 107.0$ k-ft (Short Span)

$$A_s = \frac{M \times 12}{20 \times 0.866d} = 0.694M/d$$

	Long Span				Short Span			
	Column Strip		Middle Strip		Column Strip		Middle Strip	
	Negative	Positive	Negative	Positive	Negative	Positive	Negative	Positive
t	8.5 at drop	6.5	6.5	6.5	8.5	6.5	6.5	6.5
d	7.44	5.44	5.44 / 5.50	5.44 / 5.50	6.81	4.81	4.81 / 5.00	4.81 / 5.00
M coefficient	0.50	0.20	0.15	0.15	0.50	0.20	0.15	0.15
M	60.8	24.3	18.3	18.3	53.5	21.4	16.1	16.1
A_s	5.67	3.11	2.33 / 2.31	2.33 / 2.31	5.45	3.08	2.33 / 2.23	2.33 / 2.23
Min. $A_s = 0.0025bd$			1.55	1.55			1.52	1.52
No. #5 bars	19	—	8	8	18	—	8	8
Max. spcg. #5	—	10	14.3	14.3	—	10	15.7	15.7
Allow. $2t = 13$ in.	—	11.4	N.G.	N.G.	—	11.5	N.G.	N.G.
No. #4 bars	—	O.K.	12	12	—	O.K.	12	12
USE Bent bars	10-#5	5-#5	12-#4	6-#4	10-#5	5-#5	12-#4	6-#4
Straight bars	9-#5	5-#5 / 8-#4 (for bond)	—	6-#4	8-#5	5-#5 / 8-#4 (for bond)	—	6-#4

(c) Choice of reinforcing bars

In designing the steel, it will be assumed* that steel is placed in the sequence given in Sec. 11.7. The effective depth illustrations in Table 11.2 are based on the use of #5 bars. The entire steel design calculations are summarized in this table.

The 8–#5 bars for positive and negative moment in the middle strips would give a spacing greater than twice the thickness [Art. 1002d(1)]. These bands have been redesigned with #4 bars. The effective depths in the table have been

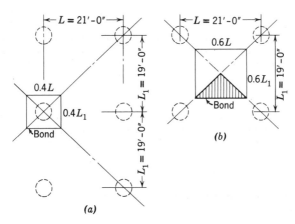

Fig. 11.19. Two sections used in bond check for slab of Sec. 11.9d.

revised accordingly, although this is a very minor correction. The illustrations were not revised.

Figure 1004g in the Code will be found helpful in detailing the steel, as in Sec. 11.8 for the flat slab without drop. These details will not be shown but for the purpose of the next paragraph the bend-up point of the bottom steel will be assumed at the 0.25L point of the span.

(d) Bond stress

As a rough check on the bond situation for the bars chosen, the bond stress will be approximated at a few points. It is probably possible to get positive moment in the column strip as close as 0.20L to the center line of the columns. On a rectangle with sides of 0.40L surrounding the column (Fig. 11.19a),

$$V = 200(21 \times 19 - 0.4 \times 21 \times 0.4 \times 19) = 67,000 \text{ lb}$$

This might be further broken down into the shear on one face across the long span.

$$V = 200(0.5 \times 19 \times 10.5 - 0.5 \times 0.4 \times 19 \times 0.2 \times 21) = 16,700 \text{ lb}$$

* Design drawings should specify the placement sequence.

This face is 0.4 × 19 ft wide and the only bottom steel crossing it consists of (0.4/0.5)5 = 4 straight #5 bars.

$$u = \frac{16,700}{4 \times 1.96 \times 0.875 \times 5.44} = 448 \text{ psi}$$

This might, with some logic, be reduced 28%, just as M_0 is reduced below the static moment. Then the bond stress would be 0.72 × 448 = 323 psi. This would be near the allowable of 300 psi. Except for the smaller d, the corresponding calculation for the short span would give the same results since the shear would work out the same and the identical bottom straight bars were used in that direction; the resulting bond stress would be some 12% larger. With development lengths carefully watched, these bond stresses might be accepted. Since the author regards $0.10f_c'$ as somewhat excessive when a small cover is used, he would prefer to substitute 8–#4 straight bars for the 5–#5 originally scheduled as bottom steel in each column strip, as shown finally in Table 11.2.

Top column strip steel on the long span near the point of inflection totals 9 straight and 5 bent #5 bars. It is obvious that this perimeter is adequate, from comparison with the bottom steel calculations.

A rough check will also be made on the middle strip steel. If the point of inflection is considered at 0.20L from the center of columns, these inflection lines form a rectangle as shown in Fig. 11.19b. The load on one quarter of this rectangle gives

$$V = 200(0.5 \times 0.6 \times 21 \times 0.3 \times 19) = 7160 \text{ lb}$$

Most of this shear can be taken as measuring the bond on the middle strip bottom bars.

$$u < \frac{7160}{6 \times 1.57 \times 0.875 \times 4.81} = 181 \text{ psi}$$

The bond on the top middle strip bars would be critical farther from the columns, beyond the bar bend-down point. There the bond would be lower since shear would be less and the perimeters would be the same as used for bottom bars.

Bond around the column capital will not be calculated since the development length of all bars there is ample. This bond stress calculation could be made as for the flat slab of Sec. 11.8. This bond stress is usually smaller than that near the points of inflection.

11.10. MINIMUM COLUMN SIZE

With slabs designed from empirical moment coefficients, columns must provide a certain minimum of stiffness, as discussed briefly in Sec. 11.6. The minimum average moment of inertia I_c of the gross concrete column section above and below the slab shall be determined by the formula:

$$I_c = \frac{t^3 H}{0.5 + w_D/w_L}, \text{ but not less than } 1000$$

where t = slab thickness, but not more than required by Code Eqs. 8 and 9 in Art. 1004d

H = story height in feet

w_D, w_L = dead and live loads.

For the flat slab with the drop designed in Sec. 11.9, $t_1 = 8.5$ in. but the minimum t_1 calculation* gives only 7.58 in., which may be used here. Assume $w_D = 95$ psf, $w_D/w_L = 95/105 = 0.904$, and $H = 10$ ft.

$$I_c = \frac{7.58^3 \times 10}{0.5 + 0.904} = 3120 \text{ in.}^4 > 1000$$

This value is the average for the columns above and below. If these columns are assumed equal, for round columns of diameter D,

$$\pi D^4/64 = 3120$$

$$\text{Min. } D = \sqrt[4]{3120 \times 64/3.14} = \sqrt[4]{63,600} = 15.85 \text{ in.}$$

This column size may not govern in comparison with the design for combined direct stress and bending (Chap. 13). Attention is called to the column moment specified in Art. 1004b(2). For interior columns the total moment on the columns above and below is

$$(WL_1 - W_D L_2)/40$$

where W = total panel load

W_D = panel dead load

L_1, L_2 = adjacent spans.

For w_D = say, 95 psf,

$$W_D = 95 \times 21 \times 19 = 37,900 \text{ lb}$$

$$W = 200 \times 21 \times 19 = 79,800 \text{ lb}$$

$$M_{\text{cols.}} = (WL_1 - W_D L_2)/f = (79,800 - 37,900)21/40 = 22,000 \text{ ft-lb}$$

This moment should be distributed between the columns above and below in proportion to their stiffness. Section 11.13b indicates that the column capital increases the relative stiffness of the column below the floor roughly

$$* \ t_1 = 0.028L\left(1 - \frac{2}{3}\frac{c}{L}\right)\sqrt{\frac{w'}{f_c'/2000}} + 1.5 = 0.028 \times 21\left(1 - \frac{2}{3}\frac{3.25}{L}\right)\sqrt{\frac{200}{3000/2000}} + 1.5$$

$$= 0.528\sqrt{133.3} + 1.5 = 7.58 \text{ in.}$$

in the ratio of 6 : 4.4. Hence 9300 ft-lb of moment will be assigned to the upper column and 12,700 ft-lb to the lower one.

11.11. ELASTIC ANALYSIS OF FLAT SLABS

The assumptions commonly made in analyzing flat slab structures as frames are stated in Art. 1003a. As in an analysis of beams and columns, the structure is subdivided into bents running each way. The entire slab width, namely, one half panel width on each side of the column, is considered in establishing the slab load and stiffness. A moment of inertia calculation based on gross concrete area, rather than on transformed area, is suggested.

The chief complications compared to ordinary frame analysis* are three in number. First, slabs and columns are usually variable section members. The value of $1/EI$ for slabs is taken as zero for the width of the column capital. Likewise, for columns $1/EI$ is considered zero from the bottom of the capital to the top of the floor above. The second complication lies in defining the maximum negative moment as that acting at a specific distance A from the center line of the column. The distance A, although defined in other terms in Art. 1000, normally extends a distance $t_1 - 0.5t_2$ beyond the column capital or $t_1 - 0.5t_2$ beyond the column when no capital is used. If no drop panel is used, $t_1 - 0.5t_2$ becomes simply $0.5t$. The same distance A is applied to column strips and middle strips alike. The third complication relates to the distribution of the total moment between column and middle strips. Table 1003c of the Code tabulates recommendations for these distributions, which differ for positive and negative moments.

11.12. FRAME CONSTANTS FOR FLAT SLAB ANALYSIS

For flat slab frame analysis, the stiffness, carry-over, and fixed-end moment coefficients are needed for members having an infinite I at one or both ends. Figure 11.20 shows carry-over factors C and stiffness coefficients k for columns and slabs. The stiffness then becomes kEI/L, where I is the minimum moment of inertia of the member cross section and L is the member length center to center of joints. It will be noted that an unsymmetrical member has different factors from each end. The first subscript denotes the end which is rotated; thus k_{TB} applies for a joint

* Ordinary moment distribution methods are given in Appendix B and permissible simplifications are stated in Code Art. 702.

REINFORCED CONCRETE FUNDAMENTALS

rotation at the top and C_{TB} gives the carry-over factor from the top to the bottom end of the member. Figure 11.21a gives fixed-end moment coefficients for a uniform load and a few other loads on a symmetrical span; Fig. 11.21b gives the coefficients for a single concentrated load.

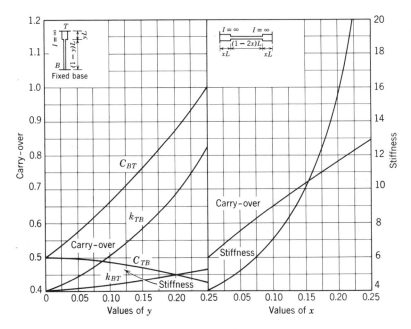

Fig. 11.20. Carry-over factors and stiffness factors for member with infinite I over part of length. Adapted from Ref. 4, Portland Cement Assn.

Unsymmetrical sections can also be analyzed easily by the column analogy method,[5, 6] or other methods developed for members of varying moment of inertia may be used.

Figure 11.22 is based on the work of R. L. Bertin as reported by Peabody.[7] Their suggestions as to the proper length of the sections of infinite I are probably more nearly correct than the Code suggestion that these extend from the top of the floor to the bottom of the capital for columns and all across the capital for beams. They suggest:

For columns, yh = distance from bottom of drop panel to bottom of capital (Fig. 11.22a).

For beams, $xL = b - (b - a)I/I_1$, where the symbols are indicated in Fig. 11.22b.

FLAT SLABS AND RELATED TYPES   309

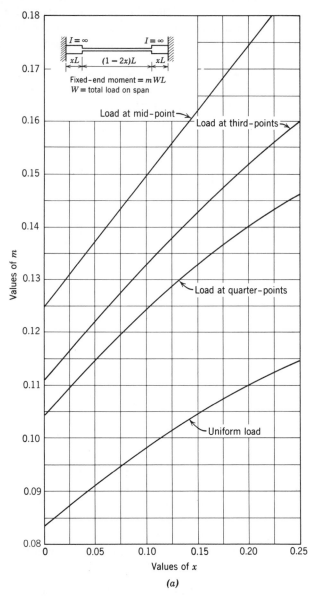

Fig. 11.21a. Fixed-end moment coefficients for members having infinite I over part of length, symmetrical loading. Adapted from Ref. 4, Portland Cement Assn.

11.13. EXAMPLE OF ELASTIC ANALYSIS FOR FLAT SLAB

(a) Data

The moments for the long strips of the flat slab of Sec. 11.9 will be analyzed to indicate the method and to enable a few comparisons to be made. The important data for use here are:

$w = 200$ psf, assumed 95 psf dead load

105 psf live load

19-ft by 21-ft continuous panels with slab 6.5 in. thick

Drop panels 7 ft square and 8.5 in. thick

Column capital, 3 ft. 3 in. in diameter, with 1.5 in.
vertical edge just below slab

Column size assumed 16-in. diameter

Story height, floor to floor assumed 10 ft.

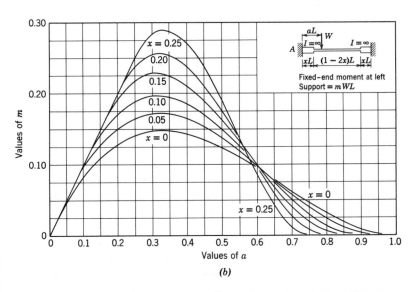

Fig. 11.21b. Fixed-end moment coefficients for members having infinite I over part of length, concentrated load. Adapted from Ref. 4, Portland Cement Assn.

(b) Moment distribution constants

The panel in question will be considered as one of a large number of equal panels.

$$I_{\text{slab}} = \tfrac{1}{12}bt^3 = \tfrac{1}{12} \times 19 \times (6.5/12)^3 = 0.252 \text{ ft}^4$$

The I within the column capital, a distance 1.62 ft at each end of the slab, may be considered infinite [Art. 1003a(3)].

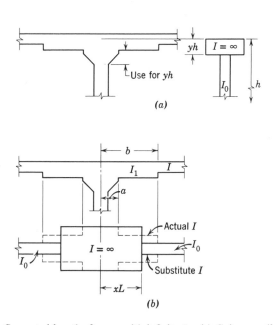

(a)

(b)

Fig. 11.22. Suggested lengths for use with infinite I. (a) Column. (b) Slab.

The drop panel gives an I greater than 0.252 ft⁴ over an additional 1.88 ft at each end. Strictly stated, the beam thus has a low I over the middle 14 ft, an increased I over an additional 1.88 ft at each end, and a nearly infinite I over the remaining 1.62 ft at each end. Since no curves for stiffness, and so forth, are available for this case, the method suggested by R. L. Bertin, who originally studied this method of analysis for inclusion in the Code, will be used as given in Sec. 11.12 and indicated in Fig. 11.22b.

$$xL = b - (b - a)I/I_1 = 3.5 - 1.88 \times 0.252/I_1$$

The slab cross section for I_1 is illustrated in Fig. 11.23. From mid-depth of the 6.5-in. slab, the centroid distance is

$$\bar{y} = \frac{-84 \times 2 \times 4.25}{228 \times 6.5 + 84 \times 2} = -0.43 \text{ in.} = -0.036 \text{ ft}$$

$$I_1 = 19 \times 0.542^3/12 + 19 \times 0.542 \times 0.036^2 + 7 \times 0.167^3/12 +$$
$$7 \times 0.167 \times 0.318^2$$

$$= 0.252 + 0.013 + 0.003 + 0.119 = 0.387 \text{ ft}^4$$

$$xL = 3.5 - 1.88 \times 0.252/0.387 = 3.5 - 1.23 = 2.27 \text{ ft}$$

$$x = 2.27/21 = 0.108$$

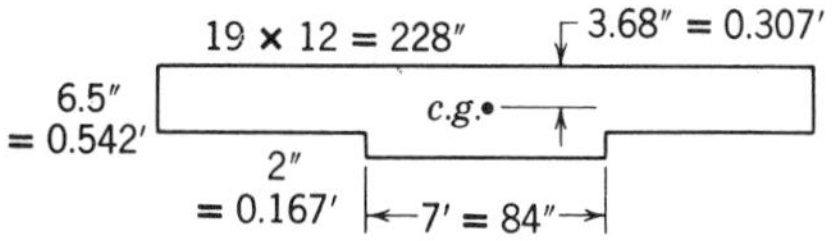

Fig. 11.23. Slab cross section used for moment of inertia.

From Fig. 11.20, for the slab,

$$k = 7.50, \qquad C = 0.660*$$
$$K = kEI/L = 7.50E \times 0.252/21 = 0.0900E$$

From Fig. 11.21,

$$m = 0.0992*$$
$$M^F_{D+L} = 0.0992 \times 200 \times 19 \times 21^2 = 166,500 \text{ ft-lb}$$
$$M_D{}^F = 0.0992 \times 95 \times 19 \times 21^2 = 79,000 \text{ ft-lb}$$

For the column, take yh as the depth of the capital below the slab, that is, $1.5/12 + 0.5(3.25 - 1.33) = 1.08$ ft, or $y = 1.08/10.0 = 0.108$. From Fig. 11.20,

$$k_{TB} = 6.30, \qquad k_{BT} = 4.44$$
$$I_0 = 3.14 \times 16^4/64 = 3220 \text{ in.}^4 = 0.155 \text{ ft}^4$$
$$K_{TB} = 6.30E \times 0.155/10 = 0.0975E$$
$$K_{BT} = 4.44E \times 0.155/10 = 0.0688E$$

---

* Column analogy, with I of infinity only within column capital, leads to

$$k = 7.38, \qquad C = 0.632, \qquad m = 0.0982$$

The distribution factors at each interior joint will be alike:

	K	D.F. $= K/\Sigma K$
Slab	0.0900E	0.260
Column above	0.0688E	0.198
Column below	0.0975E	0.282
Slab	0.0900E	0.260
ΣK	0.3463E	1.000

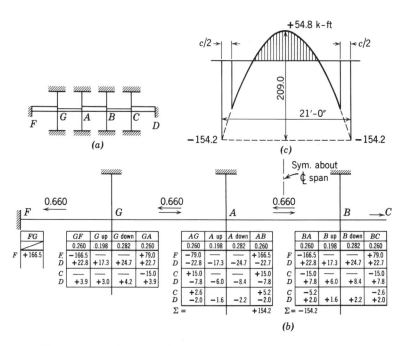

(a)

(c)

(b)

Fig. 11.24. Maximum positive moment calculation. (a) Loading pattern. (b) Moment distribution. (c) Moment diagram.

(c) Maximum positive moment

The loading for maximum positive moment is shown in Fig. 11.24a and the distribution is shown in Fig. 11.24b. The complete frame is symmetrical about the middle of span AB; hence the moments at joint B are like those at joint A, except for having opposite signs. The resulting moment diagram is plotted in Fig. 11.24c with the maximum positive moment of 54.8 k-ft determined by $WL/8 = 200 \times 19 \times 21^2/8 = 209,000$ ft-lb reduced by $M_{AB} = -154.2$ k-ft. The actual moment within the column capital width is quite different since the reaction is distributed, not concentrated at the center of the column. This does not modify the positive moment which the diagram establishes.

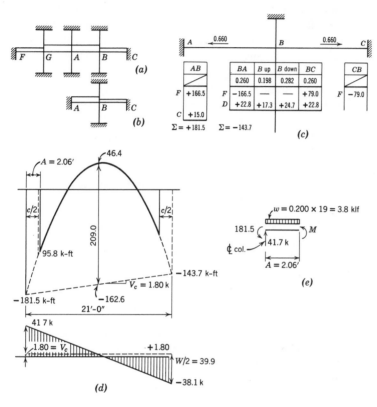

Fig. 11.25. Maximum negative moment calculation. (*a*) Loading pattern. (*b*) Equivalent reduced frame. (*c*) Moment distribution. (*d*) Moment and shear diagram. (*e*) Free body for calculation of moment at critical section at distance A from center line of column.

The positive moment is to be allocated between the column and the middle strip in the ratio of 0.6 to 0.4. Before this is done the sum of maximum negative and maximum positive moments will be compared with the empirical M_0, since Art. 1002a in this case may permit some reduction in the calculated moments. This comparison must await the calculation of the maximum negative moment.

(d) Maximum negative moment

The loading for maximum negative moment is shown in Fig. 11.25a. Since the frame and loading are symmetrical about the center column A, there is no rotation of joint B and only the reduced frame shown in Fig. 11.25b is needed for the distribution of Fig. 11.25c.

The unsymmetrical moment diagram is plotted in Fig. 11.25d. The actual moment within the column capital width c is quite different from that shown, because of the distributed reaction there, but this portion of the diagram is not needed except as a step in establishing the portion depicted as a solid line. The corresponding shear diagram is also shown with the maximum shear $V = 0.5W + V_c = 0.5 \times 0.200 \times 21 \times 19 + 1.80 = 39.9 + 1.8 = 41.7$ k.

The critical section for negative moment is defined in Art. 1003b as not more than the distance A from the center of the column. The definition of A in Art. 1000 is equivalent in this case to one-half of the column capital width plus the drop thickness minus one-half of the slab thickness $= 0.5 \times 3.25 + 8.5/12 - 0.5 \times 6.5/12 = 2.06$ ft. Based on the free body of Fig. 11.25e, the critical negative moment is:

$$M = -181.5 + 41.7 \times 2.06 - 0.2 \times 19 \times 2.06^2/2 = -103.7 \text{ k-ft}$$

According to Code Table 1003c, this moment should be distributed between the column and middle strips in the ratio of 76% and 24%.

(e) Reduction in total moment

Since the frame is one which might be designed on the basis of the empirical method of Art. 1004 and in every way satisfies this Art. 1004, the moments may be reduced as suggested in Art. 1002a:

$$\text{Maximum positive moment} = 54.8 \text{ k-ft}$$

$$\text{Maximum negative moment} = 103.7 \text{ k-ft}$$

$$\text{Total } M = 158.5 \text{ k-ft}$$

$$M_0 = 0.09WFL \left(1 - \frac{2}{3}\frac{c}{L}\right)^2$$

$$F = 1.15 - c/L = 1.15 - 3.25/21 < 1.0 \qquad \text{Use } F = 1$$

$$M_0 = 0.09 \times 0.200 \times 19 \times 21^2 \times 1 \left(1 - \frac{2}{3}\frac{3.25}{21}\right)^2 = 121.7 \text{ k-ft} < 158.5$$

Reduce the design moments in the ratio $121.7/158.5 = 0.767$

Modified positive moment = 54.8 × 0.767 = 42.0 k-ft

Column strip positive moment = 0.60 × 42.0 = 25.2 k-ft

Middle strip positive moment = 0.40 × 42.0 = 16.8 k-ft

(The empirical method gave 24.3 and 18.3 k-ft, respectively)

Modified negative moment = −103.7 × 0.767 = −79.5 k-ft

Column strip negative moment = 0.76(−79.5) = −60.4 k-ft

Middle strip negative moment = 0.24(−79.5) = −19.1 k-ft

(The empirical method gave −60.8 and −18.3 k-ft respectively)

(f) Comparison between elastic analysis and empirical method

The foregoing calculations indicate that there is little difference between the results of the two methods for a case such as this. Because the total moment is reduced to M_0, the only difference which can exist lies in the distribution of the total moment. For a less regular layout or for slabs not completely satisfying Art. 1004, where the empirical method cannot be used, the total moments will not be reduced to M_0 and the differences will be considerably greater. In such cases the frame analysis procedure *must* be used.

Because of restrictions associated with the empirical method, the frame analysis procedure may be desirable even with regular layouts. The following limitations are applied only to designs based on the empirical method:

1. Minimum of three continuous panels in each direction.
2. Length of panel not to exceed 1.33 times the width.
3. Successive spans not to differ more than 20% of the longer span.
4. The use of three-fourths of the strip (or drop panel) as the effective width in the calculation of compressive stress.
5. Minimum column size and minimum column moment.
6. Minimum thicknesses by Code Eqs. 8 and 9 of Art. 1004d.
7. Limitations on drop panel size.
8. Detailed specifications on bar lengths.
9. Restrictions on openings through flat slabs.

This does not mean that the designer is relieved of all responsibility relative to these matters. Rather, it means his analysis should be adequate to determine these matters. His frame analysis gives him moments on columns, moment diagrams for bending bars, and methods of recognizing loss of stiffness and strength due to openings through the slab. The Code allows the designer who uses an elastic analysis more freedom because he is assumed to be more competent and more capable of establishing his own standards.

11.14. FLAT PLATES

In principle, flat plate design differs almost not at all from the flat slab design of Sec. 11.8. Westergaard showed[2] that the concentration of moment around the column becomes more severe as the column capital is made smaller. With no column capital it would be logical to use a smaller width in calculating f_c (or depth for moment) than is required in Art. 1002c(1), that is, less than three-fourths of the strip width. However, this is not a requirement of the Code. [Possibly the requirement of Art. 1002c(2)b that at least 25% of the column strip negative moment steel pass through the critical diagonal tension section is related to this moment problem.]

Since the critical diagonal tension section at a distance d beyond the column is not wide and since the allowable v is usually near $0.025f_c'$, the slab thickness will often be governed by the unit shear. Many designers ignore the exact requirement as stated in the Code, using a larger unit shear and adding some form of diagonal tension reinforcement. Tests known to the author on slabs with web reinforcement are somewhat inconclusive. The Code restriction probably reflects the need for caution until such time as the effectiveness of web reinforcement in slabs has been fully verified by tests. A few tests recently reported[8] are encouraging. The author believes one essential of effective web reinforcement is that such reinforcement must tie the main tensile steel to the body of the compression concrete.

At least three forms of web reinforcement are in use. The Portland Cement Association originally suggested a spearhead type such as is shown in Fig. 11.26a. Many engineers prefer to use bent bars like those in Fig. 11.26b, which are in addition to the regular moment steel. A patented reinforcement in the form of short cantilever structural steel sections as shown in Fig. 11.26c is used in the Wheeler "Smooth Slab System."

11.15. SLABS WITH WIDE SHALLOW BEAMS ON ALL FOUR SIDES

The Code definition of a flat slab includes slabs with paneled ceilings, provided the reduced thickness lies entirely within the area of intersecting

REINFORCED CONCRETE FUNDAMENTALS

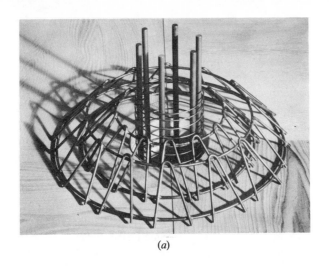

(a)

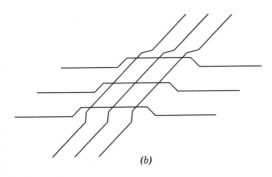

(b)

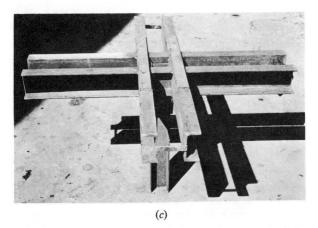

(c)

Fig. 11.26. Shear strengthening for slab. (a) Spearhead reinforcing.
(b) Special bent bars. (c) Structural sections (patented). Courtesy
Mr. Walter H. Wheeler.

FLAT SLABS AND RELATED TYPES

319

middle strips, is at least 4 in. thick, and is at least two-thirds the thickness of the remainder of the slab. Such slabs would have slightly reduced positive moments in the middle strip resulting from the local reduced stiffness and a corresponding increase in column strip negative moments, but these changes are not specified in the Code.

When the reduced thickness extends beyond the intersection of the middle strips, the construction does not qualify as a flat slab. Presumably this type of slab is to be analyzed as a two-way slab supported on all four sides. But the Code design coefficients for slabs supported on all four sides envisage supports with small deflections. In contrast, the resulting "beams" in the paneled construction may be quite wide and shallow and relatively flexible. They are thus subject to considerable deflection or sag under load. Coefficients for the central slab in the paneled construction would more properly be those for a two-way slab supported on all four sides by *flexible* supports. In the absence of specified values for the real conditions, the designer might properly (1) increase the positive moment coefficients and reduce the negative moment coefficients, (2) consider long and short strips as sharing less unequally in the load, since the long strips deflect more in this case, and (3) consider the load coming to the beams as less concentrated towards the middle of the beam spans.*

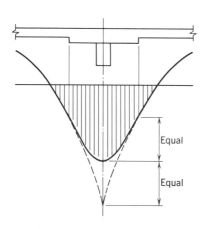

Fig. 11.27. Transverse moment across slab band or shallow beam.

Prior to the appearance of the 1956 Code, the author recommended analysis of these slabs with wide shallow beams as flat slabs, with some modification of moment coefficients and some adjustment of positive moment steel where the shallow slab extended into the column strip. Under the 1956 Code, the elastic analysis suggested for flat slabs appears proper, with the moment assigned to the "beams" equal to the difference

* If such statements seem to the student to leave too much responsibility to the designer, it is because a textbook tends to concentrate upon problems with specific answers and thereby leaves a false impression of exact, scientific procedures. The ordinary reinforced concrete designer faces situations every day which he can analyze only roughly, sometimes only vaguely. Thus design is often as much an art as a scientific procedure. Only gradually are the scientific boundaries expanded, even to the point of making three statements as definite as those above.

REINFORCED CONCRETE FUNDAMENTALS

between the total panel moment and the moment already assigned to the slabs. (Note that the total moment cannot be reduced to the flat slab M_0.) Provision should be made for transverse negative moment across the middle of all beams. Possibly a reasonable picture of this negative moment is that of Fig. 11.27 which, within the beam width, assumes the upward reaction distributed over the entire beam width.

Some designers refer to these wide shallow beams as slab bands. This term was originated for the construction described in the following section.

11.16. SLAB BANDS

The slab band[9] is a thickened section of slab acting as a wide shallow beam. The slab band has usually been used at interior column lines to parallel a spandrel beam along the exterior columns. It thus supports a one-way slab construction. Such a wide shallow support acts effectively to reduce the clear span of the one-way slab. The best analysis of this system appears to be an elastic frame analysis following closely the elastic analysis the Code suggests for flat slabs. The negative moment across the slab band might be treated as in Fig. 11.27, which assumes that the reaction for the one-way slab is distributed uniformly across the slab band. It might be noted that between columns the slab support is a rather flexible one and this leads to increased positive moment in the one-way slab.

The slab bands for such construction may be designed as ordinary beams, except that the shear around the column seems to be more nearly like that in a flat slab.

In some cases slab bands have been extended into an end panel and stopped in a manner which is quite similar to a dropped panel in flat slab construction. The corner slab itself is then supported on two adjacent spandrel beams and at the opposite corner by this special slab band, as in Fig. 11.28.

11.17. LIFT SLABS

Lift slabs are a flat plate type of slab which is cast at grade level embedding steel shoes or collars which fit loosely around the columns. After the slabs are cured they are lifted by a patented jack system to the proper level where the shoes are welded to the steel columns. Although the Code makes no special attempt to provide for this type of design, the elastic method of flat slab analysis would appear to be proper for lift slabs. Since column stiffness is small, there seems to be no section which deserves to be treated as having infinite moment of inertia. Loadings for maximum moment are also more significant in this case. A rigid joint between the collar and the column is an essential condition.

Since lift slabs do not qualify for empirical design procedures, total moment cannot be reduced to the M_0 value specified in Art. 1004. The distance A to the critical moment section seems to have little validity in

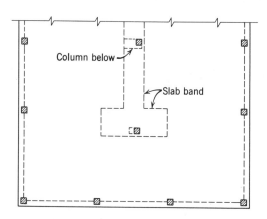

Fig. 11.28. Special case of extension of slab band into an end panel.

this case; the collar stiffness may determine whether the critical section is at the center of the column or farther out.

The designer must consider carefully the stresses caused by differential jack movements which in the field seem frequently to exceed the limits normally considered in the office.

11.18. CANTILEVERS FROM SLAB CONSTRUCTION

Lift slabs generally, and flat slabs and flat plates frequently, have the columns set back from the outside wall, thus causing the outermost section of the slab to act as a cantilever beyond the exterior columns. This is quite favorable to regular slab action. A proper overhang of the slab can provide a total negative moment which can almost eliminate the special problems associated with exterior slab panels.

The cantilever provides a total negative moment about the exterior columns which is statically determinate, but its distribution is not uniform. It is suggested that this distribution might be taken the same as that used

REINFORCED CONCRETE FUNDAMENTALS

to distribute negative moment between the column and middle strips in the elastic analysis method.   If the cantilever projects the ideal distance, it can thus balance the typical interior slab negative moments.   Longitudinal steel, as in any column strip, is needed to deliver the cantilever reaction ultimately to the columns.

It might also be noted that cantilever slabs have large deflections which become conspicuous after creep of concrete has taken place.   The use of some compression steel solely to reduce deflections is often justified.

SELECTED REFERENCES

1. J. R. Nichols, "Statical Limitations Upon the Steel Requirement in Reinforced Concrete Flat Slab Floors," *ASCE Trans.*, **77**, 1914, p. 1670.

2. H. M. Westergaard and W. A. Slater, "Moments and Stresses in Slabs," *ACI Proc.*, **17**, 1921, p. 415.

3. Raymond C. Reese, *CRSI Design Handbook*, Concrete Reinforcing Steel Institute, Chicago, 2nd ed., 1957.

4. "Frame Analysis Applied to Flat Slab Bridges," Portland Cement Association, Chicago.

5. Linton E. Grinter, *Theory of Modern Steel Structures*, Vol. II, Macmillan Co., New York, rev. ed., 1949, p. 259.

6. Chu-Kia Wang, *Statically Indeterminate Structures*, McGraw-Hill Book Co., New York, 1953, Chap. 9.

7. Dean Peabody, Jr., "Continuous Beam Analysis of Flat Slabs," *Jour. Boston Soc. Civil Engrs.*, **XXXV**, No. 1, Jan. 1948, p. 1.

8. Richard C. Elstner and Eivind Hognestad, "Shearing Strength of Reinforced Concrete Slabs," *ACI Jour.*, **28**, No. 1, July 1956; *Proc.*, **53**, p. 29.

9. Joseph H. Abel and Fred N. Severud, *Apartment Houses*, Reinhold Publishing Co., New York, 1947, p. 195.

10. Chas. S. Whitney, "Ultimate Shear Strength of Reinforced Concrete Slabs, Footings, and Frame Members Without Shear Reinforcement," *ACI Jour.*, **28**, Oct. 1957; *Proc.*, **54**, p. 265.

PROBLEMS

Prob. 11.1.   Considering shear alone, calculate the thickness required for a flat slab to carry a total load of 300 psf (which includes its own weight) over a 20-ft square panel with $f_c' = 3000$ psi.

(a) At the column if the capital has $c = 4$ ft 0 in.

(b) At the column if the capital has $c = 5$ ft 0 in.

(c) At the drop if the drop panel is 6 ft 8 in. square.

Prob. 11.2. Considering shear alone, calculate the slab thickness required to carry a total load of 150 psf (which includes its own weight) over a 20-ft square panel with $f_c' = 3000$ psi.

(a) At the column if the capital has $c = 3$ ft 6 in.

(b) At the column if an 18-in. square column is used with no capital and shear reinforcement is not used.

(c) At the column as in (b) except that the column is 15 in. square.

Prob. 11.3.

(a) Under the empirical method of Art. 1004, design a flat slab with a drop panel for a 22-ft square interior panel using $f_c' = 3750$ psi, intermediate grade steel. Assume total dead plus live load is 250 psf. For the initial trial assume $c = 4$ ft 6 in.

(b) For what moment should the interior column be designed?

Prob. 11.4. Redesign the flat slab of Prob. 11.3 without using a drop panel.

Prob. 11.5. Design a 19-ft by 22-ft interior panel of a flat slab with a drop panel using the empirical method, $f_c' = 3000$ psi, intermediate grade steel, and a total load of 225 psf (which includes the slab weight). For the first trial use $c = 4$ ft 6 in. unless otherwise instructed.

Prob. 11.6. Design the flat slab of Prob. 11.5 without a drop panel.

Prob. 11.7. Assume the flat slab with drop panel which was designed in Sec. 11.9 with $c = 3$ ft 3 in. is supported by columns 18 in. in diameter and that similar columns extend to the floor above. Assume $w_D = 85$ psf and $w_L = 115$ psf. If the story height from top of one floor to the next is 12 ft, use the elastic method of design to establish the following for the short strips:

(a) Maximum negative design moment and its distribution to column and middle strips.

(b) Maximum positive moment for design and its distribution to design strips.

(c) Maximum moment on the 18-in. part of the column.

(d) A comparison of these moments with those from the empirical method used in Sec. 11.9.

Prob. 11.8. Rework Prob. 11.7 using an ultimate load of 1.2 times the dead load and 2.4 times the live load. By what per cent does this loading increase the moments found for the working loads in Prob. 11.7?

Prob. 11.9.

(a) Under the empirical method of Art. 1004, design an exterior panel (not a corner panel) of the flat slab described in Prob. 11.3.

(b) What moment should be included in the design of the exterior column?

Prob. 11.10. Using $f_c' = 3000$ psi, intermediate grade steel, and no shear reinforcement, design an interior panel of a flat plate floor supported on columns 18 in. square spaced 18 ft on centers. The slab is to carry a total of 150 psf which includes its own weight.

Prob. 11.11. Redesign the slab of Prob. 11.10 on the assumption that a total v of $0.05f_c'$ can be used with proper shear reinforcement.

12

Distribution
of Concentrated Loads
and Other
Special Problems

12.1. CONCRETE STRUCTURES DISTRIBUTE
CONCENTRATED LOADS

The ordinary reinforced concrete structure is either monolithic or is tied together to act as a unit. Although parallel members of the structure may be analyzed somewhat independently of each other under uniform live loads, actually the entire structure is a three-dimensional frame. When moving concentrated loads are considered, their spacing and their number suggest that all parallel slab strips and all neighboring beams will not be equally loaded. The interaction of the several slab strips and beams is usually such as to make the effective slab loading less severe than if each set of loads acted separately on the individual members.

When a heavy wheel rolls over a plank floor, each plank in turn must support the total load. In contrast, when a wheel moves over a concrete slab the wheel deflects the slab locally into a saucerlike pattern and this depression moves with the wheel across or along the slab. Thus a slab strip is deflected (and must be loaded) without a wheel actually resting on it. As the wheel passes over a particular strip the deflection increases, but the single 1-ft strip of slab never carries the entire wheel load unassisted. The designer describes this by saying the wheel load in Fig. 12.1a is distributed over an effective width E (Fig. 12.1b), meaning that the moment on the most heavily loaded 1-ft strip is that which would be produced by $1/E$ parts of the total load, as in Fig. 12.1c. Likewise,

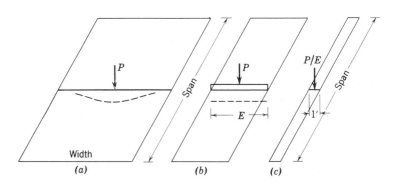

Fig. 12.1. Effective width under a single concentrated load. (*a*) Cross section through mid-span showing unequal deflections. (*b*) Design assumption of a width E with uniform deflections. (*c*) Equivalent 1-ft strip.

closely spaced beams share in carrying concentrated loads when the beams are connected by stiff floor slabs or stiff diaphragms.

The result of a theoretical study as to how a single wheel load is carried by a simple girder highway span is shown in Fig. 12.2. The load is applied to mid-span, directly over beam B, and the girder stiffness assumed is five times that of the slab for a width equal to the girder span. Girder B then deflects more than its neighbors A and C. The slab (attached to the beams) is pulled down by beam B, but it resists this movement and exerts upward forces on the beam, as shown by the shaded ordinates on the right of the figure. These upward forces on beam B total $0.88P$, leaving the net downward load only $0.12P$. The resulting moment diagram on the beam is shown to the left. The neighboring beams deflect less and carry less moment than beam B. Actually, the slab imposes heavier net loads on these beams than on beam B, but the load of $0.43P$ on A and $0.32P$ on C is better distributed and produces less moment. The load on beam D is only $0.13P$ and the load on beam E is negligible.

REINFORCED CONCRETE FUNDAMENTALS

Although such interaction of members can be approximately evaluated on a theoretical basis, design rules depend equally upon field tests. This chapter will not attempt to demonstrate how load distribution factors are established nor to tabulate them for the many possible conditions. Rather its objective is to call attention to the problem of load distribution and illustrate how it can be handled in a few typical cases.

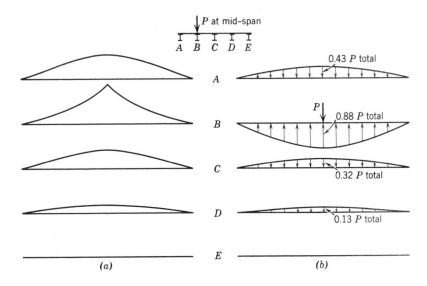

Fig. 12.2. The distribution of a single concentrated load to the girders of a bridge span, girder spacing of 0.1 span. Reproduced from Ref. 1, Highway Research Board. (*a*) Moment diagrams. (*b*) Approximate load distributions and the resulting total loads.

12.2. LOAD DISTRIBUTION IN A CONCRETE SLAB

Load distribution in a slab can be approached on two different bases which may be described as (1) the working load or deflection basis and (2) the ultimate strength or yield-line basis. The distribution at working loads is the one more commonly considered. For a wide slab having a 10-ft simple span, the effective width thus determined for a simple load is between 7 ft and 8 ft, depending somewhat upon the size of the load contact area and the particular algebraic formula[2] used. For comparison, Johansen has shown[3] that at ultimate load, the effective width would be twice the span multiplied by $\sqrt{\mu}$, where μ is the ratio of the perpendicular top steel to the longitudinal bottom steel. If μ is about one-third, this would make the effective width $2 \times 10\sqrt{0.33} = 11.5$ ft.

One complication which may make calculations at ultimate strength uncertain is the shear capacity of the slab around the load. Richart and Kluge[4] found shear failures occurring from diagonal tension, with a truncated cone of concrete punched out below the load. When those shear stresses were calculated like footings (Sec. 14.3d) on a surface at a distance d beyond the load, the unit shear stress was low, in one series from $0.044f_c'$ to $0.057f_c'$. Since the shear failures came at loads 50% greater than those producing local yielding of the steel, these low shear stresses were not considered serious. For a yield-line analysis shear stresses around the load might be more significant.

It appears that the distribution based on elastic conditions, as commonly used, is on the safe side. Its use also tends to reduce crack size at working loads. For elastic conditions, Westergaard[5] established an extreme value of maximum positive moment on a slab as $0.315P$ for any simple span when P is distributed over a circular area with the diameter equal to one-tenth of the span and the slab thickness one-twelfth of the span, Poisson's ratio 0.15. (This local moment is quite sensitive to the size of the bearing area.) The corresponding transverse moment is $0.248P$. Jensen[6] extended these results to show the effect of a rigid beam support at right angles, that is, an effect like that in a two-way slab. At this crossbeam the maximum negative moment is $-P/2\pi = -0.159P$ and it occurs with the wheel quite close to the beam.

When closely spaced multiple wheels occur, an extra slab width acts, but the effective width per wheel is reduced. The AASHO in their *Standard Specifications for Highway Bridges*[7] specify an effective width E for a slab carrying a single wheel such that the resultant design will be safe for multiple wheels without further calculations.

12.3. CALCULATION FOR CONCENTRATED LOAD ON SLAB

A specification calls for a live load of 60 psf or a moving concentrated load of 2000 lb. Determine which loading controls for a continuous 10-ft span where the moment coefficients for uniform load are $+\frac{1}{16}$ and $-\frac{1}{12}$, and for a concentrated load $+\frac{1}{8}$ and $-\frac{1}{8}$. Consider $E = 0.68S + 2c$, where S is the span and c the diameter of the loaded area.[2]

SOLUTION

For uniform load, $M_L = -60 \times 10^2/12 = -500$ ft-lb
For concentrated load, with $c = 0$ in the absence of better data, $E = 0.6 \times 10 + 0 = 6.0$ ft

REINFORCED CONCRETE FUNDAMENTALS

Effective load, $P_E = 2000/6.0 = 333$ lb/ft strip

$M_P = -PS/8 = -333 \times \frac{10}{8} = -416$ ft-lb < 500 ft-lb

Therefore, the uniform load moment governs the slab design.

It might be noted that the effective width for shear would call for the concentrated load near the support which would give much less slab deflection and a much reduced effective width. The AASHO specification says slabs designed for moment will be considered safe in bond and shear. As an extreme assumption, consider the entire load resisted by a 1-ft strip. Assume also a minimum t of 3.5 in., $d = 2.5$ in., $w_D = 44$ psf.

$$V = 2000 + 44 \times \frac{10}{2} = 2220 \text{ lb}$$

$$V = \frac{2220}{12 \times 0.875 \times 2.5} = 84.4 \text{ psi} < 0.03f_c' = 90 \text{ psi}$$

Although there are limited data as to reaction distribution, it is difficult to imagine a diagonal tension failure which would involve less than a width of four to five times the slab thickness, in the assumed case at least 14 to 17.5 in.

12.4. HIGHWAY BRIDGE LOADINGS

The basic units of loading for highway bridges are the H truck, a two-axle loading, and the H-S truck with trailer, a three-axle loading. The 20-ton truck is designated as H20-44, the last number denoting the year 1944 when this loading was established. Figure 12.3 shows the distribution of the load between the various wheels. The corresponding truck and trailer combination H20-S16-44 represents the standard 20-ton truck plus a second 16-ton axle, as shown in Fig. 12.4. For either type of truck an alternate uniform load of 640 plf for each 10-ft lane plus a concentrated load of 18,000 lb for moment or 26,000 lb for shear is to be used wherever it gives larger values, which will be the case on longer spans. The reader is referred to the AASHO specification[7] for details such as the number of loaded lanes and proper reduction factors, impact allowance, and distribution of loads. In the following examples, only the governing portion of the specification will be mentioned.

12.5. DESIGN OF A HIGHWAY SLAB SPAN

Design an interior panel of an 8 ft 6 in. span continuous slab for H20-44 loading, $f_c' = 3000$ psi, intermediate grade steel, AASHO specification. Consider that this slab spans laterally between longitudinal girders.

SOLUTION

The AASHO specification allowable stresses are $f_c = 0.40f_c' = 1200$ psi, $n = 10, f_s = 20,000$ psi.

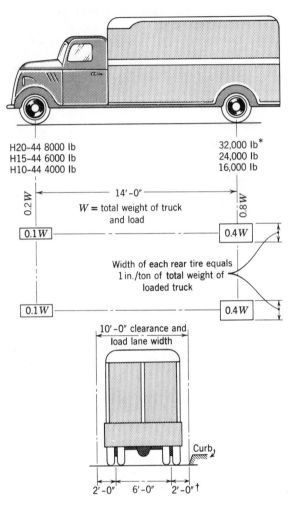

H20–44 8000 lb
H15–44 6000 lb
H10–44 4000 lb

32,000 lb*
24,000 lb
16,000 lb

14'-0"

0.2W

W = total weight of truck
and load

0.8W

0.1W   0.4W

Width of each rear tire equals
1 in./ton of total weight of
loaded truck

0.1W   0.4W

10'-0" clearance and
load lane width

Curb

2'-0"   6'-0"   2'-0" †

* In the design of floors (concrete slabs, steel grid floors, and timber floors) for H20 or H20–S16 loading, one axle load of 24,000 lb or two axle loads of 16,000 lb each spaced 4 ft apart may be used, whichever produces the greater stress, instead of the 32,000-lb axle shown.

† For slab design the center line of wheel shall be assumed to be 1 ft from the face of the curb.

Fig. 12.3. The H truck of the AASHO *Standard Specifications for Highway Bridges.*

$$kd = \frac{1200}{1200 + 20{,}000/10}\, d = 0.375d, \quad jd = 0.875d$$

$$R = 0.5 f_c kj = 0.5 \times 1200 \times 0.375 \times 0.875 = 197$$

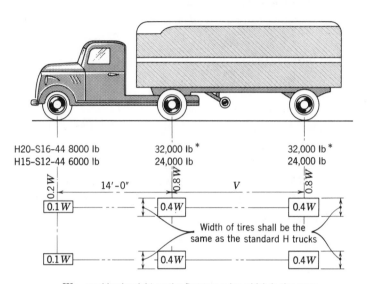

| H20-S16-44 8000 lb | 32,000 lb * | 32,000 lb * |
| H15-S12-44 6000 lb | 24,000 lb | 24,000 lb |

$0.2\,W$ 14'-0" $0.8\,W$ V $0.8\,W$

| $0.1\,W$ | $0.4\,W$ | $0.4\,W$ |

Width of tires shall be the same as the standard H trucks

| $0.1\,W$ | $0.4\,W$ | $0.4\,W$ |

W = combined weight on the first two axles which is the same as for the corresponding H truck

V = variable spacing—14 ft to 30 ft inclusive. Spacing to be used is that which produces maximum stresses

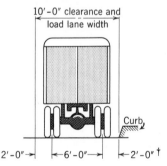

10'-0" clearance and load lane width

Curb

2'-0"   6'-0"   2'-0" †

Fig. 12.4. The H-S truck of the ASSHO *Standard Specifications for Highway Bridges.* The footnotes in Fig. 12.3 also apply here.

Since the reinforcement is perpendicular to traffic, this slab falls under Case A in the specification with an effective width $E = 0.4S + 3.75$, where S is the span. The design moment is listed as $M = \pm0.2PS/E$. The rear wheel of the H20 truck weighs $0.4 \times 20 = 8$ tons $= 16{,}000$ lb. However, the specification sets up a special loading for slabs,* namely, one axle load of 24,000 lb or two axle loads of 16,000 lb each, spaced 4 ft apart. Case A further indicates that the single 24,000-lb axle will govern for spans under 10.5 ft. This axle gives $P = 12,000$ lb.

$$E = 0.4 \times 8.5 + 3.75 = 7.15 \text{ ft}$$

Effective load $P_E = P/E = 12,000/7.15 = 1680$ lb

$$M_L = 0.2P_E S = 0.2 \times 1680 \times 8.5 = 2850 \text{ ft-lb}$$

The impact fraction is specified as

$$I = \frac{50}{L + 125} = \frac{50}{8.5 + 125} = 0.375$$

but not to exceed 0.30, which governs here.

Impact $M = M_I = 0.300 M_L = 0.300 \times 2850 = 855$ ft-lb

Assume dead load $w_D = 75$ psf and moment coefficients of $-\frac{1}{12}$ and $+\frac{1}{16}$.

$$M_D = -75 \times 8.5^2/12 = -453 \text{ ft-lb}$$

$$M_T = -2850 - 855 - 453 = -4160 \text{ ft-lb}$$

$$d = \sqrt{M/Rb} = \sqrt{4160 \times 12/(197 \times 12)} = \sqrt{21.1} = 4.60 \text{ in.}$$

Since AASHO specifies a minimum of 1.00-in. cover

$$t = 4.60 + D/2 + 1.00 = 5.60 + 0.38 \text{ (say)} = 5.98 \text{ in.}$$

USE $t = 6$ in., $d = 6.0 - 1.00 - D/2 = $ say, 4.68 in.

No revision in dead load moment is needed.

Neg. $M_T = -2850 - 855 - 453 = -4160$ ft-lb

Pos. $M_T = +2850 + 855 + 453 \times 12/16 = +4050$ ft-lb

Neg. $A_s = \dfrac{4160 \times 12}{20,000 \times 0.875 \times 4.68} = 0.610$ in.^{2}/ft $= \#6$ at 8 in. (0.660)

Pos. $A_s = 0.610 \times 4050/4160 = 0.594$ in.^{2}/ft $= \#6$ at 9 in. (0.586)

USE $\#6$ at 9 in. for positive M and $\#6$ at 8 in. for negative M.

This design ignored the possibility of using compression steel which would be available at the supports but possibly not at mid-span. The AASHO also says slabs designed for moment "shall be considered satisfactory in bond and shear."

The concentrated load requires distribution steel perpendicular to the moment steel. The amount is specified as a percentage of the positive moment steel given by $100/\sqrt{S} = 100/\sqrt{8.5} = 34.3\%$. Transverse steel must be at least $0.343 \times 0.594 = 0.203$ in.^{2}/ft $=$ say, $\#4$ at 12 in. (0.200).

12.6. DESIGN MOMENTS AND SHEARS FOR HIGHWAY GIRDER

Calculate the design live load and impact load moments and shears for a 40-ft simple span girder supporting the slab of Sec. 12.5. Consider both

* The student will note that this procedure, in the interest of simple calculations, has been specified in rather arbitrary fashion.

H20-44 and H20-S16-44 loadings on the center girder of the cross section shown in Fig. 12.5a.

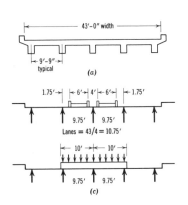

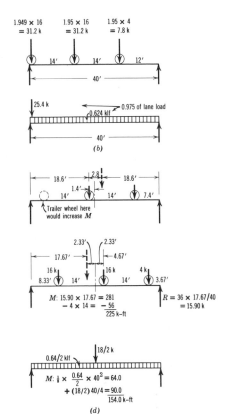

Fig. 12.5. Highway girder bridge. (a) Bridge cross section. (b) Location of wheels and lane load for maximum shear. (c) Position of loads laterally for maximum stresses in center girder. (d) Location of wheels and lane load for maximum moment.

SOLUTION

For shear calculations the AASHO says there shall be no lateral or longitudinal distribution of the wheel load at the end of the span. For other wheels the distribution shall be that applying for moment. In this case the provision for moment when two or more lanes of traffic are involved calls for the wheel loads to each stringer to be $S/5.0 = 9.75/5.0 = 1.95$ of the full load.

The longitudinal arrangement of wheels for the truck and uniform lane loads are shown in Fig. 12.5b, ignoring any complication which the end diaphragm may cause. Figure 12.5c shows the lateral arrangement of the loads on the cross section, two trucks assumed to be passing. For the truck the simple beam slab reactions would give for the end wheels:

$$(2 \times 2 \times 4.75/9.75)16 = 1.949 \times 16 \text{ k} = 31.2 \text{ k}$$

It is only by chance that this multiplier of 1.949 is so nearly identical with the 1.95 factor based on the moment distribution.

For the lane load of Sec. 12.4, the end concentrated load becomes $26 \times 9.75/10 = 25.4$ k and the uniform load $0.64 \times 9.75/10.0 = 0.624$ klf. For the trucks, max. $V = 31.2 + 31.2 \times 26/40 + 7.8 \times 12/40 = 53.7$ k. For the lane load, max. $V = 25.4 + 0.624 \times 40/2 = 37.9$ k.

$$\text{Max. } V = 53.7 \text{ k}$$

The loaded length is considered from the far load to the reaction.

$$L = 28 \text{ ft} \qquad I = \frac{50}{28 + 125} = 0.327$$

Since $I = 0.30$ governs, $V_I = 0.30 \times 53.7 = 16.1$ k

For moment three loadings must be investigated, as shown in Fig. 12.5d. For simplicity these loadings are compared on the basis of one line of wheels or one half lane load. The H20-S16-44 loading governs maximum moment. Since the number of lines of wheels is $S/5 = 1.95$,

$$M_L = 1.95 \times 225 = 438 \text{ k-ft}$$

The loaded length, by definition, is the full length, $L = 40$ ft.

$$I = \frac{50}{40 + 125} = 0.303$$

Since $I = 0.30$ governs, $M_I = 0.30 \times 438 = 131$ k-ft

The above illustrates the manner specified by AASHO for handling load distribution on stringers or longitudinal girders. The remainder of the design of the T-beams would be very similar to that of a building T-beam with these minor differences, which are usually more restrictive:

1. Different allowable unit stresses for f_c, v, and u on top bars.
2. Different rules on effective flange width.
3. Different maximum moment diagram, due to type of loading.
4. Different maximum shear diagram, due to type of loading.
5. Webs of T-beams must carry stirrups full length, at a maximum spacing not to exceed $0.75d$ where not required for stress.
6. Slightly different bar extensions.

All of these are the small differences which can be expected in changing from one specification to another.

12.7. OPENINGS IN SLABS

When openings in slabs are large, as for stairs or elevators, beams must be used around the openings. Good practice usually requires that such beams be framed into columns sufficiently to provide a stable unit without the slab.

Small openings such as pipe sleeves, if not too numerous, can be made almost anywhere in a slab, except adjacent to the columns in flat slab construction. What can be done about larger openings may require at least some rough calculations. Obviously, openings are least dangerous where shear stresses are small and bending moments are below maximum.

Electric conduits, unless closely spaced or crossing at small angles, can be included without considering any loss in moment strength. The requirements of Art. 503 might be noted in this connection.

In flat slabs designed by the empirical method, Art. 1004h defines the maximum openings which are permitted without beam framing around them, being most restrictive in areas common to the two column strips and most liberal in areas common to both middle strips. Under the elastic analysis procedure the designer is able to take openings into consideration in establishing stiffness and bending moment if he considers this necessary.

In two-way slabs supported on all four sides, openings in the corners of the slab are least damaging. Since for architectural reasons openings for ducts frequently need to be near the columns, this is a definite advantage of this type of slab. The negative moment zone of the short middle strips (near mid-span of the longer beams) is the least favorable zone for openings.

Often rough checks can be made on the strength of the construction after the openings are located. If openings should reduce a critical design section for moment, the required bd^2 for moment must be maintained by providing extra depth to offset the reduced width. The steel may be more closely spaced on each side of the opening to maintain the necessary A_s. Often it will be possible to locate openings where moment is well below the compression capacity of the slab, thereby leaving the arrangement of reinforcement as the only problem. Of course, shear strength must be maintained, but this is rarely a problem except near the columns in flat slab types.

The arrangement of bars around any but minor openings can constitute a real problem. Bars running perpendicular to the face of an opening are not fully effective when simply cut off at the opening. This would be all right if there were a beam at the opening to act as a reaction for the slab. If there is no beam it is better to fan the bars out or splay them to go around the opening, as shown in Fig. 12.6a. If this leaves too wide an area without steel, extra bars can be placed parallel to the side of the opening, as indicated.

If minor cracking at the corners of an opening is objectionable, it is always well to add one or two diagonal bars at each corner, especially at large openings (Fig. 12.6b). This is always desirable around window and door openings in concrete wall slabs. Such reinforcement helps to take care of shrinkage stresses.

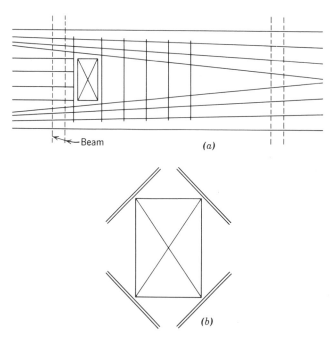

Fig. 12.6. Bars at openings in slabs. (a) Bars fanned out to miss opening. (b) Corner reinforcement to reduce shrinkage cracking.

12.8. OPENINGS IN BEAMS

Openings through slabs which encroach on the flange width of T-beams require a check on the bending strength remaining.

Openings through the beam web are always objectionable. In a region of small shear, as near the middle of a beam span, a horizontal pipe sleeve may not be serious. Elsewhere, shear strength must be closely watched and in many places bending strength as well. Large openings in beams are particularly weakening. They destroy beam action and force this reduced section to act much as a Vierendeel truss (a truss without diagonals). The average bending moment over the length of the hole is carried by axial tension and compression in the segments above and under the hole acting as chords in a truss. The shear causes secondary bending stresses in each of these segments.

SELECTED REFERENCES

1. C. P. Siess and A. S. Veletos, "Distribution of Loads to Girders in Slab-and-Girder Bridges: Theoretical Analyses and Their Relation to Field Tests," Highway Research Board *Report 14-B*, Washington, 1953, p. 58.

2. Clyde T. Morris, "Concentrated Loads on Slabs," Ohio State Univ. Eng. Exp. Sta. *Bull. No. 80*, 1933.

3. K. W. Johansen, "Bruchomente Der Kreuzweise Bewehrten Platten" (Moments of Rupture in Cross-Reinforced Slabs), International Association for Bridge and Structural Engineering, Liége, Vol. 1, 1932, p. 277.

4. Frank E. Richart and Ralph W. Kluge, "Tests of Reinforced Concrete Slabs Subjected to Concentrated Loads," Univ. of Ill. Eng. Exp. Sta. *Bull. No. 314*, 1949.

5. H. M. Westergaard, "Computation of Stresses in Bridge Slabs Due to Wheel Loads," *Public Roads*, **11**, No. 1, Mar. 1930, p. 1.

6. Vernon P. Jensen, "Solutions for Certain Rectangular Slabs Continuous Over Flexible Supports," Univ. of Ill. Eng. Exp. Sta. *Bull. No. 303*, 1938.

7. *Standard Specifications for Highway Bridges*, AASHO, Washington, 6th ed., 1953.

PROBLEMS

Prob. 12.1. Design a simple span slab to carry its own weight and a 20-k concentrated load over a 20-ft span. Assume the impact as 25 % of live load and an effective width $E = 5.6$ ft. Allowable $f_c = 1000$ psi, $f_s = 18,000$ psi, $n = 10$, cover of 1.25 in. to center of steel. Assume the load is distributed over a sufficient bearing area to avoid a punching shear failure.

Prob. 12.2. An interior span of a continuous slab with a clear span of 12 ft is to be designed for a live load of 75 psf or a single concentrated live load of 3 k, whichever is worse. If the effective width assumed for the concentrated load is 6 ft when the load is at its worst position for moment, design the slab using the moment coefficients of Code Art. 701 for uniform load and $\pm 0.20PL$ for the concentrated load. Assume zero impact.

Prob. 12.3. Design a T-beam for a 23-ft simple span assuming a 6-in. slab, beams 7 ft 6 in. on centers, allowable $f_c = 1200$ psi, $f_s = 18,000$ psi, $n = 10$, 2.5 in. to center of steel (if in one layer). Each beam may be assumed to carry

1.50 lines of wheels for moment and 1.77* lines for shear. Use H20 loading with 25% of live load for impact. The stem weight below the slab may be assumed as 250 plf and this need not be revised for this problem. Sketch the beam cross section showing the steel arrangement. $f_c' = 3000$ psi.

Prob. 12.4. Same as Prob. 12.3 but with a 40-ft span. In this case assume the stem weight below the slab as 400 plf.

* The AASHO *Standard Specifications for Highway Bridges*[7] uses a different factor *E* for load on the end of span from that used for loads out on the span. The student may ignore this and, for these problems, use this factor for each wheel.

13

Eccentrically Loaded Columns

13.1. ECCENTRICITY OF LOADING IN FRAMES

It is doubtful whether a concrete column should ever be designed for zero eccentricity. As a part of the frame, the column is subject to a moment whenever there is any joint rotation. Such a moment is equivalent in its effect to an eccentricity of load $e = M/P$, as indicated in Fig. 13.1.

The Joint Report on ultimate strength design[1, 2] and the Code Appendix (Art. A.608a) require that all members subject to axial load be designed for a minimum eccentricity of at least $0.05t$ for a spiral column and $0.10t$ for a tied column, where t is the over-all column dimension. The Code proper, for working load design, does not completely eliminate the design of axially loaded columns, but it does require (Art. 1108) that columns "be designed to resist the axial forces from loads on all floors, plus the maximum bending due to loads on a single adjacent span of the floor under

339

consideration." The rather frequent ignoring of this moment loading on columns has been in violation of the Code, rather than something encouraged by the Code. It is undoubtedly desirable that all columns be designed for eccentricity.

The remainder of this chapter will consider eccentrically loaded columns, with working load methods in Secs. 13.2–13.5 sharply separated from ultimate strength methods in Secs. 13.6–13.10.

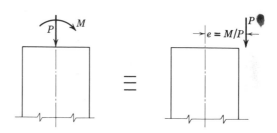

Fig. 13.1. Axial load with bending moment is equivalent to an eccentric load.

13.2. ECCENTRIC LOAD ANALYSIS—A MERGER ZONE

The working load formulas for axially loaded columns, Eqs. 2.2 and 2.4, are really *ultimate strength* formulas adapted to working load conditions. In contrast, beam analysis for working loads, in Chaps. 4 and 5, is definitely a modified *elastic* analysis, far different from ultimate strength methods. In the zone of combined direct stress and bending, members theoretically run the entire range from columns with only small eccentricity to beams with only small axial load. Such blending or merging of two diverse approaches of necessity produces rather awkward correlation formulas. This was certainly the case with the 1940 Joint Committee Specification and with the similar ACI Code from 1941 until the present 1956 Code appeared. Although stresses were not calculated on axially loaded columns because of major creep and shrinkage effects, eccentrically loaded columns were analyzed on an elastic analysis basis and an allowable stress was specified:

$$f_p = f_a \left(\frac{1 + \dfrac{De}{t}}{1 + C\dfrac{De}{t}} \right)$$

REINFORCED CONCRETE FUNDAMENTALS

where f_p = maximum allowable compression stress

f_a = average allowable stress on concrete of the column when axially loaded = (allowable axial load) ÷ (transformed area)

$C = f_a \div 0.45 f_c' = f_a \div$ (allowable stress in bending)

e/t = eccentricity relative to over-all column size

$D = t^2/2r^2$, where r is the radius of gyration of the transformed area.

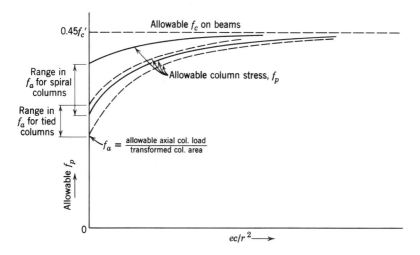

Fig. 13.2. Allowable column stresses under old ACI Code.

Such an involved relation, as illustrated in Fig. 13.2, was needed because the "allowable" stress on the axially loaded column, f_a, expressed as a fractional part of f_c', was not constant but varied between tied and spiral columns, between different percentages of steel, and different f_c' values.

The present (1956) Code does not differ much from the older Code in substance but it does differ greatly in form. It is considerably simpler in usage. Hence the working load treatment of eccentrically loaded columns will here be limited entirely to the provisions of the new Code. The awkward merger zone is still present, but most of the awkwardness has been removed by some relatively simple arbitrary procedures.

13.3. KERN POINT AND KERN AREA

The kern point is an elastic concept not used directly in the Code, but nevertheless of importance to a general understanding of eccentrically

ECCENTRICALLY LOADED COLUMNS   341

loaded members. In the following discussion, area, moment of inertia, and radius of gyration all refer to the transformed area section.

A load P at an eccentricity e produces stresses on extreme "fibers" of

$$f_c = \frac{P}{A} \pm \frac{Mc}{I} = \frac{P}{A} \pm \frac{Pec}{I} = \frac{P}{A}\left(1 \pm \frac{ec}{r^2}\right)$$

The eccentricity producing zero stress on one face can be found by considering $f_c = 0$.

$$0 = \frac{P}{A}\left(1 - \frac{ec}{r^2}\right)$$

$$ec/r^2 = 1, \qquad e = r^2/c$$

This eccentricity is the distance from the centroid of the column to what is designated as the kern point. The kern point on an axis designates the application point for a load that produces zero stress on a particular face of a column. There is a separate kern point corresponding to the zero stress on each face of the column. If these four kern points are connected as shown in Fig. 13.3, they enclose an area known as the kern area. A load anywhere in the kern area produces only compression stresses on the column; a load anywhere outside the kern area produces tension on the far corner or face of the column. The

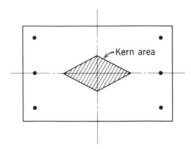

Fig. 13.3. Kern area of a column.

kern area for a plain concrete member corresponds to the middle third; for reinforced concrete it normally represents an eccentricity slightly more than one-sixth of the column dimension.

To the small extent that elastic analysis is valid for other than short-time loads, a load within the kern area produces stresses which can be calculated from elastic considerations:

$$f = \frac{P}{A} + \frac{M_y x}{I_y} + \frac{M_x y}{I_x}$$

where M_x and M_y represent the product Pe about the x-axis and y-axis. Loads outside the kern area also produce stresses which, with equal validity, can be calculated by this procedure provided the resulting tension is not enough to crack the concrete.

In effect the old ACI Code encouraged this use of the uncracked section for an e/t as great as unity in either or both planes. In the author's opinion this was a very undesirable and unrealistic situation because cracking with this e/t would be severe. The present Code sets the corresponding limit on e/t as $\frac{2}{3}$, about either or both axes. This maximum e also would undoubtedly result in some cracking, but the factor of safety in the stresses that are permitted ensures safety. In other words, rather imaginary stresses are calculated in extreme cases, much lower than actual stresses, but these are kept low enough to provide a conservative factor of safety on the load capacity.

13.4. COLUMNS WITH SMALL ECCENTRICITY— WORKING LOAD THEORY

(a) Theory

Tests at the University of Illinois[3] have shown that the load capacity of columns with eccentric loads does not decrease as rapidly with increasing eccentricity as would be predicted from the increase in calculated f_c. On this basis the 1941 Code adopted the allowable stress formula of Sec. 13.2 which increased the allowable stress from f_a with zero eccentricity to the full beam allowable f_c for infinite eccentricity. The present Code does approximately the same thing by specifying

$$\frac{f_a}{F_a} + \frac{f_b}{F_b} \lesssim 1$$

where f_a = nominal axial unit stress = actual axial load divided by the over-all or gross area of the column, A_g

F_a = nominal allowable axial unit stress = $0.225f_c' + f_s p_g$ for spiral columns and 0.8 of this value for tied columns

f_b = bending unit stress (actual) = bending moment Pe divided by section modulus of transformed area (uncracked) where A_s has been replaced by $(n - 1)A_s$.

F_b = allowable stress in pure bending = $0.45f_c'$.

The form of this equation is the same as for the corresponding equation in structural steel design specifications. The upper limit, $(f_a/F_a) + (f_b/F_b) = 1$, is the equation of the straight line shown in Fig. 13.4, but it is proper to point out here that only the upper part of this line is used. This equation is used only for $e \lesssim \frac{2}{3}t$, where t is the over-all column thickness.

Attention is called to the similarity of this curve to the one of Fig. 13.18b for ultimate load design. Although the foregoing equation is written in terms of unit stresses and Fig. 13.18*b* is in terms of loads and moments, one should note that the present equation could easily be converted into loads and moments. If the first ratio term were multiplied by A_g/A_g, one would have a ratio of actual axial load to allowable axial load. If the second ratio term were multiplied top and bottom by the section modulus, one would have the ratio of actual moment to what might be called a nominal "allowable moment."

If the student is troubled by the artificial nature of the nominal stresses f_a and F_a, he should note that the use of the transformed area in these calculations, instead of A_g, would more nearly give actual stresses. Since transformed area $= A_g[1 + (n-1)p_g]$, the term in brackets would cancel out of the ratio term, f_a/F_a.

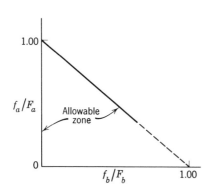

When eccentricity occurs about both axes, the governing equation is expanded to

$$\frac{f_a}{F_a} + \frac{f_{bx}}{F_{bx}} + \frac{f_{by}}{F_{by}} \lessgtr 1$$

where the added subscripts x and y designate the axis from which the eccentricity is measured and about which the section modulus is calculated. The eccentricity in either direction must not exceed two-thirds of the column thickness in that direction.

Fig. 13.4. Working load stress limits against compression failure, 1956 Code.

(b) Investigation of given column

A given column would be investigated by finding how close the sum of the ratios comes to unity, or by calculating the actual permissible load at the given eccentricity. For example, investigate the column of Fig. 13.5*a* for a load of 175 k at an eccentricity of 2.4 in., $f'_c = 2500$ psi, $n = 12$, intermediate grade steel.

SOLUTION

$f_a = P/A_g = 175,000/20^2 = 437$ psi

$F_a = $ allow. axial load $\div A_g = \dfrac{0.8(20^2 \times 0.225 \times 2500 + 4 \times 1.27 \times 16,000)}{20^2}$

$\quad = 0.8(225,000 + 81,400)/400 = 612$ psi

REINFORCED CONCRETE FUNDAMENTALS

This form of calculation for F_a is an identity with the specified form, $F_a = 0.8(0.225f_c' + f_s p_g)$.

$$I = \tfrac{1}{12} \times 20 \times 20^3 + 11 \times 4 \times 1.27 \times 7.5^2 = 13,330 + 3140 = 16,470$$

$$S = I/c = 16,470/10 = 1647$$

$$f_b = Pe/S = 175,000 \times 2.4/1647 = 255 \text{ psi}$$

$$F_b = 0.45f_c' = 1125 \text{ psi}$$

$$\frac{f_a}{F_a} + \frac{f_b}{F_b} = \frac{437}{612} + \frac{255}{1125} = 0.716 + 0.227 = 0.943 < 1.00$$

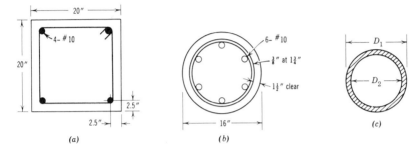

Fig. 13.5. Column of Secs. 13.4b and 13.8b.

The given 175-k load is permissible and could be increased to $175,000 \times 1.000/0.943 = 186,000$ lb at the same eccentricity.

If the column is a spiral column, either round as in Fig. 2.12d or square with a circular arrangement of the steel as in Fig. 2.12e, no special problem arises except that of the determination of the moment of inertia of the reinforcing bars. Instead of locating each bar and using a summation process for the moment of inertia of this steel, common practice imagines a ring or circular shell of steel similar to a thin-walled pipe. For example, in Fig. 13.5b, the 6–#10 bars have an area of $6 \times 1.27 = 7.62$ in.² and an effective transformed area (for $f_c' = 3000$ psi) of $9 \times 7.62 = 68.6$ in.² The center of each bar lies on a circle of diameter $= 16 - 2 \times 1.5 - 2 \times 0.375 - 1.27 = 10.98$ in.

Next consider the moment of inertia of this ring in Fig. 13.5c. The I of a circular area is $\pi D^4/64$ or $AD^2/16$, where A is the area. Then for the ring

$$I = \frac{\pi}{64}(D_1^4 - D_2^4) = \frac{\pi}{16}\left(\frac{D_1^2 - D_2^2}{4}\right)(D_1^2 + D_2^2) = \frac{A_r}{16}(D_1^2 + D_2^2)$$

where A_r is the area of the ring. Closely enough, for a thin ring,

$$I = \frac{A_r}{8}(\text{average } D)^2 = 68.6 \times 10.98^2/8 = 1030 \text{ in.}^4$$

Thus D_1 and D_2 need not be established.

ECCENTRICALLY LOADED COLUMNS

(c) Design of a column

Design a square tied column to carry an eccentric load of 150 k with a moment of 60 k-ft, using $f_c' = 3000$ psi and a small percentage, say, approximately 1.5% of rail steel.

SOLUTION

The Code, Art. 1109c, suggests that the preliminary selection of the column be made by use of an equivalent axial load given by the formula

$$P = N\left(1 + \frac{Be}{t}\right)$$

in which P is the equivalent axial load, N is the actual axial load at eccentricity e, and B is a selected factor. A footnote suggests B from 3 to 3.5 for rectangular tied columns, the lower value for columns with minimum reinforcement. (The corresponding values for circular spiral columns are B from 5 to 6.)

$$e = M/P = 60/150 = 0.40 \text{ ft} = 4.8 \text{ in.}$$

Assume $e/t = 0.25$. The trial equivalent axial load P is

$$P = N\left(1 + B\frac{e}{t}\right) = 150,000(1 + 3 \times 0.25) = 263,000 \text{ lb}$$

For $p = 0.015$,

Allow. $P = 0.8A_g(0.225f_c' + f_s p_g)$

$\qquad = 0.8(0.225 \times 3000 + 20,000 \times 0.015)A_g = 780A_g$

$263,000 = 780A_g, \qquad A_g = 337 \text{ in.}^2 = 18.3 \times 18.3 \text{ in.}$

The estimate of e/t was good. For an 18-in. column, $e/t = 4.8/18 = 0.267$. A revised e/t will give a larger A_g and make either an 18-in. by 18-in. or a 19-in. by 19-in. column a possible selection. USE 18-in. by 18-in. column, subject to exact check.

$$P = 263,000 \text{ lb}$$

$$\text{Value of concrete} = 0.8 \times 0.225 \times 3000 \times 18^2 = \overline{175,000}$$

$$0.8 \times 20,000A_s = 88,000 \text{ lb}$$

$$A_s = 5.50 \text{ in.}^2$$

Since a larger e/t would increase calculated P slightly, try 6–#9 = 6.00 in.²

$$f_a = 150,000/18^2 = 463 \text{ psi}$$

$$F_a = \frac{175,000 + 0.8 \times 6.0 \times 20,000}{18^2} = 836 \text{ psi}$$

$$I = \tfrac{1}{12} \times 18 \times 18^3 + 6.0 \times 9 \times 6.5^2 = 8760 + 2280 = 11,040 \text{ in.}^4$$

$$\text{based on } d' = 2.5 \text{ in.}$$

$S = I/c = 11,040/9 = 1227 \text{ in.}^3$

$f_b = 60,000 \times 12/1227 = 585 \text{ psi}$

$F_b = 0.45 f_c' = 1350 \text{ psi}$

$\dfrac{f_a}{F_a} + \dfrac{f_b}{F_b} = \dfrac{463}{836} + \dfrac{585}{1350} = 0.554 + 0.433 = 0.987 < 1.00$ O.K.

Although it was expected that a second trial of steel would be needed, the trial is now shown only to indicate the usual method. Try 4–#10 = 5.08 in.^{2}

$$F_a = \frac{175,000 + 5.08 \times 20,000 \times 0.8}{18^2} = 792 \text{ psi}$$

$$I = 8760 + 5.08 \times 9 \times 6.5^2 = 8760 + 1930 = 10,690 \text{ in.}^4$$

$$S = 10,690/9 = 1188 \text{ in.}^3$$

$$f_b = 720,000/1188 = 606 \text{ psi}$$

$$\frac{463}{792} + \frac{606}{1350} = 0.585 + 0.449 = 1.034 > 1.00 \qquad \text{N.G.}$$

USE 18 in. by 18 in., $A_s = 6$–#9, #3 ties at 16 in., as shown in Fig. 13.6a.

Cover to center line of steel $= 1.50 + 0.38 + 0.5 \times 1.13 = 2.44$ in.

vs. 2.5 in. assumed   say O.K.

13.5. COLUMNS WITH LARGER ECCENTRICITY— WORKING LOAD THEORY

(a) Theory

For eccentricities greater than two-thirds of the column thickness (Art. 1109d) the column is considered as a cracked section with straight-line variation in stresses and with compression steel treated as in beams (Art. 706). Both tension and compression must be investigated, the allowables being the same as in beams.

Although a cracked section should logically be weaker than an uncracked section, some of the load capacities calculated by the method of Sec. 13.4 turn out to be lower than those for a slightly larger e calculated according to Art. 1109d. In other words, there is a discontinuity in calculated load capacities as one moves from one method of calculation to the other, and some of these discontinuities are in the "wrong" direction. There has been some criticism of the Code because of this inconsistency.

(b) Investigation of given rectangular column

A given column can be investigated by comparing the calculated stresses with the allowables or by calculating the allowable load for the given

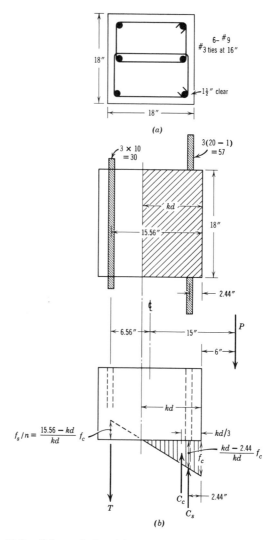

Fig. 13.6. Column designed in Sec. 13.4c and analyzed in Secs. 13.5b and 13.7b. (a) Cross section. (b) Transformed area and stresses on column with large eccentricity.

eccentricity. For example, calculate the allowable load on the column of Fig. 13.6a for an eccentricity of 15 in. (measured horizontally on this view), $f_c' = 3000$ psi, rail steel.

SOLUTION

The transformed area is shown in Fig. 13.6b. Cover to center of steel = 2.44 in.

REINFORCED CONCRETE FUNDAMENTALS

$$T = 30\,\frac{15.56 - kd}{kd}f_c \qquad C_s = 57\,\frac{kd - 2.44}{kd}f_c \qquad C_c = 18kdf_c/2 = 9kdf_c$$

ΣM about the load $P = 0$.

$$T \times 21.56 - C_c(6 + kd/3) - C_s \times 8.44 = 0$$

$$30\,\frac{15.56 - kd}{kd}f_c \times 21.56 - 9kdf_c(6 + kd/3) - 57\,\frac{kd - 2.44}{kd}f_c \times 8.44 = 0$$

$$647\,\frac{15.56 - kd}{kd} - 9kd(6 + kd/3) - 482\,\frac{kd - 2.44}{kd} = 0$$

Solution from this form by trial is about as simple as any.

$$
\begin{aligned}
\text{For } kd = 10, && 360 - 840 - 364 &= -844 \\
6, && 1033 - 432 - 286 &= +315 \\
7, && 792 - 524 - 314 &= -46 \\
6.9, && 814 - 515 - 312 &= -13 \\
6.86, && 819 - 513 - 310 &= -4 \\
6.84, && 825 - 510 - 310 &= +5
\end{aligned}
$$

Take $kd = 6.85$ in.

If $f_c = 1350$ psi,

$$f_s' = 20 \times 1350\,\frac{6.85 - 2.44}{6.85} = 17{,}400 \text{ psi} < 20{,}000 \text{ psi} \qquad \text{O.K.}$$

$$f_s = 10\,\frac{15.56 - 6.85}{6.85} \times 1350 = 17{,}150 \text{ psi} < 20{,}000 \text{ psi} \qquad \text{O.K.}$$

$f_c = 1350$ psi governs

$\Sigma F_y = 0, \qquad P + T - C_c - C_s = 0.$

$$P + 30\,\frac{15.56 - 6.85}{6.85} \times 1350 - 0.5 \times 1350 \times 18 \times 6.85$$

$$- 57\,\frac{6.85 - 2.44}{6.85} \times 1350 = 0$$

$P + 51{,}500 - 83{,}000 - 49{,}500 = 0$

Allow. $P = 132{,}500 - 51{,}500 = 81{,}000$ lb

(c) Investigation of given circular column

A circular column involves no theory beyond that used for the rectangular column, but the geometry of the circular segment and of the equivalent ring of steel introduces some mathematical complications. A solution by trial and error is necessary unless one uses column load tables such as those in the *CRSI Design Handbook*.[4]   Professor J. R. Shank of Ohio State University has simplified this problem considerably by preparing the curves shown in Fig. E.18 in Appendix E.

As an example, calculate the allowable load on the column of Fig. 13.7a for an eccentricity of 18 in., $f_c' = 3000$ psi, intermediate grade steel.

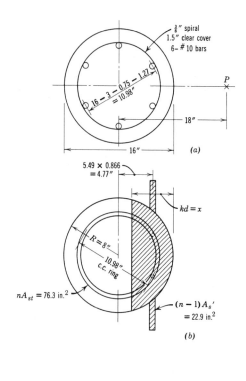

(a)

(b)

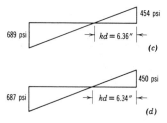

454 psi

689 psi $kd = 6.36''$

(c)

450 psi

687 psi $kd = 6.34''$

(d)

Fig. 13.7. Circular column of Sec. 13.5c. (a) Cross section. (b) Transformed area. (c) Stresses from first trial kd and $P = 10,000$ lb. (d) Stresses from second trial.

SOLUTION

Estimate $kd = 7.00$ in., as shown in Fig. 13.7b. The equivalent ring will be used to represent nA_{st}, where A_{st} represents total steel. Then $A_r = nA_{st} = 10 \times 6 \times 1.27 = 76.3$ in.² Since the compression steel A_s' is considered as

REINFORCED CONCRETE FUNDAMENTALS

furnishing a transformed area of $(2n - 1)A_s'$, add wings of $(n - 1)A_s' = 9 \times 2 \times 1.27 = 22.9$ in.[2]

The circular segment defined in Fig. E.18 by $x = 7.00$ in. or $x/d = \frac{7}{16} = 0.438$ has coefficients as follows: $A = 0.488$, $B = 0.336$, $C = 0.065$.

$$A_c = Bd^2 = 0.336 \times 16^2 = 86.0 \text{ in.}^2$$
$$\bar{x}_c = AR = 0.488 \times 8 = 3.90 \text{ in.}$$
$$I_{c0} = CR^4 = 0.065 \times 8^4 = 266 \text{ in.}^4$$

Moments about the column center line will be used to locate the centroid of the entire effective area. The column can then be analyzed as an unsymmetrical column eccentrically loaded from this centroid.

Area		Arm	Moment
A_c	86.0	3.90	335
A_r	76.3	0	0
Wings	22.9	4.77	109

$A = 185.2$ in.[2] $\qquad$ 444 in.[3] $\qquad$ $\bar{x} = 444/185.2 = 2.40$ in.

Part	I_0 of part	Ad^2	Total I
A_c	266	$86.0(3.90 - 2.40)^2 = 193$	459
A_r	$76.3 \times 10.98^2/8 = 1152$	$76.3 \times 2.40^2 \quad = 440$	1592
Wings	0	$22.9(4.77 - 2.40)^2 = 129$	129

Total I $\quad = 1418$ $\qquad$ $+$ $\qquad$ $762 = 2180$ in.[4]

$$e = 18 - 2.40 = 15.60 \qquad M = P \times 15.60$$

To avoid the algebraic term, take a token P of 10,000 lb. Then $M = 156{,}000$ in.-lb.

$$f_c = \frac{P}{A} + \frac{M_c}{I} = \frac{10{,}000}{185.2} + \frac{156{,}000(8 - 2.40)}{2180} = 53.9 + 400 = 454 \text{ psi}$$

$$f_t \text{ (imaginary but convenient)} = 53.9 - \frac{156{,}000\,(8 + 2.40)}{2180}$$

$$= 53.9 - 743 = -689 \text{ psi}$$

The plot of these values sketched in Fig. 13.7c shows that kd appears to be 6.36 in. compared to 7.00 in. assumed. Try a revised kd of 6.40 in. or $x = 6.40$ in., $x/d = 0.400$. Figure E.18 then shows $A = 0.530$, $B = 3.00$, $C = 0.050$.

$$A_c = 0.300 \times 16^2 = 76.8 \text{ in.}^2$$
$$\bar{x}_c = 0.530 \times 8 = 4.24 \text{ in.}$$
$$I_c = 0.050 \times 8^4 = 205 \text{ in.}^4$$

Centroid:			
A_c	76.8 × 4.24 = 326		
A_r	76.3 × 0 = 0		
Wings	22.9 × 4.77 = 109		

$A = 176.0$ in.[2] $\qquad$ 435 $\qquad$ $\bar{x} = 435/176.0 = 2.47$ in.

New moment of inertia:

Part	I_0	Ad^2	Total
A_c	205	$76.8(4.24 - 2.47)^2 = 240$	445
A_r	1152	$76.3 \times 2.47^2 \quad = 465$	1617
Wings	0	$22.9(4.77 - 2.47)^2 = 121$	121
	1357	$+ \qquad\qquad 826 = 2183$ in.^{4}	

$$e = 18 - 2.47 = 15.53 \text{ in.} \qquad M = 15.53P = \text{say, } 155,300 \text{ in.-lb}$$

$$f_c = \frac{10,000}{176.0} + \frac{155,300 \times 5.53}{2183} = 56.8 + 393 = 450 \text{ psi}$$

$$f_t \text{ (imaginary)} = 56.8 - \frac{155,300 \times 10.47}{2183} = 56.8 - 744 = 687 \text{ psi}$$

Similar triangles give $kd = 6.34$ in., as indicated in Fig. 13.7d, compared to 6.40 in. assumed. Say O.K.

The steel stress will be calculated at the ring:

$$f_s = 10 \left[56.8 - \frac{155,300(5.49 + 2.47)}{2183} \right] = 10[56.8 - 566] = -4990 \text{ psi}$$

Now find the allowable P by proportion.

Based on $f_c = 1350$ psi, allow. $P = \dfrac{1350}{450} \times 10,000 = 30,000$ lb

Based on $f_s = 20,000$ psi, allow. $P = \dfrac{20,000}{4990} \times 10,000 = 40,100$ lb

Allow. $P = 30,000$ lb

Check f_s' stress:

$$f_s' = \frac{30,000}{10,000} \times 20 \left[56.8 + \frac{155,300(5.49 - 2.47)}{2183} \right]$$
$$= 60[56.8 + 215] = 16,320 \text{ psi} < 20,000 \qquad \text{O.K.}$$

The steel stress calculated above at the ring may be slightly larger than that actually on any bar, depending upon whether a bar falls at this extreme location. Since one cannot be certain how bars will be oriented during construction, the procedure used is the conservative one.

(d) Design of a column

Design a tied column for a load of 100 k and a moment of 150 k-ft, $f_c' = 3000$ psi, approximately 1.5% of intermediate grade steel.

SOLUTION

$$e = 150 \times 12/100 = 18 \text{ in.}$$

Assume $e/t = 0.8$, $B = 3$. The trial equivalent axial load P is

$$P = N(1 + Be/t) = 100(1 + 3 \times 0.8) = 340 \text{ k}$$

For $p = 0.015$,

$$P = 0.8A_g(0.225f_c' + f_sp_g)$$
$$= 0.8A_g(0.225 \times 3000 + 16,000 \times 0.015) = 733A_g$$
$$340,000 = 733A_g, \qquad A_g = 464 \text{ in.}^2 = 21.5 \times 21.5 \text{ in.}$$

Since $e/t = 18/21 = 0.86 > 0.80$ assumed, the equivalent P will be > 340 k.

$\underset{\text{(Try)}}{\text{USE}}$ 22-in. by 22-in. column, $e/t = 18/22 = 0.82$, trial P slightly > 340 k if $B = 3.0$.

$$\text{Trial } P = 340,000 \text{ lb}$$
$$\text{Value of concrete} = 0.225 \times 3000 \times 22^2 \times 0.8 = 261,000$$
$$0.8 \times 16,000A_s = \quad\underline{79,000} \text{ lb}$$
$$A_s = 6.16 \text{ in.}^2 > 6-\#9 = 6.00 \text{ in.}^2$$

$\underset{\text{(Try)}}{\text{USE}}$ 6-#9 (similar arrangement to Fig. 13.6a) since trial P is only an approximation.

This column will be analyzed for actual stresses, using $d' = 2.5$ in. (Fig. 13.8).

$$T = 30\,\frac{19.5 - kd}{kd}f_c \qquad C_s = 57\,\frac{kd - 2.5}{kd}f_c \qquad C_c = 22kdf_c/2 = 11kdf_c$$

$$\Sigma M_P = 0, \qquad T \times 26.5 - C_c(7 + kd/3) - C_s \times 9.5 = 0.$$

$$30\,\frac{19.5 - kd}{kd}f_c \times 26.5 - 11kdf_c(7 + kd/3) - 57\,\frac{kd - 2.5}{kd}f_c \times 9.5 = 0$$

$$795\,\frac{19.5 - kd}{kd} - 11kd(7 + kd/3) - 543\,\frac{kd - 2.5}{kd} = 0$$

$$\text{Try } kd = 10 \text{ in.,} \qquad 755 - 1140 - 407 = -792$$
$$7, \qquad 1420 - 717 - 348 = +355$$
$$8, \qquad 1145 - 852 - 373 = -80$$
$$\text{Use } kd = 7.8 \text{ in.,} \qquad 1193 - 824 - 370 = -1.$$

For $f_c = 1350$ psi,

$$f_s = 10 \times 1350 \times 11.7/7.8 = 20,200 \text{ psi} > 20,000 \qquad f_s \text{ most critical}$$
$$f_s' = 20 \times 1350 \times 5.3/7.8 = 18,400 \text{ psi} < 20,000 \qquad \text{O.K.}$$

$$\Sigma F_y = 0, \qquad 100,000 + T - C_c - C_s = 0.$$

$$100,000 + 30\,\frac{19.5 - 7.8}{7.8}f_c - 0.5f_c \times 22 \times 7.8 - 57\,\frac{5.3}{7.8}f_c = 0$$

$$100,000 + 45.0f_c - 85.8f_c - 38.7f_c = 0$$

$$79.5f_c = 100,000, \qquad f_c = 1260 \text{ psi} < 1350 \qquad \text{O.K.}$$

$$f_s = \frac{11.7}{7.8} \times 1260 \times 10 = 18,900 \text{ psi} < 20,000 \qquad \text{O.K.}$$

Could reduce A_s slightly, say, $\dfrac{20,200 - 18,900}{20,000} \times 100 = 5.5\%$, but say O.K.

This design can also be approached as a double-reinforced beam provided unsymmetrical steel is permissible and balanced stresses are considered satisfactory. The economy of balanced stresses, as reflected in total steel requirements, has not been investigated here. (The first design fell so close to a balanced

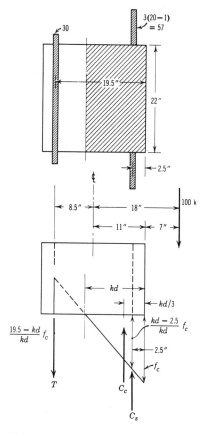

Fig. 13.8. Check on column design in Sec. 13.5*d*.

section it does not furnish a typical case for comparison.) The column will be redesigned by this method.

The value of R' is first estimated for the desired percentage of steel, as in Sec. 5.4*e*, and $R'bd^2$ is equated to the external moment calculated about a moment center on A_s. The percentage of compression steel p' will be 0.015/2 = 0.0075.

$$M_s = Rbd^2 + p'btf_s''(d - d')$$

Since $t = d + d'$, $t(d - d') = d^2 - d'^2 \doteq d^2$. Assume $f_s'' = 16{,}000$ psi.

$$M_s = 236bd^2 + 0.0075bd^2 \times 16{,}000 = 356bd^2$$

To locate A_s from the center of the column, estimate $(d - d')/2 = 7$ in. Assume also that $b = d + d' =$ say, $1.1d$.

$$M_s = 100{,}000(18 + 7) = 2{,}500{,}000 = 356bd^2 \doteq 392d^3$$

$$d = \sqrt[3]{6400} = 18.55 \text{ in.}, \qquad t = 18.55 + 2.5 = 21.05 \text{ in.}$$

Try $t = 21$ in., $d = 18.5$ in., $(d - d')/2 = 8$ in., $b = t = (21/18.5)d = 1.13d$.

$$M_s = 100{,}000(18 + 8) = 2{,}600{,}000 = 356bd^2 = 402d^3$$

$$d = \sqrt[3]{6480} = 18.65 \text{ in.}, \qquad t = 18.65 + 2.5 = 21.15 \text{ in.}$$

With slightly more steel, USE 21-in. by 21-in. column (f_s'' not yet exact).

$$M_s = 2{,}600{,}000 \text{ in.-lb}$$

$$Rbd^2 = 236 \times 21 \times 18.5^2 = \overline{1{,}700{,}000}$$

$$A_s'f_s''(d - d') = 900{,}000$$

$$f_s'' = \frac{0.403d - 2.5}{0.403d} f_c'(2n - 1) = \frac{7.48 - 2.5}{7.48} \times 1350 \times 19 = 17{,}100 \text{ psi}$$

$$A_s' \times 17{,}100 \times 16 = 900{,}000$$

USE $A_s' = 3.28$ in.², say, 3–#10 (3.81 in.²)

Total tension can be found by $\Sigma M = 0$ about C_s or C_c or any other convenient center. As an alternate, use $\Sigma F_y = 0$.

$$-100{,}000 - T + C_s + C_c = 0$$

$$-100{,}000 - A_s \times 20{,}000 + 3.28 \times 17{,}100 + 0.5 \times 1350 \times 21$$
$$\times 0.403 \times 18.5 = 0$$

$$-100{,}000 - 20{,}000A_s + 56{,}000 + 105{,}500 = 0$$

USE $A_s = 3.08$ in.², say, 4–#8 (3.16 in.²)

13.6. ASCE-ACI JOINT COMMITTEE REPORT ON ULTIMATE STRENGTH DESIGN

The ACI Code Appendix is based on the ASCE-ACI Joint Committee Report on ultimate strength design.[1, 2] The Report is framed to give the designer freedom in using either rectangular, parabolic, or trapezoidal stress distribution and consequently is somewhat more involved than it would need to be for any one pattern. The ACI Code in Sec. A609a quotes the two equilibrium equations in the Report form, as follows:

$$P_u = 0.85f_c'bdk_uk_1 + A_s'f_y - A_sf_s \qquad (13.1)$$

$$P_ue = 0.85f_c'bd^2k_uk_1(1 - k_2k_u) + A_s'f_y(d - d') \qquad (13.2)$$

The first equation is $\Sigma F_y = 0$ and the second is $\Sigma M = 0$ about the tension steel as a center. Attention is particularly called to the measurement of e from the tension steel, *not* from the center of column as in the working load calculation. The remainder of the notation is explained in Fig. 13.9. A Code footnote explains that concrete displaced by A_s' can be taken into account by reducing f_y to $f_y - 0.85f_c'$. Limitations are placed on k_1, to be taken not greater than 0.85, and on k_2/k_1, which must not be less than

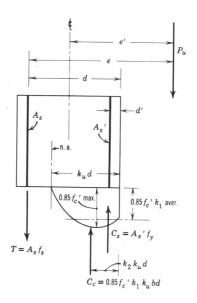

Fig. 13.9. Notation used in Report on ultimate strength design.

0.5. The 0.85 coefficient of f_c' is reduced for $f_c' > 5000$ psi. A simplified form for these equations is developed at the end of this section.

Design and analysis procedures fall into separate groups for compression and tension failures. The balanced condition where either failure is possible is defined in Art. A609b by the balanced load:

$$P_b = 0.85k_1\left(\frac{90{,}000}{90{,}000 + f_y}\right)f_c'bd + A_s'f_y{}^* - A_s f_y \qquad (13.3)$$

For this balanced condition or for a tension failure, the f_s in Eq. 13.1 becomes f_y. If the ultimate load $P_u > P_b$, the failure will be in compression; if $P_u < P_b$, the primary failure will be in tension. If k_1 is taken as 0.85, the above equation becomes the Report equation:

REINFORCED CONCRETE FUNDAMENTALS

$$P_b = 0.72 \left(\frac{90,000}{90,000 + f_y} \right) f_c'bd + A_s'f_y^* - A_sf_y \qquad (13.3a)$$

The parentheses in these equations represent the coefficient k_u, where k_ud is the distance to the neutral axis. The assumed conditions are shown in Fig. 13.10, leading to

$$k_ud = \left(\frac{0.003}{0.003 + \dfrac{f_y}{30 \times 10^6}} \right) d = \frac{90,000}{90,000 + f_y} d$$

The balanced stress conditions of Eq. 13.3a are shown in Fig. 13.11a. For $f_y = 40,000$ psi, $k_ud = 0.693d$, and $C_c = 0.498f_c'bd$; when $A_s = A_s'$, $P_b = C_c = 0.498f_c'bd$, as illustrated in Fig. 13.11b.

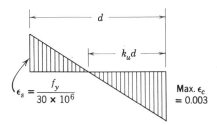

Fig. 13.10. Basis for neutral axis used in calculation of P_b.

For the tension failure, f_s on A_s remains as f_y. For the compression failure $f_s < f_y$, and for very small eccentricities of load f_s will become compression.

The above formulas from the Code Appendix and the Joint Report do not present the simplest and most direct approach to ultimate strength analysis and design. In the remainder of this chapter, the rectangular stress block idea is applied directly with the necessary equilibrium conditions. This satisfies all the conditions of the Code and Report, but emphasizes the physical concepts more than formulas.

In Eqs. 13.1 and 13.2, k_1 is defined as the ratio of the average f_c to $0.85f_c'$. For use with the rectangular stress block pioneered by Whitney[5] in this country, it is suggested that this definition of k_1 be ignored, that it be associated with k_u as the product k_1k_u, and that k_1k_ud be taken as the equivalent of Whitney's depth of stress block a. Then k_2k_ud can be

* Correction for concrete area displaced by A_s' may be made by subtracting $0.85f_c'$ from f_y in this term only.

written as $(k_2/k_1)k_1k_ud = (k_2/k_1)a = 0.5a$, when k_2/k_1 is used as 0.5, the minimum permitted by the Report. With these changes in notation, Eqs. 13.1 and 13.2 become:

$$P_u = 0.85f_c'ba + A_s'f_y - A_sf_s \tag{13.1a}$$

$$P_ue = 0.85f_c'bad(1 - a/2d) + A_s'f_y(d - d') \tag{13.2a}$$

The stress block with this notation is shown in Fig. 13.12.

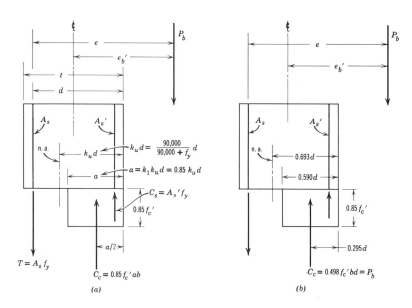

Fig. 13.11. Ultimate strength balanced load conditions. (*a*) General. (*b*) For $f_y = 40,000$ psi.

13.7. ULTIMATE STRENGTH OF RECTANGULAR COLUMNS FAILING IN TENSION—LARGE ECCENTRICITIES

(a) Theory

This discussion will be entirely in terms of symmetrical reinforcement and a rectangular stress block, with no account taken of concrete displaced by A_s'.

When a tension failure occurs, the yielding of the tension steel causes the neutral axis to move toward the compression face, reduces the compression area, and finally brings about a secondary compression failure.

REINFORCED CONCRETE FUNDAMENTALS

This final failure condition is the basis of analysis and implies that the stress on compression steel also becomes f_y.

Equilibrium of forces is very simply established from Fig. 13.13. For $A_s = A_s'$, $T = C_s$, and it follows from $\Sigma F_y = 0$ that $C_c = P_u$. For

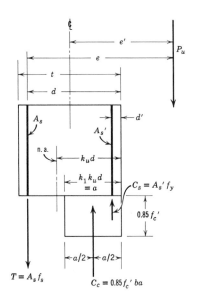

Fig. 13.12. Ultimate strength notation with rectangular stress block.

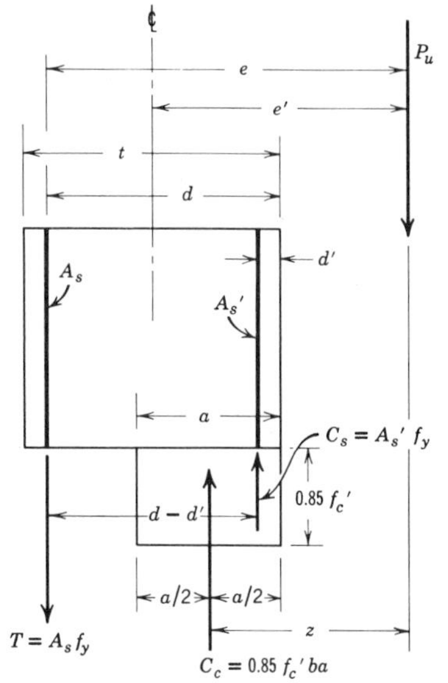

Fig. 13.13. Equilibrium of forces with tension failure, ultimate strength method.

$\Sigma M = 0$, the forces divide into two couples, one composed of T and C_s, the other of C_c and P_u.

$$C_s(d - d') = P_u z$$

where $z = e' - 0.5t + 0.5a$. (Note that e' is here defined as the distance from load to centroid.) These are both powerful and simple equations and are adequate for many problems.

(b) Investigation of given rectangular column

The ultimate load P_u on the column of Fig. 13.6a when e' is taken as 15 in. (horizontally) from the centroid, $f_c' = 3000$ psi, and $f_y = 50,000$ psi, will be calculated.

ECCENTRICALLY LOADED COLUMNS

SOLUTION

The forces acting are shown in Fig. 13.14.

$$T = A_s f_y = 3 \times 50{,}000 = 150{,}000 \text{ lb}$$
$$C_s = A_s' f_y = 3 \times 50{,}000 = 150{,}000 \text{ lb}$$
$$z = 15 - 9 + 0.5a = 6 + 0.5a$$
$$C_s(d - d') = 150{,}000(15.56 - 2.44) = 1{,}965{,}000 \text{ in.-lb}$$
$$P_u z = P_u(6 + 0.5a) = 1{,}965{,}000$$

Since $C_c = P_u$, $a = P_u/0.85 f_c' b$. This value of a could be substituted in the equation for $P_u z$ to give a quadratic in P_u. As an alternate, estimate a, solve for P_u, and revise.

Try $a = 6$ in., $\qquad P_u(6 + 0.5 \times 6) = 1{,}965{,}000$, $\qquad P_u = 218{,}000$ lb

$$a = \frac{218{,}000}{0.85 \times 3000 \times 18} = 4.75 \text{ in.}$$

Try $a = 5$ in., $\qquad P_u(6 + 2.5) = 1{,}965{,}000$, $\qquad P_u = 232{,}000$ lb

$$a = \frac{232{,}000}{0.85 \times 3000 \times 18} = 5.04 \text{ in.}$$

USE $a = 5.03$ in., $\qquad P_u(6 + 2.52) = 1{,}965{,}000$, $\qquad P_u = 231{,}000$ lb

If a load factor of 2 is used, P_u of 231,000 lb corresponds to a working $P = 115{,}500$ lb. This might be compared with the 81,000-lb value found in Sec. 13.5b for allowable P. Part of the difference is due to the use of the larger f_y for rail steel which the working load stress does not recognize with a higher allowable. Part of the difference is justified by the stricter control of f_c' specified in Art. A602f (compared to Art. 302c). Part of the difference simply recognizes the excessive factor of safety in the working load procedure.

An entirely practical alternate solution for this example would be given by a direct substitution in Eq. A9 in Art. A609 of the Code Appendix.

(c) Investigation of given circular column

Although the formula approach of Sec. 13.10 or the use of curves as in Sec. 13.13 is often convenient, circular columns can be analyzed readily using the coefficients for circular segments which have been conveniently arranged in Fig. E.18 in Appendix E. A solution by trial is recommended.

The column of Fig. 13.15a will be analyzed to establish the ultimate load capacity for a load at 12-in. eccentricity, assuming $f_c' = 3000$ psi and intermediate grade steel.

SOLUTION

Try $k_u d = 8$ in. and assume $a = 0.85 k_u d = 6.80$ in. $a/d = 6.80/20 = 0.340 = x/d$ of Fig. E.18 and corresponds to $B = 0.24$, $A = 0.60$. Hence, $\bar{x}$ of the

REINFORCED CONCRETE FUNDAMENTALS

segment from the center of the column $= AR = 0.60 \times 10 = 6.00$ in. and the
area $= Bd^2 = 0.24 \times 20^2 = 96$ in.^{2}

$$\text{Permissible } C_c = 0.85 \times 3 \times 96 = 245 \text{ k}$$

The assumed bar locations are shown in Fig. 13.15b. One pair of bars is so
close to the assumed neutral axis as to be only slightly stressed. This pair is

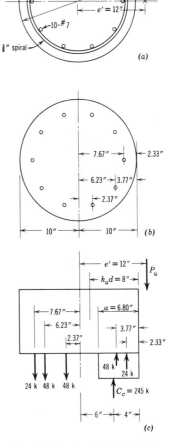

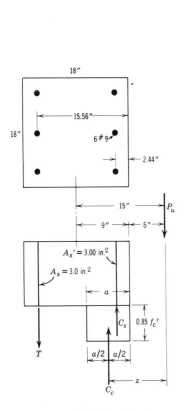

Fig. 13.14. Analysis of column
of Fig. 13.6a, ultimate strength
method with large eccentricity.

Fig. 13.15. Analysis of circular column, ultimate strength method. (a)
Column cross section. (b) Bar locations. (c) Forces in equilibrium.

ECCENTRICALLY LOADED COLUMNS

totally neglected in this calculation; the problem is discussed further in the following subsection. All other bars are assumed to carry the yield stress, leading to the forces shown in Fig. 13.15c. Moments of these forces about the center of the column must balance the moment $P_u e'$:

$$2 \times 24 \times 7.67 = \quad 368$$
$$2 \times 48 \times 6.23 = \quad 600$$
$$48 \times 2.37 = \quad 114$$
$$C_c: 245 \times 6.00 = 1470$$
$$\overline{}$$
$$2552 = 12P_u$$
$$P_u = 213 \text{ k}$$
$$T - C_s = \quad 48$$
$$\overline{}$$
$$\text{Required } C_c = 261 \text{ k}$$

This exceeds the permissible C_c of 245 k for the assumed $k_u d$.

For the second trial, take $k_u d = 8.5$ in., $a = 0.85 \times 8.5 = 7.22$ in. $a/d = 7.22/20 = 0.361$. Figure E.18 for $x/d = 0.361$ shows $B = 0.26$, $A = 0.572$.

$$\text{Permissible } C_c = (0.26 \times 20^2)(0.85 \times 3) = 265 \text{ k}$$
$$\bar{x} = 0.572 \times 10$$
$$= 5.72 \text{ in. from center}$$

$$\Sigma M: \text{As above} = \quad 368$$
$$\text{,,} \quad \text{,,} \quad = \quad 600$$
$$\text{,,} \quad \text{,,} \quad = \quad 114$$
$$C_c: 265 \times 5.72 = 1518$$
$$\overline{}$$
$$2600 = 12P_u$$
$$P_u = \quad 217 \text{ k}$$
$$T - C_s = \quad 48$$
$$\overline{}$$
$$\text{Required } C_c = \quad 265 \text{ k as assumed}$$
$$\text{O.K.}$$

Fig. 13.16. The failure of an eccentrically loaded spiral column. (Courtesy University of Illinois.)

Hence, the ultimate load $P_u = 217$ k.

The failure of such a column is shown in Fig. 13.16.

(d) Treatment of bars near neutral axis

A consideration of deformation in either rectangular or circular columns indicates that bars at the neutral axis will not be effective in carrying stress and those nearby will have stresses lower than the yield stress. For any given neutral axis it might be well to sketch the unit deformations in order to establish the status of nearby bars. The maximum unit deformation on the concrete is limited by specification to $\epsilon = 0.003$ for f'_c of 5000 psi or less. For example, Fig. 13.17a shows the deformations agreeing with the first trial value of $kd = 8$ in. used for the column of Fig. 13.15a. To make

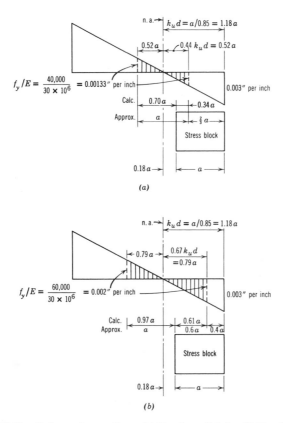

(a)

(b)

Fig. 13.17. Deformation studies. (a) For $f_y = 40$ ksi. (b) For $f_y = 60$ ksi.

$f_s = f_y = 40$ ksi, the steel deformation must be at least 0.00133. Considering the stress block depth as $a = 0.85 k_u d$, the bars falling in the shaded zone will have f_s less than f_y. A rough rule would be to say that f_s is less than an f_y of 40 ksi whenever the bar falls at a depth between $2a/3$ and $5a/3$. For $f_y = 60$ ksi the corresponding zones (Fig. 13.17b) would be roughly between depths of 0.4a and 2.0a.

The deformation sketch is quite simple to use whenever $k_u d$ is known or assumed and can lead directly to the proper f_s for each bar location. It is not a precision calculation because of the assumption that $a = 0.85k_u d$. This is in agreement with the Joint Committee Report as it has been applied to the rectangular stress block in this chapter, but its value is probably less accurate when applied to circular cross sections.

(e) Design of a column

For the sake of comparison the design will be made for the data of Sec. 13.5d. Design a tied column for a working load of 100 k with a moment of 150 k-ft, $f_c' = 3000$ psi, intermediate grade steel, approximately 1.5% steel, a load factor of 2.

SOLUTION

$$e' = 150 \times 12/100 = 18 \text{ in.}$$

A balanced design at failure will probably use more than this small amount of steel, but such design will be made to show the method as well as its limitations. The equation for balanced load (Eq. 13.3a) will be used, noting that the last two terms net zero for symmetrical steel.

$$P_b = 0.72 \left(\frac{90,000}{90,000 + f_y} \right) f_c'bd = 0.72 \left(\frac{90,000}{90,000 + 40,000} \right) f_c'bd = 0.498 f_c'bd$$

$$P_u = 2 \times 100,000 = P_b = 0.498 \times 3000bd = 1494bd$$

$$bd = 200,000/1494 = 133.6 \text{ in.}^2$$

If $b = 13$ in., $d = 10.25 + 2.5$ cover $\doteq 13$ in. for t

The balanced column will usually require excessive steel, but calculations will be continued to show the procedure. For a 13-in. by 13-in. column:

$$a = \frac{P_u}{0.85 f_c'b} = \frac{200,000}{0.85 \times 3000 \times 13} = 6.05 \text{ in.}$$

$$P_u z = 200,000(e' - 0.5t + 0.5a) = 200,000(18 - 6.5 + 3.02) = 2,910,000$$

This must be balanced by the T and C_s couple.

$$A_s'f_y(d - d') = A_s' \times 40,000(13 - 2 \times 2.5) = P_u z = 2,910,000$$

$$A_s' = 9.10 \text{ in.}^2 = A_s$$

$$\text{Total } p_t = 2 \times 9.10/13^2 = 0.108 = 10.8\%, \text{ excessive}$$

(The per cent of steel required for a balanced column increases as the eccentricity becomes larger.)

The design will now be started on a more realistic basis, on the basis of the desired p. For clarity p_t will be used for total steel, p for tension, and p' for compression steel. The desired $p' = 0.0075$.

$$C_s(d - d') = P_u z$$

$$p't^2 f_y(d - d') = P_u(e' - 0.5t + 0.5a)$$

For $d' = 2.5$ in., $d - d' = t - 2d' = t - 5$

Since the above equation for p' is not very sensitive to variation in a, assume $a =$ say, 4 in.

$$0.0075t^2 \times 40,000(t - 5) = 200,000(18 - 0.5t + 0.5 \times 4)$$
$$300t^2(t - 5) - 4,000,000 + 100,000t = 0$$

Try $t = 20$ in.: $1,800,000 - 4,000,000 + 2,000,000 = -200,000$

$t = 21$ in.: $2,120,000 - 4,000,000 + 2,100,000 = +220,000$

USE 20-in. by 20-in. column

$$a = \frac{P_u}{0.85f_c'b} = \frac{200,000}{0.85 \times 3000 \times 20} = 3.92 \text{ in.}$$

The agreement with the assumed 4 in. is unusually good, but t would be little changed anyway. The revised couple becomes

$$P_u z = 200,000(18 - 10 + 1.96) = 1,992,000 \text{ in.-lb}$$
$$A_s' f_y(20 - 2.5 \times 2) = 40,000 \times 15 A_s' = 1,992,000$$
$$A_s' = 3.32 \text{ in.}^2 = A_s$$

Check: $\qquad p = 2 \times 3.32/20^2 = 0.0166 = 1.66\%$ O.K.

USE $A_{st} = 6\text{-}\#10$

Since the formation and solution of the cubic equation is a slow process, the desired column would probably be established more quickly by a cut-and-try process, as follows. A guess at the column size would first be made. For this assumed size, a, z, A_s', and p would be calculated just as at the close of the above solution. On the basis of this result a second trial would be made. Because the results are sharply convergent and because several trials can be made while the cubic equation is set up and solved, this trial procedure would probably be favored by experienced designers.

Several comments on the numerical solution above are appropriate. For the moment always in one direction, the concrete without any A_s' is entirely capable of carrying the compression. Also, for moments in only this one plane, some saving would accrue from using a width smaller than t; not much concrete is needed for load capacity. The column size was large only in order to increase the arm for the T and C_s couple and thereby to reduce p.

13.8. ULTIMATE STRENGTH OF RECTANGULAR COLUMNS FAILING IN COMPRESSION—SMALL ECCENTRICITIES

(a) Theory

When P_u on a given column is more than P_b from Eq. 13.3a, the failure will be in compression, with the tension f_s on A_s lower than f_y. When the

ECCENTRICALLY LOADED COLUMNS

eccentricity falls well inside the column cross section, it is obvious that the stress f_s will become compression and that a tension failure is impossible; it is entirely unnecessary to calculate P_b in such a case. With larger eccentricity, it may be necessary to establish that P_u exceeds P_b in order to be certain that a compression failure is involved; the eccentricity accompanying P_b is quite sensitive to variation in the percentage of steel.

In order to analyze compression failures some elastic considerations must be introduced in connection with the stress acting on A_s. Analysis

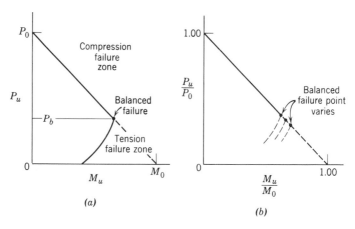

Fig. 13.18. Interaction diagrams showing limits for compression failure. (*a*) For a single given column. (*b*) Dimensionless form for general use.

of a given column on this basis, over the range between a balanced failure and zero eccentricity, leads to the conclusion that approximately a linear relationship exists between axial load and moment, as shown in Fig. 13.18*a*. The load for zero eccentricity is the ultimate strength P_0 given by Eq. 2.1 (Sec. 2.3):

$$P_0 = 0.85f_c'A_c + f_yA_{st}$$

The moment M_0 for pure bending is Whitney's[5] compression failure (balanced beam) value plus the added moment developed by the compression steel A_s'.

$$M_0 = 0.333f_c'bd^2 + A_s'f_y(d - d') \tag{13.4}$$

The dashed portion of the curve has no practical significance because there the failure would be in tension.

REINFORCED CONCRETE FUNDAMENTALS

This same curve reduced to dimensionless terms, as shown in Fig. 13.18b, is defined by the equation:

$$\frac{P_u}{P_0} + \frac{M_u}{M_0} = 1 \tag{13.5}$$

In this form it agrees well with test data from a wide range of columns. Unfortunately, no similar simplification is possible for the tension failure zone.

Whitney[5] expressed essentially* this same equation in terms of the column dimensions and this has been accepted by the Joint Report and the Code (Eq. A11 in Art. A609d):

$$P_u = \frac{A_s' f_y}{e'/(d-d') + \frac{1}{2}} + \frac{btf_c'}{(3te'/d^2) + 1.18} = \frac{A_s' f_y}{e/(d-d')} + \frac{btf_c'}{(3te'/d^2) + 1.18} \tag{13.6}$$

The notation is shown in Fig. 13.13. When $e' = 0$, this equation gives P_0 exactly as in Eq. 2.1 except that $2A_s'$ shows in place of A_{st} and bt shows instead of A_c, thus ignoring concrete displaced by the steel; when e' becomes infinite, the equation leads to M_0 as given by Eq. 13.4.

(b) Investigation of a given column

The column of Fig. 13.5a was analyzed in Sec. 13.4b for $f_c' = 2500$ psi, $n = 12$, where it was established that a load of 186 k at 2.4-in. eccentricity would be permitted as a working load. The ultimate load at this eccentricity will now be established, first from Eq. 13.5 and next from Eq. 13.6, using $f_y = 40,000$ psi.

SOLUTION

$P_0 = 0.85 f_c' A_c + f_y A_s = 0.85 \times 2500(20^2 - 4 \times 1.27) + 40,000 \times 4 \times 1.27$
$$= 839,000 + 203,000 = 1,042,000 \text{ lb} = 1042 \text{ k}$$

$M_0 = 0.333 f_c' b d^2 + A_s' f_y(d - d') = 0.333 \times 2500 \times 20 \times 17.5^2 + 2 \times 1.27$
$$\times 40,000(17.5 - 2.5) = 5,120,000 + 1,527,000$$
$$= 6,650,000 \text{ in.-lb} = 6650 \text{ k-in.}$$

$M_u = P_u e' = 2.4 P_u$

Using Eq. 13.5:

$$\frac{P_u}{1042} + \frac{2.4 P_u}{6650} = 1, \quad \text{or} \quad P_u + 0.375 P_u = 1042$$

$$P_u = 757 \text{ k}$$

* Actually Eq. 13.6 defines a line between P_0 and M_0 in Fig. 13.18a that is slightly curved, but the deviation is not important.

This indicates that the ACI Code gives an actual load factor in this case of $757/186 = 4.07$.

ALTERNATE SOLUTION

$e' = 2.4$ in., $\quad e = 2.4 + 10 - 2.5 = 9.9$ in., $\quad d - d' = 20 - 2 \times 2.5 = 15$ in.

Using Eq. 13.6:

$$P_u = \frac{2 \times 1.27 \times 40,000}{9.9/15} + \frac{20 \times 20 \times 2500}{(3 \times 20 \times 2.4)/17.5^2 + 1.18}$$

$$= 154,000 + 607,000 = 761,000 \text{ lb} = 761 \text{ k}$$

(c) Design of a column

Either Eq. 13.5 or Eq. 13.6 is suitable for design by successive approximations, but the latter seems to give more rapid convergence.

The tied column of Sec. 13.4c will be redesigned, using a load factor of 2. The working load is 150 k, moment 60 k-ft, $f_c' = 3000$ psi, rail steel ($f_y = 50,000$ psi), p_t about 0.015.

SOLUTION

$$P_u = 2 \times 150 = 300 \text{ k}, \qquad M_u = 2 \times 60 = 120 \text{ k-ft}$$

Try $t = 24$ in. (a deliberate poor choice to show convergence).

$d = 24 - 2.5 = 21.5$ in., $\quad d - d' = 21.5 - 2.5 = 19.0$ in., $\quad b = t$

$e' = M/P = 120 \times 12/300 = 4.8$ in., $\quad e = 4.8 + 9.5 = 14.3$ in.

$A_s' = 0.5 p_t bt = 0.5 \times 0.015 t^2 = 0.0075 t^2$

Substituting in Eq. 13.6, but leaving t in the numerator as unknown:

$$300,000 = \frac{0.0075 t^2 \times 50,000}{14.3/19.0} + \frac{3000 t^2}{(3 \times 24 \times 4.8)/21.5^2 + 1.18}$$

$$= 498 t^2 + 1550 t^2 = 2048 t^2$$

$$t = \sqrt{146} = 12.1 \text{ in.}$$

Since this much smaller t would lead to some increase on the next cycle, try $t = 13$ or 14 in., say, $t = 14$ in.

$d = 14 - 2.5 = 11.5$ in., $\quad d - d' = 11.5 - 2.5 = 9.0$ in. $\quad b = t$

$e' = 4.8$ in., $\quad e = 4.8 + 4.5 = 9.3$ in.

$$300,000 = \frac{0.0075 t^2 \times 50,000}{9.3/9.0} + \frac{3000 t^2}{(3 \times 14 \times 4.8)/11.5^2 + 1.18}$$

$$= 363 t^2 + 1110 t^2 = 1473 t^2$$

$$t = \sqrt{203} = 14.27 \text{ in.}$$

(The use of $t = 13$ in. as a trial would have led to $t = 14.4$ in.)

USE 14-in. by 14-in. column

REINFORCED CONCRETE FUNDAMENTALS

Use Eq. 13.6 again, leaving A_s' as the unknown:

$$300,000 = \frac{A_s' \times 50,000}{9.3/9.0} + 1110 \times 14^2 = 48,300A_s' + 217,000$$

$$A_s' = 83,000/48,300 = 1.72 \text{ in.}^2 = A_s$$

$$A_{st} = 2 \times 1.72 = 3.44 \text{ in.}^2 \quad (p_t = 0.0176)$$

$$\text{USE } 4\text{-}\#9 = 4.00 \text{ in.}^2 \quad \text{or} \quad 6\text{-}\#7 = 3.60 \text{ in.}^2$$

13.9. COMPARISON OF ULTIMATE STRENGTH AND WORKING LOAD DESIGNS

Compared to the 14-in. square column in Sec. 13.8c it should be noted that the working load design of Sec. 13.4c resulted in an 18-in. square column, which thus gives a real load factor much in excess of 2. A comparison of the large eccentricity case in Sec. 13.5d with that of Sec. 13.7e shows a similar result, with the 22-in. column for working loads replaced by a 20-in. column under ultimate design procedures.

Much of this difference represents an absolute difference in the factors of safety under the two methods, a difference which must obviously be narrowed in the next edition of the ACI Building Code. However, two factors in these designs are not comparable. First, a given f_c' in ultimate strength design represents a stronger concrete than in ordinary working load design. (Compare Code Arts. 304c and A.602f.) Second, the larger load factor used for ultimate strength design gives a larger effective ratio of design live load to dead load, which implies larger moments reaching an interior column and larger eccentricities for its design.

13.10. ULTIMATE STRENGTH OF CIRCULAR COLUMNS— FORMULAS

Since circular segments are not easy to handle algebraically, the Report formulas shown in the Code Appendix are helpful. These formulas are based on the same principles discussed in connection with rectangular columns.[9] They are the formulas presented by Whitney[5] in 1942, with some modifications of the constants.* Whitney's basic assumptions were: (1) that the circular arrangement of the steel could be approximated by considering half the steel effective on each side of the member at $D_s/3$ from the center (D_s being the diameter of a circle circumscribing the steel; and

* References 5 and 6 also cover square columns with circular cores.

(2) that the concrete could be replaced by a square having a side dimension equal to 0.8 of the outside column diameter.

For compression failure the governing formula is Eq. A13 in the Code Appendix. This equation has a form quite similar to Eq. 13.6 (Eq. A11 in the Code Appendix). The ultimate load P_u for a given column can be found by direct substitution in this equation. If one is in doubt as to whether the failure will be in compression, the value of P_u can also be calculated from Eq. A12 in the Code Appendix; the smaller P_u governs.

For design, on the basis of a compression failure, Eq. A13 in the Code Appendix can be used with a trial value of D (column diameter) in the denominators, as t was used in Sec. 13.8c with a rectangular column.

For design, on the basis of a given eccentricity e' leading to tension failure, substitution of e', a trial column diameter D, and the desired $p_t m$ value into Eq. A12 (Code Appendix) leads directly to a permissible P_u value. A proper D can thus be established in a few trials, such that the permissible P_u is approximately adequate. With this diameter D the exact $p_t m$ required can be found from the same equation.

13.11. LONG COLUMNS—ULTIMATE STRENGTH

With large eccentricities, the bending strength required to resist the moment Pe' is often greater than that required to prevent buckling as a long column. Hence P_u as already calculated for short columns often governs also for long columns. However, the Report and the Code Appendix (Art. A611) limit the load on a long column to

$$P_u' = P_0(1.6 - 0.04L/t)$$

whenever the L/t ratio exceeds 15. In this formula P_0 is the ultimate column strength for an axial load as given in Eq. 2.1 of Sec. 2.3. P_u' does not control unless it is lower than P_u.

13.12. DESIGN AIDS—WORKING LOADS

The *CRSI Design Handbook*[4] includes a comprehensive series of tables which give the allowable working loads on a wide range of column sizes and reinforcements for a considerable range of eccentricities. These tables are based on the working stress procedures of Secs. 13.4 and 13.5.

13.13. DESIGN AIDS—ULTIMATE STRENGTH

(a) Available aids

For ultimate strength design attention is called to charts for columns included in the Joint Report.[1,2] The first chart, reproduced as Fig. E.19 in Appendix E, was developed by the Portland Cement Association to solve Eqs. 13.1 and 13.2 for the case of tension failure. The unlabeled horizontal axis represents values of $k_1 k_u$. The second series of charts, reproduced as Figs. E.20 through E.33, were developed by Whitney and Cohen.[6] Eight of these charts were printed in nearly the same form in the Joint Report somewhat earlier. These charts cover both tension and compression failures for symmetrical columns. For many tension failure calculations Fig. E.19 reads more easily; it also covers unsymmetrical steel.

(b) Examples involving tension failure

The determination of P_u for a given eccentricity is awkward on Fig. E.19 and only moderately accurate for $e' > t$ when Whitney's charts (Figs. E.20 through E.31) are used. The procedure for the latter would be: (1) select the chart for the correct d/t ratio; (2) calculate $p_t m$, based on the gross area bt; (3) calculate e'/t; (4) find the point corresponding to $p_t m$ and e'/t and read $P_u/f_c' bt$ on the ordinate or $P_u e'/f_c' bt^2$ on the abscissa; (5) calculate P_u from this value as the only unknown.

The design of Sec. 13.7e will be determined from Fig. E.19.

A symmetrical design gives $(pm - p'm) = 0$. The intersection of the line marked $(pm - p'm) = 0$ with the vertical line marked "limit for f_y 40,000 psi" gives the data for a balanced section; horizontally to the left read $P_u/f_c' bd$ $= 0.504$.

$$bd = P_u/(0.504 f_c') = 200{,}000/(0.504 \times 3000) = 132.4 \text{ in.}^2$$

As noted in Sec. 13.7e, this would be too small and call for excessive steel.

Try $t = b = 18$ in., $d = 18 - 2.5 = 15.5$ in., $e = 18 + 13.0/2 = 24.5$ in.

$$P_u/f_c' bd = 200{,}000/(3000 \times 18 \times 15.5) = 0.239$$

$$P_u e/f_c' bd^2 = 0.239 e/d = 0.239 \times 24.5/15.5 = 0.379$$

Enter the chart with 0.239 on the left ordinate, move horizontally to $(pm - p'm)$ $= 0$, thence vertically (upward in this case) to $P_u e/f_c' bd^2 = 0.379$, then horizontally to read on the right ordinate $p'm(1 - d'/d) = 0.210$.

$$m = f_y/0.85 f_c' = 40{,}000/(0.85 \times 3000) = 15.7$$

$$1 - d'/d = 1 - 2.5/15.5 = 0.839 = (d - d')/d$$

$$p' = 0.210 \div m\left(\frac{d - d'}{d}\right) = 0.210 \div (15.7 \times 0.839) = 0.0159 = A_s'/bd$$

Since the desired p' is 0.0075 based on A_s'/bt, try a larger column. For the 20-in. by 20-in. column used before,

$$t = b = 20 \text{ in.}, \qquad d = 17.5 \text{ in.}, \qquad e = 18 + 15.0/2 = 25.5$$

$$1 - d'/d = 1 - 2.5/17.5 = 0.857$$

$$P_u/f_c'bd = 200{,}000/(3000 \times 20 \times 17.5) = 0.191$$

$$P_u e/f_c'bd^2 = 0.191e/d = 0.191 \times 25.5/17.5 = 0.278$$

These values on the chart give $p'm(1 - d'/d) = 0.131$

$$p' = 0.131 \div (15.7 \times 0.857) = 0.0097$$

$$A_s' = 0.0097 \times 20 \times 17.5 = 3.40 \text{ in.}^2$$

This compares with $A_s' = 3.32$ in.^{2} in Sec. 13.7e.

Whitney's charts could also be used as indicated in (c), although these cannot be read quite as accurately.

(c) Example involving compression failure

For designs involving the minimum eccentricities permitted by the Report, Figs. E.32 and E.33, prepared by Whitney and Cohen,[6] are quite convenient. Each of these covers the entire range of d/t ratios ordinarily encountered, with a separate line for each ratio.

For general analysis Whitney's charts, Figs. E.20 through E.31, are very convenient. One picks a chart on the basis of the actual d/t ratio. One next calculates $p_t m = \left(\dfrac{A_{st}}{bt}\right)\left(\dfrac{f_y}{0.85f_c'}\right)$ and e'/t and from these locates a point on the chart. The corresponding ordinate $P_u/f_c'bt$ or the corresponding abscissa $P_u e/f_c'bt^2$ establishes P_u since this is the only remaining unknown.

For design, one estimates d/t and e'/t to use with the desired $p_t m$. This procedure will be illustrated with the data of Sec. 13.8c.

The value of $d = 0.8t$ will be first assumed, indicating the use of Fig. E.23. Since e' is given as 4.8 in., assume $e'/t = 0.2$.

$$m = f_y/0.85f_c' = 50{,}000/(0.85 \times 3000) = 19.6$$

The desired p_t is 0.015, making $p_t m = 0.015 \times 19.6 = 0.294$. On Fig. E.23, $e'/t = 0.2$ and $p_t m = 0.294$ determine a point on the ordinate, $P_u/f_c'bt = 0.62$.

$$bt = P_u \div (0.62f_c') = 300{,}000 \div (0.62 \times 3000) = 161 \text{ in.}^2 \doteq 13 \text{ in. by } 13 \text{ in.}$$

This increases e'/t greatly and the required bt some.

Try $b = t = 14$ in., $e'/t = 4.8/14 = 0.343$. Read from the chart $P_u/f_c'bt = 0.48$.

$$bt = 300,000 \div (0.48 \times 3000) = 208 \text{ in.}^2 = 14.4 \text{ in. by } 14.4 \text{ in.}$$

USE 14-in. by 14-in. column

$$d = (11.5/14)t = 0.82t \quad \text{(Does not quite fit the } d = 0.8t \text{ chart used.)}$$

$$e'/t = 0.343, \quad P_u/f_c'bt = 300,000 \div (3000 \times 14^2) = 0.51$$

For these e'/t and $P_u/f_c'bt$ values read $p_t m$ from chart as 0.37.

$$p_t = 0.37/m = 0.37/19.6 = 0.0189$$

$$A_{st} = p_t bt = 0.0189 \times 14^2 = 3.70 \text{ in.}^2$$

Since this is based on $d = 0.8t$, it is proper that the earlier calculated A_{st} based on $d = 0.82t$ be slightly less, namely, 3.44 in.[2] (Sec. 13.8c). A better value could be established by interpolating between Figs. E.20 and E.21 for $d = 0.82t$.

SELECTED REFERENCES

1. "Report of ASCE-ACI Joint Committee on Ultimate Strength Design," *ASCE Proc.-Separate 809*, Oct. 1955.

2. ACI-ASCE Committee 327, "Ultimate Strength Design," *ACI Jour.*, **27**, Jan. 1956; *Proc.*, **52**, p. 505.

3. F. E. Richart and T. A. Olson, "The Resistance of Reinforced Concrete Columns to Eccentric Loads," *ACI Jour.*, **9**, Mar.-Apr. 1938; *Proc.*, **34**, p. 401.

4. R. C. Reese, *CRSI Design Handbook*, Concrete Reinforcing Steel Institute, Chicago, 2nd ed., 1957.

5. Chas. S. Whitney, "Plastic Theory of Reinforced Concrete Design," *ASCE Trans.*, **107**, 1942, p. 251.

6. Chas. S. Whitney and Edward Cohen, "Guide for Ultimate Strength Design of Reinforced Concrete," *ACI Jour.*, **28**, Nov. 1956; *Proc.*, **53**, p. 455.

7. Chas. S. Whitney, "Application of Plastic Theory to the Design of Modern Reinforced Concrete Structures," *Jour. Boston Soc. Civil Engrs.*, **XXXV**, Jan. 1948, p. 29.

8. Phil M. Ferguson, "Simplification of Design by Ultimate Strength Procedures," *Jour. ASCE*, Structural Div., **82**, No. ST4, July 1956, Paper 1022.

9. Hermann Craemer, "Skew Bending in Concrete Computed by Plasticity," *ACI Jour.*, **23**, Feb. 1952; *Proc.*, **48**, p. 516.

10. I. M. Viest, R. C. Elstner, and E. Hognestad, "Sustained Load Strength of Eccentrically Loaded Short Reinforced Concrete Columns," *ACI Jour.*, **27**, Mar. 1956; *Proc.*, **52**, p. 727.

11. Eivind Hognestad, "A Study of Combined Bending and Axial Load in Reinforced Concrete Members," Univ. of Ill. Eng. Exp. Sta. *Bull. No. 399*, 1951.

PROBLEMS

Prob. 13.1. If $f_c' = 3000$ psi and bars are rail steel with the cover 2.5 in. to the center of the bars, $h = 10$ ft., find the working load permitted by the main body of the Code on:

(a) The column of Fig. 2.12a for a load on the x-axis 6 in. to the right of the center line of the column.

(b) The column of Fig. 2.12b for a load on the x-axis 10 in. to the right of the center line of the column.

(c) The column of Fig. 2.12d for a load 8 in. off the center of the column.

(d) The column of Fig. 2.12f for a load on the axis 6 in. off the center of the column.

(e) The column of Fig. 2.12b for a load on the y-axis 6 in. above the x-axis.

(f) The column of Fig. 2.12c for a load on the y-axis 6 in. above the x-axis.

Prob. 13.2. If $f_c' = 3750$ psi and intermediate grade steel is used with the cover 2.5 in. to the center of the steel, $h = 9$ ft., find the working load permitted by the main body of the Code on:

(a) The column of Fig. 2.12a for a load on the x-axis 20 in. to the right of the center of the column.

(b) The column of Fig. 2.12b for a load on the y-axis 20 in. above the x-axis.

(c) The column of Fig. 2.12c for a load on the x-axis 18 in. to the right of the y-axis.

(d) The column of Fig. 2.12e for a load on the x-axis 18 in. to the right of the y-axis.

(e) The column of Fig. 2.12d for a load on the x-axis 18 in. to the right of the y-axis.

Prob. 13.3. If $f_c' = 3000$ psi and bars are intermediate grade steel with the cover 2.5 in. to the center of the steel, $h = 10$ ft., find the working load permitted by the main body of the Code on:

(a) The column of Fig. 2.12a for a load 6 in. to the right of the y-axis and 8 in. above the x-axis.

(b) The column of Fig. 2.12c for a load 8 in. from both axes.

(c) The column of Fig. 2.12d for a load 8 in. from both x- and y-axes.

(d) The column of Fig. 2.12e for a load acting exactly on one corner of the column.

Prob. 13.4. If $f_c' = 3750$ psi and bars are hard grade steel with the cover 2.5 in. to the center of the steel, what is the working load permitted by the main body of the Code on the column of Fig. 2.12d for a load on a 45° line 15 in. from the center of the column. Take $h = 12$ ft.

Prob. 13.5.

(a) Design a square tied column for a working load of 200 k and a moment of 100 k-ft using $f_c' = 3750$ psi, approximately 2% of hard grade steel, and $h = 10$ ft.

(b) Redesign this tied column if the moment is increased to 200 k-ft.

(c) Redesign the column of part (a) as a round spiral column.

(d) Redesign the column of part (b) as a round spiral column.

REINFORCED CONCRETE FUNDAMENTALS

(e) Redesign the column of part (a) using a square column with a round spiral.

(f) Redesign the column of part (b) using a square column with a round spiral.

Prob. 13.6. Under ultimate strength theory with an average load factor of 2.0, evaluate the permissible service load for each case of the column and loading position combinations indicated in Prob. 13.1.

Prob. 13.7. Under ultimate strength theory with an average load factor of 2.1, evaluate the permissible service load for each case of the column and eccentricity indicated in Prob. 13.2.

Prob. 13.8. Under ultimate strength theory with an average load factor of 2.0, evaluate the permissible service load on the column of Prob. 13.4.

Prob. 13.9.

(a) Without using curves, design the column of Prob. 13.5a on the ultimate strength basis using a load factor of 2.0.

(b) Repeat for the column of Prob. 13.5b.

Prob. 13.10. Design a square tied column under ultimate strength theory for a load factor of 2.0, service load of 300 k, service moment of 300 k-ft, $f_c' = 3000$ psi, about 3% intermediate grade steel, and $h = 11$ ft.

Prob. 13.11.

(a) Under ultimate strength theory with an average load factor of 2.0, evaluate and locate the ultimate load which gives a horizontal neutral axis 6 in. below the top edge of the column of Fig. 2.12c. Assume cover 2.5 in. to center of steel, $f_c' = 3000$ psi, intermediate grade steel, and consider deformations to establish the steel stresses.

(b) Repeat for a horizontal neutral axis 6 in. below the top edge of Fig. 2.12b.

CHAPTER

14

Footings

14.1. TYPES OF FOOTINGS

Although underground conditions call for many variations in foundation design, the majority of building footings can be classified as one of the following types.

Bearing walls may be supported on a continuous strip of concrete called a wall footing, as shown in Fig. 14.8.

Isolated column footings under individual columns may be square (as shown in Fig. 14.1*b*), rectangular, or round in plan.

When a single footing supports two or more column loads, as in Figs. 14.11 and 14.12, it is called a combined footing.

A cantilever footing, as in Fig. 14.14, also supports two or more columns. It is characterized by the fact that it is really two footings joined by a beam instead of by a bearing portion of the footing.

Under poor soil conditions it is sometimes desirable to support the

376

entire structure on a single mat or slab. Such a foundation is often called a floating or raft foundation.

Any of these footings may be directly supported on the soil or they may rest on piling.

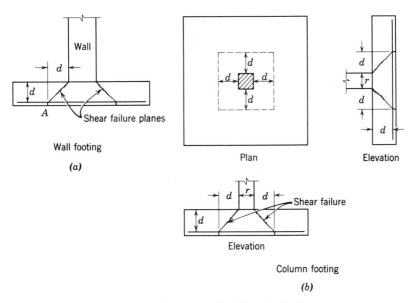

Fig. 14.1. Diagonal tension failure in footings.

14.2. TESTS ON FOOTINGS

Two noteworthy series of footing studies have influenced American practice, Talbot's tests[1] in 1907 and Richart's tests[2] in 1946.

Shear failures never occurred on vertical planes along the wall or around the column and the older design concept of punching shear around a column has now been completely abandoned. In the case of wall footings which failed in shear, a diagonal tension crack developed on an approximate 45° plane parallel to the wall, as shown at A in Fig. 14.1a. The shear causing this crack is that produced by the upward load to the left of A, that is, the load beyond a plane a distance d from the face of the wall. In an isolated square column footing a similar failure occurs, the column pushing ahead of it a truncated pyramid with an approximate 45° slope on all faces. This pyramid has a base width equal to the column width plus twice the effective depth of the footing (Fig. 14.1b). The probable reason for this type of failure lies in the heavy vertical compressive stresses produced, between the diagonal cracks, by the load as it spreads out directly beneath the column or wall, this being accentuated by the upward soil reaction. In this zone the diagonal tension normally caused by shear stresses is somewhat counteracted or reduced by this vertical compressive stress. (Compare Fig. 6.8c and the related discussion in Sec. 6.9.) The 45° failure planes mark the approximate boundaries over which substantial vertical compression is developed.

With both walls and columns of concrete, the critical section for moment and bond was found to be at the face of the wall or column. In the wall footing the one-way cantilever moment due to loads beyond the critical section is uniformly distributed along the wall (Fig. 14.8); any 1-ft wide strip can be used in this part of the design. In the column footing Richart found the distribution of this cantilever moment (in each direction) to be very nonuniform at working loads, being largest for strips passing under the column and least for strips near an edge. However, near ultimate loads the yielding of the steel in the central strips causes more moment to shift to the edge strips and moment failure does not occur until essentially all the steel has reached its yield point.* Bond was found to be less critical than expected, but was found to be maximum on the sections used for maximum moment.

14.3. SQUARE COLUMN FOOTINGS—ANALYSIS

(a) Critical stresses

Column footing must be checked or designed for six stress conditions:

1. Bearing (compression) from column on top of footing.
2. Soil pressure beneath footing.
3. Diagonal tension stress.
4. Steel stress from moment.
5. Concrete compressive stress from moment.
6. Bond stress between steel and concrete.

(b) Bearing under column

Dowel bars should be used to transfer the load from the column steel into the footing. If the footing and column are of the same grade of concrete, the footing, because only part of its area is loaded, can safely

---

* Recent tests seem to hint that the shear strength may be improved when a larger portion of the steel passes directly through the failure pyramid beneath the column.

REINFORCED CONCRETE FUNDAMENTALS

carry a higher unit bearing stress than the column. The ACI Code permits a compressive stress of $0.375f_c'$ when the bearing occurs on one-third of the total area or less and the bearing is well centered on the total area. On the full area the allowable is $0.25f_c'$ and interpolation may be used for intermediate areas (Art. 305a). If the column design stress is more than these allowables, extra dowels can provide for the surplus. Thus a column with much higher concrete strength may call for extra dowels.

(c) Soil pressure

The soil pressure is usually considered as uniform for a centered loading and trapezoidal or triangular for eccentric loadings. The assumed uniform pressure is on the safe side in the calculation of internal moments and shears in isolated footings, but the student should note the different situation in the case of a combined footing, as discussed in the last paragraph of Sec. 14.10.

The allowable soil pressure is a matter of soil mechanics and will not be discussed here. The footing base area must be adequate to care for the column load, footing weight, and any overburden weight, all within the permissible soil pressure, assumed uniformly distributed under the footing. Sometimes this over-all pressure is called the gross soil pressure to distinguish it from net soil pressure, which is a convenient design concept. Since the weight of footing and overburden is usually nearly uniform over the footing area, the design moment or shear on any section will be the result of the gross soil pressure upward less the footing and other overburden weight downward. It is convenient to think in terms of the resultant load or "net soil pressure" which is the difference between these upward and downward unit pressures. The net pressure is usually found most simply by dividing the column load (alone) by the footing area.

(d) Diagonal tension

The diagonal tension is calculated for the shear caused by loads outside the dashed square in Fig. 14.1b and is resisted by a width equal to the perimeter of that square $= 4(r + 2d)$. The use of d_v as the average depth to the two layers of steel appears justified. The author prefers to use one-quarter of this shear and a width equal to one side of this square, not because it is simpler but because it also fits into the pattern for rectangular footings. The lower allowable v (maximum of 75 psi) in Art. 305a is the result of an unsatisfactory scatter in values from diagonal tension tests on footings.

(e) Bending stress

Bending stresses in steel and concrete will be discussed together. The author recommends that the simple cantilever moment be used for both these stress calculations. The ACI Code (Art. 1204a) specifies that 85%

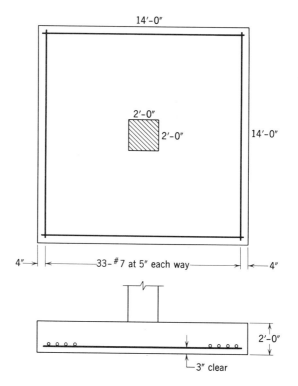

Fig. 14.2. Square column footing.

of this moment may be used in calculating the steel stress. This factor is a hangover from an earlier erroneous method of calculating the bending moment. Richart's tests[2] clearly showed that it had no physical significance and that it should be abandoned. The calculation of total moment on the full footing width and the calculation of the total area of steel are recommended rather than the use of a 1-ft strip.

The moment in each direction is a matter of statics and can be varied only by a change in the distribution of soil pressure. The steel in each direction should thus be adequate for the moment in that direction;

REINFORCED CONCRETE FUNDAMENTALS

excess steel in the y-direction cannot make up for a steel shortage in the x-direction. Hence it appears desirable that the smaller depth to the upper steel layer be used for calculation of the moment resistance in a square footing. Economy will be achieved by using a j value corresponding to the actual percentage of steel used, this value usually being 0.90 or larger.

The compressive bending stress will normally be low, the diagonal tension requirements calling for a depth greater than is needed for moment.

(f) Bond stress

Bond stress is calculated on the moment section at the face of the column, counting all bars crossing the section, that is, all bars in one direction. The author recommends the use of the full static shear [ignoring the 85% factor in Art. 1205e(2)]. The lower allowable bond stress ($0.08f_c'$ on two-way footings) is specified because moment cracks perpendicular to one set of steel are parallel to bars in the other direction. It is reasoned that cracks parallel to the bars may actually lie along these bars and lower their resistance to bond.

(g) Example of square footing analysis

Check the footing of Fig. 14.2, assuming $f_c' = 3000$ psi for both column and footing, intermediate grade steel, and an allowable soil pressure of 3000 psf. The column load is 510 k. Assume no overburden.

SOLUTION

Since the column is of same strength concrete as the footing, the bearing on top of the footing will be adequate. Dowels should be provided to match the column steel.

$$\text{Net soil pressure} = p_{net} = \frac{510,000}{14 \times 14} = 2600 \text{ psf}$$

$$\text{Wt. of footing} = 2.0 \times 150 \qquad = 300$$

$$p_{gross} = 2900 \text{ psf} < 3000 \text{ allow.} \qquad \text{O.K.}$$

Could use slightly smaller footing.

In a square footing the use of average d is recommended for shear calculations, with the depth to upper steel layer used for bond and moment calculations.

$$d_v = 24 - 3 - 0.88 \text{ (bar diam.)} = 20.12 \text{ in.}$$

Diagonal tension will be calculated on one quadrant (Fig. 14.3) at a distance d from the face of the column.

$$V_v = \frac{5.36 + 14}{2} \times 4.32 \times 2600 = 108,600 \text{ lb}$$

$$v = \frac{V}{bjd} = \frac{108,600}{64.2 \times 0.88 \times 20.12} = 96.0 \text{ psi}$$

Allow. v on two-way footings = 75 psi. $\therefore v$ is N.G.

Moment and bond must be calculated at the face of the column (Fig. 14.3).

$$M = 14 \times 6 \times 2600 \times 3 = 655,000 \text{ ft-lb}$$

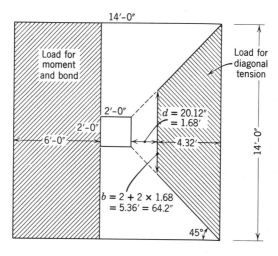

Fig. 14.3. Critical sections on square column footing.

The author does not approve the provision of the ACI Code (Art. 1204*e*) which bases the steel calculation on 85% of this moment.

$$d_M = 24 - 3 - 1.5 \times 0.88 = 19.68 \text{ in.}$$

$$p = \frac{33 \times 0.60}{14 \times 12 \times 19.68} = 0.00600 \quad \text{Curves show } j = 0.903$$

$$\text{Reqd. } A_s = \frac{655,000 \times 12}{20,000 \times 0.903 \times 19.68} = 22.1 \text{ in.}^2 \text{ vs. } 33 \times 0.60 = 19.8 \text{ in.}^2 \quad \text{N.G.}$$

$$\text{Reqd. } d_M = \sqrt{\frac{M}{Rb}} = \sqrt{\frac{655,000 \times 12}{236 \times 14 \times 12}} = 14.1 \text{ in.} < 19.68 \text{ in. actual} \quad \text{O.K.}$$

$$V_u = 14 \times 6 \times 2600 = 218,000 \text{ lb}$$

REINFORCED CONCRETE FUNDAMENTALS

This shear also ignores ACI Art. 1205e(2), which authorizes an 85% factor.

$$\text{Reqd. } \Sigma o = \frac{V}{ujd} = \frac{218{,}000}{0.08 \times 3000 \times 0.88 \times 19.68}$$

$$= 52.6 \text{ in. vs. } 33 \times 2.75 = 90.6 \text{ in.} \qquad \text{O.K.}$$

Some designers would prefer to use $j = 0.90$ for v and u, but the accuracy of these formulas scarcely justifies any refinement.

This footing needs to be deepened to care for diagonal tension which might then permit less steel to be used. A larger bar size is feasible on the basis of bond requirements.

14.4. SQUARE COLUMN FOOTING—DESIGN

Design a square column footing using $f_c' = 3000$ psi, intermediate grade steel, and allowable soil pressure of 3500 psf, to carry an 18-in. square spiral column made of 5000 psi concrete and carrying a load of 550 k.

SOLUTION

The load assigned to the concrete in the spiral column is based on a nominal stress of $0.225f_c' = 0.225 \times 5000 = 1125$ psi. The allowable bearing on the footing is $0.375f_c' = 0.375 \times 3000 = 1125$ psi, since the column will occupy less than one-third of the footing area. Hence, no extra dowels are required over these needed to match the column steel.

Assume the footing will weigh about 300 psf, leaving an allowable net soil pressure of $3500 - 300 = 3200$ psf.

$$\text{Reqd. } A = \frac{\text{col. load}}{p_{net}} = \frac{550{,}000}{3200} = 172 \text{ ft}^2$$

Try 13 ft 2 in. square (area $= 173$ ft²)

$$p_{net} = 550{,}000/173 = 3180 \text{ psf}$$

If t is assumed 24 in. and 3-in. clear cover is used (ACI Code Art. 504a), average $d = 24 - 3 - D =$ say, 20 in. The critical section for diagonal tension is then 20 in. from the face of the column, as shown in Fig. 14.4a.

$$V_v = \frac{4.83 + 13.17}{2} \times 4.17 \times 3180 = 119{,}300 \text{ lb}$$

Allow. $v = 75$ psi

$$\text{Reqd. } d_v = \frac{V}{bjv} = \frac{119{,}300}{58 \times 0.88 \times 75} = 31.3 \text{ in.} > 20 \text{ in. assumed} \qquad \text{N.G.}$$

The initial estimate of thickness was not very good and must be revised upward. Since b increases twice as much as d, the calculation for d_v is sensitive to changes in assumed d. The footing size will also have to be increased but a better value of d will be found first. Assume that t is 29 in. and that $d = 29 - 3 - D =$ say, 25 in. From Fig. 14.4b,

$$b = 18 + 2 \times 25 = 68 \text{ in.}$$

$$V_v = \frac{5.67 + 13.17}{2} \times 3.75 \times 3180 = 112,500 \text{ lb.}$$

$$d_v = \frac{112,500}{68 \times 0.88 \times 75} = 25.1 \text{ in.} > 25 \text{ in. assumed}$$

This is nearly satisfactory. The increased footing weight will call for a lower net soil pressure and a larger footing. Assume little change in required d, say, $t = 29$ in. The footing weight is then $\frac{29}{12} \times 150 = 362$ psf.

$$\text{Allow. } p_{net} = 3500 - 362 = 3140 \text{ psf}$$

$$\text{Reqd. } A = \frac{550,000}{3140} = 175 \text{ ft}^2, \text{ say, 13 ft 3 in. square}$$

$$\text{Actual } p_{net} = \frac{550,000}{13.25 \times 13.25} = 3140 \text{ psf}$$

When areas are fitted as closely as this, the calculation of the actual p_{net} is scarcely necessary. As on the second trial, $d_v = 25$ in. and $b = 68$ in. Figure 14.4c gives

$$V_v = \frac{5.67 + 13.25}{2} \times 3.79 \times 3140 = 113,000 \text{ lb}$$

$$\text{Reqd. } d_v = \frac{113,000}{68 \times 0.88 \times 75} = 25.1 \text{ in.}$$

$$\text{USE } t = 29 \text{ in., } d = 25 \text{ in. } (0.4\% \text{ overstress, say O.K.})$$

$$\text{Ftg. 13 ft 3 in. by 13 ft 3 in.}$$

This assumes $D = 1$ in., that is, #8 bars. d may vary slightly when bars are chosen. For moment, available $d_M = 29 - 3 - 1.5D =$ say, 24.5 in.

$$M = 13.25 \times 5.87 \times 3140 \times 2.94 = 716,000 \text{ ft-lb}$$

$$d_M = \sqrt{\frac{M}{Rb}} = \sqrt{\frac{716,000 \times 12}{236 \times 13.25 \times 12}} = \sqrt{229} = 15.1 \text{ in.} < 24.5 \text{ in.} \qquad \text{O.K.}$$

Again ignoring the 85% factor in the ACI Code [Arts. 1204e and 1205e(2)]:

$$\text{Reqd. } A_s = \frac{M}{f_s j d} = \frac{716,000 \times 12}{20,000 \times 0.90 \times 24.5} = 19.5 \text{ in.}^2$$

$$p = 19.5/(13.25 \times 12 \times 24.5) = 0.0050, \qquad j = 0.910$$

With 3 in. from the edge to the first bar,

25–#8 at 6.38 in. = 19.8 in.²		
20–#9 at 8.25 = 20.0	(d_M reduced to 24.31 in.)	
16–#10 at 10.20 = 20.3	(d_M reduced to 24.10 in.)	
13–#11 at 12.75 = 20.3	(d_M reduced to 23.88 in.)	
32–#7 at 4.78 = 19.8	(d_M increased to 24.69 in.)	

The #8 bars look best for this case, with #7 available if bond proves difficult. The #9 bars also look good. USE 25-#8 at approx. 6.5-in. spcg. each way ($d = 24.5$ in.)

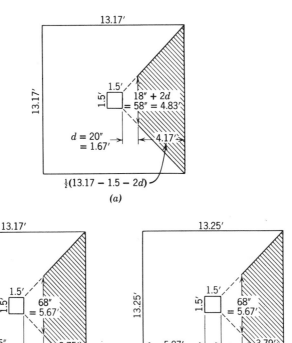

Fig. 14.4. Trial sections for diagonal tension in square footing design. (a) First trial. (b) Second trial. (c) Final design.

$V_v = 13.25 \times 5.87 \times 3140 = 244{,}000$ lb

Reqd. $\Sigma o = \dfrac{V}{ujd} = \dfrac{244{,}000}{0.08 \times 3000 \times 0.88 \times 24.5}$

$$= 47.2 \text{ in. vs. } 25 \times 3.14 = 78.4 \text{ in.} \qquad \text{O.K.}$$

14.5. RECTANGULAR COLUMN FOOTINGS—ANALYSIS

Analyze the rectangular footing of Fig. 14.5, assuming $f_c' = 3000$ psi, intermediate grade steel, and an allowable soil pressure of 3000 psf. The column load is 500 k and there is no overburden.

SOLUTION

$$\text{Net soil pressure} = \frac{500,000}{11.0 \times 18.0} = 2525 \text{ psf}$$

$$\text{Wt. of footing} = \tfrac{3\,2}{1\,2} \times 150 \qquad = \;400$$

$$p_{\text{gross}} = 2925 \text{ psf} < 3000 \text{ psf} \qquad \text{O.K.}$$

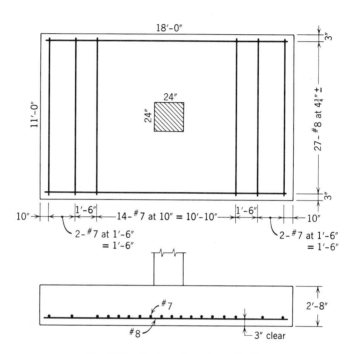

Fig. 14.5. Rectangular column footing.

For the long projection, $d = 32 - 3 - 0.5 = 28.5$ in. For the short projection, $d = 32 - 3 - 1.0 - 0.44 = 27.56$ in. Diagonal tension will be more critical on the long projection (Fig. 14.6).

$$V_v = (11.0 \times 5.62 - 2 \times \tfrac{1}{2} \times 2.12^2)2525 = 57.2 \times 2525 = 144,500 \text{ lb}$$

$$\text{Reqd. } d_v = \frac{V}{bjv} = \frac{144,500}{81 \times 0.88 \times 75} = 27.0 \text{ in.} < 28.5 \text{ in. available}$$

The footing could be approximately 1 in. shallower, which would decrease b by 2 in. In the long direction, $M_L = 8.0 \times 11.0 \times 2525 \times 4.0 = 887,000$ ft-lb.

$$p = \frac{27 \times 0.79}{11.0 \times 12 \times 28.5} = 0.0057^- \qquad j = 0.905$$

REINFORCED CONCRETE FUNDAMENTALS

Ignoring the 0.85% factor in Arts. 1204e and 1205e(2),

$$\text{Reqd. } A_s = \frac{M_L}{f_s jd} = \frac{887,000 \times 12}{20,000 \times 0.90 \times 28.5}$$

$$= 20.8 \text{ in.}^2 \text{ vs. } 27 \times 0.79 = 21.3 \text{ in.}^2 \qquad \text{O.K.}$$

$$V_{uL} = 8.0 \times 11.0 \times 2525 = 222,000 \text{ lb}$$

$$\text{Reqd. } \Sigma o = \frac{222,000}{0.08 \times 3000 \times 0.88 \times 28.5}$$

$$= 37.0 \text{ in. vs. } 27 \times 3.14 = 84.8 \text{ in.} \qquad \text{O.K.}$$

$$\text{Reqd. } d_M = \sqrt{\frac{M}{Rb}} = \sqrt{\frac{887,000 \times 12}{236 \times 11.0 \times 12}}$$

$$= \sqrt{342} = 18.5 \text{ in. vs. } 28.5 \text{ in.} \qquad \text{O.K.}$$

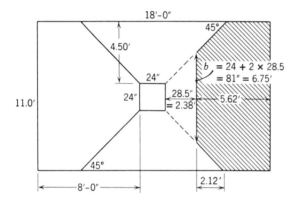

Fig. 14.6. Diagonal tension analysis for rectangular footing.

In the short direction, $M_s = 18.0 \times 4.50 \times 2525 \times 2.25 = 460,000$ ft-lb

$$p = \frac{18 \times 0.60}{18.0 \times 12 \times 27.56} = 0.00181, \qquad j = 0.94$$

$$\text{Reqd. } A_s = \frac{460,000 \times 12}{20,000 \times 0.94 \times 27.56}$$

$$= 10.65 \text{ in.}^2 \text{ vs. } 18 \times 0.60 = 10.80 \text{ in.}^2 \qquad \text{O.K.}$$

The total steel satisfies this calculation but is still open to some criticism. The strength of a plain concrete slab or beam is nearly as great without any steel as it is when reinforced with this small a percentage of steel. Probably Code Art. 702e(2) should be considered to apply, with 0.25% as a minimum (for a yield point of 40,000 psi), which would be 0.0025 × 18 × 12 × 27.56 = 14.9 in.²
= 25–#7.

This short steel must be distributed in accordance with Art. 1204g. The central 11-ft width (equal to the short side of the footing) must contain a proportion of the total short steel given by the relation $2 \div (S + 1)$, where S is the ratio of the long to the short side, in this case $\frac{18}{11} = 1.64$. Hence $2/(1.64 + 1) = 0.76$ of the short steel, or $0.76 \times 18 = 14$ bars, must be in this 11-ft width. This leaves 4 bars, 2 for each of the 3.5-ft widths at each end. The original steel is properly distributed but is only some 73% of that deemed desirable, as noted above.

For bond: $V_u = 18.0 \times 4.5 \times 2525 = 205,000$ lb

$$\text{Reqd. } \Sigma o = \frac{205,000}{0.08 \times 3000 \times 0.88 \times 27.56}$$

$$= 35.2 \text{ in. vs. } 18 \times 2.75 = 49.5 \text{ in.} \qquad \text{O.K.}$$

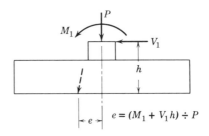

Fig. 14.7. Equivalent eccentricity of load.

14.6. FOOTINGS CARRYING MOMENT

Footings must often carry moment from a column or wall. Combined with direct load this gives the equivalent of an eccentric load, as in Fig. 14.7. If the moment were constant it would be desirable to put the center of the footing under this eccentric load. In the case of the retaining wall (Sec. 7.5d, e), the base was adjusted to make the resultant load fall between the center and third point. Usually the varying nature of the moment makes it impossible to avoid all eccentricity on the footing and a trapezoidal soil pressure results. This modifies the magnitude of the design moment and shears, but not the general design procedure.

14.7. WALL FOOTINGS

The uniform nature of a wall loading leads to the use of a typical 1-ft width as a design strip, as in Fig. 14.8. For heavy walls, the design is quite similar to that of column footings, but simpler because the bending is in only one direction. For light walls, the design is frequently based on rather arbitrary minimum sizes. In such cases plain concrete is often the appropriate material.

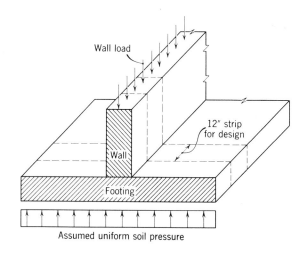

Fig. 14.8. Part of wall footing, with heavy loading.

Examples

(a) Design a wall footing for a 13-in. brick wall carrying a total load of 20 k per running foot, using $f_c' = 2500$ psi, intermediate grade steel, and an allowable soil pressure of 4000 psf, negligible overburden.

SOLUTION

Assume the footing weight is 150 psf.

Assumed $p_{net} = 4000 - 150 = 3850$ psf

Ftg. width $= 20,000/3850 = 5.20$ ft, say, 5 ft 3 in.   USE

$p_{net} = 20,000/5.25 = 3820$ psf

If d is assumed 8 in., the critical section for diagonal tension (Fig. 14.9) lies 1 ft 5 in. or 1.42 ft from the edge.

Reqd. $d_v = \dfrac{V}{bjv} = \dfrac{1.42 \times 3820}{12 \times 0.88 \times 75} = 6.85$ in. < 8 in. assumed

Try $d = 7$ in.

Reqd. $d_v = \dfrac{1.50 \times 3820}{12 \times 0.88 \times 75} = 7.24$ in. > 7 in.

USE $t = 11$ in., $d = 11 - 3$ cover $- D/2 =$ say, 7.5 in.

The footing weight changes so little it will be neglected. For a brick wall the critical section for moment lies at the quarter-point of the wall thickness, that is, in this case $1.08/4 = 0.27$ ft inside the face of the wall [Art. 1204b(2)]

$$M = (2.08 + 0.27) \times 3820 \times 2.35/2 = 10,500 \text{ ft-lb}$$

$$\text{Reqd. } d_M = \sqrt{\frac{M}{Rb}} = \sqrt{\frac{10,500 \times 12}{196 \times 12}}$$

$$= \sqrt{53.7} = 7.33 \text{ in.} < 7.5 \text{ in.} \qquad \text{O.K.}$$

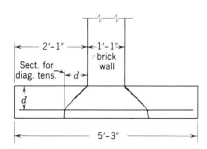

Fig. 14.9. Reinforced concrete wall footing, design.

$$\text{Reqd. } A_s = \frac{M}{f_s jd} = \frac{10,500 \times 12}{20,000 \times 0.866 \times 7.5} = 0.97 \text{ in.}^2/\text{ft} = 0.081 \text{ in.}^2/\text{in.}$$

$$\text{Reqd. } \Sigma o = \frac{V \text{ at face of wall}}{ujd} = \frac{2.08 \times 3820}{0.10 \times 2500 \times 0.88 \times 7.5}$$

$$= 4.83 \text{ in.}/\text{ft} = 0.402 \text{ in.}/\text{in.}$$

For $\#6$, spcg. for $A_s = 0.44/0.081 = 5.45$ in.

spcg. for $\Sigma o = 2.36/0.402 = 5.88$ in.

USE $\#6$ at 5 in.

Note that with $\#6$ bars, d becomes $11 - 3 - 0.38 = 7.62$ in. Thus it is permissible to use $\#6$ at $5\frac{1}{2}$ in. if that spacing is considered acceptable for field use.

(*b*) Redesign the wall footing of (*a*) as a plain concrete footing in accordance with ACI Code, Art. 1207b.

SOLUTION

Assume the footing weight is 300 psf.

$$p_{\text{net}} = 4000 - 300 = 3700 \text{ psf}$$

Ftg. width $= 20,000/3700 = 5.42$ ft $= 5$ft 5 in.

Moment will probably be critical with tension limited to $0.03f_c' = 75$ psi.

Moment is taken at the quarter-point of the wall, Fig. 14.10.

$$M = 2.44 \times 3700 \times 1.22 = 11,050 \text{ ft-lb}$$
$$11,050 \times 12 = f_t bh^2/6 = 75 \times 12h^2/6$$
$$h^2 = 882, \qquad h = 29.7 \text{ in.}$$

The bottom inch of concrete placed against the ground should not be considered for strength. Hence a 31-in. over-all depth is indicated, which requires a weight revision. Assume 32-in. thickness and a footing weight of 400 psf.

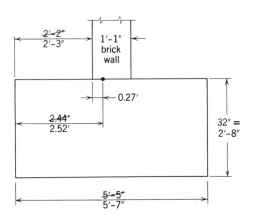

Fig. 14.10. Plain concrete wall footing, design.

$$p_{\text{net}} = 4000 - 400 = 3600 \text{ psf}$$

Ftg. width $= 20,000/3600 = 5.56$ ft, say, 5 ft 7 in. USE

Actual $p_{\text{net}} = 20,000/5.58 = 3580$ psf

$$M = 2.52 \times 3580 \times 1.26 = 11,350 \text{ ft-lb}$$
$$11,350 \times 12 = 75 \times 12h^2/6$$
$$h^2 = 910, \qquad h = 30.2 \text{ in.} + 1 \text{ in. lost} = 31.2 \text{ in.}$$

USE $t = 32$ in.

Diagonal tension is rarely significant in plain concrete footings. If d is considered 31 in., the critical section for diagonal tension will fall 31 in. from the face of the wall or outside the footing.

(c) Design a wall footing for a 13-in. brick wall carrying a total load of 3 k per running foot using $f_c' = 2500$ psi and an allowable soil pressure of 3000 psf.

SOLUTION

By inspection, soil pressure would call for a footing width less than the thickness of the wall. A minimum projection of 1 to 4 in. is generally used on walls.

USE footing width $= 1$ ft 3 in., $\qquad t = 8$ in.

Code Art. 1209*b* calls for the minimum thickness of 8 in. for plain concrete, which will be used. The moment will be calculated (at the quarter-point of wall thickness), although one senses that it will be negligible.

$$\text{Actual } p_{\text{net}} = 3000/1.25 = 2400 \text{ psf}$$

$$M = 0.35 \times 2400 \times 0.18 = 151 \text{ ft-lb}$$

This is of no significance, even on 7 in. of plain concrete, giving a calculated stress of less than 19 psi.

14.8. FOOTINGS ON ROCK

In many cases only a nominal footing is required on rock since good rock is usually at least as strong as concrete and, moreover, is usually loaded on only a small part of its surface. Where a significant footing is required, as under a heavy steel column, deformations and relative stiffness become more significant than calculated unit stresses. A reinforced concrete footing cannot function normally unless the steel elongates and the cantilever elements deflect. Since the underlying rock is stiffer against compressive deformation than the reinforced concrete footing is against bending deflection, such a footing cannot effectively distribute the load laterally to any significant extent. A reinforced concrete footing on rock is thus of little value. The designer must depend more on the transfer of stress through shear with its smaller deformations. This calls for a deep footing and suggests that plain concrete may be just as effective as reinforced. It should be noted that, on the usual rough rock surface, friction (and interlock) forces are ample to prevent any significant stretching of the bottom of the footing. A footing on rock requires a large depth to give it shear stiffness and little concern needs to be given to tension on its bottom face.

14.9. BALANCING FOOTING PRESSURES

Many years ago it was commonly accepted that footings would undergo essentially uniform settlements if they developed the same soil loading per unit area under the usual loads on the structure. Such footings were said to have balanced footing areas.

Modern soil mechanics has greatly restricted the field of usefulness of this concept. It has shown in most practical cases that uniform soil pressure does not lead to uniform settlement. Proportioning for balanced footing pressures usually results in an increased size for outside wall footings. In a heavy structure on a thick stratum of material which consolidates slowly under additional load, such an increase in exterior footing size will actually *increase* the final differential settlement. In many areas, such as in the Southwest, foundation movement on ordinary residence and commercial structures is as apt to be upward due to expansive soils as downward due to applied loads. The engineer who uses the balanced footing design should be certain that his special foundation situation justifies this approach. In many cases it increases rather than reduces differential settlements.

For a balanced footing design, the term "usual load" will be applied to the average load or the load most commonly on the structure. This might vary from dead load alone, for a church or a school, up to nearly full live load plus dead load, for certain types of warehouses.

If all footings were designed for the usual load, at full working stresses, that footing caring for the greatest percentage of live load (compared to dead load) would be the most overstressed when full live load was acting. This gives the clue for balanced footing area design. That footing having the largest ratio of live load to dead load is designed first by the usual procedures, using maximum load and the full allowable soil pressure. The usual soil pressure under this footing is next established for the usual load, most frequently something between dead load alone and dead load plus half live load. The bearing areas of all other footings are then chosen to give this same usual soil pressure under the usual footing loads. (This will automatically give them less than the maximum permissible soil pressure under the maximum live load.) The individual footings are then designed for thickness and steel using these balanced areas and full live load.

Example

Balance the areas for footings given in Table 14.1 for dead load plus one-fourth live load if the allowable net soil pressure is 3 ksf.

TABLE 14.1

Footing	Dead Load	Live Load
A	100 k	200 k
B	75	200
C	50	150
D	100	150

SOLUTION

Footing C has the largest ratio of live load to dead load, that is, 150/50 = 3.00. Choose the area of this footing for full dead load plus live load and the full allowable soil pressure.

$$\text{Area } C = (50 + 150)/3 = 66.7 \text{ ft}^2$$

$$\text{Usual } p = (50 + 0.25 \times 150)/66.7 = 1.31 \text{ ksf}$$

Choose the other footing areas for this usual soil pressure and the specified usual load; see Table 14.2. The maximum pressure column is based on full

TABLE 14.2

Footing	Dead Load	Live Load	Usual Load	Usual p	Area	Max. p
A	100 k	200 k	150 k	1.31 ksf	114.5 ft²	2.62 ksf
B	75	200	125	1.31	95.4	2.89
C	50	150	87.5	1.31	66.7	3.00
D	100	150	137.5	1.31	105.0	2.37

dead and live load and is shown only to demonstrate that under this procedure one need not consider maximum pressures after the usual pressure has been properly established.

14.10. COMBINED FOOTINGS

When two or more columns are carried on a single footing, it is called a combined footing. Two circumstances, especially, call for a combined footing: (1) two columns so closely spaced that separate footings would overlap or be of uneconomic proportions, Fig. 14.11a; (2) an exterior column footing which cannot be made symmetrical because of property line limitations or other restrictions, Fig. 14.11b. In each case the centroid of the combined footing must coincide with the resultant of the two column loads, noted as O.

In Fig. 14.11b, the length of a rectangular footing is fixed by the fact that it must be symmetrical about axis y-y through this resultant load point O. The width in turn is fixed by the required soil-bearing area to carry the combined column loads.

In Fig. 14.11a, the designer has some choice in the length and width he chooses, but the centroid of the area chosen must fall at O.

Design of combined footings, like the design of many other reinforced concrete structures, has not been standardized. The ACI Code specifically states that it makes no recommendations for such. The old Joint Committee Specification (Art. 868) was as follows:

(a) For reinforced concrete columns, the critical section for transverse bending should be taken at the faces of the columns or pedestals. For footings under metallic column bases, the critical section should be assumed midway between the face of column and the edge of the metallic base. The transverse reinforcement should be divided into groups proportionate in sectional area to the column loads. The transverse reinforcement at each column should be placed uniformly within a band having a width not greater than the width of column plus twice the effective depth of the footing. Longitudinal reinforcement should be distributed over the whole width.

(b) The critical sections for diagonal tension in combined footings should be taken at the faces of the supported members for all beam elements and also for all projecting cantilevers.

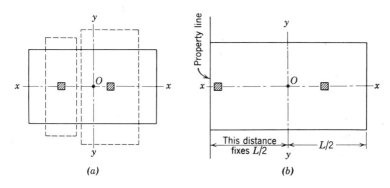

Fig. 14.11. Combined footings.

This concentrates the short steel near the columns, apparently assuming that the transverse strips under the columns act as transverse beams to do the entire job of distributing the load laterally (Fig. 14.12). The longitudinal slab is then treated as a slab supported on these two transverse

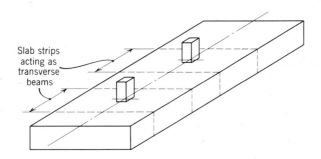

Fig. 14.12. Transverse "beams" in combined footing.

beams. Moments *and diagonal tension shears* are considered as critical at the *face* of columns, except as modified for loads brought in through metallic column bases. This type of design provides a logical analysis, but the specification fails to relate the diagonal tension resistance of the transverse "beams" to a definite width. The designer must provide this diagonal tension strength in a reasonable width to complete a logical analysis. This design pattern lends itself most naturally to footings of relatively narrow transverse dimensions, that is, to lateral projections beyond the columns which are relatively short compared to the longitudinal cantilever beyond the heavier column.

The author prefers to consider that the cantilever projections on three sides of the heavier column act much like those in an isolated column

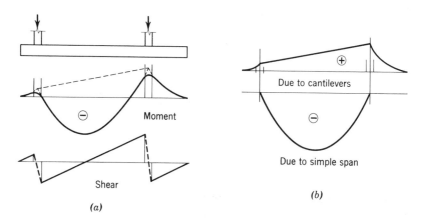

Fig. 14.13. Moment and shear diagrams for combined footing.

footing. This leads to optimum proportions when these projections are equal. This is not inconsistent with some concentration of transverse steel under the columns but would call for some transverse steel throughout the length. This method of design is obviously most suited to combined footings of moderate length and considerable width.

Reasonably typical moment and shear diagrams for the longitudinal strips of a combined footing are shown in Fig. 14.13a. Design is concerned only with the portions outside the column widths. The moment diagram can be visualized as a simple beam moment (negative due to upward loads) superimposed on the positive moment diagram produced by the upward loads on the two end cantilevers. These two diagrams going into the total moment diagram of Fig. 14.13a are shown separately in Fig. 14.13b. These diagrams present no special design problem except one relating to the negative moment between columns. If the columns are closely spaced, no top steel may be required, because the simple span moment may be small compared to the cantilever moment.

Attention should be called to that fact that it is *not* on the safe side to assume a uniform soil pressure in the design of this center negative steel. If the pressure is nonuniform, it is probably larger near the center than it is towards the ends. A uniform load assumption gives too much positive cantilever moment and too little negative moment from the center span. These errors add to indicate a negative moment smaller than the actual value. The designer should be liberal in providing this negative moment steel, even introducing some steel when the uniform pressure assumption indicates a small remnant of positive moment.

14.11. CANTILEVER FOOTINGS

When an exterior column footing, because of property line restrictions, calls for some kind of combined footing but when the nearest interior footing is some distance away, the ordinary combined footing becomes long and narrow and subject to excessive bending moment. The cantilever footing is then more economical.

The cantilever footing is really two separate column footings joined by a beam which preferably should not contribute to the bearing area. In Fig. 14.14a, footing A under the exterior column is eccentric by a distance e from the column. By itself it would produce a very unsatisfactory soil pressure distribution. The stiff beam C is attached to footing A to balance the overturning moment P_1e and is carried to the concentric footing B for its necessary balancing reaction. This beam must be stiff in order to function well. It functions most simply if it is relieved of soil pressure from below, except enough to carry the beam's weight. This condition is approached in several ways, most commonly by loosening or spading the soil under the beam, occasionally by forming the beam free from the soil, and so forth. Each of these measures leaves some question as to its effectiveness, which causes some engineers to shun this type of footing.

Under the simplest assumption, that the beam weight is carried by the soil, the analysis of the cantilever footing is quite simple. The beam is then effectively weightless. The reaction from the exterior column alone is R_1 on footing A (Fig. 14.14b) and ΔR downward on the beam at the interior column, which means ΔR is an uplift on this footing at B (Fig. 14.14c). Hence

$$\Delta R = P_1e/(L - e)$$
$$R_1 = P_1 + \Delta R$$
$$R_2 = P_2 - \Delta R$$

Hence footing A must be slightly larger than needed for P_1 alone and footing B can be slightly reduced in area below that needed for P_2 alone.

The beam C must carry a constant shear ΔR and a moment as shown in Fig. 14.14b.

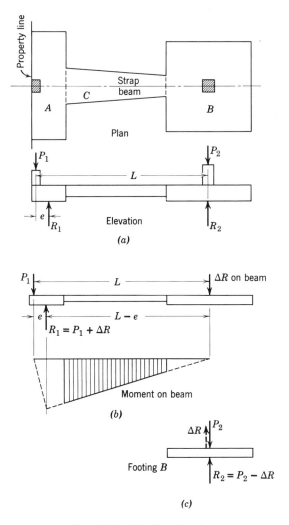

Fig. 14.14.   Cantilever footing.

14.12. RAFT FOUNDATIONS

It is sometimes desirable to utilize the soil pressure under the entire building area by covering the site with a thick slab or mat foundation.

REINFORCED CONCRETE FUNDAMENTALS

Such a foundation is often called a raft foundation, particularly when enough soil is excavated to offset the increased load due to the structure. Such a foundation may consist of a uniform slab several feet thick, or a slab stiffened by beams (either above or below the slab), or an inverted flat slab floor (Chap. 11).

No special design problems are involved in the concrete for such foundations other than those of a heavy floor design to resist upward pressures, with the columns furnishing the downward reactions.

14.13. FOOTINGS ON PILES

Many footings must be built on piles. The piles act as a series of relatively concentrated reactions for the footing and in design are usually considered as concentrated loads. Since it is usually difficult to drive piles exactly where they are desired, the designer must expect that piles will be from a few inches to a foot from the spot he assigns to them. Accordingly, the Code provides a stricter requirement for diagonal tension in this case (Art. 1205a, f), using a section $d/2$ from the face of the column instead of d from the face.

14.14. STEPPED AND SLOPED FOOTINGS

Specifications now permit thinner footings than were formerly used. Hence there is less reason now for stepped or sloped footings and fewer are used. Such footings must definitely be cast as a monolith to avoid horizontal shearing weakness. Stresses must usually be checked at more than one section. For instance, bond may be higher at a step than at the face of the column.

Stepped footings are more appropriate for massive footings. A step can sometimes be used to advantage with a combined footing.

SELECTED REFERENCES

1. A. N. Talbot, "Reinforced Concrete Wall and Column Footings," Univ. of Ill. Eng. Exp. Sta. *Bull. No. 67*, 1913.

2. F. E. Richart, "Reinforced Concrete Wall and Column Footings," *ACI Jour.*, **20**, Oct. and Nov., 1948; *Proc.*, **48**, pp. 97, 237.

3. Eivind Hognestad, "Shearing Strength of Reinforced Concrete Column Footings," *ACI Jour.*, **25**, Nov. 1953; *Proc.*, **50**, p. 189.

4. Richard E. Elstner and Eivind Hognestad, "Shearing Strength of Reinforced Concrete Slabs," *ACI Jour.*, **28**, July 1956; *Proc.*, **53**, p. 29.

5. Chas. S. Whitney, "Ultimate Shear Strength of Reinforced Concrete Flat Slabs, Footings, and Frame Members Without Shear Reinforcement," *ACI Jour.*, **29**, Oct. 1957; *Proc.*, **54**, p. 265.

PROBLEMS

Prob. 14.1. Redesign the rectangular footing of Sec. 14.5 and Fig. 14.5 as a square footing.

Prob. 14.2. Redesign the square column footing of Sec. 14.4 as a rectangular footing having a width of 11 ft 6 in.

Prob. 14.3. Design a square column footing for a 16-in. by 16-in. column (of 3750 psi concrete) to carry a column load of 250 k using an allowable soil pressure of 4000 psf, $f_c' = 3000$ psi, hard grade steel.

Prob. 14.4. Redesign the footing of Prob. 14.3 as a plain concrete footing of uniform thickness.

Prob. 14.5. Design a reinforced concrete wall footing to carry a uniform load of 10 klf from a concrete wall 12 in. thick. Use an allowable soil pressure of 3000 psf, $f_c' = 3000$ psi, intermediate grade steel.

Prob. 14.6. Redesign the footing of Prob. 14.5 using plain concrete.

Prob. 14.7. Redesign the wall footing of Prob. 14.5 if the allowable soil pressure is only 2000 psf.

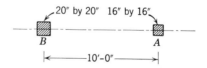

Fig. 14.15. Column layout for Prob. 14.8.

Prob. 14.8.

(*a*) Lay out the plan view of a combined footing for the columns of Fig. 14.15 where the loads are 250 k for *A* and 400 k for *B*, using an allowable *net* soil pressure of 3200 psf. Try to achieve equal projections around the heavier column.

(*b*) Lay out again on the assumption that there is a property line 4 in. beyond the outside face of column *A*.

(c) Lay out again for conditions of (a) on the assumption that lateral projections beyond column B are to be about half the longitudinal projection.

Prob. 14.9. If the columns of Fig. 14.16 carry loads of 250 k for A and 400 k for B, lay out the plan view of a cantilever footing (without dimensions on the beam) based on a *net* soil pressure of 3200 psf. Draw the M and V diagrams for the strap beam which connects the two footing elements:

(a) If the footing under column A extends 4 ft from the property line.
(b) If the dimension in (a) is changed to 5 ft.
(c) If the dimension in (a) is changed to 6 ft.

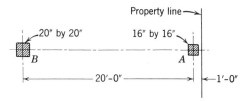

Fig. 14.16. Column layout for Prob. 14.9.

Prestressed
Concrete
Analysis

15.1. SCOPE OF PRESENTATION

This discussion of prestressed concrete covers some of the fundamental concepts and presents a general idea of how such concrete responds to loads. No attempt is made to develop design procedures. For ease of presentation, simple rectangular sections are used in the examples rather than the more practical I or T shapes.

15.2. THE NATURE OF PRESTRESS

Reinforced concrete becomes prestressed concrete when permanently loaded in such a way as to build up initial stresses opposite to those which later will be developed by service loads.

A circular tank, designed to resist circumferential or ring tensile stresses, as in Fig. 15.1a, is prestressed by being placed in initial circumferential compression. This compression is produced by wrapping the tank with wire under high tensile stress as indicated in Fig. 15.1b.

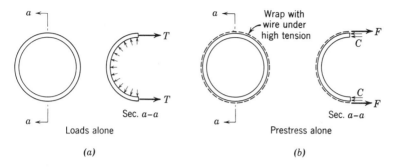

Loads alone

(a)

Prestress alone

(b)

Fig. 15.1. Prestress largely eliminates ring tension in tanks.

A simple span beam is prestressed (Fig. 15.2) by introducing (1) a negative moment to offset the expected positive moment and at the same time (2) a longitudinal compression to offset the tensile stresses from bending moment. Both effects are obtained by embedding highly stressed tension members eccentrically below the middle of the beam, giving both a P/A effect from the load F and a negative bending moment effect

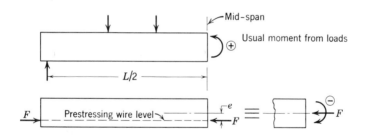

Fig. 15.2. Beam prestress produces axial compression and a moment opposite in sign to dead load moment.

measured by Fe. The tension prestressing element, called a tendon, may be wire, twisted wire strands, or rods.

Continuous beams are prestressed in similar fashion but for best results require an effective eccentricity above mid-depth in negative moment zones. Their analysis is more involved because the prestress may modify the external reactions, shears, and moments.

PRESTRESSED CONCRETE ANALYSIS   403

For piles, plank, and other members subject to moments both positive and negative, or subject to loading on either face, longitudinal wires without any resultant eccentricity are used solely for their P/A effect, as in Fig. 15.3. Since eccentric prestressing wires in a simple span build up

Fig. 15.3. Beam with uniform prestress.

negative moment to offset the ordinary positive moment, such prestressing would actually weaken the member if it were inverted or put under negative moment.

15.3. OBJECTIVES OF PRESTRESSING

Proper prestressing completely prevents the formation of tension cracks under working loads. This alone is adequate reason for prestressing tanks to avoid leakage, or for prestressing structural members subject to severe corrosion conditions.

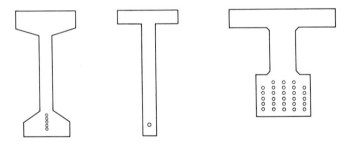

Fig. 15.4. Cross section of prestressed beams.

With this lack of cracking, the entire cross section remains effective for stress; a smaller required section normally results. With lighter sections, precasting of longer members becomes possible. Precasting has been a most important economic factor in promoting prestressed concrete in this country.

REINFORCED CONCRETE FUNDAMENTALS

Since prestress puts camber into a member under dead loading, deflections at working loads are much reduced.

Because tension cracking of prestressed concrete at working loads is avoided, very high strength steel (and smaller steel areas) can be used to provide the necessary tension. In some countries prestressed concrete is thus a device to make small supplies of steel serve more efficiently. In this country prestress is a device to permit high strength steel to compete economically with ordinary grades of steel.

Prestress reduces diagonal tension stresses at working loads. This has led to the general use of modified I and T shapes with less web area than conventional beams, as in Fig. 15.4.

Most of the advantages of prestressed concrete are construction or working stress advantages. Under ultimate load conditions the strength of a prestressed beam is about the same as without prestress; its deflection increases after cracking and stirrups are needed.

15.4. NOTATION AND SIGNS

The key to prestressed concrete analysis lies in a good bookkeeping system. All of the usual calculations are individually simple, but they consist of a number of small pieces which must be assembled into various combinations. Good bookkeeping requires a consistent set of signs for stresses and an adequate notation. For the beginner numerous illustrations, such as those in Figs. 15.7, 15.8, and 15.9, are helpful.

In this chapter a tensile stress will carry a plus sign and a compressive stress a negative sign. Although this is contrary to the signs used by many writers for prestressed concrete, it is in accord with general structural practice and is recommended also in Professor Lin's book.[1] No sign convention is needed for ordinary reinforced concrete since the kind of stress in such calculations is never in doubt.

Notation for stresses is necessarily involved because it must distinguish between (1) concrete stress at the top and the bottom of the beam, (2) initial stresses and those after creep and shrinkage have occurred, and (3) stresses with and without live load. No subscript is used to specify that a stress is on concrete but a subscript s is used to designate a steel stress. The recommended notation[2] for concrete stresses uses a superscript t for top and b for bottom and uses multiple subscripts to define load conditions. The first subscript indicates the prestress condition (with or without losses) and subsequent subscripts the various loadings. The notation listed here[2] is only that applying to this chapter and sometimes differs from that used elsewhere in this text. It also differs in minor respects from notation used in the 1958 report[3, 4] of the Joint ACI-ASCE Committee on Prestressed Reinforced Concrete.

Cross-sectional constants

A_c = area of entire concrete section (steel area not deducted)

A_c' = area of transformed section $A_c' = A_c + (n-1)A_s$

c.g.c.   = center of gravity of entire concrete section

c.g.c.$'$ = center of gravity of transformed section

c.g.s.   = center of gravity of steel area

y_b, y_t = distance of bottom (top) fiber to c.g.c.

y_b', y_t' = distance of bottom (top) fiber to c.g.c.$'$

e = eccentricity of c.g.s. with regard to c.g.c.

e' = eccentricity of c.g.s. with regard to c.g.c.$'$

I_c = moment of inertia of entire concrete section about c.g.c.

I_c' = moment of inertia of transformed section about c.g.c.$'$

Loads

w_G = dead load per unit length when the prestress is being established (dead load of prestressed girder)

w_L = distributed live load per unit length

M_G = bending moment due to w_G

M_L = bending moment due to live load

Prestressing force

F_i = initial prestress force

F_o = prestress force after release

F = effective prestress force after deduction of all losses

Stresses

Concrete

f_{ci}' = cylinder strength at the age of prestressing

f_{cp} = permissible compressive stress

f_{cpi} = permissible compressive stress at the age of prestressing

$f_{Fo}{}^b, f_{Fo}{}^t$ = stress at bottom (top) fiber due to initial prestressing only

$f_F{}^b, f_F{}^t$ = stress at bottom (top) fiber due to effective prestressing only

$f_G{}^b, f_G{}^t$ = stress at bottom (top) fiber due to dead load w_G only

$f_L{}^b, f_L{}^t$ = stress at bottom (top) fiber due to live load only

$f_{F_0G}^b, f_{F_0G}^t$ = stress at bottom (top) fiber due to prestressing at release F_o and dead load w_G

$f_{FG}{}^b, f_{FG}{}^t$ = stress at bottom (top) fiber due to effective prestressing F and dead load w_G

$f_{FT}{}^b, f_{FT}{}^t$ = stress at bottom (top) fiber due to effective prestressing F and total load

f_{tp} = permissible tensile stress

Steel

$f_s{}'$ = ultimate strength of steel

f_{si} = steel stress due to initial prestressing

f_{so} = steel stress due to prestressing after release

f_{se} = steel stress due to effective prestress force after deduction of all losses

f_{su} = stress at failure

15.5. PRE-TENSION METHOD OF PRESTRESSING

Since prestressing calculations follow closely the physical process of prestressing, both the pre-tensioning and post-tensioning procedures must be clearly understood. Sketches of the beam and stresses at each stage will be helpful to the beginner in making his summations. The individual calculations are quite simple.

In the pre-tension process the first step is to stretch high strength wires between abutments or end piers of a (long) prestressing bed, as indicated schematically in Fig. 15.5a. This total initial wire tension is designated F_i, the unit stress f_{si}. The forms are placed around the wire, with a number of such units along the total length, and in these forms the members are cast and cured (often by accelerated curing). The wires are then cut between members (Fig. 15.5b).

The resulting release of wire tension F_i is equivalent to F_i applied as an external compressive force on the entire transformed area of the member $A_c{}'$. The wires are usually eccentric, below the centroid of the member, and thus the external force F_i introduces a negative moment F_ie, which causes the beam to curve upward and pick up its dead load moment M_G. Due to F_i alone, rather large calculated tensile stresses develop on the top beam fibers, but this need not be dangerous because these never exist

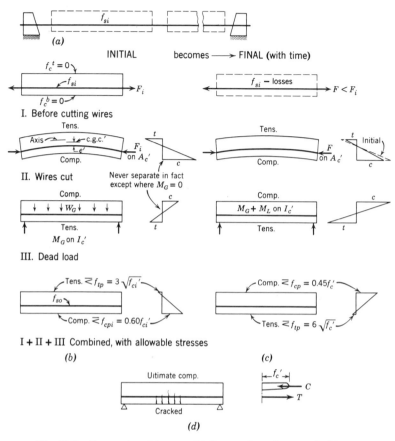

Fig. 15.5. Pre-tensioned beam. (*a*) Prestressing wire stretched between casting yard abutments. (*b*) Initial stresses at mid-span, separated for calculation purposes; also allowable concrete stresses. (*c*) Stresses at mid-span under full load, separated for calculation purposes; also allowable concrete stresses. (*d*) Ultimate strength conditions.

without the counteracting compression from dead load moment.* This combined top tensile stress is one of the more critical design stresses with a recommended limit[3, 4] of $3\sqrt{f_{ci}'}$ unless top steel is used, f_{ci}' being the cylinder strength at this early age. To turn such a beam on its side, or invert it, or lift it by a sling at the middle will be unsafe and may cause

* With straight wires and straight members, stresses would be critical near the ends where M_G is small. Present practice often reduces the eccentricity near the ends to keep the center stresses the critical ones (Sec. 15.12).

failure. The bottom stress in compression may also be a controlling stress, limited[3,4] to $0.60f_{ci}'$. Shrinkage is usually omitted from this calculation. Although some shrinkage will have occurred by the time the wires are cut, and these calculations apply, the shrinkage reduces both of these critical stresses.

With time, shrinkage of concrete and the creep of concrete and steel under stress reduce the length of the concrete holding the wires and thereby reduce F_i some 35,000 psi[3,4] to the effective prestress F. Thus the top tension and bottom compression are reduced below the initial values. As shown in Fig. 15.5c, it is upon these lowered stresses that live load stresses are superimposed. The final result is compression critical at the top and tension at the bottom, with the allowable stresses for buildings noted in the combined load sketch in Fig. 15.5c.

At ultimate load, the beam will be cracked as indicated in Fig. 15.5d and conditions will not differ greatly from those of an ordinary reinforced concrete beam.

15.6. POST-TENSION METHOD OF PRESTRESSING

In the post-tension method the plain concrete member is first cast with a tube or slot for future introduction of steel as indicated at I in Fig. 15.6a. A variation in procedure is to embed the steel in the member but separate it from the concrete by an enclosing metal or plastic tube or mastic coating. After the concrete has cured, the steel tendons are stressed by jacking against the concrete and are then locked under stress by appropriate end anchorages or clamps. Since the concrete simultaneously shortens under compression, the jacking must account for both steel stretch and concrete shortening; and this is complicated by friction losses and by the fact that beam curvature under this stressing causes the dead load moment also to become active (Fig. 15.6a).

The figure shows the steel tension as F_o acting on the plain concrete section A_c (compared to F_i on A_c' for pre-tension). In the pre-tensioned case F_o had to be calculated from the known value of F_i;* in the post-tensioned case there exists nothing comparable to F_i. The forces w_F between cable and concrete are discussed in Sec. 15.12. The allowable stresses are also marked at the bottom of Fig. 15.6a.

The calculations for full load are diagrammed in Fig. 15.6b. These calculations start with a loss of prestress slightly less than was used for the pre-tension case; some shrinkage will have occurred prior to prestressing

* In the pre-tension case F_o on the net concrete area would give the same result as F_i on the transformed area, but F_i is the known starting point.

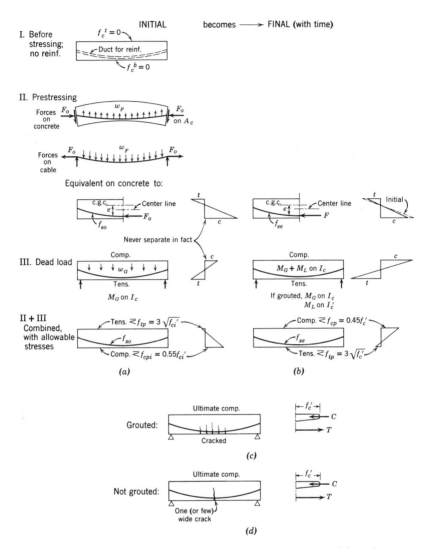

Fig. 15.6. Post-tensioned beam. (*a*) Initial stresses separated for calculation purposes; also allowable concrete stresses. (*b*) Stresses under full load separated for calculation purposes; also allowable concrete stresses. (*c*) Ultimate strength when grouted. (*d*) Ultimate strength, when ungrouted, is lower.

and all the elastic deformation of the concrete occurs during jacking to the f_{so} stress. The recommended allowance for loss[3, 4] is 25,000 psi.

Unless the tendons are grouted into place, the calculations for the effect of live load must also be based on the plain (net) concrete section. Actually, the live load moment does increase the steel stress slightly, but to less total stress than the original F_o. This change in steel stress is not usually calculated.

If the tendons are grouted effectively, as is usually attempted under present practice, the live load stresses are based on the entire transformed area.

Ultimate strength when the beam is grouted (Fig. 15.6c) is about the same as for a pre-tensioned beam. Without grouting the strength is somewhat less, the cracks being fewer and individually much wider, as indicated in Fig. 15.6d.

The possibility of aligning the post-tensioned cable in any desired shape gives this construction an advantage in taking care of shear and varying moments. However, means of deflecting the pre-tension wires are coming into use which may approximate the same advantages.

15.7. CRACKING LOAD AND ULTIMATE STRENGTH

European specifications have placed considerable emphasis on the cracking load, requiring that no cracks be formed for a given (usually small) overload. American practice has placed greater emphasis on ultimate strength.

Each of these methods is an attempt to provide an adequate factor of safety, the first slightly indirect, the second rather direct. The need for both working stress and ultimate strength calculations lies in the radical change in beam behavior when cracks form. Prior to cracking the gross area of the beam is effective. As a crack develops, all the tension from the concrete must be picked up by the steel. If the percentage of steel is small, there may be very little added capacity between cracking and failure. Cracking may be assumed to take place when the calculated tensile stress reaches $7.5\sqrt{f_c'}$.

15.8. EXAMPLE OF PRESTRESS WITHOUT ECCENTRICITY

The hollow member of Fig. 15.7a is reinforced with the equivalent of four wires of 0.10 in.^{2} each, pre-tensioned to $f_{so} = 140$ ksi. If $f_c' = 5000$ psi, $n = 6$, determine the stresses when the wires are cut between members; also the moment that can be carried at a maximum tension of $3\sqrt{f_c'}$* and a maximum f_c of $0.45f_c'$. If 25 ksi* of the prestress is lost (in addition to the elastic load) determine this limiting moment.

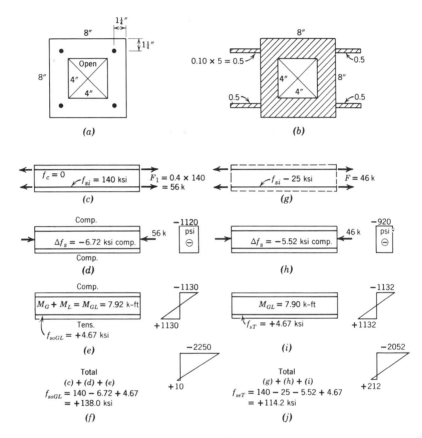

Fig. 15.7. Prestress without eccentricity, pre-tensioned. (*a*) Beam cross section. (*b*) Effective transformed area. (*c*) Wires under initial tension. (*d*) Effect of cutting wires. (*e*) Permissible moment for initial loading. (*f*) Total stresses for initial loading. (*g*) Equivalent initial tension after losses. (*h*) Equivalent reduction due to compression of concrete. (*i*) Permissible moment for later loading. (*j*) Total stresses for later loading.

SOLUTION

Transformed area (Fig. 13.7*b*) $= A_c' = 64 - 16 + 4 \times 0.5 = 50.0$ in.^{2}

$I_c' = 8 \times 8^3/12 - 4 \times 4^3/12 + 4 \times 0.5 \times 2.75^2 = 342 - 21 + 15 = 336$ in.^{4}

* Note that the 1958 recommendations[3, 4] would use $6\sqrt{f_c'}$ and 35 ksi for these values.

The starting stresses of Fig. 15.7c are $f_c = 0$ and $f_{si} = 140$ ksi. When the wires are cut, the 56-k force acts on the transformed area (Fig. 15.7d) to add these stresses:

$$f_c = -F_i/A_c' = -56 \times 1000/50.0 = -1120 \text{ psi comp.}$$
$$\Delta f_s = nf_{Fo} = -6 \times 1120 = -6720 \text{ psi} = -6.72 \text{ ksi comp.}$$

The total stresses before loading are thus:

$$f_{Fo} = 0 - 1120 = -1120 \text{ psi comp.}$$
$$f_{so} = 140 - 6.72 = +133.3 \text{ ksi tens.}$$

Before any prestress losses take place, $M_D + M_L$ can be enough to bring f_c^t to $0.45 f_c' = 2250$ psi compression or to bring f_c^b to $3\sqrt{f_c'} = 212$ psi tension.

Allowable: $f_{GL}^t = -2250 + 1120 = -1130$ psi. Controls (Fig. 15.7e).

$$f_{GL}^b = +212 + 1120 = +1332 \text{ psi}$$
$$M_{GL} = 1130 \times I_c'/y_t = 1130 \times 336/4 = 95,000 \text{ in.-lb} = 7.92 \text{ k-ft}$$

Under this loading,

$$f_{FoGL}^b = f_{Fo} + f_{GL}^b = -1120 + 1130 = +10 \text{ psi tens.}$$
$$f_{soGL} = f_{so} + nf_{GL}^b \times 2.75/4 = 133.3 + 6(1.130)2.75/4$$
$$= 133.3 + 4.67 = +138.0 \text{ ksi (bottom steel)}$$

After 25 ksi of prestress is lost, F_i is in effect reduced to $(140 - 25)0.4 = 46.0\,k$, as in Fig. 15.7g, h, giving uniform stresses:

$$f_F = -1120 \times 46.0/56 = -920 \text{ psi comp.}$$
$$f_{se} = 115 - 6 \times 0.92 = +109.5 \text{ ksi tens.}$$

M_{GL} may safely change f_c^t by $-2250 + 920 = -1330$ psi and f_c^b by $+212 + 920 = +1132$ psi.

$$M_{GL} = 1132 \times 336/4 = 94,800 \text{ in.-lb} = 7.90 \text{ k-ft}$$

Accompanying stresses, Fig. 15.7j, are:

$$f_{FT}^t = -920 - 1132 = -2052 \text{ psi} < 0.45 f_c'$$
$$f_{seT} = 109.5 + 6 \times 1.132 \times 2.75/4 = 109.5 + 4.67 = +114.2 \text{ ksi}$$
$$\text{tens. (bottom)}$$

The notations on some of the above steel stresses are a little awkward. In actual practice such steel stresses are not usually calculated.

15.9. EXAMPLE OF PRE-TENSIONED BEAM WITH ECCENTRICITY

The pre-tensioned beam of Fig. 15.8 will be investigated for $f_c' = 5000$ psi, $n = 6, f_{si} = 135$ ksi, and a creep and shrinkage loss (from f_{so}) of 35 ksi. $M_G = 65$ k-ft, $M_L = 80$ k-ft. The concrete strength when wires

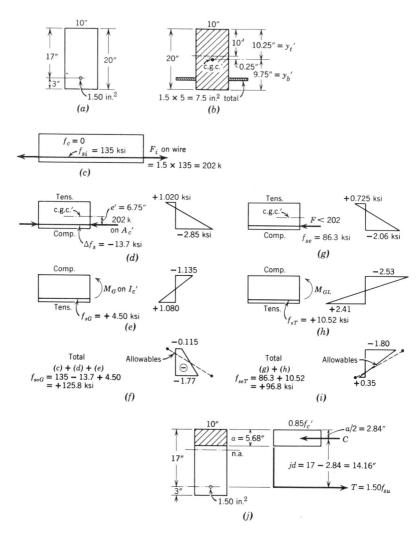

Fig. 15.8. Pre-tensioned beam. (*a*) Cross section. (*b*) Transformed area, A_c'. (*c*) Wires under initial tension. (*d*) Effect of cutting wires, eccentric load on A_c'. (*e*) Dead load stresses. (*f*) Total initial stresses. (*g*) Effective pre-tension stresses are 87.8/107.8 times those in (*c*) and (*d*). (*h*) Dead plus live load stresses. (*i*) Total stresses under full load. (*j*) Ultimate strength calculation.

are released is assumed to be $f_{ci}' = 4000$ psi, but for simplicity the same n will be used. Assume that the beam axis (or wire) is curved so that stresses under dead load and prestress do not require a check other than at mid-span. Allowable concrete stresses are shown in Fig. 15.5b, c.

SOLUTION

$A_c' = 10 \times 20 + 7.50 = 208$ in.^{2}

$\bar{y}$ from mid-depth $= -7.50 \times 7/208 = -0.25$ in. (below)

$I_c' = 10 \times 20^3/12 + 200 \times 0.25^2 + 7.50 \times 6.75^2$
$$= 6667 + 12 + 342 = 7020 \text{ in.}^4$$

Figure 15.8c shows forces before cutting wires and Fig. 15.8d and e shows the stress changes occurring after cutting wires. Actually these two sets of changes occur together and cannot be separated.

$f_{Fo}{}^t = -F_i/A_c' + F_i e y_t'/I_c' = -202/208 + (202 \times 6.75) \times 10.25/7020$
$$= -0.968 + 1.988 = +1.020 \text{ ksi tens.}$$

$f_{Fo}{}^b = -F_i/A_c - F_i e y_b'/I_c' = -0.968 - (202 \times 6.75) \times 9.75/7020$
$$= -0.968 - 1.888 = -2.85 \text{ ksi comp.}$$

$f_{so} = 135 + 6(-0.968 - 1.888 \times 6.75/9.75) = 135 - 6(0.968 + 1.310)$
$$= 135 - 13.7 = +121.3 \text{ ksi tens.}$$

$f_G{}^t = M_G y_t'/I_c' = -65 \times 12 \times 10.25/7020 = -1.135$ ksi comp.

$f_G{}^b = M_G y_b'/I_c' = +65 \times 12 \times 9.75/7020 = +1.080$ ksi tens.

$f^t{}_{FoG} = +1.020 - 1.135 = -0.115$ ksi comp. $< f_{tp} = 3\sqrt{f_{ci}'}$
$$= 0.189 \text{ ksi tens.} \qquad \text{O.K.}$$

$f^b{}_{FoG} = -2.85 + 1.080 = -1.77$ ksi comp. $< f_{cp} = 0.60f_{ci}'$
$$= 2.40 \text{ ksi comp.} \qquad \text{O.K.}$$

$f_{soG} = 121.3 + 6 \times 1.080 \times 6.75/9.75 = 121.3 + 4.50 = +125.8$ ksi

A prestress some 22% larger would be possible since both stresses in Fig. 15.8f are low. (One objection to the rectangular beam shape is the large prestress required for full effectiveness.)

When f_{so} drops 35 ksi (due to losses) from 121.3 ksi, as in Fig. 15.8g:

$f_{se} = 121.3 - 35 = 86.3$ ksi

$f_F{}^t = +1.020 \times 86.3/121.3 = +0.725$ ksi tens.

$f_F{}^b = -2.85 \times 86.3/121.3 = -2.06$ ksi comp.

$M_{GL} = 65 + 80 = 145$ k-ft (Fig. 15.8h)

$f_{GL}{}^t = -145 \times 12 \times 10.25/7020 = -2.53$ ksi comp.

$f_{GL}{}^b = +145 \times 12 \times 9.75/7020 = +2.41$ ksi tens.

$f_{FT}{}^t = +0.725 - 2.53 = -1.80$ ksi comp. $< 0.45f_c' = 2.25$ ksi $\qquad$ O.K.

$f_{FT}{}^b = -2.06 + 2.41 = +0.35$ ksi tens. $< 6\sqrt{f_c'} = 0.423$ ksi $\qquad$ O.K.

$f_{seT} = 86.3 + 6 \times 2.41 \times 6.75/9.75 = 86.3 + 10.0 = +96.3$ ksi

The total moment could be increased some 3 % or the prestress could be reduced nearly 3 % and still keep the bottom tension within the allowable.

The check cannot be considered complete without an investigation of the ultimate moment capacity (Sec. 15.11).

15.10. EXAMPLE OF POST-TENSIONED BEAM WITH ECCENTRICITY

The post-tensioned beam of Fig. 15.9a will be investigated for $f_c' = f_{ci}' = 5000$ psi, $n = 6$, $f_{so} = 135$ ksi, 25-ksi loss in prestress with time, $M_G = 60$ k-ft, $M_L = 70$ k-ft. It is assumed that the cables are positioned along the span so as to make the mid-span section the critical one. The cables will first be considered as ungrouted; then the effect of grouting will be investigated. Allowable concrete stresses are shown in Fig. 15.6a, b.

SOLUTION

$A_c = 10 \times 20 - 4 \times 2.5 = 190$ in.^{2} (Fig. 15.9b)

$\bar{y}$ from mid-depth $= (-4 \times 2.5) \times (-7.25)/190 = +0.38$ in. (above)

$I_c = 10 \times 20^3/12 + 10 \times 20 \times 0.38^2 - 4 \times 2.5^3/12 - 4 \times 2.5 \times 7.63^2$
$$= 6110 \text{ in.}^4$$

$e = 16.75 - 10.0 + 0.38 = 7.13$ in.

Figure 15.9c and d shows prestress effects artificially separated from M_G stresses. For prestress alone:

$F_o = 1.5 \times 135 = 202$ k

$f_{Fo}{}^t = -F_o/A_c + F_o e y_t/I_c = -202/190 + 202 \times 7.13 \times 9.62/6110$
$$= -1.060 + 2.26 = +1.20 \text{ ksi tens.}$$

$f_{Fo}{}^b = -202/190 - 202 \times 7.13 \times 10.38/6110 = -1.060 - 2.44$
$$= -3.50 \text{ ksi comp.}$$

For M_G alone:

$$f_G{}^t = -60 \times 12 \times 9.62/6110 = -1.135 \text{ ksi comp.}$$
$$f_G{}^b = +60 \times 12 \times 10.38/6110 = +1.225 \text{ ksi tens.}$$

Combined prestress and dead load (Fig. 15.9e):

$$f^t{}_{FoG} = +1.20 - 1.135 = +0.06 \text{ ksi} < 3\sqrt{f_{ci}'} = 0.212 \text{ ksi} \qquad \text{O.K.}$$
$$f^b{}_{FoG} = -3.50 + 1.225 = -2.28 \text{ ksi} < 0.55 f_{ci} = 2.75 \text{ ksi} \qquad \text{O.K.}$$

With time, f_{so} drops to $f_{se} = 135 - 25 = 110$ ksi, and the effect of prestress drops in like ratio, as indicated in Fig. 15.9f.

$$f_F{}^t = +1.20 \times 110/135 = +0.975 \text{ ksi tens.}$$
$$f_F{}^b = -3.50 \times 110/135 = -2.85 \text{ ksi comp.}$$

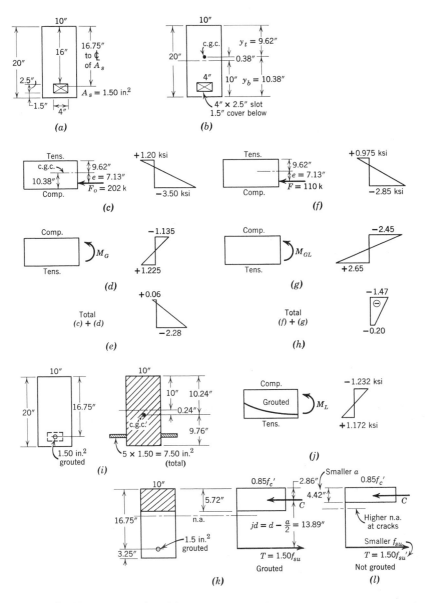

Fig. 15.9. Post-tensioned beam. (*a*) Cross section. (*b*) Effective area, plain concrete only, A_c. (*c*) Initial prestressing. (*d*) Dead load stresses. (*e*) Total initial stresses. (*f*) Prestress effects after losses. (*g*) Dead plus live load stresses (ungrouted). (*h*) Total full load stresses (ungrouted). (*i*) Effective section for live load when effectively grouted. (*j*) Live load stresses, effectively grouted. (*k*) Ultimate strength calculation, grouted. (*l*) Effect of lack of grouting on ultimate strength conditions.

PRESTRESSED CONCRETE ANALYSIS 417

For dead and live load, $M_{GL} = 60 + 70 = 130$ k-ft

$f_{GL}{}^t = -130 \times 12 \times 9.62/6110 = -2.45$ ksi comp.

$f_{GL}{}^b = +130 \times 12 \times 10.38/6110 = +2.65$ ksi tens.

$f_{FT}{}^t = +0.975 - 2.45 = -1.47$ ksi comp. $< 0.45 f_c{}' = 2.25$ ksi

$f_{FT}{}^b = -2.85 + 2.65 = -0.20$ ksi comp. $\ll 3\sqrt{f_c{}'} = 0.212$ ksi tens.

For an ungrouted beam the changes in f_s due to live load are small (significantly less than n times the concrete live load stress at that level). These changes in f_s are not usually calculated.

Neglecting the complications the grouted section may involve in the matter of loss of prestress, the only change in working stress calculations resulting from grouting is that the live load stresses will be based on the transformed area.

If the beam were effectively grouted, and again neglecting the variation in n, the transformed area would become that of Fig. 15.9i.

$A_c{}' = 20 \times 10 + 5 \times 1.50 = 207.5$ in.^{2}

$\bar{y}$ from mid-depth $= -7.50 \times 6.75/207.5 = -0.24$ in.

$I_c{}' = 10 \times 20^3/12 + 10 \times 20 \times 0.24^2 + 7.50 \times 6.51^2 = 6667 + 12 + 318$
$$= 7000 \text{ in.}^4$$

$f_L{}^t = -70 \times 12 \times 10.24/7000 = -1.232$ ksi comp.

$f_L{}^b = +70 \times 12 \times 9.76/7000 = +1.172$ ksi tens.

$f_{seL} = 110 + 6 \times 1.172(6.75 - 0.24)/9.76 = 110 + 4.68 = +114.7$ ksi

$f_{FT}{}^t = +0.975 - 1.135 - 1.232 = -1.392$ ksi comp. $< 0.45 f_c{}'$

$f_{FT}{}^b = -2.85 + 1.225 + 1.172 = -0.45$ ksi comp. $< 3\sqrt{f_c{}'}$ tens.

These totals put together stresses from Fig. 15.9f, 15.9d, and 15.9j.

The differences as a result of grouting are small at working stress, about 0.08 ksi less compression on the top and 0.25 ksi more compression on the bottom. The ultimate moment is more noticeably improved by grouting, as noted in the next section.

15.11. ULTIMATE STRENGTH OF PRESTRESSED BEAMS

Since the high strength steels lack a sharp and distinct yield point (Fig. 15.10) and since prestress may modify the neutral axis location at failure, it is not possible to use ultimate strength relations developed for ordinary beams without some concern or caution. Theoretical considerations would seem to call for a calculation process correlating strains on steel and concrete at failure.

Nevertheless, for beams with bonded wire and a percentage of steel low enough to ensure a tension failure, Whitney's method of analysis (Sec. 3.4) gives approximate values which seem to agree fairly well with tests. Since there is no sharp yield point, the ACI-ASCE Joint Committee on prestressed concrete uses average steel stress f_{su} at ultimate beam load in this

REINFORCED CONCRETE FUNDAMENTALS

calculation rather than f_y. Fundamentally the determination of f_{su} depends upon stress-strain diagrams and strain relationships, which means that f_{su} is not a quantity easily established without detailed data. Professor Lin accordingly uses the ultimate strength f_s' in ultimate strength calculations. The committee eases this situation by providing approximate formulas for f_{su} that may be used for rather typical cases:

For bonded members, $\quad f_{su} = f_s'(1 - 0.5pf_s'/f_c')$

For unbonded members, $\quad f_{su} = f_{se} + 15{,}000$

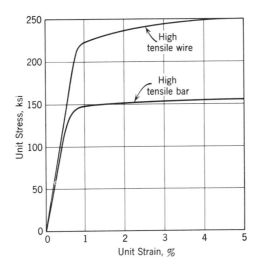

Fig. 15.10. Typical stress-strain curves for prestressing steel. (From Lin.[1])

The ultimate moment for rectangular beams, or for flanged beams with the neutral axis within the flange, is expressed by the relation

$$M_u = A_s f_{su} d(1 - 0.6pf_{su}/f_c')$$

This is almost the same relation given in Sec. 3.5 for ordinary reinforced concrete beams except that f_{su} takes the place of f_y and that 0.6 is used instead of 0.59. The small change in coefficient is ignored in the calculations which follow.

To avoid approaching the overreinforced beam condition the committee recommends for rectangular sections that steel not exceed that representing $pf_{su}/f_c' = 0.30$. For larger steel ratio the value of M_u is to be taken as $M_u = 0.25f_c'bd^2$ which corresponds to a value of $a = 0.353d$ by a straight Whitney analysis.

As an example of approximate ultimate strength analysis, the pretensioned beam of Sec. 15.9 and Fig. 15.8 will be investigated assuming $f_s' = 195$ ksi. The failure conditions of Fig. 15.8j give:

$$f_{su} = f_s'(1 - 0.5pf_s'/f_c') = 195[1 - 0.5 \times 1.50 \times 195/(10 \times 17 \times 5)]$$
$$= 161 \text{ ksi}$$

$$a = \frac{A_s f_{su}}{0.85 f_c' b} = \frac{1.50 \times 161}{0.85 \times 5 \times 10} = 5.68 \text{ in.} < 0.353d = 6.04 \text{ in.}$$

$$M_u = 1.50 \times 161(17 - 2.84) = 3420 \text{ k-in.} = 285 \text{ k-ft}$$

Reqd. $M_u = 1.2M_G + 2.4M_L = 1.2 \times 65 + 2.4 \times 80 = 270$ k-ft

This comparison shows about a 5% surplus strength, compared to about 3% by the working stress method. The agreement is quite good.

For the post-tensioned beam of Sec. 15.10 and Fig. 15.9a with $f_s' = 195$ ksi and the steel well grouted, the failure conditions of Fig. 15.9k give:

$$f_{su} = f_s'(1 - 0.5pf_s'/f_c') = 195[1 - 0.5 \times 1.50 \times 195/(10 \times 16.75 \times 5)]$$
$$= 162 \text{ ksi}$$

$$a = \frac{162 \times 1.50}{0.85 \times 5 \times 10} = 5.72 \text{ in.} < 0.353d = 5.92 \text{ in.}$$

$$M_u = 1.5 \times 162(16.75 - 5.72/2) = 3370 \text{ k-in.} = 282 \text{ k-ft}$$

Reqd. $M_u = 1.2M_G + 2.4M_L = 1.20 \times 60 + 2.4 \times 70 = 240$ k-ft

The section provides about 18% more capacity than required compared to nearly 28% under the working stress analysis. The ultimate strength analysis is slightly more restrictive in this example.

If the beam of Sec. 15.10 were left ungrouted, a straight Whitney analysis would give the same M_u value as for the bonded case just calculated. Nevertheless, ungrouted beams are weaker because the unbonded steel leads to failure after only one crack opens, or at most a few. These few cracks open widely, crowd the neutral axis upward, and thereby cause a secondary compression failure at lower moment, as indicated in Fig. 15.9l. Some tests by Baker[5] indicate cracks three to ten times as wide as for the bonded case where many small cracks occur.

The committee suggests that this condition be recognized by using a lower f_{su} as given by the formula quoted earlier in this section.

For the beam just investigated, if grouting is omitted (Fig. 15.9l) the calculations become:

$$f_{su} = f_{se} + 15,000 = 110,000 + 15,000 = 125,000 \text{ psi} = 125 \text{ ksi}$$

$$a = \frac{125 \times 1.50}{0.85 \times 5 \times 10} = 4.42 \text{ in.} < 0.353d = 5.92 \text{ in.}$$

$$M_u = 1.50 \times 125(16.75 - 4.42/2) = 2720 \text{ in.-lb} = 227 \text{ k-ft}$$

This compares to a required M_u of 240 k-ft. Thus the ungrouted beam shows a 5% deficiency whereas the grouted beam showed an 18% surplus.

If calculations for ungrouted sections are based on correlating strains, as suggested in the second paragraph of this section, it is not difficult to introduce a factor to represent relative crack width. The effective steel strain (beyond initial prestress) can simply be taken as about one-fifth of the strain indicated by the strain triangles. This reduced steel strain, when added to the initial prestress strain, gives the total to be used with the stress-strain curve.

15.12. CABLE EFFECT CONSIDERED AS A NEGATIVE LOADING

Since simple beam cable eccentricity develops a negative moment which offsets much or all of the dead load moment, this eccentricity must be reduced where dead load moment is small; otherwise a negative moment failure can occur as prestressing is applied. With post-tensioned steel the tendons or cables can be formed to any desired shape. With pre-tensioned wires or strands recent practice is using hold-down devices to give the effect of bent-up steel. Other pre-tensioned beams have been made with a curved soffit, the curved beam axis thus producing a varying eccentricity.

A complete analysis can be made by considering all critical sections with their respective eccentricities. The relieving moment is (almost) proportional to the eccentricity, since the slope angles are small and the horizontal component of the prestress is essentially a constant. Hence the relieving moment diagram has the same shape as the curve of plotted e values.

A more convenient way for some to visualize the effect of curvature is in terms of a negative or upward load on the beam. A curved cable under heavy tension requires vertical load to deflect it from a nearly horizontal line. A concentrated load at the center will deflect the cable as in Fig. 15.11a, loads at both third points as in Fig. 15.11b, and a uniform load as in Fig. 15.11c, a parabolic curve. When embedded in a concrete beam in a slot having one of these shapes, the cable after prestressing exerts upward forces on the concrete opposite to those required to deform the free tension cable into the same shape.

If the parabolic cable shape is used, the free body of Fig. 15.11d indicates from ΣM that $Fe = (w_F L/2)(L/4) = w_F L^2/8$, or $w_F = 8Fe/L^2$. Hence the cable can be visualized as contributing an axial load and an upward uniform load w_F, both acting on the plain concrete section. The cable can be shaped in such a way as to offset nearly completely any dead load distribution that exists.

15.13. SHEAR AND DIAGONAL TENSION

A cable with varying eccentricity acts somewhat as a suspension cable, partially relieving the concrete not only of bending stress but also of shear stress. The shear thus carried by the cable can be calculated either as the vertical component of the cable pull or as the shears created by the equivalent upward loads discussed in Sec. 15.12. The remainder of the external load creates a shear which must be resisted by the concrete.

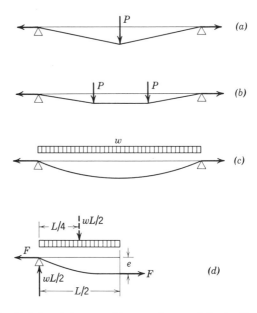

Fig. 15.11. Relation between cable curvature and load. Prestressed cable exerts similar upward forces on (plain) concrete.

The axial compression from prestress reduces the diagonal tension stresses so long as the beam is uncracked from moment stress. Cracking reduces this beneficial effect and inelastic steel deformations at loads near the ultimate largely eliminate it. Thus working load analysis for diagonal tensile stresses gives little information on the behavior of a beam under overload conditions.

The ACI-ASCE Joint Committee indicates[3, 4] that a beam will fail in moment and will not develop inclined cracks requiring web reinforcement if $pf_s'/f_c' = 0.3f_{se}b'/(f_s'b)$, where b' = web thickness, $p = A_s/bd$, and b = flange width. At the same time their report suggests that this criterion may be conservative if the ratio of span to depth exceeds 15, or if uniformly loaded members are involved. However, the limited knowledge on shear failures causes the committee to suggest that some web reinforcement always be provided. The maximum spacing for stirrups is recommended at three-quarters of the depth but not to exceed the clear height of the web in the case of thin webs.

The more critical sections for shear are at points where moment also exists. For simply supported beams uniformly loaded, the committee suggests that the maximum shear be taken at a distance from the support equal to the depth of the member, with the resulting web steel continued on to the support. Likewise, the web reinforcement needed at the third point should be carried across the entire middle third.

For members fully prestressed and needing web reinforcement that portion of the ultimate load shear assigned to vertical stirrups is in effect taken as 0.5 of the shear in excess of $0.06f_c'$. The stirrups' capacity is then based on the yield point of the stirrup steel. The 0.5 factor represents a 50% reduction in the stirrup requirement from what would be used for ordinary reinforced concrete. A minimum $A_v = 0.0025b's$ is suggested in this case, although the recommendation states that this may be excessive for thick webs.

15.14. BOND STRENGTH

On pre-tensioned beams the self-anchorage of wires and strands at the ends of the beams leads to high bond stresses. The ACI-ASCE Joint Committee makes no recommendation on this, simply stating that transfer length seems to be a problem only on short members. Obviously the post-tensioned beam must substitute end anchors for anchorage by bond.

Although the committee states that flexural bond stress should be investigated if cracking is anticipated under design loads, it goes on to say that for the usual span lengths bond failure at ultimate load is not a significant design factor. In extremely short members bond failure should be investigated by test.

15.15. DESIGN CONSIDERATIONS

Design considerations will be treated very briefly. Allowable working load stresses have already been mentioned in analysis examples.

Since the optimum total prestress approximates half the allowable f_c

multiplied by the total concrete area, economy is provided by reducing the concrete area near the centroid, where it is less effective in resisting moment, and by increasing the area near the extreme fibers. Hence I, T, and ⌐⌐ shapes are the general types which prove economical. Tables of section modulus values for such shapes are helpful in picking a size.

It is sometimes stated that the prestress carries the dead load and that the size of the beam depends only on the live load. At working loads the negative moment $F_o e$ can be made to offset the dead load moment. Of course, as F_o decreases in time to F, part of this offsetting moment is lost. Furthermore, at ultimate strength the effect of prestress is largely lost and the beam must carry all the moment, essentially as an ordinary beam.

Referring to Fig. 15.5b, it will be noted that the top stress under prestress and dead load may be a tension as large as f_{tp}. Under full load (Fig. 15.5c) this stress may be the full allowable compression f_{cp}. Thus, except for the effect of prestress losses, the full range of $f_{tp} + f_{cp}$ is available to take care of M_L. Likewise, on the bottom the stress range for M_L can be from f_{cpi} to f_{tp}, except for the effect of prestress losses. Magnel[6] has thus worked out design requirements for a section modulus established from M_L divided by the major part of this stress range. This approach is most suitable when M_L is large compared to M_G. It indicates the saving sometimes possible in beam size compared to an ordinary beam which must be sized for $M_G + M_L$.

As American specifications develop, it is probable that more designs will be made on the basis of ultimate strength design.

Lin has developed[1] design procedures for elastic designs based on visualizing the internal resisting couple. These appear very straightforward in application.

15.16. CONTINUOUS BEAMS

Continuous beams cannot be considered here except to mention one special condition which often controls. Since an eccentrically placed prestressing tendon itself develops bending moment and curvature in a beam, the prestressing operation may well require reactions (up or down) to hold the member in contact with its supports. These reactions change the prestressing moment from the simple Fe value to something more involved. Cables can be so arranged as to cause zero external reactions, but this appears to be an unnecessary restriction. Lin[1] gives a complete discussion of this problem following basic methods originally suggested by Guyon.

SELECTED REFERENCES

1. T. Y. Lin, *Design of Prestressed Concrete Structures*, John Wiley & Sons, New York, 1955.

2. ACI-ASCE Committee 323, "Proposed Definitions and Notation for Prestressed Concrete," *ACI Jour.*, Oct. 1952; *Proc.*, **49**, p. 85.

3. *ACI-ASCE* Joint Committee 323, "Recommended Practice for Prestressed Concrete," *ACI Jour.*, **29**, Jan. 1958; *Proc.*, **54**, p. 545.

4. Report of the Joint ACI-ASCE Committee on Prestressed Reinforced Concrete, "Tentative Recommendations for Prestressed Concrete," *Jour. ASCE*, Structural Div., **84**, No. ST1, Jan. 1958, p. 1519–1; also *ACI Jour.*, Jan. 1958; *Proc.*, **54**, p. 545.

5. Y. Guyon, *Prestressed Concrete*, John Wiley & Sons, New York, 1953.

6. Gustave Magnel, *Prestressed Concrete*, Concrete Publications Ltd., London, 2nd ed., 1950.

7. Kurt Billig, *Prestressed Concrete*, D. Van Nostrand Co., New York, 1953.

PROBLEMS

Prob. 15.1. The rectangular beam of Fig. 15.12 has pre-tensioned steel at two levels as shown with $f_{si} = 150$ ksi. Consider $f_{ci}' = f_c' = 5000$ psi, $n = 6$, and a simple span of 40 ft.

(a) Calculate concrete stresses at top and bottom and both steel stresses when prestressed wires are first cut between units.

(b) Recalculate stresses after shrinkage and creep have decreased f_s by 35 ksi below the value found in (a).

(c) Calculate all stresses when a live load of 600 plf is added to the conditions in (b).

Prob. 15.2. The post-tensioned beam of Fig. 15.13 has a 40-ft simple span. It has two holes as shown, for wires with a total area of 2.33 in.^{2} which after tensioning will be 16.5 in. below the top of beam. $f_c' = 5000$ psi, $f_{so} = 150$ ksi. Considering the holes ungrouted and without using the approximation of area as the gross area of the concrete, calculate:

(a) Stresses under dead weight alone after post-tensioning.

(b) Stresses after shrinkage and creep reduce the steel stress to $f_{se} = 125$ ksi and a live load of 625 plf acts on the beam.

Prob. 15.3.

(a) Recalculate condition (b) of Prob. 15.2 if the beam hole is well grouted.

(b) Calculate the ultimate moment capacity of this beam and its over-all factor of safety assuming it is well grouted and has $f_s' = 220$ ksi.

Prob. 15.4.

(a) If the pre-tensioned beam of Fig. 15.8 is changed to $f_c' = 5000$ psi, $f_{si} = 150$ ksi, $n = 6$, $A_s = 1.00$ in.^{2} with M_G still 65 k-ft, calculate all stresses after the wires are cut.

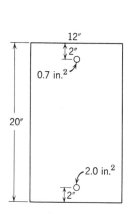

Fig. 15.12. Beam for Prob. 15.1.

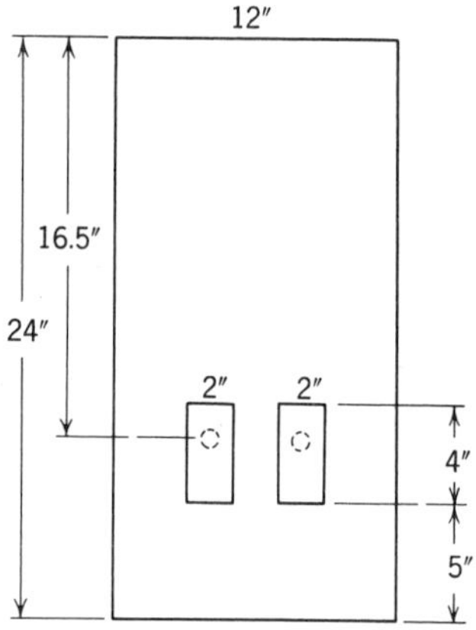

Fig. 15.13. Beam for Probs. 15.2 and 15.3.

(b) If the wires are straight and concrete stresses are limited to a (bottom) compression of 2400 psi and a tension of $3\sqrt{f_c'}$, what is the maximum wire eccentricity that can be used? [The student should note that M_G at the support would be zero. The change in c.g.c.' from that used in part (a) above may be ignored.]

(c) If the wires are draped such that the condition at the end of the span does not control, and if f_{so} decreases to f_{se} of 115 ksi, what live load moment is permissible with the allowable f_{cp} of $0.45f_c'$ and f_{tp} of $3\sqrt{f_c'}$?

REINFORCED CONCRETE FUNDAMENTALS

A

Deflections:
Area Moment Method

A.1. DEFLECTIONS RELATIVE TO A TANGENT;
THE AREA MOMENT METHOD

The area moment method, developed by Professor Charles E. Greene of the University of Michigan in 1873, determines deflections *relative* to a specific *tangent* to the elastic curve, not absolute deflections. These relative movements are here called tangential deviations to emphasize that absolute deflections can be directly obtained only when a fixed reference tangent is available. However, the absolute deflection can be found for any beam by a two-step process, since the movement of certain reference tangents can be established simply. The area moment method is not always the shortest one; but it keeps the physical picture to the fore, is readily usable for variable section members, and is quite useful for proofs. In its usual form it applies only to members within their elastic range. Section A.9 discusses briefly inelastic action.

A.2. ANGULAR DEFLECTION

Figure A.1a shows a beam AD fixed at end A and of gradually varying cross section, gradual enough to justify the use of the relation $Mc = fI$. Its loading develops a moment diagram which is shown as positive for

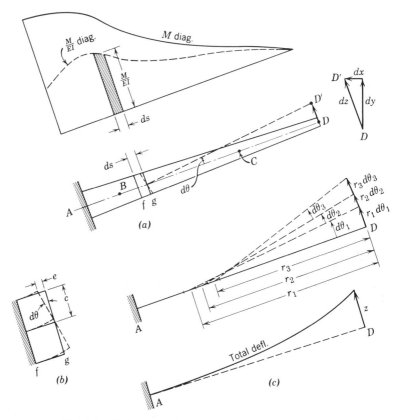

Fig. A.1. Deflection of beam elements, straight beam axis.

simplicity in signs, rather than the more common negative moment for this type of beam. The straight beam axis is indicated in order to make it easier to sketch the moment diagram; the proof applies equally to a curved beam axis, provided the relation $Mc = fI$ is also applicable.

Consider initially that the ds length fg is elastic while all other elements remain rigid. Face f is held fixed by its rigid attachment to A. The elastic deformation of the ds element rotates face g and the entire length gD through an angle $d\theta = e/c$, as shown in Fig. $A.1b$.

$$e = \int ds/E = Mc\,ds/EI$$
$$d\theta = e/c = M\,ds/EI$$

But $M\,ds/EI$ is also the area of the M/EI diagram for the ds length between f and g. For the entire beam, each ds element contributes its own $d\theta$. Thus the total angular change between any two points B and C becomes

$$\theta_{CB} = \int_B^C d\theta = \int_B^C (M/EI)\,ds = \text{area of } M/EI \text{ diagram between } B \text{ and } C$$

and

$$\theta_{DA} = \theta_D = \int_A^D d\theta = \int_A^D (M/EI)\,ds = \text{total area of } M/EI \text{ diagram } A \text{ to } D$$

Because A is fixed, this is also the absolute rotation θ_D of point D. In comparison, θ_{CB} is a relative rotation, because both C and B rotate.

> The total angular movement, or the change in slope of the elastic curve due to load, between any two points is equal to the area of the M/EI diagram between these two points.

A positive θ indicates a predominant positive moment with the right end rotating counterclockwise with respect to the left end or the left end rotating clockwise with respect to the right end.

A.3. LINEAR DEFLECTION

Consider the deflection of point D in Fig. A.1c. The $d\theta$ change in element fg moves D a distance $dz = r_1\,d\theta_1$ perpendicular to r_1, where r_1 is the line joining D to the element. The next element adds a $d\theta_2$ rotation and a movement $r_2\,d\theta_2$ to D, the next $r_3\,d\theta_3$, and so forth. With small deflections, and for a beam with a straight axis, all such small dz movements, as essentially parallel vectors, can be added algebraically to give the total deflection of D, that is,

$$z = \int_A^D r\,d\theta = \int_A^D r(M\,ds/EI)$$

$= $ moment about D of the total area of the M/EI diagram

Here z is perpendicular to r, that is, perpendicular to the axis of the beam. For area moments the M/EI diagram may best be visualized as cut from cardboard and erected (perpendicular to the page) on the axis of the beam.

For the usual case of a horizontal beam axis, r would be a horizontal dimension x, and z would be the vertical deflection, that is,

$$z_D = \int_A^D x(M\,ds/EI)$$

For members with curved or bent axes, x and y deflections are more usable than z deflections, because x and y components can be added algebraically whereas z components must be added vectorially (Fig. A.2).

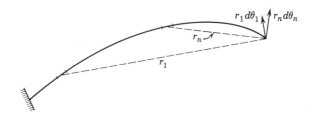

Fig. A.2. Deflection of beam elements, curved beam axis.

In Fig. A.3, the deflection DD' or dz (same as in Fig. A.1a) is shown resolved into dx and dy components. Let x_1 and y_1 be the horizontal and vertical coordinates of the ds element fg, measured from point D. Since right triangles $x_1y_1r_1$ and dy, dx, dz are similar triangles,

$$\frac{dx}{dz} = \frac{y_1}{r_1} \quad \text{or} \quad dx = \frac{y_1}{r_1} dz$$

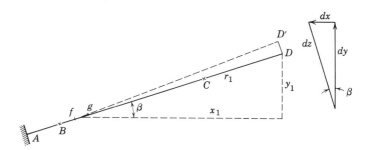

Fig. A.3. Components of deflection.

Since $dz = r_1\, d\theta = r_1(M\, ds/EI)$,

$$dx = \frac{y_1}{r_1} \times r_1(M\, ds/EI) = y_1(M\, ds/EI)$$

and
$$dy = x_1(M\, ds/EI)$$

Then the total deflection of D in Fig. A.1 becomes

$$\Delta x = \int_A^D y(M\,ds/EI)$$

$$\Delta y = \int_A^D x(M\,ds/EI)$$

These are the moments about D of the total area of the M/EI diagram from A to D, using the y or x lever arms measured from D. It should be noted

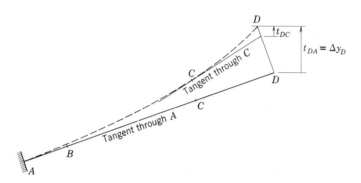

Fig. A.4. Significance of reference tangent.

that the lever arm used is perpendicular to the deflection desired. Likewise, the vertical deflection of C is given by $\int_A^C x(M\,ds/EI)$, where x is measured from C and the area is from A to C. These are true deflections since A is fixed.

In general, however, the area moment relation gives only the tangential deviation, that is, the deflection of a point relative to that of a reference tangent. For example, in Fig. A.4, Δy_D is also t_{DA}, the vertical deviation of point D from a reference tangent through A, because this reference tangent is fixed, that is, the tangent at A does not rotate. However, the moment of the area of the M/EI diagram C to D about D as a center and with x arms gives only t_{DC}, the vertical deviation of D from a reference tangent through C. Obviously, a fixed reference tangent, such as the one through A, is the simpler one to use.

It should be noted that if the arm is taken as positive, t will be positive whenever the moment is predominantly positive. Hence a positive t means that the elastic curve has moved above the tangent.

A.4. CHOICE OF REFERENCE TANGENT

Any beam reference point fixed against both deflection and rotation provides the simplest possible reference tangent. This includes the fixed end of a cantilever beam, or the fixed end of a continuous beam. The next simplest case is that of a symmetrical beam where the tangent at the point of symmetry remains horizontal, but may deflect vertically. For other cases, a tangent through a supported point (reaction point which does not move up or down) is recommended.

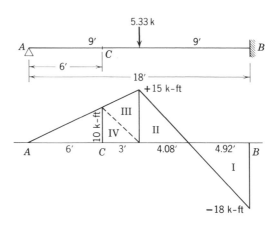

Fig. A.5. Deflection problem with fixed reference tangent at *B*.

A.5. DEFLECTION USING A FIXED REFERENCE TANGENT

The deflection of point *C* on the beam of Fig. A.5 will be calculated for $E = 30 \times 10^6$ psi, $I = 60$ in.[4], and the *M* diagram shown. In many cases the use of the simple beam moment diagram plus separate moment diagram for the moments due to continuity* will be simpler than using the final combined diagram, but in this case the combined diagram is already of simple form.

Use a fixed reference tangent through *B*.

$$y_C = t_{CB} = \frac{1}{EI} \text{ (mo. abt. } C \text{ of area of } M \text{ diag. } B \text{ to } C)$$

---

* The student not entirely familiar with continuous span moment and shear diagrams will do well to review these subjects in Sec. A.10.

	Area	Arm abt. C	Mo. abt. C
I	$-\frac{18}{2} \times 4.92 = -44.3$ k-ft^2	$7.08 + 3.28 = 10.36$ ft	-459 k-ft^3
II	$+\frac{15}{2} \times 4.08 = +30.6$	$3 + 1.36 = 4.36$	$+133.6$
III	$+\frac{15}{2} \times 3 = +22.5$	2.0	$+ 45.0$
IV	$+\frac{10}{2} \times 3 = +15.0$	1.0	$+ 15.0$

$$\Sigma = -265 \text{ k-ft}^3$$

$$y_C = \frac{-265 \times 1000 \times 1728}{30 \times 10^6 \times 60} = -0.255 \text{ in.} \downarrow$$

The 1000 and 1728 terms are necessary to convert to pound and inch units. The negative sign indicates the elastic curve is below the reference tangent.

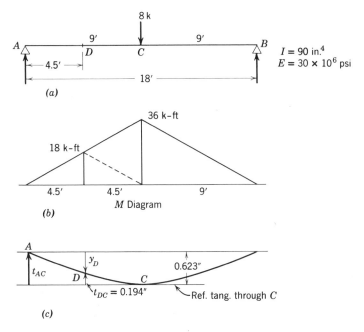

Fig. A.6. Deflection problem with symmetry.

A.6. DEFLECTION OF A SYMMETRICAL BEAM AND LOADING

The quarter-point deflection of the beam of Fig. A.6 illustrates the use of a reference tangent which deflects but does not rotate. From symmetry, the elastic curve is horizontal at mid-span.

Use a reference tangent through C and locate it by calculating t_{AC} at A where the real vertical movement is known to be zero.

$$t_{AC} = \frac{1}{EI} \text{(mo. abt. } A \text{ of area of } M \text{ diag. } A \text{ to } C\text{)}$$

$$= \frac{1}{EI} \left(+\frac{36}{2} \times 9 \times 6.0 \right) = \frac{+972 \times 1000 \times 1728}{30 \times 10^6 \times 90} = +0.623 \text{ in. } \uparrow$$

Since A lies 0.623 in. above the reference tangent through C, the reference tangent must have deflected 0.623 in. downward.

$$t_{DC} = \frac{1}{EI} \text{(mo. abt. } D \text{ of area of } M \text{ diag. } D \text{ to } C\text{)}$$

$$= \frac{1}{EI} (+\tfrac{36}{2} \times 4.5 \times 3.0 + \tfrac{18}{2} \times 4.5 \times 1.5)$$

$$= \frac{+(243 + 60.8) \times 1000 \times 1728}{30 \times 10^6 \times 90} = +0.194 \text{ in. } \uparrow$$

The net deflection, as shown in Fig. A.6a, is

$$y_D = \text{defl. of ref. tang.} + t_{DC}$$

$$= -0.623 + 0.194 = -0.429 \text{ in. } \downarrow$$

A.7. GENERAL CASE OF DEFLECTION

Calculate the deflection of mid-span C and of the free end F of the beam of Fig. A.7a for $E = 29 \times 10^6$ psi and $I = 100$ in.[4]

SOLUTION

The moment diagram is shown in Fig. A.7b. The two separate diagrams making up this total are shown in Fig. A.7c and these will be used in the calculations. The student should note the sequence of calculations to be given now and follow it in other problems. Use a reference tangent through D, which does not deflect vertically. Locate this tangent by calculating the apparent deflection of point B, which actually does not move.

$$t_{BD} = \frac{1}{EI} \text{(mo. abt. } B \text{ of area } B \text{ to } D\text{)}$$

$$= \frac{1}{EI} (-\tfrac{36}{2} \times 24 \times 8 - \tfrac{18}{2} \times 24 \times 16 + \tfrac{2}{3} \times 72 \times 24 \times 12)$$

$$= \frac{(-3460 - 3460 + 13{,}850) \times 1000 \times 1728}{29 \times 10^6 \times 100} = +4.12 \text{ in. } \uparrow$$

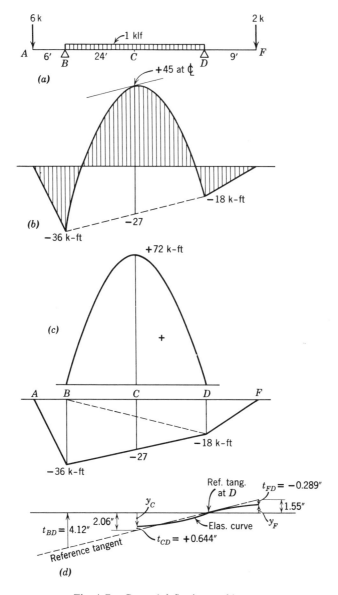

Fig. A.7. General deflection problem.

Since B lies above the reference tangent, the tangent must be shown below B, as in Fig. A.7d. At point C, by proportion, the tangent lies $4.12/2 = 2.06$ in. below the original position of C.

$$t_{CD} = \frac{1}{EI}(\text{mo. abt. } C \text{ of area of } M \text{ diag. } C \text{ to } D)$$

$$= \frac{1}{EI}(-\tfrac{27}{2} \times 12 \times 4 - \tfrac{18}{2} \times 12 \times 8 + \tfrac{2}{3} \times 72 \times 12 \times \tfrac{3}{8} \times 12)$$

$$= \frac{(-648 - 865 + 2590)1000 \times 1728}{29 \times 10^6 \times 100} = +0.644 \text{ in. } \uparrow$$

Based on Fig. A.7d,

$$y_C = -2.06 + t_{CD} = -2.06 + 0.644 = -1.42 \text{ in. } \downarrow$$

The same reference tangent can be used to calculate y_F. In fact, its convenience for this purpose was the reason for originally using it in preference to one through B. At F the reference tangent, by similar triangles, lies $+4.12 \times 9/24 = +1.55$ in. above the original position of F.

$$t_{FD} = \frac{1}{EI}(\text{mo. abt. } F \text{ of area of } M \text{ diag. } D \text{ to } F)$$

$$= \frac{(-\tfrac{18}{2} \times 9 \times 6)1000 \times 1728}{29 \times 10^6 \times 100} = -0.289 \text{ in. } \downarrow$$

Again referring to Fig. A.7d, one finds

$$y_F = +1.55 + t_{DF} = +1.55 - 0.289 = +1.26 \text{ in. } \uparrow$$

A.8. LIMITATIONS AS APPLIED TO REINFORCED CONCRETE

(a) General

A reinforced concrete beam is by no means a truly elastic member. Hence all ordinary deflection calculations relating to it, whether by the area moment method or any other conventional method, are approximate. Some of the complications are now discussed.

(b) Value of EI as a measure of beam stiffness

Even for a given specimen in the working stress range, the value of f_c/ϵ, the apparent E, is not constant (Sec. 1.6), and between different samples of the same mix there appears to be much more variation in the apparent E than in f_c'. The concrete strength increases with time under favorable conditions with a resultant increase in E that is somewhat obscured by the creep effect to be discussed in (c).

REINFORCED CONCRETE FUNDAMENTALS

The effective moment of inertia varies considerably along the length of even a simple span. Near the ends of the span, the concrete is uncracked and the effective area is the entire concrete cross section (including cover under the steel) plus the reinforcing steel (treated as a transformed area). At mid-span the concrete on the tension side of the beam will be cracked, say, to mid-height, although this is dependent somewhat upon the percentage of steel. The extent of the cracking along the length of the span depends upon the shape of the moment diagram, that is, upon the loading. In a continuous T-beam the variation in moment of inertia is even more serious, with the entire section effective in the vicinity of the points of inflection and cracked sections elsewhere, these being quite different for positive and negative moment as suggested in Fig. 8.3c.

The arbitrary procedure in common use is to treat the beam as a member of constant cross section. The entire concrete section is used as though uncracked throughout and the steel is not counted except as offsetting the cracking effect. For short-time loading the usual secant modulus is used for E. Further study is needed to establish what EI is really effective.

(c) Effect of creep

Creep is discussed briefly in Sec. 1.7. Since deformation of concrete under stress increases with time, deflections will also increase with time. Creep and shrinkage effects in time will add from 100% to 200% to the initial deflection under load. This effect can be approximated by using a reduced modulus value or by introducing a simple multiplier of 2 to 3.

(d) Effect of shrinkage

Uniform shrinkage of plain concrete will not produce warping or curvature, but the usual reinforced concrete member is reinforced unsymmetrically on the two faces. Since any reinforcement resists shrinkage, the effect of positive moment steel is to reduce this shortening on the bottom of the beam and its eccentric action causes extra shortening on the top of the beam. (This effective eccentricity of steel is large in the case of the cracked section.) Thus shrinkage causes deflection in the same direction as that produced by the external moment. A similar condition exists for negative moment regions. Compression steel reduces shrinkage deflection and could be so arranged as to eliminate it.

(e) Effect of high steel stress

Concern has been expressed by some about the increased deflections which will result from ultimate strength design procedures which utilize high yield-point steel. Section 3.5 mentions the steel limitation of $p = 0.40f_c'/f_y$ and the deflection warning when p exceeds $0.18f_c'/f_y$. The following tests indicate that such concern about the use of high steel percentages and high yield-point steel may be unnecessary.

The Portland Cement Association laboratory constructed two frames identical except for their reinforcing steel. The first frame was designed under the straight-line theory in accordance with the ACI Code with $f_s = 20$ ksi, and $p = 0.18f_c'/f_y$, the allowable load being 7.1 k. The second frame was reinforced according to ultimate strength theory with $p = 0.40f_c'/f_y$ using a steel having $f_y = 60$ ksi. On the basis of a load factor of 1.8, this second frame had a service load capacity of 15.7 k. Each frame was continuously loaded under its service load. The "beam" deflections resulting are shown in Fig. A.8a, excluding column shortening. The final deflections per kip of load are nearly identical for the two frames, as shown in Fig. A.8b, being some 10% in excess of computed values based on the plain concrete section and an effective modulus of one-third of the ordinary value. There thus appears to be no ill result from the use of the higher yield-point steel and the higher working stress except the proportionate increase to be expected from the increased size of the working load.

(f) Characteristic deflection curve

A typical complete deflection curve for a simple span slab with moderate reinforcement is shown in Fig. A.8c, for initial loading. The dashed line shows the deflection that would be calculated on the basis of using the cracked section for the moment of inertia. The early deflection is much less since all the slab is uncracked. Cracking at the section of maximum moment may be relatively sudden when it occurs, but for the slab as a whole it is a gradual process, more and more sections cracking as they become subject to the initial cracking moment. The slab never becomes completely cracked. The deflection curve gradually curves over towards the dashed line as cracks open.

When the reinforcing steel reaches the yield point, ϵ_s increases rapidly with small changes in load. The increasing steel deformation crowds the neutral axis upward at this section and brings about increasing concrete deformations and finally a secondary compression failure. For an ordinary simple span slab the difference between the load at yield point and the failure load will be only a few per cent, say, 5% or possibly 10%. The deflection before failure will be many times that at the first yielding of the steel. The total relative deflection will depend on the percentage of steel, the span, and the type of loading, but ten times the yield-point deflection would be quite usual. This deflection would be almost entirely due to the

REINFORCED CONCRETE FUNDAMENTALS

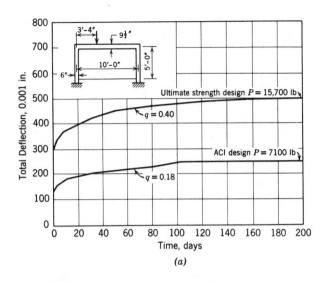

(a)

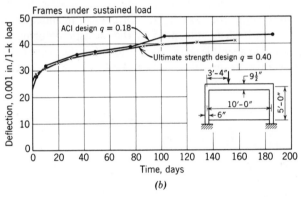

(b)

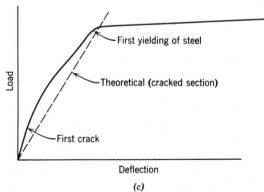

Deflection

(c)

Fig. A.8. Load-deflection curves. (*a*) Frames with varying steel ratio under long-time load. (*b*) Frame deflections per kip of load. (*c*) Simple span-slab deflection under increasing load.

DEFLECTIONS: AREA MOMENT METHOD

large angle change at the yielding section, the slab tending to fold about this point as though it constituted a stiff hinge.

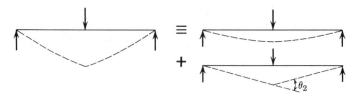

Fig. A.9. Beam deflection after a plastic hinge forms equals elastic deflection plus hinge deflection.

A.9. EFFECT OF INELASTIC ACTION

The calculation of deflections is more complex when inelastic action occurs. If the relation between moment and angle change is known, it is possible to calculate deflections by a summation process in which real $d\theta$ values are substituted for $(M\,ds)/EI$. Of course, in indeterminate structures the moment itself is influenced by the inelastic deformations.

When yielding in a simple span has developed to the point of establishing a hingelike section, as described in Sec. A.8f, the added deflection is due

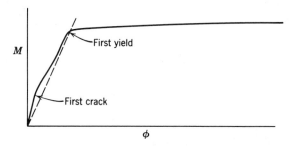

Fig. A.10. $M\text{-}\phi$ curve for unit length of moderately reinforced concrete slab.

almost entirely to the angle change occurring at this section, as shown in Fig. A.9. Except for the general uncertainties as to partially elastic action prior to yielding, the total deflection is easy to calculate for any given θ_2 value. If the load-deflection diagram became truly horizontal, θ_2 would increase indefinitely to failure. If, however, there is a definite relation known between M and the angle change ϕ per unit length, as in Fig. A.10,

REINFORCED CONCRETE FUNDAMENTALS

the simple beam moment diagram permits ϕ to be established for each section and particularly for those critical sections near the point of maximum moment, that is, at the so-called "plastic hinge" section.

In an indeterminate frame, the moments are modified by the yielding at any section. The calculation of deflections between yielding and failure points is thereby further complicated. In any case the yielding section is much like a hinge which refuses to accept a larger bending moment. For further load, the moment elsewhere on the member increases as though a real hinge existed at the yielding section. This action is sometimes called a redistribution of moment; actually only the added moment is distributed differently. There will be a relatively abrupt change of slope angle at each such "plastic hinge."

The moments between first yielding and final failure are not usually calculated because they are difficult to obtain and not essential to design. Just at failure or collapse the determination of moments is simpler. This is discussed briefly in Appendix C under the title of *limit design*.

The area moment theorems are restated in Ref. 1 in a manner consistent with inelastic and plastic hinge action.

A.10. MOMENT AND SHEAR DIAGRAMS FOR CONTINUOUS BEAMS

The combination and subdivision of moment diagrams as discussed in this section will often be helpful in connection with area moment calculations.

For any member as a whole or for any shorter length, the complete moment diagram can be constructed if one knows the loads and the end moments. In Fig. A.11a the uniformly loaded section is in equilibrium with the known end moments M_1 and M_2 and some necessary end shears. It is convenient to divide this system into two sets of forces (Fig. A.11b and c), each in equilibrium. The first set of forces represents the external loading without end moments, in effect, a simply supported span leading to the simple beam M and V diagrams as shown. The second set of forces consists of the end moments and the end shears necessary for their equilibrium. The end shears represent a constant shear from end to end, here designated as the continuity shear. The continuity shear can be calculated from the equilibrium of moments or from the slope of the moment diagram. The total moment is the sum of the moment ordinates for the two cases, as in Fig. A.11d. The total shear is similarly obtained and enables the point of zero shear and point of maximum moment to be established.

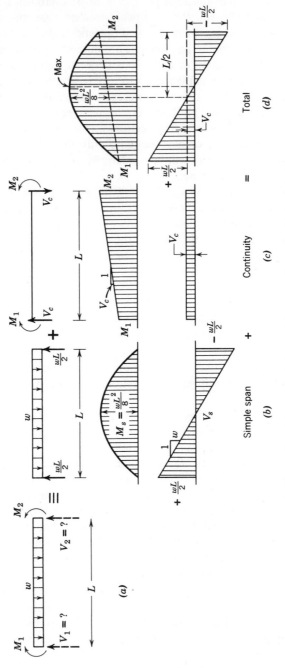

Fig. A.11. Moment and shear diagrams as the sum of two parts.

REINFORCED CONCRETE FUNDAMENTALS

It follows that if a chord is cut across any moment diagram, as in Fig. A.12, the portion above the chord has vertical ordinates which correspond exactly to those of a simple span moment diagram for a beam of length a. For a uniform load this small diagram is a parabola. It should be noted that the zero base line of the original moment diagram can also be considered as such a chord. It follows that the portion of the moment diagram above the base line is a symmetrical parabola with

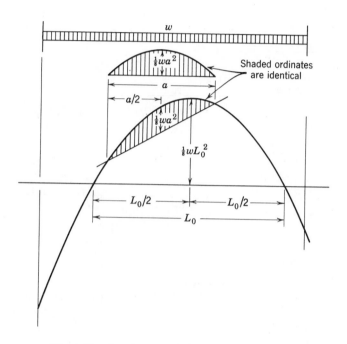

Fig. A.12. A segment is a simple beam diagram.

maximum ordinate $wL_0^2/8$, where L_0 is the distance between points of inflection. If the maximum positive moment is known, the points of inflection can be located easily as symmetrical distances each side of the point of maximum moment.

Example

Plot the moment and shear diagram for a 20-ft span carrying a uniform load of 3 klf and having $M_{AB} = -100$ k-ft, $M_{BA} = -50$ k-ft, as shown in Fig. A.13a.

DEFLECTIONS: AREA MOMENT METHOD   443

SOLUTION

The simple span has reactions of 30 k each, a maximum moment of $wL^2/8 = 3 \times 20^2/8 = +150$ k-ft, and end shears of $+30$ k and -30 k as shown in Fig. A.13a.

The end moments as loads require a positive V_c for equilibrium equal to $(100 - 50)/20 = +2.5$ k. This is also the slope of this part of the moment diagram (Fig. A.13b).

The two sets of M and V diagrams can be combined for the total.

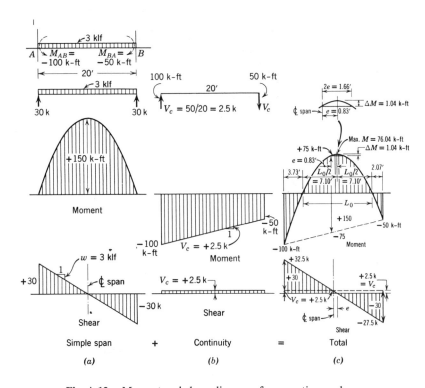

Fig. A.13. Moment and shear diagrams for a continuous beam.

It is just as simple to build this total diagram without sketching the separate diagrams in such detail. First, plot the end moments and complete this part of the moment diagram with a dashed line as shown in Fig. A.13c. The slope of this line is V_c, in this case, $+50/20 = +2.5$ k. This continuity shear can also be plotted as a dashed line for the start of the shear diagram. The simple beam moment diagram can be plotted as vertical ordinates from the sloping (dashed) continuity moment line as a base line. This gives an ordinate of $-75 + 150 = +75$ k-ft at mid-span. The slope of the moment diagram at mid-span is parallel to the dashed continuity moment line and the maximum moment obviously lies to the right of the mid-span. The shear diagram can also be completed by adding the simple beam shears to the dashed value of V_c. The point of maximum moment can be located at the point of zero shear, a distance e from mid-span. The small shear triangle at mid-span shows that $e = V_c/w = +2.5/3.0 = +0.83$ ft and the increase in moment over that at mid-span is given by the area of this triangle, that is, $\triangle M = 2.5 \times 0.83/2 = +1.04$ k-ft. Therefore the maximum moment is $+75$ (at mid-span) $+ 1.04 = 76.04$ k-ft. As an alternate, $\triangle M$ is the simple beam moment on a span of $2e$, that is, $\triangle M = w(2e)^2/8 = 3 \times 1.66^2/8 = +1.04$ k-ft.

The points of inflection are located by equating maximum positive moment to $wL_0^2/8$.

$$76.04 = \tfrac{1}{8} \times 3 \times L_0^2$$

$$L_0 = \sqrt{\frac{8 \times 76.04}{3}} = \sqrt{202.5} = 14.20 \text{ ft}$$

The points of inflection lie at $L_0/2 = 7.10$ ft to the right and left of the point of maximum moment.

SELECTED REFERENCES

1. Geo. C. Ernst, "Ultimate Slopes and Deflections—A Brief for Limit Design," *ASCE Proc.-Separate 583*, Jan. 1955.

2. Herbert A. Sawyer, Jr., "Elasti-Plastic Design of Single-Span Beams and Frames," *ASCE Proc.-Separate 851*, Dec. 1955.

3. G. W. Washa and P. G. Fluck, "Effect of Compressive Reinforcement on the Plastic Flow of Reinforced Concrete Beams," *ACI Jour.*, **24**, Oct. 1952; *Proc.*, **49**, p. 89.

4. G. W. Washa and P. G. Fluck, "Plastic Flow (Creep) of Reinforced Concrete Continuous Beams," *ACI Jour.*, **27**, Jan. 1956; *Proc.*, **52**, p. 549.

5. George A. Hool and W. S. Kinne, *Structural Members and Connections*, McGraw-Hill Book Co., New York, 2nd ed., Sec. 1.63, 1943.

PROBLEMS

Prob. A.1. An 8-in. I weighing 18.4 plf cantilevers 4 ft from a fixed end as shown in Fig. A.14. $I = 56.9$ in.^{4}, $E = 30 \times 10^6$ psi. If a couple M large enough to make $f_s = 20,000$ psi acts on the end of the beam, what will be the end slope in degrees? What will be the end deflection? Up or down?

Prob. A.2.

(a) If a concrete beam, as in Fig. A.15, has $f_c = 1350$ psi and $f_s = 20,000$ psi between the load points, what would be the slope of the beam under the left load

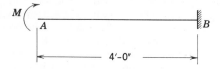

Fig. A.14.   Cantilever beam for Prob. A.1.

point, assuming $E_c = 3 \times 10^6$ psi, $E_s = 30 \times 10^6$ psi, and no complication from concrete carrying tension? (Note that unit stresses establish deformations.)

(b) If angle change per unit length were proportional to moment, what would be the slope at the left support?

(c) What would be the center deflection under the conditions of part (b)?

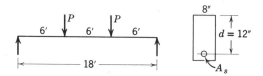

Fig. A.15.   Simple span beam for Prob. A.2.

Prob. A.3.   Calculate the fixed end moments on the constant section beams of Fig. A.16 using the area moment principles.

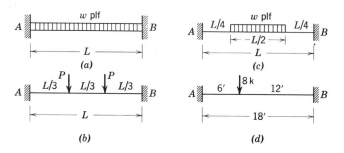

Fig. A.16.   Fixed end beams for Prob. A.3.

Prob. A.4.   By making use of area moments and the idea of Fig. A.12, calculate the deflection of point D of the beam of Fig. A.17, $E = 3 \times 10^6$ psi, $I = 4000$ in.⁴

Prob. A.5.   Calculate the deflection of the beam of Fig. A.13 at a point 12 ft to the right of A, assuming $I = 6000$ in.⁴ and $E = 3 \times 10^6$ psi. (*Suggestion:*

REINFORCED CONCRETE FUNDAMENTALS

The idea of Fig. A.12 should be used to get the area of the parts of the parabola. The separate moment diagrams of Fig. A.13a and b are probably simpler to use than the resultant moment.)

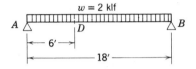

Fig. A.17. Simple span beam for Prob. A.4.

Prob. A.6. Find the deflection of points D and F on the beam of Fig. A.18 if $I = 3000$ in.^{4} and $E_c = 3.5 \times 10^6$ psi.

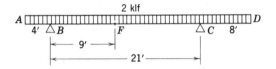

Fig. A.18. Beam with overhanging ends for Prob. A.6.

Prob. A.7.

(a) Use area moment ideas to establish M_A if the right support of the beam of Fig. A.19 settles 0.25 in., $I = 10,000$ in.^{4}, $E = 3 \times 10^6$ psi.

(b) If the loading is on a long-time basis and the settlement takes place slowly such that effective $E = 1 \times 10^6$ psi, calculate a new value of M_A.

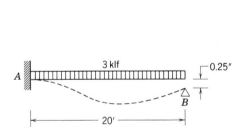

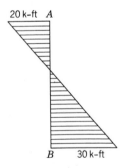

Fig. A.19. Beam with settlement at B, for Prob. A.7.

Fig. A.20. Moment diagram for column AB, Prob. A.8.

Prob. A.8. Calculate the mid-point deflection of a column (to right or left?) when it carries the bending moment shown in Fig. A.20 and the ends do not

DEFLECTIONS: AREA MOMENT METHOD

move laterally. The moment value has been plotted on the compression face of the member; that is, compression is on the right face of the column at B. $I = 2000$ in.^{4}, $E = 2.5 \times 10^6$ psi, $h = 12$ ft.

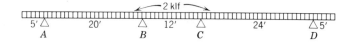

Fig. A.21. Continuous beam for Prob. A.9.

Prob. A.9. Plot the moment and shear diagrams for the beam of Fig. A.21, using the methods of Sec. A.10, $M_A = -25$ k-ft, $M_B = -51.1$ k-ft, $M_c = -91.1$ k-ft, $M_D = -25$ k-ft. Determine the maximum moments and points of inflection in each span.

REINFORCED CONCRETE FUNDAMENTALS

Frame Analysis:
Moment Distribution

B.1. THE GENERAL PROCESS OF MOMENT DISTRIBUTION

Moment distribution is a method of analysis for frames in the elastic range which was originated by Professor Hardy Cross and is often referred to as the Hardy Cross method. It involves a series of simple steps taken in sequence such that the moments shown to be acting on the several joints approach closer and closer to the true values resulting from the given loads. Since the calculated moments converge (usually rapidly) on the true moments, any degree of accuracy desired is obtainable.

Consider the frame in Fig. B.1a with lateral movement of all joints prevented, that is, with no sidesway. It is assumed that each joint holds the members at fixed angles to each other and that any rotation of a joint requires all attached members to rotate through the same angle. This means the joints are rigid compared to the stiffness of the members.

449

The moment distribution process follows these steps:

1. Lock or clamp all joints in their unloaded position. Temporarily, this fixes every member at each end.

2. Calculate and record the fixed end moments due to loads, that is, the moments at each end of each member. With the ends fixed, this calculation is relatively simple. Unloaded members have zero fixed end moment.

3. Unlock or unclamp one set of alternate joints. Where unbalanced fixed end moments exist, joints will rotate until they build up resisting moments in adjacent members sufficient to bring them into equilibrium. It should be noted that this release of alternate joints forms a checkerboard

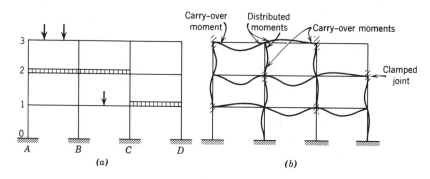

Fig. B.1. Joint rotations with alternate joints clamped.

pattern with each rotating joint surrounded by members having their far ends still fixed at locked joints, as shown in Fig. B.1*b*.

4. Write the distributed moments around each rotating joint, that is, the changes in end moments necessary to bring the joint into equilibrium. Each member framing into the joint shares in the distributed moment.

5. Write the carry-over moments, that is, the changes in moments that occur at the far (fixed) ends of each member because of the above joint rotations. These are directly related to the distributed moments at the rotating ends.

6. Now relock or reclamp this first set of alternate joints in their rotated or equilibrium positions.

7. Unlock or release the other set of alternate joints. These will rotate to equilibrium under the combined influence of fixed end moments and such carry-over moments as have already been developed there.

8. Write distributed moments for all members at these rotating joints and the carry-over moments at the far ends of such members.

REINFORCED CONCRETE FUNDAMENTALS

9. Again lock or clamp this second set of alternate joints in these equilibrium positions.

10. Release the first set of joints, which will now rotate again under the influence of the moments carried over to them in step 8. Write distributed moments at the rotating joints and carry-over moments out at the fixed ends. Then clamp this set of joints in its equilibrium position.

11. Release the second set of joints and continue the process until the unbalanced moments are negligible (for the accuracy desired).

12. At each end of each member add the original fixed end moment and all subsequent distributed moments and carry-over moments, with due regard to signs. The total is the final moment for this end of the member.

It will be noted that one requires for this process:

1. Fixed end moments for various loadings (Sec. B.2).

2. Distribution factors, to establish the proper allotment of distributed moment to each adjacent member when a joint rotates (Sec. B.6).

3. Carry-over factors, to establish the moment at the fixed end of a member when the joint at the other end is rotated (Sec. B.3).

4. The stiffness of each member, as a step in establishing the distribution factors in item 2 (Sec. B.4).

It is also helpful to have:

5. A convenient set of signs for moments (Sec. B.5).

6. A convenient form for tabulating the various moments acting at each end of each member (Sec. B.7).

B.2. FIXED END MOMENTS

Fixed end moments can be calculated from deflection methods such as the area moment relations or from the three moment equations. Many handbooks tabulate them for a variety of loads. A few cases, for uniform I and E, are given in Fig. B.2. The following symbols are all in use: $M_{AB}{}^{F}$, $M_{f,AB}$, F.E.M., F.

B.3. CARRY-OVER FACTOR

The beam AB of Fig. B.3 is fixed at A and supported, but free to rotate, at B. Assume that a moment M_B acts at B, rotating the end of the beam and setting up bending moments M_{AB} and M_{BA} *in the beam* at A and B. Since the shear is constant from A to B, the moment diagram is a straight line. It is sketched as though both M_{AB} and M_{BA} were positive, even though the sketch of the elastic curve indicates a negative value at A.*

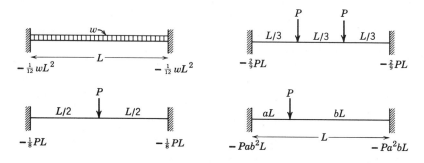

Fig. B.2. Fixed end moment values, signs according to beam bending moments.

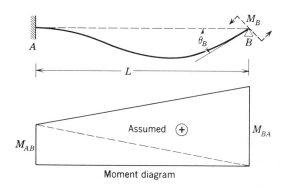

Fig. B.3. Assumed moments for rotation at one end.

Since the vertical deflection of B from the tangent at A is zero, and EI is constant,

$$t_{BA} = \frac{1}{EI} \text{(moment abt. } B \text{ of area of } M \text{ diag. betw. } A \text{ and } B)$$

$$= \frac{1}{EI} (\tfrac{1}{2} M_{AB} L \tfrac{2}{3} L + \tfrac{1}{2} M_{BA} L \tfrac{1}{3} L) = 0$$

* Errors in signs are more easily avoided if all unknown algebraic quantities are assumed as positive when writing equilibrium equations. The solution of the equation will indicate by a negative sign those quantities assumed incorrectly.

REINFORCED CONCRETE FUNDAMENTALS

$$2M_{AB} + M_{BA} = 0$$

$$M_{AB} = -M_{BA}/2 \quad \text{(beam or bending moment signs)}$$

The moment M_{AB} developed or carried over to the far end of the beam is thus equal to $\frac{1}{2}M_{BA}$ but of opposite sign. This moment is called the *carry-over moment* (C.O.M.). The ratio $M_{AB}/M_{BA} = -\frac{1}{2}$ is called the *carry-over factor* (C.O.F.). The sign is modified later to fit new joint signs (Sec. B.5).

B.4. STIFFNESS OF A BEAM

Consider further the beam of Fig. B.3 and evaluate θ_B for the given M_B and for $M_{AB} = -M_{BA}/2$, as found in the foregoing section.

$$\theta_B = \frac{1}{EI}(\text{area of } M \text{ diag. betw. } A \text{ and } B)$$

$$= \frac{1}{EI}(\text{average ordinate of } M \text{ diag.})L$$

$$= \frac{1}{EI}\frac{M_{BA} + M_{AB}}{2}L = \frac{L}{2EI}(M_{BA} - M_{BA}/2)$$

$$= M_{BA}\frac{L}{4EI}$$

$$M_{BA} = 4E\theta_B I/L = 4E\theta_B K, \quad \text{where } K = I/L$$

The size of this moment measures the resistance of the beam to rotation at end B, that is, how stiff it is. *The stiffness of a beam* fixed at the far end is defined as the ratio M_{BA}/θ_B, or stiffness $= 4EK$.

It will be noted later that in most cases only relative stiffness is required. For such cases K is just as useful a measure of stiffness as $4EK$. Thus K is often referred to as the stiffness of the member, although actually it is only the *relative* stiffness.

B.5. SIGN CONVENTION FOR MOMENT DISTRIBUTION—JOINT SIGNS

Ordinary bending moment signs are useful in describing a beam because *plus* always means compression in the top, and *minus* always means tension in the top. Such a sign convention is essential to drawing a moment diagram and designing a beam. It is the only convention usable with the area moment method of calculating deflections.

In frame analysis, however, the determination of the moments is simpler if one deals entirely with the moments exerted by the various members *on*

Positive
joint moments

Negative
joint moments

Fig. B.4. Signs for joint moments.

the joints; and for these, joint signs are recommended. (The final joint moments must eventually be interpreted in terms of the usual bending moment signs to make them usable for M diagrams and design purposes.) For joint moments in frame analysis the following convention is recommended:

> When the moment a member exerts *on a joint tends* to rotate the *joint* in a clockwise direction, this joint moment is designated as positive; when it tends to rotate the joint in a counterclockwise direction the joint moment is negative, as indicated in Fig. B.4.

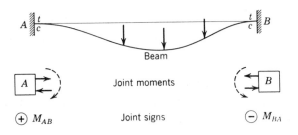

Beam

A Joint moments B

$\oplus M_{AB}$ Joint signs $\ominus M_{BA}$

Fig. B.5. Joint signs for fixed end moments.

Under the usual vertical loads, a fixed-ended beam has a negative *bending* moment at each end, producing tension in the top of the beam, as indicated in Fig. B.5. The moment at A tends to rotate the joint clockwise, making M_{AB} positive by joint signs. Likewise, the moment at B

tends to rotate the joint counterclockwise, making M_{BA} negative by joint signs.

Consider now the carry-over relationship found above, which for bending moment signs is $M_{AB} = -M_{BA}/2$. For the beam of Fig. B.3, the bending moments and joint moments have the signs indicated in Fig. B.6. Since in joint signs a positive M_{BA} causes a positive M_{AB}, the relation becomes

$$M_{AB} = M_{BA}/2 \quad \text{(joint signs)}$$

The carry-over factor is thus *plus* one-half for joint signs.

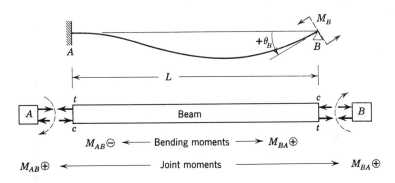

Fig. B.6. Joint moment signs for a member rotated at one end.

For moments at the right end of a beam, bending moment signs and joint moment signs are identical; but at the left end of the beam the signs disagree.

If θ_B is considered positive when counterclockwise (as in trigonometry), a positive θ causes a positive joint moment to be built up, as shown in Fig. B.6. Thus the relation between M_{BA} and θ_B is

$$M_{BA} = +4EK\theta_B \quad \text{(joint signs)}$$

This relation holds whether the member is on the right or left of the joint. (For bending moment signs, the sign may be either positive or negative, depending upon whether the beam is to the left or right of the joint.)

The following sections use joint signs for all moment distribution calculations.*

* Nevertheless the student must understand that these signs are for moment distribution only. The final moments must be reinterpreted in terms of beam bending moment signs before moment diagrams can be drawn and the beams designed.

B.6. DISTRIBUTION FACTORS

Consider a counterclockwise (negative) moment M_0 applied to joint B of Fig. B.7, causing the ends of all the members framing into the joint to rotate through a counterclockwise (positive) angle θ_B. Since the joint is assumed to maintain fixed angles between its members, all members rotate through the same angle. This counterclockwise rotation is resisted by clockwise moments (positive joint sign) developed by each member at

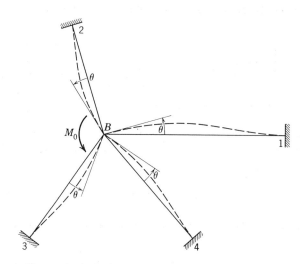

Fig. B.7. Joint rotated by moment M_0.

B. Such resisting moments increase with θ_B until the joint ceases to rotate farther, at which time the equilibrium equation becomes:

$$M_0 + M_{B1} + M_{B2} + M_{B3} + \cdots = 0$$

or

$$\sum_0^n M_B = -M_0$$

It has been established in Art. B.4 that

$$M_{B1} = +4EK_1\theta_B, \qquad M_{B2} = +4EK_2\theta_B, \cdots$$

$$\sum_0^n M_B = +4E\theta_B\sum_0^n K = -M_0$$

$$\theta_B = -M_0/(4E\sum_0^n K)$$

REINFORCED CONCRETE FUNDAMENTALS

Substituting this value of θ_B in the above equations:

$$M_{B1} = +4EK_1\theta_B = -M_0 \left(\frac{K_1}{\sum\limits_{0}^{n} K} \right)$$

$$M_{B2} = +4EK_2\theta_B = -M_0 \left(\frac{K_2}{\sum\limits_{0}^{n} K} \right), \cdots$$

All the distributed moments (D.M.) thus carry the same sign, opposite to that of the unbalanced joint moment M_0. The ratio $K/\Sigma K$ is called the distribution factor (D.F.). It is obvious that only relative values of K are required in order to determine distribution factors.

Although the foregoing relation for distributed moment is in the most usable form, it is helpful to note that the moment is distributed to the beams in direct proportion to their stiffnesses, that is,

$$\frac{M_{B1}}{M_{B2}} = \frac{K_1}{K_2}, \cdots$$

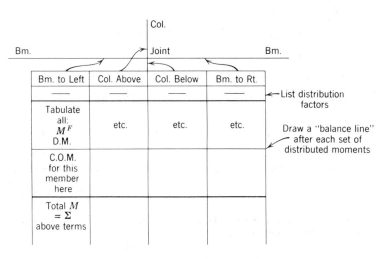

Fig. B.8. Standard tabulation form for each joint.

B.7. TABULATION FORM

Moment distribution calculations can best be superimposed on a skeleton picture of the frame, grouping the moments around the joints where they apply. For this purpose the skeleton frame need not be to scale.

The Portland Cement Association has used a tabulation form at each joint which has great merit. Its use as an arbitrary standard form should be unvarying. Figure B.8 shows this form superimposed on a typical joint.

B.8. EXAMPLES OF MOMENT DISTRIBUTION— BASIC PROCESS

(a) Alternate joint procedure

Find the joint moments for the continuous beam of Fig. B.9a.

SOLUTION

Fixed end moments (signs are obtained from the joint sketches in Fig. B.9a):

$$M_{AB}{}^F = +Pab^2L = +40 \times \tfrac{8}{20} \times (\tfrac{12}{20})^2 \times 20 = +115.2 \text{ k-ft}$$

$$M_{BA}{}^F = -Pa^2bL = -40 \times (\tfrac{8}{20})^2 \times \tfrac{12}{20} \times 20 = -76.8 \text{ k-ft}$$

$$M_{BC}{}^F = +\tfrac{1}{12}wL^2 = +\tfrac{1}{12} \times 2 \times (25)^2 = +104.2 \text{ k-ft}$$

$$M_{CB}{}^F = -\tfrac{1}{12}wL^2 = -104.2 \text{ k-ft}$$

$$M_{CD}{}^F = +\tfrac{1}{2}wL^2 = +\tfrac{1}{2} \times 2 \times 6^2 = +36 \text{ k-ft}$$

Distribution factors:

Joint A: Since the fixed end at A is infinitely stiff, no rotation occurs and no D.F. is needed for the beam. Technically, beam D.F. $= \dfrac{I/L}{\infty + I/L} = 0$.

Joint B:

	K	Rel. K	D.F.
BA	$I_{AB}/20$	1.00	$1.00/2.60 = 0.384$
BC	$I_{BC}/25 = 2I_{AB}/25$	1.60	$1.60/2.60 = 0.616$
	$\Sigma K = 2.60$		ΣD.F. $= 1.000$

Joint C: The stiffness of a cantilever overhang is zero, since this length does not *resist* any rotation about C.

	K	D.F.
CD	0	0
CB	$I_{BC}/25$	1.00

The moment distribution is carried out in Fig. B.9b, with successive steps shown on separate lines. (The more usual form is shown in Fig. B.9c.) Since there are no vertical members, the form of Fig. B.8 becomes somewhat simplified. The choice of which set of alternate joints to unlock and balance first is arbitrary. Usually the convergence is more rapid if the set with the largest unbalances is used first.

REINFORCED CONCRETE FUNDAMENTALS

The initial unbalance at C is $-104.2 + 36.0 = -68.2$; therefore $+68.2$ is distributed, in this case entirely to CB because of the D.F. of 1.00. Half of this distributed moment is carried over to BC with the sign unchanged. The fixed end at joint A gives no rotation nor distribution.

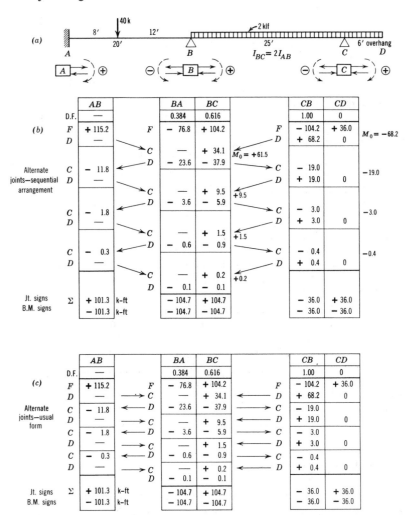

Fig. B.9. Alternate joint procedure in moment distribution.

Joints A and C are next locked and B is released. The unbalanced moment of $-76.8 + 104.2 + 34.1 = +61.5$ is distributed $-0.384 \times 61.5 = -23.6$ to BA and $-0.616 \times 61.5 = -37.9$ to BC. Half of these distributed moments are carried over to the far ends of members.

The process is continued until the carry-over moments are negligible or small enough to neglect for the accuracy desired. The columns are totaled to obtain final moments (joint signs). These must then be changed into beam or bending moment signs.

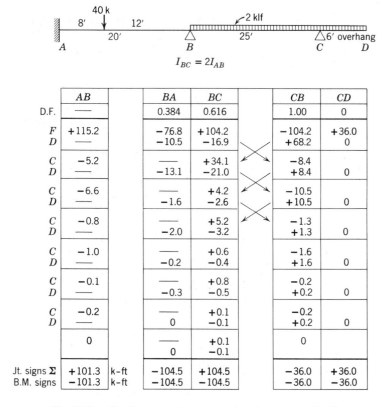

Fig. B.10. Simultaneous release procedure in moment distribution.

(b) Simultaneous joint release

The same results are obtained by a slightly different sequence of calculations which many prefer. In this sequence the distributions are first made at all joints (with the distribution factors unchanged) as though all joints were simultaneously released. The carry-over moments which occur simultaneously are not written until all these distributed moments have been calculated and recorded. Then all carry-over moments are written, another complete distribution is made, another set of carry-over moments, and so forth. This sequence eliminates the need for keeping track of

REINFORCED CONCRETE FUNDAMENTALS

alternate joints, but is often slightly slower in converging. Figure B.10 shows this solution form for the same problem.

(c) Example with vertical members

Find the joint moments in the double box frame of Fig. B.11 subject to the loads shown. Consider I as constant and any sidesway prevented.

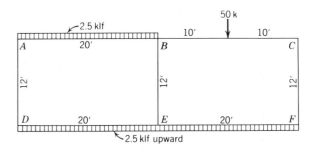

Fig. B.11. Moment distribution problem with vertical members.

SOLUTION

For AB, DE, and EF, $M^F = \frac{1}{12}wL^2 = \frac{1}{12} \times 2.5 \times (20)^2 = \pm\ 83.3$ k-ft.

For BC, $M^F = \frac{1}{8}PL = \frac{1}{8} \times 50 \times 20 = \pm 125$ k-ft.

Corner joints:

	K	Rel. K	D.F.
Beam	$I/20$	1.00	0.375
Wall	$I/12$	1.67	0.625
	$\Sigma = 2.67$	1.000

Center joints:

	K	Rel. K	D.F.
Beam	$I/20$	1.00	0.272
Beam	$I/20$	1.00	0.272
Wall	$I/12$	1.67	0.456
	$\Sigma = 3.67$	1.000

Figure B.12 shows the solution carried out until the unbalance appears to be negligible. It should be noted that, with this form, carry-over moments on vertical members are always from lower left to upper right, or upper right to lower left in columns of data adjacent to the vertical member. No carry-over moves from second to fourth quadrant or from fourth to second. The blank columns can be omitted from the tabulation completely if desired, as illustrated in Fig. B.20.

A   B   C

	AD	AB		BA		BE	BC		CB		CF	
	0.625	0.375		0.272		0.456	0.272		0.375		0.625	
F	0	+83.3		−83.3		0	+125.0		−125.0		0	
D	−52.0	−31.3		−11.4		−19.0	−11.3		+46.7		+78.3	
C	+26.0	−5.7		−15.6		0	+23.4		−5.6		−26.0	
D	−12.7	−7.6		−2.1		−3.6	−2.1		+11.8		+19.8	
C	+8.1	−1.0		−3.8		+2.2	+5.9		−1.0		−12.3	
D	−4.4	−2.7		−1.1		−2.0	−1.2		+5.0		+8.3	
C	+1.6	−0.6		−1.4		+1.0	+2.5		−0.6		−3.5	
D	−0.6	−0.4		−0.6		−0.9	−0.6		+1.5		+2.6	
C	+0.5	−0.3		−0.2		+0.4	+0.8		−0.3		−1.5	
D	−0.1	−0.1		−0.3		−0.4	−0.3		+0.7		+1.1	
C	0	−0.2		0		+0.2	+0.4		−0.2		−0.5	
D	+0.1	+0.1		−0.2		−0.2	−0.2		+0.3		+0.4	
Jt. Σ	−33.5	+33.5		−120.0		−22.3	+142.3		−66.7		+66.7	
B.M.	−33.5	−33.5		−120.0		−22.3	−142.3		−66.7		+66.7	

D   E   F

	DA		DE		ED	EB		EF		FE	FC	
	0.625		0.375		0.272	0.456		0.272		0.375	0.625	
F	0		−83.3		+83.3	0		−83.3		+83.3	0	
D	+52.0		+31.3		0	0		0		−31.3	−52.0	
C	−26.0		0		+15.6	−9.5		−15.6		0	+39.2	
D	+16.2		+9.8		+2.6	+4.3		+2.6		−14.7	−24.5	
C	−6.4		+1.3		+4.9	−1.8		−7.4		+1.3	+9.9	
D	+3.2		+1.9		+1.2	+2.0		+1.1		−4.2	−7.0	
C	−2.2		+0.6		+1.0	−1.0		−2.1		+0.6	+4.2	
D	+1.0		+0.6		+0.6	+0.9		+0.6		−1.8	−3.0	
C	−0.3		+0.3		+0.3	−0.4		−0.9		+0.3	+1.3	
D	0		0		+0.3	+0.4		+0.3		−0.6	−1.0	
C	0		+0.2		0	−0.2		−0.3		+0.2	+0.6	
D	−0.1		−0.1		+0.1	+0.3		+0.1		−0.3	−0.5	
Σ	+37.4		−37.4		+109.9	−5.0		−104.9		+32.8	−32.8	
B.M.	−37.4		+37.4		+109.9	+5.0		+104.9		+32.8	+32.8	

For bending moment signs on vertical members: View from right side.

Fig. B.12. Solution of frame of Fig. B.11 using simultaneous joint releases.

B.9. PIN ENDS AND ENDS WITH MOMENTS STATICALLY DETERMINED

(a) Simplified procedure

The convergence in the example of Figs. B.9 and B.10 is slow because the distribution factor is 1.00 at joint C. A slight modification of the general procedure may be used to shorten this process. This modification

REINFORCED CONCRETE FUNDAMENTALS

consists of leaving joint C unlocked throughout the process and modifying the fixed end moments, stiffness factors, and carry-over moments as necessary to agree with this condition.

(b) Modified fixed end moments

Modified end moments for member BC are needed for B fixed and C not fixed, and this automatically involves member CD as well. These moments can be established by a simple (separate) moment distribution as shown in Fig. B.13. The first line of fixed end moments is the same as in Fig. B.9. The release of C establishes the moments needed for starting

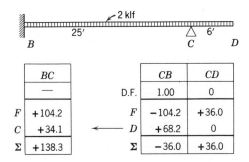

Fig. B.13. Modified fixed end moment with far end statically determinate.

the analysis with joint C unlocked. The author sometimes uses the notation $M_{BC}{}^{FH}$ for this modified moment.

For beams without overhangs, handbooks show these modified moments for many loadings. However, the above process is so simple that a handbook is not necessary.

(c) Modified stiffness

The overhang CD does not affect the moment required to rotate end B of beam BC, either with joint C fixed or not fixed. The modified stiffness can be established by another simple moment distribution. Sections B.3 and B.4 established the stiffness with far end fixed as $4EK$. In Fig. B.14, C is first considered fixed as B is rotated to give $M_{BC}{}^{F} = +4EK\theta_B$ and a carry-over moment $M_{CB}{}^{F} = +2EK\theta_B$. When joint C is released, the final moment at B becomes $+3EK\theta_B$ and the modified stiffness is $M_{BC}/\theta_B = +3EK$. This is three-fourths of the stiffness with end C fixed. Hence, when relative stiffness is used, the modified value may be taken as $\frac{3}{4}(I/L)$.

Obviously, this relationship applies to all pin end members as well as to those with overhangs. It is not limited to this particular example.

(d) Carry-over moment

When the far joint is never locked, its moment remains statically determined. The joint thus receives *no* carry-over moment as a result of rotations at the other end of the beam.

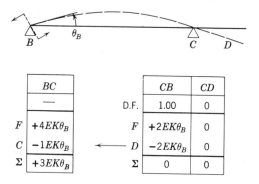

	BC			CB	CD
	—		D.F.	1.00	0
F	$+4EK\theta_B$		F	$+2EK\theta_B$	0
C	$-1EK\theta_B$	←	D	$-2EK\theta_B$	0
Σ	$+3EK\theta_B$		Σ	0	0

Fig. B.14. Stiffness with far end hinged or on knife edge.

(e) Final solution of example of Sec. B.8a

In Fig. B.15, the fixed end moments for member AB are taken from the original solution and those for BCD from Sec. B.9b. New distribution factors must be calculated at B:

	K	Rel. K	D.F.
BA	$I_{AB}/20$	1.00	0.455
BC	$\dfrac{3}{4}\dfrac{I_{BC}}{25} = \dfrac{3}{4}\dfrac{2I_{AB}}{25}$	1.20	0.545
		$\Sigma K = 2.20$	1.000

This solution is unusually short because only one joint must rotate to equilibrium.

(f) Example with columns

Find the joint moments for the frame of Fig. B.16.

REINFORCED CONCRETE FUNDAMENTALS

SOLUTION

All members except BC, CD, and CJ are pinned at their outer ends. Hence the modified stiffness procedure with joints A, F, G, and H remaining unlocked will be much shorter.

$$I_{BC} = 2I_{AB}$$

	AB		BA	BC		CB	CD
	—		0.455	0.545		—	—
F	+115.2	F	−76.8	+138.3	F	−36.0	+36.0
C	−14.0	← D	−27.9	−33.6	---→		
Σ	+101.2	Σ	−104.7	+104.7	No C.O.M. for a		
					$\frac{3}{4}\frac{I}{L}$ member		

Fig. B.15. Example showing use of modified stiffness and modified end moments. The solution is unusually short, as noted in text.

Fixed end moments (and modified values):

$$M_{AB}^F = +Pab^2L = +40 \times \tfrac{8}{20} \times (\tfrac{12}{20})^2 \times 20 = +115.2 \text{ k-ft}$$
$$M_{BA}^F = -Pa^2bL = -40 \times (\tfrac{8}{20})^2 \times \tfrac{12}{20} \times 20 = -76.8 \text{ k-ft}$$

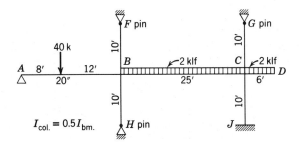

Fig. B.16. Frame to illustrate modified stiffness.

These are modified in Fig. B.17a to $M_{AB} = 0$ and $M_{BA}^{FH} = -134.4$ k-ft

$$M_{BC}^F = +\tfrac{1}{12}wL^2 = +\tfrac{1}{12} \times 2 \times (25)^2 = +104.2 \text{ k-ft}$$
$$M_{CB}^F = -\tfrac{1}{12}wL^2 = -104.2 \text{ k-ft}$$
$$M_{CD}^F = +\tfrac{1}{2}wL^2 = +\tfrac{1}{2} \times 2 \times 6^2 = +36 \text{ k-ft}$$

Distribution factors:

Joint A: none.

Joint B:

	K	Rel. K	D.F.
BA	$0.75I/20$	0.75	0.246
BF	$0.75 \times 0.5I/10$	0.75	0.246
BC	$I/25$	0.80	0.262
BH	$0.75 \times 0.5I/10$	0.75	0.246
		$\Sigma K = 3.05$	1.000

Joint C:

CB	$I/25$	0.80	0.313
CG	$0.75 \times 0.5I/10$	0.75	0.294
CD	0	0	0
CJ	$0.5I/10$	1.00	0.393
		$\Sigma K = 2.55$	1.000

The final solution is shown in Fig. B.17b. Advantage has been taken of the fact that joint J does not rotate to make one total carry-over of the distributed moments at CJ rather than several individual carry-over operations.

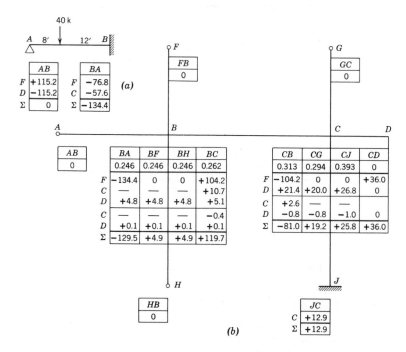

Fig. B.17. Solution of frame of Fig. B.16.

REINFORCED CONCRETE FUNDAMENTALS

B.10. MEMBERS OF VARIABLE CROSS SECTION

For members of variable cross section, the fixed end moments are different, the stiffness is greater than $4EI_0/L$ (where I_0 is the minimum I), and the carry-over factor is different from 0.5. Unless the member is symmetrical about mid-span, the stiffness and carry-over factors are different from each end of the member. However, the procedures of moment distribution are unchanged for frames containing such members, as in the analysis of Sec. 11.3 and especially Figs. 11.24 and 11.25.

The constants for fixed end moment, stiffness, and carry-over factor for many variable section members are tabulated in the Portland Cement Association pamphlet "Handbook of Frame Constants."[9]

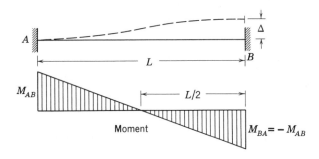

Fig. B.18. Moments due to joint movement perpendicular to member axis.

B.11. FIXED END MOMENTS FOR DEFLECTION OF JOINTS

Consider the beam AB of Fig. B.18, with constant I, deflected upward a distance Δ at B, but without any joint rotation. The moment diagram is a straight line, since the shear is constant. Since there is no angle change from A to B, the net area of the M/EI diagram is zero and this requires that $M_{AB} = -M_{BA}$ (bending moment signs). Thus the M diagram must be that of Fig. B.18. By the area moment principle,

$$\Delta = \frac{1}{EI}(\text{moment abt. } B \text{ of } M \text{ diag. from } A \text{ to } B)$$

$$= \frac{1}{IE}\left(\frac{M_{AB}}{2}\frac{L}{2}\frac{5}{6}L + \frac{M_{BA}}{2}\frac{L}{2}\frac{L}{6}\right)$$

$$= \frac{1}{EI}\left(\frac{5}{24}M_{AB}L^2 - \frac{1}{24}M_{AB}L^2\right) = \frac{1}{EI}\frac{M_{AB}L^2}{6}$$

$$M_{AB} = +6EI\ \Delta/L^2 = +6EK\ \Delta/L$$
$$M_{BA} = -M_{AB} = -6EK\ \Delta/L \quad \} \quad \text{Bending moment signs}$$

$$M_{AB} = M_{BA} = -6EK\ \Delta/L \quad \text{Joint signs}$$

Here Δ is positive when it "rotates" the member in counterclockwise fashion as shown. It should be noted that this relation requires absolute or real values of E and K, not the relative values which are often used elsewhere.

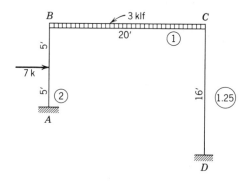

Fig. B.19. Frame where sidesway is significant.

B.12. FRAMES WITH SIDESWAY

For frames carrying lateral load and for many frames under vertical load, sidesway cannot be ignored. Generally, this sidesway effect must be calculated in a separate operation. The general procedure will be developed on the basis of a numerical example.

Consider the frame of Fig. B.19 with all members of equal I. The relative stiffness of members is indicated in a circle alongside each.

The effect of loads between joints, with sidesway prevented, will be considered first, as Case I. This requires an external holding force at B or C, called a restraining force. By the method presented here, the magnitude of this restraining force is of no interest. Figure B.20a shows the distribution for Case I.

Without the restraining force at C, the frame would sway, probably to the right (but it is not necessary to know the direction). When the correct amount of sway is added, the frame will be in equilibrium without any external restraints. The correct sway moments might be calculated separately and added as indicated diagrammatically in Fig. B.21a. As an

REINFORCED CONCRETE FUNDAMENTALS

alternate, and a more practical one, the frame might be given an arbitrary sway Δ, and the equilibrium statement could then be that X parts of these

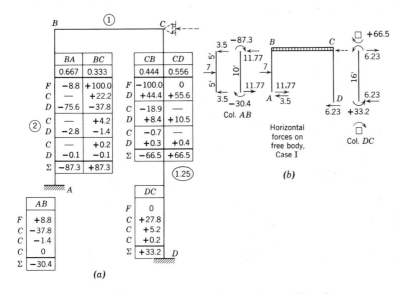

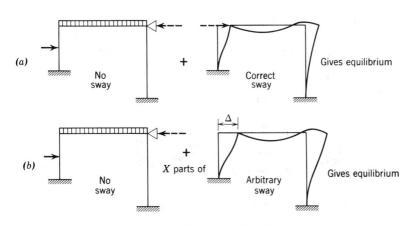

Fig. B.20. Frame solution without sidesway (Case I).

(a)

No sway $+$ Correct sway Gives equilibrium

(b)

No sway $+$ X parts of Arbitrary sway Gives equilibrium

Fig. B.21. Corrections for sidesway.

arbitrary sway moments would put the frame in equilibrium, as diagrammed in Fig. B.21b. In either case the correct sway moments must be established from an equilibrium equation of statics, in this case, $\Sigma F_x = 0$.

FRAME ANALYSIS: MOMENT DISTRIBUTION 469

In Fig. B.22a the moment distribution (Case II) for an arbitrary side-sway, enough to make $M_{AB}{}^F = M_{BA}{}^F = -1000$ k-ft, has been completed. A sway to the left, contrary to the apparent real movement, has been used to indicate that one is not required to know the direction of sway.

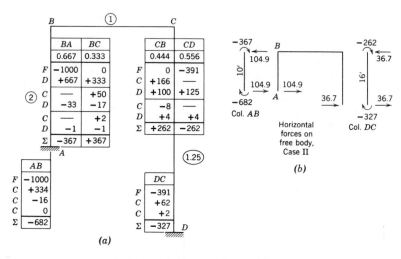

Fig. B.22. Arbitrary sidesway (Case II).

For E, I, and Δ in foot units:

$$M_{AB}{}^F = -6EK\,\Delta/L = -6E\frac{I}{10} \times \frac{\Delta}{10} = -1000 \text{ k-ft}$$

$$M_{DC}{}^F = -6E\,\frac{I}{16} \times \frac{\Delta}{16}$$

$$\frac{M_{DC}{}^F}{-1000} = \frac{-6E\dfrac{I}{16} \times \dfrac{\Delta}{16}}{-6E\dfrac{I}{10} \times \dfrac{\Delta}{10}} = \frac{1/256}{1/100} = \frac{100}{256}$$

$$M_{DC}{}^F = -391 \text{ k-ft}$$

The equilibrium equation $\Sigma F_x = 0$ will now be applied to the entire frame as a free body. Figure $B.20b$ shows the horizontal forces for Case I, omitting vertical and moment reactions which are not required for this equation. Note that the end shears on CD form a couple to balance the end moments such that $V_{DC} = V_{CD} = (M_{CD} + M_{DC})/L$, using the *joint*

REINFORCED CONCRETE FUNDAMENTALS

signs for moments.   Likewise, the shear on AB is the simple beam shear plus

$$V_{AB1} = (M_{AB} + M_{BA})/L = (-30.4 - 87.3)/10 = -11.77 \text{ k}$$

Similarly, in Fig. B.22b for Case II:

$$V_{AB} = (-367 - 682)/10 = -104.9 \text{ k}$$

$$V_{DC} = (-262 - 327)/16 = -36.7 \text{ k}$$

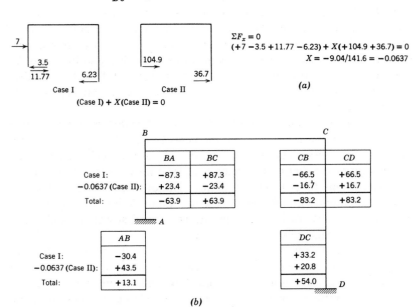

Fig. B.23.   Final moment determination for frame of Figs. B.19, B.20, and B.22.

Figure B.23a shows the forces finally used in the equilibrium equation:

$$(\text{Case I}) + X(\text{Case II}) = 0$$

Based on horizontal forces, this becomes

$$(+7 - 3.5 + 11.77 - 6.23) + X(+104.9 + 36.7) = 0$$

$$X = -9.04/141.6 = -0.0637$$

The final shears, moments, reactions, and so forth, are each given as (Case I) $+ X$ (Case II) values, that is, as (Case I) $- 0.0637$ (Case II) values.   Moments calculated on this basis are tabulated in Fig. B.23b.

In multiple story structures sidesway involves simultaneous equations or an entirely different procedure. It is fortunate that sidesway is not very significant in multibay frames under vertical loads. It must, of course, be considered wherever wind force analysis is required.

B.13. ELASTIC ANALYSIS AND REINFORCED CONCRETE

The preceding discussion of moment distribution has assumed that all members remain within their elastic range. With reinforced concrete members, however, elastic conditions do not exist. There is not only some uncertainty as to effective beam stiffness, as discussed in Sec. A.8b, but in addition ultimate strength design (Chap. 3) frankly considers yielding of the reinforcing steel not as failure, but as an approach to maximum strength.

The ASCE-ACI Joint Committee Report on ultimate strength design[11, 12] accepts the inconsistency of using moments based on elastic action with the design of cross sections based on yielding of the steel. This is tacit recognition of the fact that a frame is at least no weaker after one of its members begins to yield at one point. Although this is true, it is not entirely apparent without some analysis. Limit design, in Appendix C, considers the behavior of beams and frames after first yielding and shows that the above statement is conservative.

The best reinforced concrete design practice at the present time uses moments based on elastic analysis. However, attention is called to the fact that ultimate strength design is based on load factors which, in effect, increase the ratio of live to dead load. An elastic analysis for these ultimate loads slightly increases the resulting maximum moment coefficients.

SELECTED REFERENCES

1. Hardy Cross and Newlin D. Morgan, *Continuous Frames of Reinforced Concrete*, John Wiley & Sons, New York, 1932.
2. L. E. Grinter, *Theory of Modern Steel Structures*, Vol. 2, The Macmillan Co., New York, rev. ed., 1949.
3. John I. Parcel and Robert B. B. Moorman, *Analysis of Statically Indeterminate Structures*, John Wiley & Sons, New York, 1955.
4. Chu-Kia Wang, *Statically Indeterminate Structures*, McGraw-Hill Book Company, New York, 1953.

5. Phil M. Ferguson and Ardis H. White, "The Statics Ratio for Analysis of Frames that Deflect," Univ. of Tex. Bur. of Eng. Res. *Bull. No. 45*, 1950.
6. "Moment Distribution Applied to Continuous Concrete Structures," Portland Cement Association, Chicago.
7. "Concrete Building Frames Analyzed by Moment Distribution," Portland Cement Association, Chicago.
8. "Continuity in Concrete Building Frames," Portland Cement Association, Chicago, 3rd ed.
9. "Handbook of Frame Constants," Portland Cement Association, Chicago.
10. "Frame Analysis Applied to Flat Slab Bridges," Portland Cement Association, Chicago.
11. "Report of ASCE-ACI Joint Committee on Ultimate Strength Design," *ASCE Proc.-Separate 809*, Oct. 1955.
12. ACI-ASCE Committee 327, Leo H. Corning, Chairman, "Ultimate Strength Design," *ACI Jour.*, **27**, Jan. 1956; *Proc.*, **52**, p. 505.

PROBLEMS

In all moment distribution problems use the standard tabulation form shown in Fig. B.8. In plotting moment diagrams plot the moment ordinates on the face of member that is in compression due to flexure.

Prob. B.1. Find the final moments for the frame of Fig. B.24 and sketch the moment diagram.

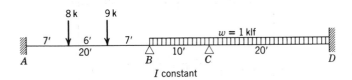

Fig. B.24. Frame for Prob. B.1.

Prob. B.2. In Fig. B.24 substitute knife edge supports ($M = 0$) at A and D and find the final moments from basic principles (without use of modified stiffness).

Prob. B.3. Find the final moments for the frame of Fig. B.25. The I of beams is double the I of columns. Plot the resulting moment diagram on the frame outline.

Prob. B.4. Find the final moments for the symmetrical frame (no sidesway) of Fig. B.26 and plot the M diagram.

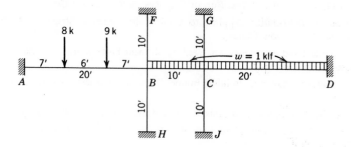

Fig. B.25. Frame for Prob. B.3.

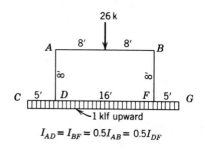

$$I_{AD} = I_{BF} = 0.5I_{AB} = 0.5I_{DF}$$

Fig. B.26. Frame for Prob. B.4.

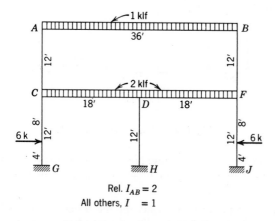

Rel. $I_{AB} = 2$
All others, $I = 1$

Fig. B.27. Frame for Prob. B.5.

REINFORCED CONCRETE FUNDAMENTALS

Prob. B.5. Find the final moments for the symmetrical frame (no sidesway) of Fig. B.27 and plot the M diagram.

Prob. B.6. Solve Prob. B.2 using modified stiffness where applicable.

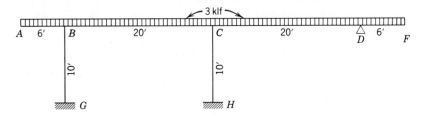

Fig. B.28. Frame for Prob. B.9.

Prob. B.7. In Prob. B.3 (Fig. B.25) recalculate the moments if the columns are hinged at F, G, H, and J. Use modified stiffness.

Prob. B.8. Find the moments in the frame of Fig. B.27 if hinges are inserted at G and H. Neglect sidesway.

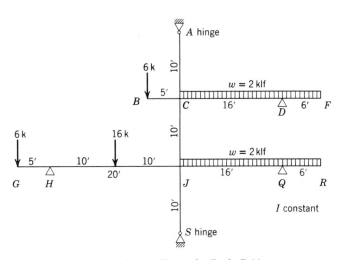

Fig. B.29. Frame for Prob. B.11.

Prob. B.9. Solve for the moments in the frame of Fig. B.28 (no sidesway permitted), making maximum use of modified stiffness ideas and assuming I is the same throughout.

Prob. B.10. Solve the frame of Fig. B.19 if a hinge is inserted at A.

FRAME ANALYSIS: MOMENT DISTRIBUTION   475

Prob. B.11. Assuming no sidesway, find the moments on the frame of Fig. B.29, making maximum use of modified stiffness. Plot the assembled moment diagram.

Prob. B.12.

(a) In Fig. B.24 assume that joint B settles 0.25 in., $E = 3 \times 10^6$ psi, $I = 8000$ in.^{4} Find the final moments caused by settlement alone. Plot the M diagram.

(b) Since settlement usually occurs gradually, a reduced E of 1×10^6 psi might be more logical. Plot the M diagram for this case.

Prob. B.13. Solve for the moments in the frame of Fig. B.28 changing the support at H to a pin support. Assume no sidesway and constant I. Use modified stiffness ideas to the maximum extent.

REINFORCED CONCRETE FUNDAMENTALS

Frame Analysis: Limit Design

C.1. TERMINOLOGY

Limit design and plastic design are often considered as synonymous terms. A distinction is made here and in most recent discussions of reinforced concrete. In steel design, the term *plastic design* includes not only the change in the pattern of moments beyond the yield point but also the increased resistance of a cross section after its extreme fiber reaches the yield point. In reinforced concrete, *limit design* is used only to refer to the changing moment pattern; ultimate strength design already includes the increase in strength of a given cross section after some stress reaches the yield point.

C.2. LIMIT DESIGN FOR REINFORCED CONCRETE

When yielding starts, deflections increase sharply and repeated loading introduces an element of fatigue. Hence under working load conditions yielding is certainly rather undesirable. On the other hand, as a reserve against final failure or collapse, the strength between yielding and failure has proved to be quite significant in the case of structural steel, and the fact that this stage involves larger deflections does not seem too important. There appear to be places where recognition of limit design is also significant in reinforced concrete. Although designated by a different name, the yield-line theory of slabs (Chap. 10) is such a case. The joint ASCE-ACI Committee on Limit Design will presumably mark out in the near future the necessary boundaries and controls on limit design for reinforced concrete. The type of members which can form plastic hinges (Sec. C.3) must be clearly distinguished from those having insufficient toughness.

Limit design is significant because it points out that: (1) a statically indeterminate member or frame cannot collapse as the result of a single yielding section; and (2) between first yielding and final frame failure there normally exists a large reserve of strength.

The remainder of this discussion will present some elementary ideas of limit design as these have been found useful in structural steel design. Presumably, similar procedures will be found satisfactory for some reinforced concrete frames once the necessary limitations have been established.

C.3. THE PLASTIC HINGE IDEA

Bending moment produces curvature and angle changes in a member. Let ϕ designate the angle change which develops over a unit length of the member. The general relation existing between M and ϕ, or the M-ϕ curve, for a concrete slab is shown in Fig. A.10. The corresponding M-ϕ curve for a steel beam is somewhat similar (Fig. C.1a). The idealized M-ϕ curve used as the basis of limit design is shown in Fig. C.1b.

The significant part of these M-ϕ curves for limit design lies beyond the first yield moment, in the zone where the moment $M_p{}^*$ remains unchanged over a very large range in ϕ values. When a point along the beam develops a moment M_p, it will act as a plastic hinge. This means it will continue

---

* The idealized value of M_p for a steel I-beam assumes the stress distribution of Fig. C.2 which leads to $M_p = f_y Z$, where $Z = 2 \int_0^c y \, dA$.

REINFORCED CONCRETE FUNDAMENTALS

to resist the moment M_p but further loading will result only in an increased angle change ϕ rather than an increased moment. If an ordinary structural hinge is thought of as frictionless, a plastic hinge may be considered

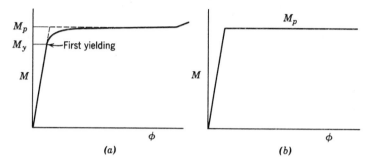

Fig. C.1. M-ϕ curve for steel I-beam. (a) Actual. (b) Idealized.

as a "rusty hinge" having a definite, but limited, resistance to rotation. Thus, for further loading on the member the moment changes produced elsewhere on the member are the same as though a real hinge existed at the plastic hinge point.

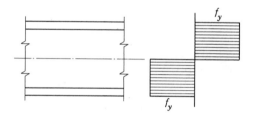

Fig. C.2. Idealized bending stresses with M_p.

C.4. THE COLLAPSE MECHANISM

In limit design, the ultimate strength considered is that which brings the frame to the verge of failure or collapse, assuming perfect plastic hinge action. The strain-hardening effect in steel actually increases the resistance beyond M_p when ϕ becomes quite large. Such increased resistance provides an extra factor against total collapse; this factor is not included in the usual computations. For this reason some object to designating the calculated load as the collapse load.

FRAME ANALYSIS: LIMIT DESIGN

A member cannot collapse under moment loading (except by buckling) until there are enough actual or plastic hinges to transform it into a mechanism. A cantilever beam thus collapses when a single hinge forms at the support, but a simple or continuous beam must have three hinges to collapse, as indicated in Fig. C.3. For the simple beam this requires the formation of only one plastic hinge and this moment is entirely statically determinate. For the usual continuous beam three plastic hinges are

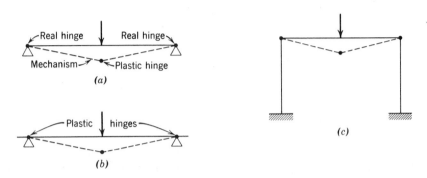

Fig. C.3. Local collapse mechanism. (*a*) Simple span. (*b*) Continuous span. (*c*) Frame member.

required; and these hinges greatly modify the moments from their elastic analysis values.

A frame may collapse as a whole without any individual member developing the three hinges, provided the frame as a whole develops enough hinges to act as a mechanism, as in Fig. C.4.

C.5. FRAME ACTION BETWEEN FIRST YIELDING AND COLLAPSE

In Sec. C.2 it was stated that yielding under working loads is objectionable, although this does not mean that such a condition will be totally prohibited under all circumstances. Generally, however, a study under working loads would involve analysis on an elastic basis.

As overloads are applied, one or more of the moments might be expected to pass the M_y value and reach the M_p value. However, it would be quite an unusual frame which would have its maximum moments so equalized that all the plastic hinges required to form a mechanism would develop at any one loading stage and thus lead to an immediate collapse. The usual

REINFORCED CONCRETE FUNDAMENTALS

pattern is for a single highly stressed section (or several) to develop first M_y and then M_p, with more load necessary before some other plastic hinge forms; and several such loading increments would be required to produce all the plastic hinges necessary for a mechanism.

Although it might be interesting to trace out this sequence of loads and moment diagrams, it would be a lengthy process. Fortunately it is an unnecessary process. The collapse pattern and the collapse loading can be established entirely independently of the original elastic moment pattern or of the intervening elastic-plastic stages.

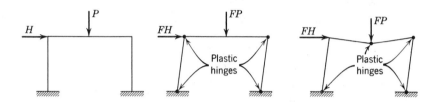

Fig. C.4.   Mechanisms for collapse of frame as a whole.

C.6. THE LOAD FACTOR OR FACTOR OF SAFETY

Although the term *safety factor* is more commonly used in discussions of limit design, the term *load factor* seems more in accord with developments in reinforced concrete notation and will be used here.

$$\text{Load factor} = \text{safety factor} = \frac{\text{collapse load}}{\text{working load}} = F$$

A given analysis, as presented here, applies only to one specific loading. For example, if the frame of Fig. C.4 were analyzed and F were established as 3, it would mean that if all loads were increased in proportion, the frame would not collapse until it carried loads of $3H$ and $3P$. This would not mean it could carry $3H$ alone or $3P$ alone or $3H$ along with P or any other combination except $3H$ and $3P$. If the load factor for H alone is needed, this requires a separate analysis.

The student should also note that the collapse load is far beyond the elastic range; hence the effect of the two loads H and P may be far different from the sum of their individual effects.

The following discussion will be directed towards methods of establishing the actual load factor or designing to maintain the desired load factor.

C.7. UPPER BOUND OR LIMIT ON LOAD FACTOR

If a frame is on the verge of collapse, it must have developed a sufficient number of plastic hinges to change it into a mechanism. As the mechanism starts to collapse, the loads move in such a way as to contribute energy to the system while rotations occur at the plastic hinges which absorb energy. For a specific given or assumed mechanism a token deflection establishes specific angle changes at all plastic hinges. The required external load to produce this movement can be established by equating internal energy absorbed at the plastic hinges to the external energy input by the loads.

The true load factor for the frame can be no larger than the ratio of P (collapse) obtained for this particular mechanism to P (working load); it may be smaller for some other (more probable) mechanism. The mechanism-energy approach thus establishes an upper bound or upper limit on the value of the true load factor.

If all possible mechanisms are investigated the lowest load factor will be the true one; but it is desirable to check this load factor against the lower bound discussed in the next section. For this purpose it should be noted that the moments are all statically determinate when M_p values are used at each plastic hinge in a mechanism.

C.8. LOWER BOUND OR LIMIT ON LOAD FACTOR

A lower bound or lower limit on the real load factor is determined from a moment diagram, *any* moment diagram that is consistent with the given loads, that is, *any* moment diagram that satisfies statics.

The fundamental idea may be very simply indicated in terms of the elastic moment diagram. Let M_p represent the plastic moment (different values for different members) and M_w represent the corresponding working load moments from the moment diagram. If M_p/M_w is determined for every member, the smallest ratio found is a lower bound on the true load factor. Why? Up to value M_p the idealized M-ϕ diagram assumes elastic action, which means the moment is directly proportional to the load. Hence the ratio M_p/M_w indicates how much the load may be increased without inelastic action and before any readjustment of the moment diagram shape occurs. This is a *lower* limit on how much the load may be increased because the moment diagram will probably shift to a more favorable shape as this critical section begins to act as a plastic hinge. For further loading the critical moment at the hinge remains constant at M_p while other parts of the moment diagram increase towards the M_p values.

REINFORCED CONCRETE FUNDAMENTALS

Greenberg and Prager have proved[1] mathematically that any moment diagram satisfying statics may be used as the basis of a lower bound. Normally it is easier to develop an "arbitrary" moment diagram than to establish the elastic moment values.

As one tries different possible moment diagrams, one discovers that higher values of this lower bound are obtained when more individual ratios of M_p/M_w become equal to this bound. The moment diagram can thus be "equalized" towards values establishing the true load factor. It is desirable finally, however, to assume plastic hinges at these high moment points and check such a solution by the energy-mechanism procedure (Sec. C.7) which fixes an upper bound.

C.9. COMBINATION SYSTEMS OF CALCULATION

Some designers find it desirable to use the methods of Secs. C.7 and C.8 somewhat alternately to establish upper and lower bounds and to work between the two methods to close the gap as much as the case demands.

C.10. UPPER BOUND APPROACH TO AN ANALYSIS EXAMPLE

The frame of Fig. C.5a will be investigated on a limit design basis to establish the possible load factor F under the loads shown.

The upper bound is established from the energy-mechanism approach. Each loaded member will first be investigated for mechanisms which represent local collapse, as shown in Fig. C.5b for member BC. The center deflection is 10θ and the energy introduced by the ultimate load $10F$ is $10F \times 10\theta = 100F\theta$ k-ft. Since $M_p = 50$ k-ft, the energy absorbed in the plastic hinge at B is 50θ, at C 50θ, and at mid-span $50 \times 2\theta$. These two energy statements can be equated.

$$100F\theta = 50\theta + 50\theta + 100\theta = 200\theta \qquad F \gtrless 2.00$$

For member CD (Fig. C.5c) by similar reasoning,

$$8F \times 10\theta = 50\theta + 50\theta + 100\theta = 200\theta \qquad F \gtrless 2.50$$

The frame might fail as a whole in what is sometimes designated as a panel mechanism (Fig. C.5d). The 10-k load contributes no energy because, for the small movements involved, BC may be considered as moving entirely in the horizontal direction.

$$8F \times 10\theta = 4 \times 50\theta \qquad F \gtrless 2.50$$

To see whether a lower F is possible, mechanisms need to be combined in such a way as to reduce the number of hinges absorbing energy while at the same time

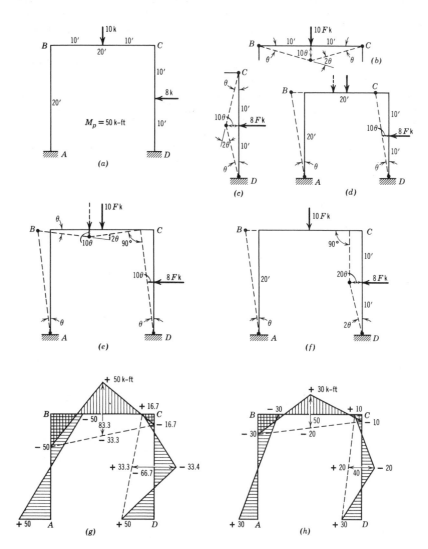

Fig. C.5. Limit design analysis by energy-mechanism equation, Sec. C.10. (*a*) Loaded frame. (*b, c*) Local collapse mechanisms. (*d, e, f*) Other possible collapse mechanisms. (*g, h*) Moment diagrams for mechanism shown in (*e*).

increasing the energy input. When the panel deformation is combined with the beam mechanism of BC, it is possible to get the mechanism of Fig. C.5e.

$$8F \times 10\theta + 10F \times 10\theta = 50(\theta + 2\theta + 2\theta + \theta) \qquad F \lessgtr 300/180 = 1.67$$

Another possible combination of mechanisms is shown in Fig. C.5f, leading to:

$$8F \times 20\theta = 50(\theta + \theta + 2\theta + 2\dot\theta) \qquad F \lessgtr 300/160 = 1.87$$

It appears that the upper bound value of 1.67 is the minimum F, but to be certain that a weaker mechanism has not been overlooked, the moment diagram should be drawn and used to establish the lower bound. Since all M_p values at the plastic hinges are known and since the direction of each angle change establishes the sign of its moment, the moment diagram is strictly a matter of statics.

The moment diagram of Fig. C.5g was constructed in the following sequence. First the M_p values were plotted at the four hinges of Fig. C.5e. The simple beam moment for BC is $M_s = 10F \times 20/4 = 10 \times 1.67 \times 20/4 = 83.3$ k-ft. At mid-span this establishes the dashed base line value as -33.3 which leads to an ordinate of -16.7 at C. Likewise, for member CD, $M_s = -8F \times 20/4 = -8 \times 1.67 \times 20/4 = -66.7$ k-ft. Plotted from a mid-span base value of $+33.3$ k-ft, this gives a -33.4 k-ft value at mid-span. Since no moment value exceeds 50 k-ft, this upper bound value of $F = 1.67$ used in this construction is also a lower bound and hence the true load factor.

The ultimate load moment diagram reduced to working load terms may be preferred by some. The moment plotted at the hinges is then $50/F = 50/1.67 = 30.0$ k-ft and the M_s values then do not involve an F term, as shown in Fig. C.5h.

C.11. LOWER BOUND APPROACH TO AN ANALYSIS EXAMPLE

The same example used in Sec. C.10 will be solved from the lower bound approach. The frame and loading are repeated in Fig. C.6a.

The governing statical relations are three in number. For BC, $M_s = 0.25PL = 0.25 \times 10 \times 20 = 50$ k-ft. For CD, $M_s = -0.25 \times 8 \times 20 = -40$ k-ft. For AB and CD to resist properly the horizontal forces, ΣF_x in Fig. C.6b must be in equilibrium:

$$V_{AB} + V_{DC} - 4 + 8 = 0$$

where V_{DC} represents only the shear due to continuity. With bending moment signs, $V_{AB} = (M_{BA} - M_{AB})/20$, $V_{DC} = (M_{CD} - M_{DC})/20$, and the equation becomes:

$$(M_{BA} - M_{AB})/20 + (M_{CD} - M_{DC})/20 - 4 + 8 = 0$$

$$M_{BA} + M_{CD} - M_{AB} - M_{DC} = -80 \text{ k-ft}$$

The moment diagram in Fig. C.6c was constructed by first equalizing center and end moments on BC. This gave $M_{BA} = -25$ and $M_{CD} = +25$, leaving

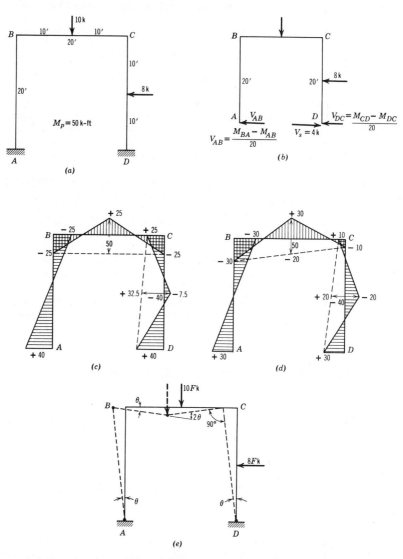

Fig. C.6. Limit design analysis by lower bound concept, Sec. C.11. (*a*) Loaded frame. (*b*) Horizontal forces for equilibrium equation. (*c, d*) Trial moment diagrams. (*e*) Mechanism for moment diagram of (*d*).

REINFORCED CONCRETE FUNDAMENTALS

$M_{AB} + M_{DC} = +80$; for the simplest arrangement each was taken as $+40$. On CD the dashed base line value at mid-height becomes $+32.5$ and the center moment becomes -7.5.

The next trial attempts to reduce the 40-k-ft maximum moment. A reduction in the 40-k-ft values will almost surely increase some of the several 25-k-ft values. In Fig. C.6d a $+30$ moment at A and D and a -30 at B were tried. Then M_{CD} must be $+10$ to give the -80 control summation. On BC the base line value at mid-span is -20, making the mid-span moment $+30$. On CD the mid-height value is $+20$ for the base line and -20 for the moment.

It does not appear possible to rearrange the moment diagram for maximum values to be less than 30 k-ft. To attain this final condition in only two trials is not typical. This was a combination of a lucky trial choice plus the fact that the critical value happened to be a round number (not something like 31.4) that brought about this short solution. The load factor $\geqslant M_p/30 = 50/30 = 1.67$.

The corresponding mechanism in Fig. C.6e should be checked to see whether this is actually the upper bound and hence the true value of load factor. This case has already been solved in Sec. C.10, giving a load factor of 1.67, which verifies this as the true value.

C.12. DESIGN PROCEDURE WITH LIMIT DESIGN

If one could ignore the complications mentioned in the next section, design for simple load arrangements would be easier than analysis. Horne[2] has developed a procedure which may be based on a form of moment distribution, as he proposes, or simply on a study of moment diagrams. He has extended this method to handle more than a single group of loads, but only the single loading will be discussed here.

Any moment diagram satisfying statics may be used as a starting point. This moment diagram would then be adjusted by varying the moments at the ends of members, or by varying the distribution of resisting moments between the several members at a joint, or by varying the percentage of shear (moments) assigned to specific columns. One accustomed to elastic analysis may at first be astonished at how ruthlessly these changes may be made.

Consider first a frame to be constructed entirely from a single beam section. The moment diagram would be adjusted to bring the maximum moments on different members down to as small a moment as seems to be feasible, as in Fig. C.6d. This moment times the load factor would determine M_p and hence the Z required, since $M_p = Zf_y$.

The more general problem with members of various size available would be to distribute the necessary moment resistance of the various members in such a way as to use available members efficiently. A number of different designs of nearly equal efficiency may be possible, each fitting closely a particular variation of the moment diagram.

C.13. COMPLICATIONS IN LIMIT DESIGN THEORY

The fact that the M-ϕ curve for a concrete beam involves a gradual rather than a sharp change from elastic conditions to an M_p value may require some modifications in the above theory.[3] Diagonal tension resistance and bond resistance when ϕ is large are further uncertainties. Compression failures do not lead to a significant constant ϕ zone; what is the maximum reinforcing steel consistent with plastic hinge formation?

Complications are not absent in the case of structural steel members, although experimental work has advanced further than with reinforced concrete. Since a member which develops the full moment $M_p = f_y Z$, as in Fig. C.2, could carry no shear, some portion of the web depth must be reserved for elastic action and shear resistance. In columns, resistance to axial load reduces the moment capacity M_p and this must be taken into account when the column load exceeds 15% of its critical (buckling) value.[4] Flange thickness relative to its projecting length from the web must be watched and compression flanges must be well braced to prevent local buckling and lateral buckling failures. When loads are variable, care must be taken that stress reversals from one yield point to the reversed stress yield point do not occur; also that repeated cycles of loading do not lead to increasing deflections with each cycle. For steel construction, Ref. 4 outlines these problems in more detail.

SELECTED REFERENCES

1. H. J. Greenberg and W. Prager, "Limit Design of Beams and Frames," *ASCE Proc.-Separate 59*, Feb. 1951; *Trans.*, **117**, p. 447.

2. Michael Rex Horne, "A Moment Distribution Method for the Analysis and Design of Structures by the Plastic Theory," *Jour. Inst. Civil Engrs.*, **3**, Pt. III, Apr. 1954, p. 51.

3. Herbert A. Sawyer, Jr., "Elasti-Plastic Design of Single Span Beams and Frames," *ASCE Proc.-Separate 851*, Dec. 1955.

4. Lynn S. Beedle, Bruno Thurliman, and Robert L. Ketter, *Plastic Design in Structural Steel*, published jointly by Fritz Engineering Laboratory at Lehigh University and American Institute of Steel Construction, 1955.

5. G. C. Ernst, "Ultimate Slopes and Deflections—A Brief for Limit Design," *ASCE Proc.-Separate 583*, Jan. 1955.

6. G. C. Ernst, "Plastic Hinging at the Intersection of Beams and Columns," *ACI Jour.*, **28**, June 1957; *Proc.*, **53**, p. 1119.

7. Herbert A. Sawyer, "The Behavior of Under-Reinforced Concrete Beams Under Long-Term Loads," Univ. of Conn. Eng. Exp. Sta. *Bull. No. 12*, 1956.

8. A. L. L. Baker, *The Ultimate-Load Theory Applied to the Design of Reinforced and Prestressed Concrete Frames,* Concrete Publications, Ltd., London, 1956.

9. B. G. Neal, *The Plastic Methods of Structural Analysis,* Chapman and Hall, London, 1956.

PROBLEMS

Prob. C.1. The frame in Fig. C.7 has $M_p = 80$ k-ft for BC and $M_p = 40$ k-ft for each vertical member. Use the lower bound method of attack to find the available load factor. Verify by using the mechanism concept for the final moment diagram.

Prob. C.2. The frame in Fig. C.8 has $M_p = 80$ k-ft for BC and $M_p = 40$ k-ft for each vertical member. Find the available load factor using the lower bound approach and verify by using the mechanism corresponding to the final moment diagram.

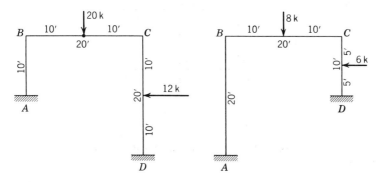

Fig. C.7. Frame for Probs. C.1 and C.3.

Fig. C.8. Frame for Probs. C.2 and C.4.

Prob. C.3. Solve Prob. C.1 by considering different possible mechanisms. Verify the final result by establishing the moment diagram for the collapse mechanism.

Prob. C.4. Solve Prob. C.2 by considering different possible mechanisms and verify by the moment diagram corresponding to collapse.

Prob. C.5. The arrangement of loads shown on AB and BC of Fig. C.9 often is used to approximate the same total load uniformly distributed. $M_p = 36$ k-ft for column CG, 108 k-ft for beam BC, and 18 k-ft for each other member. Find the available load factor:

FRAME ANALYSIS: LIMIT DESIGN   489 (*a*) Using the lower bound and verifying the result by considering the mechanism.

(*b*) Using the mechanism idea, verifying the result by the moment diagram.

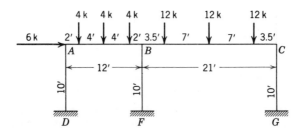

Fig. C.9. Frame for Prob. C.5.

Prob. C.6. Find the available load factor for the Vierendeel truss of Fig. C.10 if M_p is 100 k-ft for each vertical and 50 k-ft for each horizontal member.

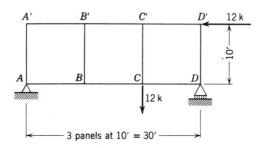

Fig. C.10. Vierendeel truss for Prob. C.6.

Prob. C.7. Find the available load factor for the frame of Fig. C.11 if M_p for *ABC* is 100 k-ft, for *DEF* is 200 k-ft, and for each vertical is 75 k-ft.

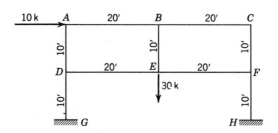

Fig. C.11. Frame for Prob. C.7.

REINFORCED CONCRETE FUNDAMENTALS

APPENDIX

D

ACI Building Code Requirements for Reinforced Concrete

The following articles of the 1956 "Building Code Requirements for Reinforced Concrete" have been included by permission of the American Concrete Institute. This Code is subject to revision whenever the studies of the Committee responsible indicate that developments in concrete design and construction warrant a change. Inquiries concerning the revision should be made periodically. A complete Code can be obtained from the American Concrete Institute, P.O. Box 4754, Redford Station, Detroit 19, Mich.

ACI Standard

Building Code Requirements for Reinforced Concrete (ACI 318-56)*

Reported by ACI Committee 318

FRANK KEREKES
Chairman

J. P. THOMPSON
Secretary

W. C. E. BECKER
FRANK H. BEINHAUER
DELMAR L. BLOEM
FRANK B. BROWN
MILES N. CLAIR
A. BURTON COHEN†
T. F. COLLIER
JOSEPH DI STASIO
MALCOLM S. DOUGLAS
A. EPSTEIN
PHIL M. FERGUSON
E. I. FIESENHEISER
THOR GERMUNDSSON
EIVIND HOGNESTAD

JOHN W. HUBLER
HARRY F. IRWIN
ROBERT O. JAMESON
VERNON P. JENSEN
ROBERT C. JOHNSON
OLIVER G. JULIAN
GEORGE E. LARGE
FRED F. McMINN
NOLAN D. MITCHELL
I. E. MORRIS
NATHAN M. NEWMARK
DOUGLAS E. PARSONS
JOSEF C. PATCHEN
ORLEY O. PHILLIPS

RAYMOND C. REESE
THEODORE O. REYHNER
PAUL ROGERS
ROBERT SAILER
CHESTER P. SIESS
HOWARD SIMPSON
L. C. URQUHART
A. CARL WEBER
C. H. WESTCOTT
WALTER H. WHEELER
C. S. WHITNEY (ex officio)
C. A. WILLSON
GEORGE WINTER
HOWARD M. ZIMMERMAN

SYNOPSIS

This code covers the proper design and construction of buildings of reinforced concrete. In such structures as arches, tanks, reservoirs, and chimneys where specialization relates principally to the mechanics of design and details of construction, the provisions of this code may be applied with the modifications necessary to suit the special conditions. It is written in such a form that it may be incorporated verbatim or adopted by reference in a general building code, and earlier editions of it have been widely used in this manner.

Among the subjects covered are: quality of concrete; allowable stresses; mixing, placing, curing, and cold weather protection of concrete; forms; cleaning, bending, placing, splicing, and protection of reinforcement; embedment of pipe and conduits in concrete; construction joints; general design considerations; flexural computations; shear and diagonal tension; bond and anchorage; flat slabs; columns and walls; footings; and precast concrete. The quality and testing of materials used in the construction are covered by references to the appropriate ASTM standard specifications.

*Adopted as a Standard of the American Concrete Institute at its 52nd Annual Convention, Feb. 21, 1956, as reported by Committee 318; ratified by Letter Ballot Apr. 30, 1956. ACI 318-56 supersedes ACI 318-51 published Apr. 1951.

Title No. 52-57 is a part of copyrighted JOURNAL OF THE AMERICAN CONCRETE INSTITUTE, V. 27, No. 9, May 1956, *Proceedings* V. 52. Separate prints in covers are available at $1.00 each (50 cents to ACI Members).

†Deceased.

CHAPTER 1—GENERAL

101—Scope

(*a*) This code covers the use of reinforced concrete and plain concrete in any structure to be erected under the provisions of the general building code of which it forms a part. It is intended to supplement the provisions of the general code in order to provide for the proper design and construction of structures of these materials. In all matters pertaining to design and construction where this code is in conflict with other provisions of the general code, this code shall govern.

(*b*) With the exception of Section 103, the provisions of this code are not intended to apply to prestressed concrete.

_ _ _ _ _ _ _ _ _ _ _ _ _ _ _ _ _ _

103—Special systems of reinforced concrete

(*a*) The sponsors of any system of design or construction of reinforced concrete which has been in successful use, or the adequacy of which has been shown by test, and the design of which is either in conflict with, or not covered by this code shall have the right to present the data on which their design is based to a "Board of Examiners for Special Construction" appointed by the Building Official. This Board shall be composed of competent engineers, architects, and builders, and shall have the authority to investigate the data so submitted and to formulate rules governing the design and construction of such systems. These rules when approved by the Building Official shall be of the same force and effect as the provisions of this code.

104—Definitions

(*a*) The following terms are defined for use in this code:

Aggregate, fine—Natural sand, or sand prepared from stone, blast furnace slag, or gravel, or, subject to the approval of the Building Official, other inert materials having similar characteristics.

Aggregate, coarse—Crushed stone, gravel, blast furnace slag, or other approved inert materials of similar characteristics, or combinations thereof having hard, strong, durable pieces, free from adherent coatings.

Column—An upright compression member the length of which exceeds three times its least lateral dimension.

Combination column—A column in which a structural steel member, designed to carry the principal part of the load, is wrapped with wire and encased in concrete of such quality that some additional load may be allowed thereon.

Composite column—A column in which a steel or cast-iron structural member is completely encased in concrete containing spiral and longitudinal reinforcement.

Concrete—A mixture of portland cement, fine aggregate, coarse aggregate, and water.

Deformed bar—A reinforcing bar conforming to "Specifications for Minimum Requirements for the Deformations of Deformed Steel Bars for Concrete

Reinforcement" (ASTM A 305). Wire mesh with welded intersections not farther apart than 6 in. in the direction of the principal reinforcement and with cross wires not smaller than No. 10 AS&W gage may be rated as a deformed bar.

Effective area of concrete—The area of a section which lies between the centroid of the tensile reinforcement and the compression face of the flexural member.

Effective area of reinforcement—The area obtained by multiplying the right cross-sectional area of the reinforcement by the cosine of the angle between its direction and the direction for which the effectiveness is to be determined.

Panel length—The distance along a panel side from center to center of columns of a flat slab.

Pedestal—An upright compression member whose height does not exceed three times its least lateral dimension.

Plain bar—Reinforcement which does not conform to the definition of deformed bar shall be classed as a plain bar.

Plain concrete—Concrete without reinforcement, or reinforced only for shrinkage or temperature changes.

Precast concrete—A plain or reinforced concrete building element cast in other than its final position in the structure.

Prestressed concrete—Concrete in which there have been introduced internal stresses of such magnitude and distribution that the stresses resulting from service loads are counteracted to a desired degree. In reinforced concrete the prestress is commonly introduced by tensioning the reinforcement.

Reinforced concrete—Concrete in which reinforcement other than that provided for shrinkage or temperature changes is embedded in such a manner that the two materials act together in resisting forces.

Surface water—The water carried by the aggregate except that held by absorption within the aggregate particles themselves.

— — — — — — — — — — — — — — — — —

CHAPTER 2—MATERIALS AND TESTS

200—Notation

D = deflection, produced by a test load, of a member relative to the ends of the span

L = span of member under load test (the shorter span of flat slabs and of floors supported on four sides)

t = total thickness or depth of a member under load test

201—Tests

(a) The Building Official, or his authorized representative, shall have the right to order the test of any material entering into concrete or reinforced concrete to determine its suitability for the purpose; to order reasonable tests of the concrete from time to time to determine whether the materials and methods in use are such as to produce concrete of the necessary quality; and to order the test under load of any portion of a completed structure, when conditions have been such as to leave doubt as to the adequacy of the structure to serve the purpose for which it is intended.

(b) Tests of materials and of concrete shall be made in accordance with the requirements of the American Society for Testing Materials as noted elsewhere in this code. The complete records of such tests shall be available for inspection during the progress of the work and for 2 years thereafter, and shall be preserved for that purpose by the engineer or architect.

(c) Tests for safe load ratings for reinforced concrete structures which are subject to approval under Section 103 shall be made at an age not greater than the minimum age at which the structure is to be put in service or is assumed to have the design strength (usually 28 days).

202—Load tests of existing structures

(a) A load test of an existing structure to determine its adequacy (stiffness and strength) for the intended use shall not be made until the portion subjected to the load is at least 56 days old, unless the owner of the structure agrees to the test being made at an earlier age.

(b) When a load test is required and the whole structure is not to be tested, the portion of the structure thought to provide the least margin of safety shall be selected for loading. Prior to the application of the test load, a load which simulates the effect of that portion of the design dead load which is not already present shall be applied and shall remain in place until after a decision has been made regarding the acceptability of the structure. The test load shall not be applied until the structural members to be tested have borne the full design dead load for at least 48 hr.

(c) Immediately prior to the application of the test load, the necessary initial readings shall be made for the measurements of deflections (and strains, if these are to be determined) caused by the application of the test load. The members selected for loading shall be subjected to a superimposed test load of two times the design live load, but not less than 80 psf for floor construction nor less than 60 psf for roof construction. The superimposed load shall be applied without shock to the structure and in a manner to avoid arching of the loading materials. Unless otherwise directed by the Building Official, the load shall be distributed to simulate the distribution of the load assumed in the design.

203—Loading and criteria of acceptability

The test load shall be left in position for 24 hr when readings of the deflections shall again be made. The test load shall be removed and additional readings of deflections shall then be made 24 hr after the removal of the test load. The following criteria shall be used in determining conformity with the load test requirements.

(*a*) If the structure shows evident failure, the changes or modifications needed to make the structure adequate for the rated capacity shall be made; or a lower rating may be established.

(*b*) Floor and roof construction shall be considered to conform to the load test requirements if there is no evidence of failure and the maximum deflection does not exceed:

$$D = \frac{L^2}{12,000\ t} \quad \dotfill \quad (1)$$

in which all terms are in the same units. Constructions with greater deflections shall meet the requirements of subsections (c), (d), and (e).

(*c*) The maximum deflection of a floor or roof construction shall not exceed the limit in Table 203(c) considered by the Building Official to be appropriate for the construction.

TABLE 203(c)—MAXIMUM ALLOWABLE DEFLECTION

Construction	Deflection
1. Cantilever beams and slabs	$L^2/1800\ t$
2. Simple beams and slabs	$L^2/4000\ t$
3. Beams continuous at one support and slabs continuous at one support for the direction of the principal reinforcement	$L^2/9000\ t$
4. Flat slabs (L = the longer span)	$L^2/10,000\ t$
5. Beams and slabs continuous at the supports for the direction of the principal reinforcement	$L^2/10,000\ t$

(*d*) The maximum deflection shall not exceed $L/180$ for a floor construction intended to support or to be attached to partitions or other construction likely to be damaged by large deflections of the floor.

(*e*) Within 24 hr after the removal of the test load the recovery of deflection caused by the application of the test load shall be at least 75 percent of the maximum deflection if this exceeds $L^2/12,000\ t$. However, constructions failing to show 75 percent recovery of the deflection may be retested. The second test loading shall not be made until at least 72 hr after the removal of the test load for the first test. The maximum deflection in the retest shall conform to the requirements of Sections 203(c) and (d) and the recovery of deflection shall be at least 75 percent.

204—Supervision

(*a*) Concrete work shall be supervised preferably by the engineer or architect responsible for its design, or by a competent representative responsible to him.

A record shall be kept of such supervision, which record shall cover the quality and quantity of concrete materials, the mixing and placing of the concrete, the placing of the reinforcing steel, and the general progress of the work. When the temperature falls below 40 F, a complete record of the temperatures and of the protection given to the concrete while curing shall be kept. This record shall be available for inspection during the progress of the work and for 2 years thereafter and shall be preserved by the engineer or architect for that purpose.

————————————————————

CHAPTER 3—CONCRETE QUALITY AND ALLOWABLE STRESSES

300—Notation

f_c = compressive unit stress in extreme fiber of concrete in flexure

f_c' = compressive strength of concrete at age of 28 days unless otherwise specified

f_r = compressive unit stress in the metal core of a composite column

f_s = tensile unit stress in longitudinal reinforcement; nominal allowable stress in vertical column reinforcement

f_v = tensile unit stress in web reinforcement

n = ratio of modulus of elasticity of steel to that of concrete

u = bond stress per unit of surface area of bar

v = shearing unit stress

v_c = shearing unit stress permitted on the concrete

301—Concrete quality

(*a*) For the design of reinforced concrete structures, the value of f_c' used for determining the allowable stresses as stipulated in Section 305 shall be based on the specified minimum 28-day compressive strength of the concrete, or on the specified minimum compressive strength at the earlier age at which the concrete may be expected to receive its full load. All plans, submitted for approval or used on the job, shall clearly show the assumed strength of concrete at a specified age for which all parts of the structure were designed.

(*b*) Concrete without air entrainment which will be exposed to the action of freezing weather shall have a water content not exceeding 6 gal. per sack of cement.*

---

*Detailed recommendations for quality of concrete and requirements for air content for various exposures are given in "Recommended Practice for Selecting Proportions for Concrete" (ACI 613).

302—Methods for determining strength of concrete

(*a*)   The determination of the proportions of cement, aggregate, and water to attain the required strengths shall be made by one of the following methods:

Method 1—Without preliminary tests

Where preliminary test data on the materials to be used in the concrete are not available, the water-cement ratio shall not exceed the values shown in Table 302 (a).† When strengths in excess of 4000 psi are required or when lightweight aggregates or admixtures (other than those exclusively for the purpose of entraining air) are used, the required water-cement ratio shall be determined in accordance with Method 2.

TABLE 302(a)—PERMISSIBLE WATER-CEMENT RATIOS FOR CONCRETE

Specified minimum compressive strength at 28 days, psi	Maximum permissible water-cement ratio, U.S. gal. per 94-lb sack of cement*	
	Non-air-entrained concrete	Air-entrained concrete
2000	8	7¼
2500	7¼	6¼
3000	6½	5¼
3500	5¾	4½
4000	5	4

*Including free surface moisture on aggregates.

Method 2—With preliminary tests

Water-cement ratios or strengths greater than shown in Table 302(a) may be used provided that the relationship between strength and water-cement ratio for the materials to be used has been previously established. Where previous data are not available, concrete of proportions and consistency suitable for the work shall be made using at least three different water-cement ratios which will produce a range in strengths encompassing those required for the work. These tests shall be made in accordance with the procedure given in the appendix to "Recommended Practice for Selecting Proportions for Concrete" (ACI 613). For each water-cement ratio, at least three specimens shall be made and cured in accordance with "Method of Making and Curing Concrete Compression and Flexure Test Specimens in the Laboratory" (ASTM C 192) and tested for strength in accordance with "Method of Test for Compressive Strength of Molded Concrete Cylinders" (ASTM C 39).

The strength tests shall be made at 28 days or the earlier age at which the concrete is to receive its full working load, as indicated on the plans. A curve shall be

---

†The tabulated water-cement ratios are more conservative than those given in ACI 613 and will generally produce appreciably higher strengths than indicated.

REINFORCED CONCRETE FUNDAMENTALS

established showing the relationship between water-cement ratio and compressive strength. The maximum permissible water-cement ratio for the concrete to be used in the structure shall be that shown by the curve to produce a strength 15 percent greater than called for on the plans, except when a lower value of the water content is required by Section 301(b). Where different materials are to be used for different portions of the work, each combination shall be evaluated separately.

303—Concrete proportions and consistency

(a) The proportions of aggregate to cement for any concrete shall be such as to produce a mixture which will work readily into the corners and angles of the forms and around reinforcement with the method of placing employed on the work, but without permitting the materials to segregate or excess free water to collect on the surface. The combined aggregates shall be of such composition of sizes that when separated on the No. 4 standard sieve, the weight passing the sieve (fine aggregate) shall not be less than 30 percent nor greater than 50 percent of the total, except that these proportions do not necessarily apply to lightweight aggregates.

(b) The methods of measuring concrete materials shall be such that the proportions can be accurately controlled and easily checked at any time during the work.*

304—Strength tests of concrete

(a) The Building Official may require a reasonable number of tests to be made during the progress of the work. At least three specimens shall be made for each test, and not less than one test shall be made for each 250 cu yd of concrete, but in no case shall there be less than one test for each day's concreting. Samples from which compression test specimens are molded shall be secured in accordance with "Method of Sampling Fresh Concrete" (ASTM C 172). Specimens made to check the adequacy of the design for strength of concrete or as a basis for acceptance of concrete shall be made and laboratory cured in accordance with "Method of Making and Curing Concrete Compression and Flexure Test Specimens in the Field" (ASTM C 31). Additional tests of specimens

---

*Detailed recommendations for proportioning concrete other than lightweight concrete are given in "Recommended Practice for Selecting Proportions for Concrete" (ACI 613).

cured entirely under field conditions may be required by the Building Official to check the adequacy of curing and protection of the concrete during cold weather. Strength tests shall be made in accordance with "Method of Test for Compressive Strength of Molded Concrete Cylinders" (ASTM C 39).

(*b*) The age for strength tests shall be 28 days, or, where specified, the earlier age at which the concrete is to receive its full working load. Additional tests may be made at earlier ages to obtain advance information on the adequacy of strength development where age-strength relationships have been established for the materials and proportions used.

(*c*) To conform to the requirements of these specifications, the average strength of the laboratory cured specimens representing each class of concrete as well as the average of any five consecutive strength tests representing each class of concrete shall be equal to, or greater than, the specified strength, and not more than one strength test in ten shall have an average value less than 90 percent of the specified strength. When it appears that tests of laboratory cured cylinders will fail to meet this requirement the Building Official shall have the right to order a change in the proportions or the water-cement ratio of the concrete sufficient to increase the strength to the specified value. The strengths of cylinders cured on the job are intended to indicate the adequacy of protection and curing of the concrete and may be used to determine when forms may be stripped, shoring removed, or the structure placed in service. When, in the opinion of the Building Official, the strengths of the job cured cylinders are excessively below those of the standard cured cylinders, the contractor may be required to improve the procedures for protecting and curing the concrete.

(*d*) In addition, where there is question as to the quality of the concrete in the structure, the Building Official may require tests in accordance with "Methods of Securing, Preparing and Testing Specimens from Hardened Concrete for Compressive and Flexural Strengths" (ASTM C 42) or order load tests as outlined in Section 202 for that portion of the structure where the questionable concrete has been placed.

305—Allowable unit stresses in concrete

(*a*) The unit stresses in pounds per square inch on concrete to be used when designs are made in accordance with Section 601(a) shall not exceed the values of Table 305(a) where f_c' equals the minimum specified compressive strength at 28 days, or at the earlier age at which the concrete may be expected to receive its full load.

TABLE 305(a)—ALLOWABLE UNIT STRESSES IN CONCRETE

Description		For any strength of concrete in accordance with Section 302 $n = \dfrac{30{,}000}{f_c'}$	Maximum value, psi	For strength of concrete shown below				
				$f_c' = 2000$ psi $n = 15$	$f_c' = 2500$ psi $n = 12$	$f_c' = 3000$ psi $n = 10$	$f_c' = 3750$ psi $n = 8$	$f_c' = 5000$ psi $n = 6$
Flexure: f_c								
Extreme fiber stress in compression	f_c	$0.45f_c'$		900	1125	1350	1688	2250
Extreme fiber stress in tension in plain concrete footings	f_c	$0.03f_c'$		60	75	90	113	150
Shear: v (as a measure of diagonal tension)								
Beams with no web reinforcement	v_c	$0.03f_c'$	90	60	75	90	90	90
Beams with longitudinal bars and with either stirrups or properly located bent bars	v	$0.08f_c'$	240	160	200	240	240	240
Beams with longitudinal bars and a combination of stirrups and bent bars (the latter bent up suitably to carry at least $0.04f_c'$.............	v	$0.12f_c'$	360	240	300	360	360	360
Footings*	v_c	$0.03f_c'$	75	60	75	75	75	75
(For flat slabs, see Chapter 10)								
Bond: u								
Deformed bars (as defined in Section 104)								
Top bars†	u	$0.07f_c'$	245	140	175	210	245	245
In two-way footings (except top bars)	u	$0.08f_c'$	280	160	200	240	280	280
All others	u	$0.10f_c'$	350	200	250	300	350	350
Plain bars (as defined in Section 104) (must be hooked)								
Top bars	u	$0.03f_c'$	105	60	75	90	105	105
In two-way footings (except top bars)	u	$0.036f_c'$	126	72	90	108	126	126
All others	u	$0.045f_c'$	158	90	113	135	158	158
Bearing: f_c								
On full area	f_c	$0.25f_c'$		500	625	750	938	1250
On one-third area or less‡	f_c	$0.375f_c'$		750	938	1125	1405	1875

*See Sections 905 and 809.

†Top bars, in reference to bond, are horizontal bars so placed that more than 12 in. of concrete is cast in the member below the bar.

‡This increase shall be permitted only when the least distance between the edges of the loaded and unloaded areas is a minimum of one-fourth of the parallel side dimension of the loaded area. The allowable bearing stress on a reasonably concentric area greater than one-third but less than the full area shall be interpolated between the values given.

306—Allowable unit stresses in reinforcement

Unless otherwise provided in this code, steel for concrete reinforcement shall not be stressed in excess of the following limits:

(a) *Tension*

(f_s = tensile unit stress in longitudinal reinforcement)

and (f_v = tensile unit stress in web reinforcement)

20,000 psi for rail-steel concrete reinforcing bars, billet-steel concrete reinforcing bars of intermediate and hard grades, axle-steel concrete reinforcing bars of intermediate and hard grades, and cold-drawn steel wire for concrete reinforcement.

18,000 psi for billet-steel concrete reinforcing bars of structural grade, and axle-steel concrete reinforcing bars of structural grade.

(b) *Tension in one-way slabs of not more than 12-ft span*

(f_s = tensile unit stress in main reinforcement)

For the main reinforcement, ⅜ in. or less in diameter, in one-way slabs, 50 percent of the minimum yield point specified in the specifications of the American Society for Testing Materials for the particular kind and grade of reinforcement used, but in no case to exceed 30,000 psi.

(c) *Compression, vertical column reinforcement*

(f_s = nominal allowable stress in vertical column reinforcement)

Forty percent of the minimum yield point specified in the specifications of the American Society for Testing Materials for the particular kind and grade of reinforcement used, but in no case to exceed 30,000 psi.

(f_r = allowable unit stress in the metal core of composite and combination columns)

Structural steel sections .... 16,000 psi
Cast iron sections .... 10,000 psi
Steel pipe .... See limitations of Section 1106(b)

(d) *Compression, flexural members*

For compression reinforcement in flexural members see Section 706(b).

CHAPTER 4—MIXING AND PLACING CONCRETE

——————————————————————

405—Curing

(*a*) In all concrete structures, concrete made with normal portland cement shall be maintained in a moist condition for at least the first 7 days after placing and high-early-strength concrete shall be so maintained for at least the first 3 days.

——————————————————————

CHAPTER 5—FORMS AND DETAILS OF CONSTRUCTION

——————————————————————

503—Conduits, pipes, etc., embedded in concrete

(*a*) Electric conduits and other pipes whose embedment is allowed shall not, with their fittings, displace that concrete of a column on which stress is calculated or which is required for fire protection, to greater extent than 4 percent of the area of the cross section. Sleeves or other pipes passing through floors, walls, or beams shall not be of such size or in such location as to impair unduly the strength of the construction; such sleeves or pipes may be considered as replacing structurally the displaced concrete, provided they are not exposed to rusting or other deterioration, are of uncoated iron or steel not thinner than standard steel pipe, have a nominal inside diameter not over 2 in., and are spaced not less than three diameters on centers. Except when plans of conduits and pipes are approved by the structural engineer, embedded pipes or conduits, other than those merely passing through, shall not be larger in outside diameter than one-third the thickness of the slab, wall, or beam in which they are embedded, nor shall they be spaced closer than three diameters on center, nor so located as to impair unduly the strength of the construction. Circular uncoated or galvanized electric conduit of iron or steel may be considered as replacing the displaced concrete.

(*b*) Pipes which will contain liquid, gas, or vapor may be embedded in structural concrete under the following conditions:

(1) The temperature of the liquid, gas, or vapor shall not exceed 150 F.

(2) The maximum pressure to which any piping or fittings shall be subjected shall be 200 psi above atmospheric pressure.

(3) All piping and fittings shall be tested as a unit for leaks immediately prior to concreting. The testing pressure per square inch above atmospheric pressure shall be 50 percent in excess of the pressure to which the piping and fittings may be subjected but the minimum testing pressure shall be not less

than 150 psi above atmospheric pressure. The pressure test shall be held for 4 hr with no drop in pressure except that which may be caused by air temperature.

(4) Pipes carrying liquid, gas, or vapor which is explosive or injurious to health shall again be tested as specified in paragraph (3) after the concrete has hardened.

(5) No liquid, gas or vapor, except water not exceeding 90 F nor 20 psi pressure, is to be placed in the pipes until the concrete has thoroughly set.

(6) In solid slabs the piping shall be placed between the top and bottom reinforcement.

(7) The concrete covering of the pipes shall be not less than 1 in.

(8) Reinforcement with an area equal to at least 0.2 percent of the area of the concrete section shall be provided normal to the piping.

(9) The piping and fittings shall be assembled by welding, brazing, solder-sweating, or other equally satisfactory method. Screw connections shall be prohibited. The piping shall be so fabricated and installed that it will not require any cutting, bending, or displacement of the reinforcement from its proper location.

(10) No liquid, gas, or vapor which may be injurious or detrimental to the pipes shall be placed in them.

(11) Drain pipes and other piping designed for pressures of not more than 1 psi above atmospheric pressure need not be tested as required in paragraph (3) above.

504—Cleaning and bending reinforcement

(*a*) Metal reinforcement, at the time concrete is placed, shall be free from loose rust scale or other coatings that will destroy or reduce the bond. Bends for stirrups and ties shall be made around a pin having a diameter not less than two times the minimum thickness of the bar. Hooks shall conform to the requirements of Section 906. Bends for other bars shall be made around a pin having a diameter not less than six times the minimum thickness of the bar, except that for bars larger than 1 in., the pin shall be not less than eight times the minimum thickness of the bar. All bars shall be bent cold.

505—Placing reinforcement

(*a*) Metal reinforcement shall be accurately placed and adequately secured in position by concrete or metal chairs or spacers. The clear distance between parallel bars, except in columns, shall be not less than the nominal diameter of the bars, $1\frac{1}{3}$ times the maximum size of the coarse aggregate, nor 1 in. Where reinforcement in beams or girders is placed in two or more layers, the clear distance between layers shall not be less than 1 in., and the bars in the upper layers shall be placed directly above those in the bottom layer.

(*b*) When wire or other reinforcement, not exceeding 1/4 in. in diameter is used as reinforcement for slabs not exceeding 10 ft in span, the reinforcement may be curved from a point near the top of the slab over the support to a point near the bottom of the slab at midspan; provided such reinforcement is either continuous over, or securely anchored to the support.

506—Splices in reinforcement

(*a*) In slabs, beams and girders, splices of reinforcement at points of maximum stress shall be avoided wherever possible. Such splices where used shall be welded, lapped, or otherwise fully developed, but, in any case, shall transfer the entire stress from bar to bar without exceeding the allowable bond and shear stresses listed in Table 305(a). The minimum overlap for a lapped splice shall be 24 bar diameters, but not less than 12 in. for bars. The clear distance between bars shall also apply to the clear distance between a contact splice and adjacent splices or bars.

507—Concrete protection for reinforcement

(*a*) The reinforcement of footings and other principal structural members in which the concrete is deposited against the ground shall have not less than 3 in. of concrete between it and the ground contact surface. If concrete surfaces after removal of the forms are to be exposed to the weather or be in contact with the ground, the reinforcement shall be protected with not less than 2 in. of concrete for bars larger than #5 and 1½ in. for #5 bars or smaller.

(*b*) The concrete protective covering for reinforcement at surfaces not exposed directly to the ground or weather shall be not less than ¾ in. for slabs and walls; and not less than 1½ in. for beams, girders, and columns. In concrete joist floors in which the clear distance between joists is not more than 30 in., the protection of reinforcement shall be at least ¾ in.

(*c*) If the general code of which this code forms a part specifies, as fire-protective covering of the reinforcement, thicknesses of concrete greater than those given in this section, then such greater thicknesses shall be used.

(*d*) Concrete protection for reinforcement shall in all cases be at least equal to the diameter of bars.

(*e*) Exposed reinforcing bars intended for bonding with future extensions shall be protected from corrosion by concrete or other adequate covering.

508—Construction joints

(*a*) Joints not indicated on the plans shall be so made and located as to least impair the strength of the structure. Where a joint is to be made, the surface of the concrete shall be thoroughly cleaned and all laitance removed. In addition to the foregoing, vertical joints shall be thoroughly wetted, and slushed with a coat of neat cement grout immediately before placing of new concrete.

(*b*) At least 2 hr must elapse after depositing concrete in the columns or walls before depositing in beams, girders, or slabs supported thereon. Beams, girders, brackets, column capitals, and haunches shall be considered as part of the floor system and shall be placed monolithically therewith.

(c) Construction joints in floors shall be located near the middle of the spans of slabs, beams, or girders, unless a beam intersects a girder at this point, in which case the joints in the girders shall be offset a distance equal to twice the width of the beam. In this last case provision shall be made for shear by use of inclined reinforcement.

CHAPTER 6—DESIGN—GENERAL CONSIDERATIONS

601—Design methods

(a) The design of reinforced concrete members shall be made with reference to allowable stresses, working loads, and the accepted straightline theory of flexure except as permitted by Section 601 (b). In determining the ratio n for design purposes, the modulus of elasticity for the concrete shall be assumed as $1000 f_c'$, and that for steel as 30,000,000 psi. It is assumed that the steel takes all the tension stresses in flexural computations.

(b) The ultimate strength method of design may be used for the design of reinforced concrete members.*

602—Design loads

(a) The provisions for design herein specified are based on the assumption that all structures shall be designed for all dead and live loads coming upon them, the live loads to be in accordance with the general requirements of the building code of which this forms a part, with such reductions for girders and lower story columns as are permitted therein.

603—Resistance to wind and earthquake forces

(a) The resisting elements in structures required to resist wind and earthquake forces shall be limited to the integral structural parts.

(b) The moments, shears, and direct stresses resulting from wind or earthquake forces determined in accordance with recognized methods shall be added to the maximum stresses which exist at any section for dead and live loads.

(c) Members subject to stresses produced by wind or earthquake forces combined with other loads may be proportioned for unit stresses 33⅓ percent greater than those specified in Sections 305 and 306, provided that the section thus required is not less than that required for the combination of dead and live load.

---

*For ready reference see appendix to this code for an abstract of the report of the ACI-ASCE joint committee on ultimate strength design.

CHAPTER 7—FLEXURAL COMPUTATIONS

700—Notation

b = width of rectangular flexural member or width of flanges for T- and I- sections

b' = width of web in T and I flexural members

d = depth from compression face of beam or slab to centroid of longitudinal tensile reinforcement; the diameter of a round bar

E = modulus of elasticity

I = moment of inertia of a section about the neutral axis for bending

l = span length of slab or beam

l' = clear span for positive moment and shear and the average of the two adjacent clear spans for negative moment (see Section 701)

t = minimum total thickness of slab

w = uniformly distributed load per unit of length of beam or per unit area of slab

701—General requirements

(*a*) All members of frames or continuous construction shall be designed to resist at all sections the maximum moments and shears produced by dead load, live load, earthquake and wind load, as determined by the theory of elastic frames in which the simplified assumptions of Section 702 may be used.

(*b*) Approximate methods of frame analysis are satisfactory for buildings of usual types of construction, spans, and story heights.

(*c*) In the case of two or more approximately equal spans (the larger of two adjacent spans not exceeding the shorter by more that 20 percent) with loads uniformly distributed, where the unit live load does not exceed three times the unit dead load, design for the following moments and shears is satisfactory:

Positive moment

End spans

If discontinuous end is unrestrained ....$\dfrac{1}{11} wl'^2$

If discontinuous end is integral with the support ....$\dfrac{1}{14} wl'^2$

Interior spans ....$\dfrac{1}{16} wl'^2$

Negative moment at exterior face of first interior support

Two spans ....$\dfrac{1}{9} wl'^2$

More than two spans ....$\dfrac{1}{10} wl'^2$

Negative moment at other faces of interior supports ....$\dfrac{1}{11} wl'^2$

Negative moment at face of all supports for, (a) slabs with spans not exceeding 10 ft, and (b) beams and girders where ratio of sum of column stiffnesses to beam stiffness exceeds eight at each end of the span ....$\dfrac{1}{12} wl'^2$

Negative moment at interior faces of exterior supports for members built integrally with their supports

Where the support is a spandrel beam or girder ....$\dfrac{1}{24} wl'^2$

Where the support is a column ....$\dfrac{1}{16} wl'^2$

Shear in end members at first interior support.....................$1.15 \dfrac{wl'}{2}$

Shear at all other supports..$\dfrac{wl'}{2}$

702—Conditions of design*

(a) *Arrangement of live load*

1. The live load may be considered to be applied only to the floor under consideration, and the far ends of the columns may be assumed as fixed.

2. Consideration may be limited to combinations of dead load on all spans with full live load on two adjacent spans and with full live load on alternate spans.

(b) *Span length*

1. The span length, l, of members that are not built integrally with their supports shall be the clear span plus the depth of the slab or beam but shall not exceed the distance between centers of supports.

2. In analysis of continuous frames, center to center distances, l and h, may be used in the determination of moments. Moments at faces of supports may be used for design of beams and girders.

3. Solid or ribbed slabs with clear spans of not more than 10 ft that are built integrally with their supports may be designed as continuous slabs on knife edge supports with spans equal to the clear spans of the slab and the width of beams otherwise neglected.

(c) *Stiffness*

1. Any reasonable assumption may be adopted for computing the relative

---

*For moments in columns see Section 1108.

stiffness of columns and of floor systems. The assumption made shall be consistent throughout the analysis.

2. In computing the value of I for relative stiffness of slabs, beams, girders, and columns, the reinforcement may be neglected. In T-shaped sections allowance shall be made for the effect of flange.

(d) *Haunched floor members*

1. The effect of haunches shall be considered both in determining bending moments and in computing unit stresses.

(e) *Limitations*

1. Wherever at any section positive reinforcement is indicated by analysis, the amount provided shall be not less than 0.005 $b'd$ except in slabs of uniform thickness. (Use b instead of b' for rectangular flexural members.)

2. In structural slabs of uniform thickness the minimum amount of reinforcement in the direction of the span shall be:

For structural, intermediate, and hard grades and rail steel .... 0.0025 bd
For steel having a minimum yield point of 56,000 psi .... 0.0020 bd

3. In slabs other than concrete joist construction or flat slabs, the principal reinforcement shall be centered not farther apart than three times the slab thickness nor more than 18 in.

703—Depth of beam or slab

(a) The depth of the beam or slab shall be taken as the distance from the centroid of the tensile reinforcement to the compression face of the structural members. Any floor finish not placed monolithically with the floor slab shall not be included as a part of the structural member. When the finish is placed monolithically with the structural slab in buildings of the warehouse or industrial class, there shall be placed an additional depth of ½ in. over that required by the design of the member.

704—Distance between lateral supports

(a) The clear distance between lateral supports of a beam shall not exceed 32 times the least width of compression flange.

705—Requirements for T-beams

(a) In T-beam construction the slab and beam shall be built integrally or otherwise effectively bonded together. The effective flange width to be used in the design of symmetrical T-beams shall not exceed one-fourth of the span length of the beam, and its overhanging width on either side of the web shall not exceed eight times the thickness of the slab nor one-half the clear distance to the next beam.

(b) For beams having a flange on one side only, the effective overhanging flange width shall not exceed 1/12 of the span length of the beam, nor six times the thickness of the slab, nor one-half the clear distance to the next beam.

(c) Where the principal reinforcement in a slab which is considered as the flange of a T-beam (not a joist in concrete joist floors) is parallel to the beam, transverse reinforcement shall be provided in the top of the slab. This reinforcement shall be designed to carry the load on the portion of the slab required for the flange of the T-beam. The flange shall be assumed to act as a cantilever. The spacing of the bars shall not exceed five times the thickness of the flange, nor in any case 18 in.

(d) Provision shall be made for the compressive stress at the support in continuous T-beam construction, care being taken that the provisions of Section 505 relating to the spacing of bars, and 404 (d) relating to the placing of concrete shall be fully met.

(e) The overhanging portion of the flange of the beam shall not be considered as effective in computing the shear and diagonal tension resistance of T-beams.

(f) Isolated beams in which the T-form is used only for the purpose of providing additional compression area, shall have a flange thickness not less than one-half the width of the web and a total flange width not more than four times the web thickness.

706—Compression steel in flexural members

(a) Compression steel in beams or girders shall be anchored by ties or stirrups not less than ¼ in. in diameter spaced not farther apart than 16 bar diameters, or 48 tie diameters. Such stirrups or ties shall be used throughout the distance where the compression steel is required.

(b) To approximate the effect of creep, the stress in compression reinforcement resisting bending may be taken at twice the value indicated by using the straight-line relation between stress and strain, and the modular ratio given in Section 601 (a), but not of greater value than the allowable stress in tension.

707—Shrinkage and temperature reinforcement

(a) Reinforcement for shrinkage and temperature stresses normal to the principal reinforcement shall be provided in structural floor and roof slabs where the principal reinforcement extends in one direction only. Such reinforcement shall provide for the following minimum ratios of reinforcement area to concrete area bt, but in no case shall such reinforcing bars be placed farther apart than five times the slab thickness nor more than 18 in.

Slabs where plain bars are used.................................0.0025

Slabs where deformed bars are used 0.0020

Slabs where wire fabric is used, having welded intersections
    not farther apart in the direction of stress than 12 in. 0.0018

708—Concrete joist floor construction

(*a*) In concrete joist floor construction consisting of concrete joists and slabs placed monolithically with or without burned clay or concrete tile fillers, the joists shall not be farther apart than 30 in. face to face. The ribs shall be straight, not less than 4 in. wide, and of a depth not more than three times the width.

(*b*) When burned clay or concrete tile fillers of material having a unit compressive strength at least equal to that of the designed strength of the concrete in the joists are used, the vertical shells of the fillers in contact with the joists may be included in the calculations involving shear or negative bending moment. No other portion of the ~~~~~~~~~~~~~~~~luded in the design calculations.

(*c*) The concrete slab over the fillers shall be not less than 1½ in. in thickness, nor less in thickness than 1/12 of the clear distance between joists. Shrinkage reinforcement shall be provided in the slab at right angles to the joists as required in Section 707.

(*d*) Where removable forms or fillers not complying with Section 708(b) are used, the thickness of the concrete slab shall not be less than 1/12 of the clear distance between joists and in no case less than 2 in. Such slab shall be reinforced at right angles to the joists with at least the amount of reinforcement required for flexure, giving due consideration to concentrations, if any, but in no case shall the reinforcement be less than that required by Section 707.

(*e*) When the finish used as a wearing surface is placed monolithically with the structural slab in buildings of the warehouse or industrial class, the thickness of the concrete over the fillers shall be ½ in. greater than the thickness used for design purposes.

(*f*) Where the slab contains conduits or pipes as allowed in Section 503, the thickness shall not be less than 1 in. plus the total over-all depth of such conduits or pipes at any point. Such conduits or pipes shall be so located as not to impair the strength of the construction.

(*g*) Shrinkage reinforcement shall not be required in the slab parallel to the joists.

709—Two-way systems with supports on four sides*

(*a*) This construction, reinforced in two directions, includes solid reinforced concrete slabs; concrete joists with fillers of hollow concrete units or clay tile, with or without concrete top slabs; and concrete joists with top slabs placed monolithically with the joists. The slab shall be supported by walls or beams on all sides and if not securely attached to supports, shall be reinforced as specified in Section 709(b).

---

*The requirements of this section are satisfied by either of the methods of design which follow this section.

(*b*) Where the slab is not securely attached to the supporting beams or walls, special reinforcement shall be provided at exterior corners in both the bottom and top of the slab. This reinforcement shall be provided for a distance in each direction from the corner equal to one-fifth the longest span. The reinforcement in the top of the slab shall be parallel to the diagonal from the corner. The reinforcement in the bottom of the slab shall be at right angles to the diagonal or may be of bars in two directions parallel to the sides of the slab. The reinforcement in each band shall be of equivalent size and spacing to that required for the maximum positive moment in the slab.

(*c*) The slab and its supports shall be designed by approved methods which shall take into account the effect of continuity at supports, the ratio of length to width of slab and the effect of two-way action.

(*d*) In no case shall the slab thickness be less than 4 in. nor less than the perimeter of the slab divided by 180. The spacing of reinforcement shall be not more than three times the slab thickness and the ratio of reinforcement shall be at least 0.0025.

METHOD 1

Notation—

L = length of clear span

L_1 = length of clear span in the direction normal to L

g = ratio of span between lines of inflection to L in the direction of span L, when span L only is loaded

g_1 = ratio of span between lines of inflection to L_1 in the direction of span L_1, when span L_1, only is loaded

$$r = \frac{gL}{g_1 L_1}$$

w = total uniform load per sq ft

W = total uniform load between opposite supports on slab strip of any width or total slab load on beam when considered as one-way construction

x = ratio of distance from support to any section of slab or beam, to span L or L_1

B = bending moment coefficient for one-way construction

C = factor modifying bending moments prescribed for one-way construction for use in proportioning the slabs and beams in the direction of L of slabs supported on four sides

C_s = ratio of the shear at any section of a slab strip distant xL from the support to the total load W on the strip in direction of L

C_b = ratio of the shear at any section of a beam distant xL from the support to the total load W on the beam in the direction of L

W_1, C_1, C_{s1}, C_{b1}, are corresponding values of W, C, C_s, C_b, for slab strip or beam in direction of L_1

(*a*) *Lines of inflection for determination of r*—The lines of inflection shall be determined by elastic analysis of the continuous structure in each direction, when only the span under consideration is loaded.

When the span L or L_1 is at least 2/3 and at most 3/2 of the adjacent continuous span or spans, the values of g or g_1 may be taken as 0.87 for exterior spans and 0.76 for interior spans. (See Fig. 1.)

For spans discontinuous at both ends, g or g_1 shall be taken as unity.

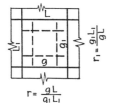

When L or L_1 is at least $^2/_3$ or at most $^3/_2$ of the adjacent continuous span or spans, obtain r or r_1 from cases 1 to 6. Beyond these limits, compute g and g_1 by elastic analysis when only the span under consideration is loaded.

$$r = \frac{gL}{g_1 L_1}$$

General

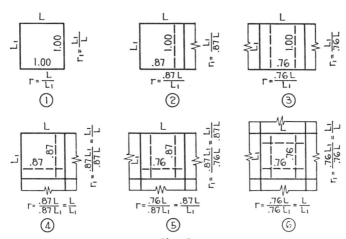

Fig. 1

(b) *Bending moments and shear*—Bending moments shall be determined in each direction with the coefficients prescribed for one-way construction in Sections 701 and 702 and modified by factor C or C_1 from Tables 1 or 2

	In L direction	In L_1 direction
Bending moment for slab strip	$M = CBWL$	$M_1 = C_1 BW_1 L_1$
Bending moment for beam	$M = (1{-}C)BWL$	$M_1 = (1{-}C_1)BW_1 L_1$

When the coefficients prescribed in 701(c) are used, the average value of Cw or $C_1 w$ for the two spans adjacent to a support shall be used in determining the negative bending moment at the face of the support.

The shear at any section distant xL or xL_1 from supports shall be determined by modifying the total load on the slab strip or beam by the factors C_s, C_{s1}, C_b, or C_{b1} taken from Tables 1 or 2

	In L direction	In L_1 direction
Shear for slab strip	$V = C_s W$	$V_1 = C_{s1} W_1$
Shear for beam	$V = C_b W$	$V_1 = C_{b1} W_1$

For spans where the end moments are unbalanced, shear values at any section shall be adjusted in accordance with Sections 701 and 702.

(c) *Arrangement of reinforcement*

1. In any panel, the area of reinforcement per unit width in the long direction shall be at least one-third that provided in the short direction

TABLE 1—SLABS

Upper figure C_s / Lower figure C_{s1}		Values of x					C / C_1
r	$\dfrac{1}{r}$	0 0	0.1	0.2	0.3	0.4	
0 00		0.50	0.40	0 30	0.20	0.10	1 00
	∞	0 00	0 00	0 00	0 00	0 00	0 00
0.50		0.44	0.36	0.27	0.18	0.09	0 89
	2.00	0 06	0.03	0 02	0 00	0 00	0 06
0.55		0.43	0.33	0.23	0.15	0.07	0.79
	1 82	0.07	0 04	0 02	0.01	0 00	0 08
0 60		0.41	0.30	0 20	0.12	0.05	0.70
	1 67	0.09	0.05	0 03	0 01	0 00	0 10
0.65		0.39	0.28	0.18	0.10	0.04	0 64
	1.54	0 11	0.06	0 03	0 01	0.00	0.13
0.70		0.37	0.26	0.16	0.09	0.03	0.58
	1.43	0.13	0.08	0 04	0 01	0 00	0 15
0.80		0.33	0.22	0.13	0.07	0.02	0.48
	1.25	0.17	0.10	0.06	0 02	0 00	0 21
0.90		0.29	0.19	0.11	0 05	0 01	0.40
	1.11	0.21	0.13	0.07	0 03	0 01	0 27
1.00		0.25	0.16	0.09	0.04	0 01	0 33
	1.00	0 25	0.16	0 09	0 04	0 01	0 33
1.10		0.21	0.13	0.07	0.03	0.01	0.28
	0.91	0 29	0.19	0 11	0 05	0 01	0 39
1.20		0.18	0.11	0 06	0.02	0.00	0.23
	0.83	0 32	0 21	0.13	0 06	0.02	0 45
1.30		0.16	0.10	0 05	0.02	0.00	0 19
	0.77	0.34	0 23	0.14	0 07	0.03	0 51
1.40		0.13	0.08.	0.04	0.02	0.00	0.16
	0.71	0 37	0.25	0.16	0.09	0.03	0 57
1.50		0.11	0.07	0.04	0.01	0.00	0.14
	0.67	0 39	0.27	0.17	0.10	0.04	0 61
1.60		0.10	0.06	0.03	0.01	0.00	0.12
	0.63	0.40	0 29	0 19	0.11	0.05	0.66
1 80		0.07	0.04	0.02	0.01	0.00	0.08
	0.55	0.43	0.33	0.23	0.15	0 07	0.79
2 00		0.06	0.03	0.02	0.00	0.00	0 06
	0 50	0.44	0.36	0.36	0.27	0.18	0 89
∞		0.00	0.00	0.00	0.00	0.00	0 00
	0 00	0.50	0.40	0.30	0 20	0 10	1 00

2. The area of positive moment reinforcement adjacent to a continuous edge only and for a width not exceeding one-fourth of the shorter dimension of the panel may be reduced 25 percent.

3. At a noncontinuous edge the area of negative moment reinforcement per unit width shall be at least one-half of that required for maximum positive moment.

METHOD 2

Notation—

C = moment coefficient for two-way slabs as given in Table 3

m = ratio of short span to long span for two-way slabs

S = length of short span for two-way slabs. The span shall be considered as the center-to-center distance between supports or the clear span plus twice the thickness of slab, whichever value is the smaller.

w = total uniform load per sq ft

(a) *Limitations*—A two-way slab shall be considered as consisting of strips in each direction as follows:

TABLE 2—BEAMS

		C_b					$1-C$
Upper figure				C_{b1}			$1-C_1$
Lower figure							
r	$\dfrac{1}{r}$	0.0	0.1	0.2	0.3	0.4	
0.00	∞	0.00 / 0 50	0.00 / 0.40	0.00 / 0.30	0.00 / 0.20	0.00 / 0 10	0.00 / 1.00
0.50	2.00	0.06 / 0.44	0.04 / 0.37	0.03 / 0.28	0.02 / 0.20	0.01 / 0.10	0.11 / 0 94
0.55	1.82	0.07 / 0.43	0.07 / 0.36	0.07 / 0.28	0.05 / 0.19	0.03 / 0.10	0.21 / 0.92
0.60	1.67	0.09 / 0.41	0.10 / 0.35	0.10 / 0.27	0.08 / 0 19	0.05 / 0.10	0.30 / 0.90
0.65	1.54	0.11 / 0.39	0.12 / 0.34	0.12 / 0.27	0.10 / 0.19	0.06 / 0.10	0.36 / 0 87
0.70	1.43	0.13 / 0.37	0.14 / 0.32	0.14 / 0.26	0.11 / 0.19	0.07 / 0.10	0.42 / 0.85
0.80	1 25	0.17 / 0.33	0.18 / 0.30	0.17 / 0 24	0.13 / 0.18	0.08 / 0.10	0 52 / 0.79
0.90	1.11	0.21 / 0.29	0.21 / 0.27	0.19 / 0.23	0.15 / 0.17	0.09 / 0 09	0 60 / 0.73
1.00	1.00	0.25 / 0.25	0.24 / 0.24	0 21 / 0.21	0.16 / 0.16	0.09 / 0.09	0.67 / 0.67
1.10	0.91	0.29 / 0.21	0.27 / 0.21	0.23 / 0.19	0.17 / 0.15	0.09 / 0 09	0.72 / 0.61
1.20	0.83	0.32 / 0.18	0.29 / 0.19	0.24 / 0.17	0.18 / 0.14	0.10 / 0.08	0.77 / 0.55
1.30	0.77	0.34 / 0.16	0.30 / 0.17	0.25 / 0.16	0.18 / 0.13	0.10 / 0.07	0.81 / 0 49
1.40	0.71	0.37 / 0.13	0.32 / 0.15	0.26 / 0.14	0.18 / 0.11	0.10 / 0.07	0.84 / 0.43
1.50	0.67	0.39 / 0.11	0.33 / 0.13	0.26 / 0.13	0.19 / 0.10	0.10 / 0.06	0.86 / 0.39
1.60	0.63	0.40 / 0.10	0.34 / 0.11	0.27 / 0.11	0.19 / 0.09	0.10 / 0.05	0.88 / 0.34
1.80	0.55	0.43 / 0.07	0.36 / 0 07	0.28 / 0.07	0.19 / 0.05	0.10 / 0.03	0.92 / 0.21
2.00	0.50	0.44 / 0.06	0.37 / 0.04	0.28 / 0.03	0.20 / 0.02	0.10 / 0.01	0.94 / 0.11
∞	0.00	0.50 / 0.00	0.40 / 0.00	0.30 / 0.00	0.20 / 0.00	0.10 / 0.00	1.00 / 0.00

A middle strip one-half panel in width, symmetrical about panel center-line and extending through the panel in the direction in which moments are considered.

A column strip one-half panel in width, occupying the two quarter-panel areas outside the middle strip.

Where the ratio of short to long span is less than 0.5, the middle strip in the short direction shall be considered as having a width equal to the difference between the long and short span, the remaining area representing the two column strips.

The critical sections for moment calculations are referred to as principal design sections and are located as follows:

For negative moment, along the edges of the panel at the faces of the supporting beams.

For positive moment, along the centerlines of the panels.

(b) *Bending moments*—The bending moments for the middle strips shall be computed from the formula

$$M = CwS^2$$

The average moments per foot of width in the column strip shall be two-thirds of the corresponding moments in the middle strip. In determining the spacing of the reinforcement in the column strip, the moment may be assumed to vary from a maximum at the edge of the middle strip to a minimum at the edge of the panel.

Where the negative moment on one side of a support is less than 80 percent of that on the other side, two-thirds of the difference shall be distributed in proportion to the relative stiffnesses of the slabs.

TABLE 3—MOMENT COEFFICIENTS

Moments	Short span						Long span, all values of m
	Values of m						
	1.0	0.9	0.8	0.7	0.6	0.5 and less	
Case 1—Interior panels							
Negative moment at—							
Continuous edge	0.033	0.040	0.048	0.055	0.063	0.083	0.033
Discontinuous edge	—	—	—	—	—	—	—
Positive moment at midspan	0.025	0.030	0.036	0.041	0.047	0.062	0.025
Case 2—One edge discontinuous							
Negative moment at—							
Continuous edge	0.041	0.048	0.055	0.062	0.069	0.085	0.041
Discontinuous edge	0.021	0.024	0.027	0.031	0.035	0.042	0.021
Positive moment at midspan	0.031	0.036	0.041	0.047	0.052	0.064	0.031
Case 3—Two edges discontinuous							
Negative moment at—							
Continuous edge	0.049	0.057	0.064	0.071	0.078	0.090	0.049
Discontinuous edge	0.025	0.028	0.032	0.036	0.039	0.045	0.025
Positive moment at midspan	0.037	0.043	0.048	0.054	0.059	0.068	0.037
Case 4—Three edges discontinuous							
Negative moment at—							
Continuous edge	0.058	0.066	0.074	0.082	0.090	0.098	0.058
Discontinuous edge	0.029	0.033	0.037	0.041	0.045	0.049	0.029
Positive moment at midspan	0.044	0.050	0.056	0.062	0.068	0.074	0.044
Case 5—Four edges discontinuous							
Negative moment at—							
Continuous edge	—	—	—	—	—	—	—
Discontinuous edge	0.033	0.038	0.043	0.047	0.053	0.055	0.033
Positive moment at midspan	0.050	0.057	0.064	0.072	0.080	0.083	0.050

(c) *Shear*—The shearing stresses in the slab may be computed on the assumption that the load is distributed to the supports in accordance with (d).

(d) *Supporting beams*—The loads on the supporting beams for a two-way rectangular panel may be assumed as the load within the tributary areas of the panel bounded by the intersection of 45-deg lines from the corners with the median line of the panel parallel to the long side.

The bending moments may be determined approximately by using an equivalent uniform load per lineal foot of beam for each panel supported as follows:

For the short span: $\dfrac{wS}{3}$

For the long span: $\dfrac{wS}{3} \dfrac{(3-m^2)}{2}$

REINFORCED CONCRETE FUNDAMENTALS

CHAPTER 8—SHEAR AND DIAGONAL TENSION

800—Notation

A_v = total area of web reinforcement in tension within a distance of s (measured in a direction parallel to that of the main reinforcement), or the total area of all bars bent up in any one plane

α = angle between inclined web bars and axis of beam

b = width of rectangular flexural member or width of flange for T- and I-sections

b' = width of web in T and I flexural members

d = depth from compression face of beam or slab to centroid of longitudinal tensile reinforcement

f_c' = compressive strength of concrete at age of 28 days unless otherwise specified

f_v = tensile unit stress in web reinforcement

j = ratio of distance between centroid of compression and centroid of tension to the depth d

s = spacing of stirrups or of bent bars in a direction parallel to that of the main reinforcement

v = shearing unit stress

V = total shear

V' = total shear carried by the web reinforcement

801—Shearing unit stress

(a) The shearing unit stress v, as a measure of diagonal tension, in reinforced concrete flexural members shall be computed by formula (2):

$$v = \frac{V}{bjd} \dots\dots\dots\dots\dots\dots\dots\dots\dots\dots\dots\dots\dots\dots\dots\dots\dots\dots\dots\dots\dots (2)$$

(b) For beams of I- or T- section, b' shall be substituted for b in formula (2).

(c) In concrete joist floor construction, where burned clay or concrete tile are used, b' may be taken as a width equal to the thickness of the concrete web plus the thickness of the vertical shells of the concrete or burned clay tile in contact with the joist as in Section 708(b).

(d) Wherever the value of the shearing unit stress computed by formula (2) exceeds the shearing unit stress v_c permitted on the concrete of an unreinforced web (see Section 305), web reinforcement shall be provided to carry the excess. Such reinforcement shall also be provided for a distance equal to the depth, d, of the member beyond the point theoretically required.

(e) Where continuous or restrained beams or frames do not have a slab so cast as to provide T-beam action, the following provisions shall apply. Web reinforcement shall be provided from the support to a point beyond the extreme position of the point of inflection a distance equal to either 1/16 of the clear span or the depth of the member, whichever is greater, even though the shearing unit stress does not exceed v_c. Such reinforcement shall be designed to carry at least two-thirds of the total shear at the section. Web reinforcement shall be provided sufficient to carry at least two-thirds of the total shear at a section in which there is negative reinforcement.

802—Types of web reinforcement

(*a*) Web reinforcement may consist of:
1. Stirrups or web reinforcing bars perpendicular to the longitudinal steel.
2. Stirrups or web reinforcing bars welded or otherwise rigidly attached to the longitudinal steel and making an angle of 30 deg or more thereto.
3. Longitudinal bars bent so that the axis of the inclined portion of the bar makes an angle of 15 deg or more with the axis of the longitudinal portion of the bar.
4. Special arrangements of bars with adequate provisions to prevent slip of bars or splitting of the concrete by the reinforcement [see Section 804(f)].

(*b*) Stirrups or other bars to be considered effective as web reinforcement shall be anchored at both ends, according to the provisions of Section 904.

803—Stirrups

(*a*) The area of steel required in stirrups placed perpendicular to the longitudinal reinforcement shall be computed by formula (3).

$$A_v = \frac{V's}{f_v j d} \quad\dots\dots\dots\dots\dots\dots\dots\dots\dots\dots\dots\dots\dots\dots\dots\dots\dots\dots\dots\dots\dots\dots\dots\dots\dots \quad (3)$$

(*b*) Inclined stirrups shall be proportioned by formula (5) [Section 804(d)].
(*c*) Stirrups placed perpendicular to the longitudinal reinforcement shall not be used alone as web reinforcement when the shearing unit stress, v, exceeds $0.08 f_c'$ or 240 psi.

804—Bent bars

(*a*) Only the center three-fourths of the inclined portion of any longitudinal bar that is bent up for web reinforcement shall be considered effective for that purpose, and such bars shall be bent around a pin having a diameter not less than six times the bar size.
(*b*) When the web reinforcement consists of a single bent bar or of a single

group of parallel bars all bent up at the same distance from the support, the required area of such bars shall be computed by formula (4).

$$A_v = \frac{V'}{f_v \sin \alpha} \dots\dots\dots\dots\dots\dots\dots\dots\dots\dots\dots\dots\dots\dots\dots\dots \quad (4)$$

(c) In formula (4), V' shall not exceed $0.04 f_c'bjd$, or $120\ bjd$.

(d) Where there is a series of parallel bars or groups of bars bent up at different distances from the support, the required area shall be determined by formula (5).

$$A_v = \frac{V's}{f_vjd\ (\sin \alpha + \cos \alpha)} \dots\dots\dots\dots\dots\dots\dots\dots\dots\dots\dots\dots \quad (5)$$

(e) When bent bars, having a radius of bend of at least six bar diameters are used alone as web reinforcement, they shall be so spaced that the effective inclined portion described in Section 804(a) meets the requirements of Section 806, and the allowable shearing unit stress shall not exceed $0.08\ f_c'$ nor 240 psi.

(f) The shearing unit stress permitted when special arrangements of bars are employed shall be that determined by making comparative tests, to destruction, of specimens of the proposed system and of similar specimens reinforced in conformity with the provisions of this code, the same factor of safety being applied in both cases.

805—Combined web reinforcement

(a) Where more than one type of reinforcement is used to reinforce the same portion of the web, the total shearing resistance of this portion of the web shall be assumed as the sum of the shearing resistances computed for the various types separately. In such computations the shearing resistance of the concrete shall be included only once, and no one type of reinforcement shall be assumed to resist more than $2V'/3$.

806—Maximum spacing of web reinforcement

(a) Where web reinforcement is required it shall be so spaced that every 45-deg line (representing a potential crack) extending from the middepth of the beam to the longitudinal tension bars shall be crossed by at least one line of web reinforcement. If a shearing unit stress in excess of $0.06\ f_c'$ is used, every such line shall be crossed by at least two such lines of web reinforcement.

807—Minimum web reinforcement

Where web reinforcement is required, the amount used shall be not less than

0.15 percent of the area computed as the product of the width of the member at middepth and the horizontal spacing of the web reinforcement.

808—Shearing stresses in flat slabs [see Section 1002(c)]

809—Shear and diagonal tension in footings

(*a*) In isolated footings the shearing unit stress computed by formula (2) on the critical section [see Section 1205(a)] shall not exceed 0.03 f_c' nor in any case shall it exceed 75 psi.

CHAPTER 9—BOND AND ANCHORAGE

900—Notation

d = depth from compression face of beam or slab to centroid of longitudinal tensile reinforcement

f_c' = compressive strength of concrete at age of 28 days unless otherwise specified

j = ratio of distance between centroid of compression and centroid of tension to the depth d

Σo = sum of perimeters of bars in one set

u = bond stress per unit of surface area of bar

V = total shear

901—Computation of bond stress in beams

(*a*) In flexural members in which the tensile reinforcement is parallel to the compression face, the bond stress at any cross section shall be computed by formula (6).

$$u = \frac{V}{\Sigma ojd} \quad \dots \quad (6)$$

in which V is the shear at that section and Σo is taken as the perimeter of all effective bars crossing the section on the tension side. Bent-up bars that are not more than $d/3$ from the level of the main longitudinal reinforcement may be included. Critical sections occur at the face of the support, at each point where tension bars terminate within a span, and at the point of inflection.

(*b*) Bond shall be similarly computed on compressive reinforcement, but the shear used in computing the bond shall be reduced in the ratio of the compressive force assumed in the bars to the total compressive force at the section. Anchorage shall be provided by embedment past the section to develop the assumed compressive force in the bars at the bond stress in Table 305(a).

(*c*) Adequate end anchorage shall be provided for the tensile reinforcement in all flexural members to which formula (6) does not apply, such as sloped, stepped or tapered footings, brackets or beams in which the tensile reinforcement is not parallel to the compression face.

902—Anchorage requirements

(*a*) Tensile negative reinforcement in any span of a continuous, restrained or cantilever beam, or in any member of a rigid frame shall be adequately anchored by bond, hooks, or mechanical anchors in or through the supporting member. Within any such span every reinforcing bar, except in a lapped splice, whether required for positive or negative reinforcement, shall be extended at least 12 diameters beyond the point at which it is no longer needed to resist stress. At least one-third of the total reinforcement provided for negative moment at the support shall be extended beyond the extreme position of the point of inflection a distance sufficient to develop by bond one-half the allowable stress in such bars, not less than 1/16 of the clear span length, or not less than the depth of the member, whichever is greater. The tension in any bar at any section must be properly developed on each side of the section by hook, lap, or embedment (see Section 906). If preferred, the bar may be bent across the web at an angle of not less than 15 deg with the longitudinal portion of the bar and be made continuous with the reinforcement which resists moment of opposite sign.

(*b*) Of the positive reinforcement in continuous beams not less than one-fourth the area shall extend along the same face of the beam into the support a distance of 6 in.

(*c*) In simple beams, or at the freely supported end of continuous beams, at least one-third the required positive reinforcement shall extend along the same face of the beam into the support a distance of 6 in.

903—Plain bars in tension

Plain bars in tension shall terminate in standard hooks except that hooks shall not be required on the positive reinforcement at interior supports of continuous members.

904—Anchorage of web reinforcement

(*a*) The ends of bars forming simple U- or multiple stirrups shall be anchored by one of the following methods:

1. By a standard hook, considered as developing 10,000 psi, plus embedment sufficient to develop by bond the remaining stress in the bar at the unit stress specified in Table 305(a). The effective embedded length of a stirrup leg shall be taken as the distance between the middepth of the beam and the tangent of the hook.

2. Welding to longitudinal reinforcement.

3. Bending tightly around the longitudinal reinforcement through at least 180 deg.

4. Embedment above or below the middepth of the beam on the compression side, a distance sufficient to develop the stress to which the bar will be subjected at a bond stress of not to exceed 0.045 f_c' on plain bars nor 0.10 f_c' on deformed bars, but, in any case, a minimum of 24 bar diameters.

(*b*) Between the anchored ends, each bend in the continuous portion of a U- or multiple U-stirrup shall be made around a longitudinal bar.

(*c*) Hooking or bending stirrups around the longitudinal reinforcement shall be considered effective only when these bars are perpendicular to the longitudinal reinforcement.

(*d*) Longitudinal bars bent to act as web reinforcement shall, in a region of tension, be continuous with the longitudinal reinforcement. The tensile stress in each bar shall be fully developed in both the upper and the lower half of the beam as specified in Section 904(a)1 or 904 (a)4.

(*e*) In all cases web reinforcement shall be carried as close to the compression surface of the beam as fireproofing regulations and the proximity of other steel will permit.

905—Anchorage of bars in footing slabs

(*a*) Plain bars in footing slabs shall be anchored by means of standard hooks. The outer faces of these hooks and the ends of deformed bars shall be not less than 3 in. nor more than 6 in. from the face of the footing.

906—Hooks

(*a*) The terms "hook" or "standard hook" as used herein shall mean either
1. A complete semicircular turn with a radius of bend on the axis of the bar of not less than three and not more than six bar diameters, plus an extension of at least four bar diameters at the free end of the bar, or
2. A 90-deg bend having a radius of not less than four bar diameters plus an extension of 12 bar diameters, or
3. For stirrup anchorage only, a 135-deg turn with a radius on the axis of the bar of three diameters plus an extension of at least six bar diameters at the free end of the bar.

Hooks having a radius of bend of more than six bar diameters shall be considered merely as extensions to the bars.

(*b*) No hook shall be assumed to carry a load which would produce a tensile stress in the bar greater than 10,000 psi.

(*c*) Hooks shall not be considered effective in adding to the compressive resistance of bars.

(*d*) Any mechanical device capable of developing the strength of the bar without damage to the concrete may be used in lieu of a hook. Tests must be presented to show the adequacy of such devices.

CHAPTER 10—FLAT SLABS WITH SQUARE OR RECTANGULAR PANELS

1000—Notation

A = distance in the direction of span from center of support to the intersection of the centerline of the slab thickness with the extreme 45-deg diagonal line lying wholly within the concrete section of slab and column or other support, including drop panel, capital and bracket

b = width of section

c = effective support size [see Section 1004(c)]

d = depth from compression face of beam or slab to centroid of tensile reinforcement

f_c' = compressive strength of concrete at age of 28 days unless otherwise specified

H = story height in feet of the column or support of a flat slab center to center of slabs

j = ratio of distance between centroids of compression and tension to depth d

L = span length of a flat slab panel center to center of supports

M_0 = numerical sum of assumed positive and average negative moments at the critical design sections of a flat slab panel [see Section 1004(f)1]

t = thickness of slab in inches at center of panel

t_1 = thickness in inches of slabs without drop panels, or through drop panel, if any

t_2 = thickness in inches of slabs with drop panels at points beyond the drop panel

v = shearing unit stress

V = total shear

w' = uniformly distributed unit dead and live load

W = total dead and live load on panel

W_D = total dead load on panel

W_L = total live load on panel, uniformly distributed

1001—Definitions and scope

(a) *Flat slab*—A concrete slab reinforced in two or more directions, generally without beams or girders to transfer the loads to supporting members. Slabs with recesses or pockets made by permanent or removable fillers between reinforcing bars may be considered flat slabs. Slabs with paneled ceilings may be considered as flat slabs provided the panel of reduced thickness lies entirely within the area of intersecting middle strips, and is at least two-thirds the thickness of the remainder of the slab, exclusive of the drop panel, and is not less than 4 in. thick.

(b) *Column capital*—An enlargement of the end of a column designed and built to act as an integral unit with the column and flat slab. No portion of the column capital shall be considered for structural purposes which lies outside of the largest right circular cone with 90-deg vertex angle that can be included within the outlines of the column capital. Where no capital is used, the face of the column shall be considered as the edge of the capital.

(c) *Drop panel*—The structural portion of a flat slab which is thickened throughout an area surrounding the column, column capital, or bracket.

(d) *Panel strips*—A flat slab shall be considered as consisting of strips in each direction as follows:

A middle strip one-half panel in width, symmetrical about panel centerline.

A column strip consisting of the two adjacent quarter-panels either side of the column centerline.

1002—Design procedures

(a) *Methods of analysis*—All flat slab structures shall be designed in accordance with a recognized elastic analysis subject to the limitations of Sections 1002 and 1003, except that the empirical method of design given in Section 1004 may be used for the design of flat slabs conforming with the limitations given therein. Flat slabs within the limitations of Section 1004, when designed by elastic analysis, may have resulting analytical moments reduced in such proportion that the numerical sum of the positive and average negative bending moments used in design procedure need not exceed M_o as specified under Section 1004(f).

(b) *Critical sections*—The slab shall be proportioned for the bending moments prevailing at every section except that the slab need not be proportioned for a greater negative moment than that prevailing at a distance A from the support centerline.

(c) *Size and thickness of slabs and drop panels*

1. Subject to limitations of Section 1002(c)3, the thickness of a flat slab and the size and thickness of the drop panel, where used, shall be such that the compressive stress due to bending at any section, and the shear about the column, column capital, and drop panel shall not exceed the unit stresses allowed in concrete of the quality used. When designed under Section 1004, three-fourths of the width of the strip shall be used as the width of the section in computing compression due to bending, except that on a section through a drop panel, three-fourths of the width of the drop panel shall be used. Account shall be taken of any recesses which reduce the compressive area.

2. The shearing unit stress on vertical sections which follow a periphery, b, at distance, d, beyond the edges of the column or column capital and parallel or concentric with it, shall not exceed the following values for the concrete when computed by the formula

$$v = \frac{V}{bjd}$$

a. 0.03 f_c' but not more than 100 psi when at least 50 percent of the total negative reinforcement required for bending in the column strip passes through the periphery.

b. 0.025 f_c' but not more than 85 psi when 25 percent, which is the least value permitted, of the total negative reinforcement required for bending in the column strip passes through the periphery.

c. Proportionate values of the shearing unit stress for intermediate percentages of reinforcement.

3. Where drop panels are used, the shearing unit stress on vertical sections which lie at a distance, d, beyond the edges of the drop panel, and parallel with them, shall not exceed 0.03 f_c' nor 100 psi. At least 50 percent of the total negative reinforcement required for bending in the column strip shall be within the width of strip directly above the drop panel.

4. Slabs with drop panels whose length is at least one-third the parallel span length and whose projection below the slab is at least one-fourth the slab thickness shall be not less than $L/40$ nor 4 in. in thickness.

Slabs without drop panels as described above shall be not less than $L/36$ nor 5 in. in thickness.

5. For determining reinforcement, the thickness of the drop panel below the slab shall not be assumed to be more than one-fourth of the distance from the edge of the drop panel to the edge of the column capital.

(d) *Arrangement of slab reinforcement*

1. The spacing of the bars at critical sections shall not exceed two times the slab thickness, except for those portions of the slab area which may be of cellular or ribbed construction. In the slab over the cellular spaces, reinforcement shall be provided as required by Section 707.

2. In exterior panels, except for bottom bars adequately anchored in the drop panel, all positive reinforcement perpendicular to the discontinuous edge shall extend to the edge of the slab and have embedment, straight or hooked, of at least 6 in. in spandrel beams, walls, or columns where provided. All negative reinforcement perpendicular to the discontinuous edge shall be bent, hooked, or otherwise anchored in spandrel beams, walls, or columns.

3. The area of reinforcement shall be determined from the bending moments at the critical sections but shall not be less than 0.0025 bd at any section.

4. Required splices in bars may be made wherever convenient, but preferably away from points of maximum stress. The length of any such splice shall be at least 36 bar diameters.

(e) *Openings in flat slabs*—Openings of any size may be provided in flat slabs if provision is made for the total positive and negative moments and for shear without exceeding the allowable stresses except that when design is based on Section 1004, the limitations given therein shall not be exceeded.

(f) *Design of columns*

1. All columns supporting flat slabs shall be designed as provided in Chapter 11 with the additional requirements of this chapter.

1003—Design by elastic analysis

(*a*) *Assumptions*—In design by elastic analysis the following assumptions may be used and all sections shall be proportioned for the moments and shears thus obtained.

1. The structure may be considered divided into a number of bents, each consisting of a row of columns or supports and strips of supported slabs, each strip bounded laterally by the centerline of the panel on either side of the centerline of columns or supports. The bents shall be taken longitudinally and transversely of the building.

2. Each such bent may be analyzed in its entirety; or each floor thereof and the roof may be analyzed separately with its adjacent columns as they occur above and below, the columns being assumed fixed at their remote ends. Where slabs are thus analyzed separately, it may be assumed in determining the bending at a given support that the slab is fixed at any support two panels distant therefrom beyond which the slab continues.

3. The joints between columns and slabs may be considered rigid, and this rigidity (infinite moment of inertia) may be assumed to extend in the slabs from the center of the column to the edge of the capital, and in the column from the top of slab to the bottom of the capital. The change in length of columns and slabs due to direct stress, and deflections due to shear, may be neglected.

4. Where metal column capitals are used, account may be taken of their contributions to stiffness and resistance to bending and shear.

5.. The moment of inertia of the slab or column at any cross section may be assumed to be that of the cross section of the concrete. Variation in the moments of inertia of the slabs and columns along their axes shall be taken into account.

6. Where the load to be supported is definitely known, the structure shall be analyzed for that load. Where the live load is variable but does not exceed three-quarters of the dead load, or the nature of the live load is such that all panels will be loaded simultaneously, the maximum bending may be assumed to occur at all sections under full live load. For other conditions, maximum positive bending near midspan of a panel may be assumed to occur under full live load in the panel and in alternate panels; and maximum negative bending in the slab at a support may be assumed to occur under full live load in the adjacent panels only.

(*b*) *Critical sections*—The critical section for negative bending, in both the column strip and middle strip, may be assumed as not more than the distance *A* from the center of the column or support and the critical negative moment shall be considered as extending over this distance.

(*c*) *Distribution of panel moments*—Bending at critical sections across the slabs of each bent may be apportioned between the column strip and middle strip, as given in Table 1003(c). For design purposes, any of these percentages may be

REINFORCED CONCRETE FUNDAMENTALS

TABLE 1003(c)—DISTRIBUTION BETWEEN COLUMN STRIPS AND MIDDLE STRIPS IN PERCENT OF TOTAL MOMENTS AT CRITICAL SECTIONS OF A PANEL

Strip		Moment section			
		Negative moment at interior support	Positive moment	Negative moment at exterior support	
				Slab supported on columns and on beams of total depth equal to the slab thickness*	Slab supported on reinforced concrete bearing wall or columns with beams of total depth equal or greater than 3 times the slab thickness*
Column strip		76	60	80	60
Middle strip		24	40	20	40
Half column strip adjacent and parallel to marginal beam or wall	Total depth of beam equal to slab thickness*	38	30	40	30
	Total depth of beam or wall equal or greater than 3 times slab thickness*	19	15	20	15

*Interpolate for intermediate ratios of beam depth to slab thickness.
Note: The total dead and live load reaction of a panel adjacent to a marginal beam or wall may be divided between the beam or wall and the parallel half column strip in proportion to their stiffnesses, but the moment provided in the slab shall not be less than given in Table 1003(c).

varied by not more than 10 percent of its value, but their sum for the full panel width shall not be reduced.

1004—Design by empirical method

(a) General limitations—Flat slab construction may be designed by the empirical provisions of this section when they conform to all of the limitations on continuity and dimensions given herein.

1. The construction shall consist of at least three continuous panels in each direction.

2. The ratio of length to width of panels shall not exceed 1.33.

3. The grid pattern shall consist of approximately rectangular panels. The successive span lengths in each direction shall differ by not more than 20 percent of the longer span. Within these limitations, columns may be offset a maximum of 10 percent of the span, in direction of the offset, from either axis between centerlines of successive columns.

4. The calculated lateral force moments from wind or earthquake may be combined with the critical moments as determined by the empirical method, and the lateral force moments shall be distributed between the column and middle strips in the same proportions as specified for the negative moments in the strips for structures not exceeding 125 ft high with maximum story height not exceeding 12 ft 6 in.

(b) *Columns*

1. The minimum dimension of any column shall be 10 in. For columns or other supports of a flat slab, the required minimum average moment of inertia, I_c, of the gross concrete section of the columns above and below the slab shall be determined from the following formula, and shall be not less than 1000 in.[4] If there is no column above the slab, the I_c of the column below shall be twice that given by the formula with a minimum of 1000 in.[4]

$$I_c = \frac{t^3 H}{0.5 + \dfrac{W_D}{W_L}} \dotfill (7)$$

where t need not be taken greater than t_1 or t_2 as determined in Section 1004 (d), H is the average story height of the columns above and below the slab, and W_L is the greater value of any two adjacent spans under consideration.

2. Columns supporting flat slabs designed by the empirical method shall be proportioned for the bending moments developed by unequally loaded panels, or uneven spacing of columns. Such bending moment shall be the maximum value derived from

$$(WL_1 - W_D L_2)\ \frac{1}{f}$$

L_1 and L_2 being lengths of the adjacent spans ($L_2 = 0$ when considering an exterior column) and f is 30 for exterior and 40 for interior columns.

This moment shall be divided between the columns immediately above and below the floor or roof line under consideration in direct proportion to their stiffness and shall be applied without further reduction to the critical sections of the columns.

(c) Determination of "c" (effective support size)

1. Where column capitals are used, the value of c shall be taken as the diameter of the cone described in Section 1001(b) measured at the bottom of the slab or drop panel.

2. Where a column is without a concrete capital, the dimension c shall be taken as that of the column in the direction considered.

3. Brackets capable of transmitting the negative bending and the shear in the column strips to the columns without excessive unit stress may be substituted for column capitals at exterior columns. The value of c for the span where a bracket is used shall be taken as twice the distance from the center of the column to a point where the bracket is $1\frac{1}{2}$ in. thick, but not more than the thickness of the column plus twice the depth of the bracket.

4. Where a reinforced concrete beam frames into a column without capital or bracket on the same side with the beam, for computing bending for strips parallel to the beam, the value of c for the span considered may be taken as the width of the column plus twice the projection of the beam above or below the slab or drop panel.

5. The average of the values of c at the two supports at the ends of a column strip shall be used to evaluate the slab thickness t_1 or t_2 as prescribed in Section 1004(d).

(d) Slab thickness

1. The slab thickness, span L being the longest side of the panel, shall be at least:

$L/36$ for slab without drop panels conforming with Section 1004(e), or where a drop panel is omitted at any corner of the panel, but not less than 5 in. nor t_1 as given below.

$L/40$ for slabs with drop panels conforming to Section 1004(e) at all supports, but not less than 4 in. nor t_2 as given below.

2. The total thickness, t_1, in inches, of slabs without drop panels, or through the drop panel if any, shall be at least

$$t_1 = 0.028L \left(1 - \frac{2c}{3L} \right) \sqrt{\frac{w'}{f_c'/2000}} + 1\frac{1}{2}* \quad \dots\dots\dots\dots\dots (8)$$

3. The total thickness, t_2, in inches, of slabs with drop panels, at points beyond the drop panel shall be at least

$$t_2 = 0.024L \left(1 - \frac{2c}{3L} \right) \sqrt{\frac{w'}{f_c'/2000}} + 1* \quad \dots\dots\dots\dots\dots (9)$$

4. Where the exterior supports provide only negligible restraint to the slab, the values of t_1 and t_2 for the exterior panel shall be increased by at least 15 percent.

---

*In the above formulas, t_1 and t_2 are in inches and L and c are in feet.

TABLE 1004(f)—MOMENTS IN FLAT SLAB PANELS IN PERCENTAGES OF M_0

Strip	Column head	Side support type	End support type	Exterior panel Exterior negative moment	Positive moment	Interior negative moment	Interior panel Positive moment	Negative moment
Column strip	With drop		A	44				
			B	36	24	56	20	50
			C	6	36	72		
	Without drop		A	40				
			B	32	28	50	22	46
			C	6	40	66		
Middle strip	With drop		A	10				
			B	20	20	17*	15	15*
			C	6	26	22*		
	Without drop		A	10				
			B	20	20	18*	16	16*
			C	6	28	24*		
Half column strip adjacent to marginal beam or wall	With drop	1	A	22				
			B	18	12	28	10	25
			C	3	18	36		
		2	A	17				
			B	14	9	21	8	19
			C	3	14	27		
		3	A	11				
			B	9	6	14	5	13
			C	3	9	18		
	Without drop	1	A	20				
			B	16	14	25	11	23
			C	3	20	33		
		2	A	15				
			B	12	11	19	9	18
			C	3	15	25		
		3	A	10				
			B	8	7	13	6	12
			C	3	10	17		

Percentage of panel load to be carried by marginal beam or wall in addition to loads directly superimposed thereon	Side support parallel to strip	Type of support listed in Table 1004 (f) Side or end edge condition of slabs of depth t	End support at right angles to strip
0	1	Columns with no beams	
20	2	Columns with beams of total depth $1\frac{1}{4}t$	A
40	3	Columns with beams of total depth $3t$ or more	B
		Reinforced concrete bearing walls integral with slab	
		Masonry or other walls providing negligible restraint	C

*Increase negative moments 30 percent of tabulated values when middle strip is continuous across support of type B or C. No other values need be increased.

Note: For intermediate proportions of total beam depth to slab thickness, values for loads and moments may be obtained by interpolation. See also Fig. 1004 (f)a and b.

REINFORCED CONCRETE FUNDAMENTALS

Fig. 1004(f)a—Moments in flat slab panels in percentages of M_0—Without drops

See Table 1004(f) for notes and classification of conditions of end supports and side supports

PANEL		INTERIOR				EXTERIOR				
MOMENT		SUPPORT	CENTER OF SPAN	1ST INTERIOR SUPPORT	CENTER OF SPAN	EXTERIOR SUPPORT (B)	EXTERIOR SUPPORT (A)	1ST INTERIOR SUPPORT	CENTER OF SPAN	EXTERIOR SUPPORT (C)
END SUPPORT	SIDE SUPPORT									
MARGINAL HALF COLUMN STRIP	3	-12	+6	-13	+7	-8	-10	-17	+10	-3
	2	-18	+9	-19	+11	-12	-15	-25	+15	-3
	1	-23	+11	-25	+14	-16	-20	-33	+20	-3
MIDDLE STRIP		-16*	+16	-18*	+20	-20	-10	-24*	+28	-6
COLUMN STRIP		-46	+22	-50	+28	-32	-40	-66	+40	-6

DIRECTION OF ALL MOMENTS →

*Increase negative moments 30 percent when middle strip is continuous across a support of type B or C. No other values need be increased.

Fig. 1004(f)b—Moments in flat slab panels in percentage of M_0—With drops

See Table 1004(f) for notes and classification of conditions of end supports and side supports

*Increase negative moments 30 percent when middle strip is continuous across a support of type B or C. No other values need be increased.

532   REINFORCED CONCRETE FUNDAMENTALS

TABLE 1004 (g)1—MINIMUM LENGTH OF NEGATIVE REINFORCEMENT

Strip	Percentage of required reinforcing steel area to be extended at least as indicated	Minimum distance beyond centerline of support to end of straight bar or to bend point of bent bar*			
		Flat slabs without drop panels		Flat slabs with drop panels	
		Straight	Bend point where bars bend down and continue as positive reinforcement	Straight	Bend point where bars bend down and continue as positive reinforcement
Column strip reinforcement	Not less than 33 percent	0.30L†		0.33L‡	
	Not less than an additional 34 percent	0.27L†		0.30L‡	
	Remainder§	0.25L	or　0.20L	0.25L	or drop but at least 0 20L / To edge of
Middle strip reinforcement	Not less than 50 percent	0.25L		0.25L	
	Remainder§	0.25L	or　0.15L	0.25L	or　0.15L

*At exterior supports where masonry walls or other construction provide only negligible restraint to the slab, the negative reinforcement need not be carried further than 0.20L beyond the centerline of such support.

†Where no bent bars are used, the 0.27L bars may be omitted, provided the 0.30L bars are at least 50 percent of total required.

‡Where no bent bars are used, the 0.30L bars may be omitted provided the 0.33L bars provide at least 50 percent of the total required.

§Bars may be straight, bent, or any combination of straight and bent bars. All bars are to be considered straight bars for the end under consideration unless bent at that end and continued as positive reinforcement.

Note: See also Fig. 1004(g).

(e) *Drop panels*

1. The maximum total thickness at the drop panel used in computing the negative steel area for the column strip shall be $1.5t_2$.

2. The side or diameter of the drop panel shall be at least 0.33 times the span in the parallel direction.

3. The minimum thickness of slabs where drop panels at wall columns

TABLE 1004(g)2—MINIMUM LENGTH OF POSITIVE REINFORCEMENT

Strip	Percentage of required reinforcing steel area to be extended at least as indicated	Maximum distance from centerline of support to end of straight bar or bend point of bent bar			
		Flat slabs without drop panels		Flat slabs with drop panels	
		Straight	Bend point where bars bend up and continue as negative reinforcement	Straight	Bend point where bars bend up and continue as negative reinforcement
Column strip reinforcement	Not less than 33 percent	0.125L		Minimum embedment in drop panel of 16 bar diameters but at least 10 in.	
	Not less than 50 percent*	3 in. or 0.25L			
	Remainder*	0.125L or 0.25L		Minimum embedment in drop panel of 16 bar diameters but at least 10 in. or 0.25L	
Middle strip reinforcement	50 percent	0.15L		0.15L	
	50 percent*	3 in. or 0.25L		3 in. or 0.25L	

*Bars may be straight, bent, or any combination of straight and bent bars. All bars are to be considered straight bars for the end under consideration unless bent at that end and continued as negative reinforcement.

Note: See also Fig. 1004(g).

are omitted shall equal $(t_1 + t_2)/2$ provided the value of c used in the computations complies with Section 1004(c).

(f) Bending moment coefficients

1. The numerical sum of the positive and negative bending moments in the direction of either side of a rectangular panel shall be assumed as not less than

$$M_o = 0.09 \ WLF \left(1 - \frac{2c}{3L} \right)^2 \dots\dots\dots\dots\dots\dots\dots\dots\dots (10)$$

in which $F = 1.15 - c/L$ but not less than 1.

2. Unless otherwise provided, the bending moments at the critical sections of the column and middle strips shall be at least those given in Table 1004(f).

REINFORCED CONCRETE FUNDAMENTALS

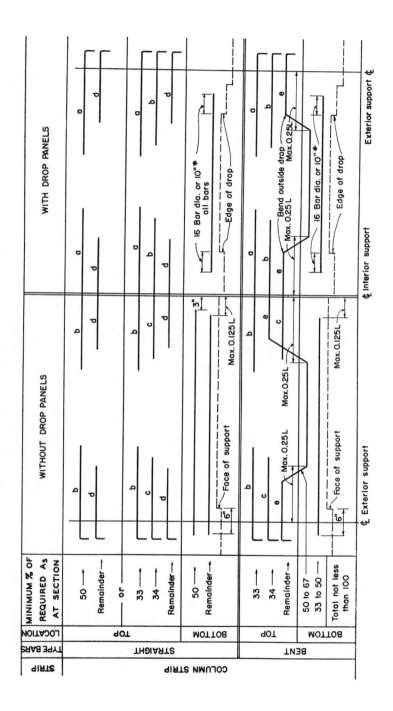

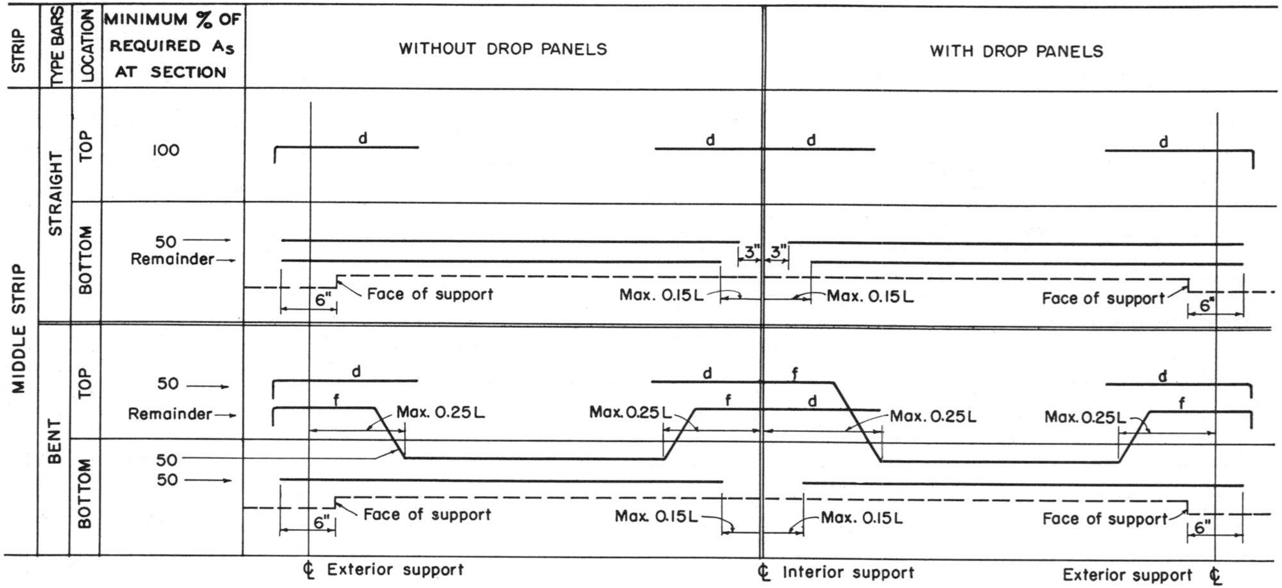

WITHOUT DROP PANELS

WITH DROP PANELS

d

d

d

d

6" Face of support

Max. 0.15L

3" 3"

Max. 0.15L

Max. 0.15L Face of support 6"

f Max. 0.25L

d

Max. 0.25L

Max. 0.25L

d

f

f Max. 0.25L

6" Face of support

Max. 0.15L

d

Max. 0.15L Face of support 6"

℄ Exterior support

℄ Interior support

℄ Exterior support

STRIP	TYPE BARS	LOCATION	MINIMUM % OF REQUIRED A_s AT SECTION
MIDDLE STRIP	STRAIGHT	TOP	100
		BOTTOM	50 → Remainder
	BENT	TOP	50 → Remainder
		BOTTOM	50 → / 50 →

MINIMUM LENGTH OF BAR FROM ℄ SUPPORT

MARK	a	b	c	d	e	f
LENGTH	0.33L	0.30L	0.27L	0.25L	0.20L	0.15L

At interior supports, L is longer of adjacent spans.

Fig. 1004(g)—Minimum length of flat slab reinforcement

At exterior supports, where masonry walls or other construction provide only negligible restraint to the slab, the negative reinforcement need not be carried further than 0.20L beyond the centerline of such support. Any combination of straight and bent bars may be used provided minimum requirements are met

*For bars not terminating in drop panel use lengths shown for panels without drops.

536 REINFORCED CONCRETE FUNDAMENTALS

3. The average of the values of c at the two supports at the ends of a column strip shall be used to evaluate M_o in determining bending in the strip. The average of the values of M_o, as determined for the two parallel half column strips in a panel, shall be used in determining bending in the middle strip.

4. Bending in the middle strips parallel to a discontinuous edge shall be assumed the same as in an interior panel.

5. For design purposes, any of the moments determined from Table 1004(f) may be varied by not more than 10 percent, but the numerical sum of the positive and negative moments in a panel shall be not less than the amount specified.

(g) *Length of reinforcement*—In addition to the requirements of Section 1002(d), reinforcement shall have the minimum lengths given in Tables 1004(g)1 and 1004(g)2. Where adjacent spans are unequal, the extension of negative reinforcement on each side of the column centerline as prescribed in Table 1004(g)1 shall be based on the requirements of the longer span.

(h) *Openings in flat slabs*
1. Openings of any size may be provided in a flat slab in the area common to two intersecting middle strips provided the total positive and negative steel areas required in Section 1004(f) are maintained.

2. In the area common to two column strips, not more than one-eighth of the width of strip in any span shall be interrupted by openings. The equivalent of all bars interrupted shall be provided by extra steel on all sides of the openings. The shearing unit stresses given in Section 1002(c)2 shall not be exceeded.

3. In any area common to one column strip and one middle strip, openings may interrupt one-quarter of the bars in either strip. The equivalent of the bars so interrupted shall be provided by extra steel on all sides of the opening.

4. Any opening larger than described above shall be analyzed by accepted engineering principles and shall be completely framed as required to carry the loads to the columns.

CHAPTER 11—REINFORCED CONCRETE COLUMNS AND WALLS

1100—Notation

A_c = area of core of a spirally reinforced column measured to the outside diameter of the spiral; net area of concrete section of a composite column

A_g = over-all or gross area of spirally reinforced or tied columns; the total area of the concrete encasement of combination columns

A_r = area of the steel or cast-iron core of a composite column; the area of the steel core in a combination column

A_s = effective cross-sectional area of reinforcement in compression in columns

B = trial factor (see Section 1109(c) and footnote thereto)

e = eccentricity of the resultant load on a column, measured from the gravity axis

F_a = nominal allowable axial unit stress $(0.225f_c' + f_s p_g)$ for spiral columns and 0.8 of this value for tied columns

F_b = allowable bending unit stress that would be permitted if bending stress only existed

f_a = nominal axial unit stress = axial load divided by area of member, A_g

f_b = bending unit stress (actual) = bending moment divided by section modulus of member

f_c = computed concrete fiber stress in an eccentrically loaded column where the ratio of e/t is greater than 2/3

f_c' = compressive strength of concrete at age of 28 days, unless otherwise specified

f_r = allowable unit stress in the metal core of a composite column

f_r' = allowable unit stress on unencased steel columns and pipe columns

f_s = nominal allowable stress in vertical column reinforcement

f_s' = useful limit stress of spiral reinforcement

h = unsupported length of column

K_c = radius of gyration of concrete in pipe columns

K_s = radius of gyration of a metal pipe section (in pipe columns)

N = axial load applied to reinforced concrete column

p' = ratio of volume of spiral reinforcement to the volume of the concrete core (out to out of spirals) of a spirally reinforced concrete column

p_g = ratio of the effective cross-sectional area of vertical reinforcement to the gross area A_g

P = total allowable axial load on a column whose length does not exceed ten times its least cross-sectional dimension

P' = total allowable axial load on a long column

t = over-all depth of rectangular column section, or the diameter of a round column

1101—Limiting dimensions

(a) The following sections on reinforced concrete and composite columns, except Section 1107(a), apply to a short column for which the unsupported length is not greater than ten times the least dimension. When the unsupported length exceeds this value, the design shall be modified as shown in Section 1107(a). Principal columns in buildings shall have a minimum diameter of 12 in., or in the case of rectangular columns, a minimum thickness of 8 in., and a minimum gross area of 120 sq in. Posts that are not continuous from story to story shall have a minimum diameter or thickness of 6 in.

1102—Unsupported length of columns

(*a*) For purposes of determining the limiting dimensions of columns, the unsupported length of reinforced concrete columns shall be taken as the clear distance between floor slabs, except that

1. In flat slab construction, it shall be the clear distance between the floor and the lower extremity of the capital, the drop panel or the slab, whichever is least.

2. In beam and slab construction, it shall be the clear distance between the floor and the under side of the deeper beam framing into the column in each direction at the next higher floor level.

3. In columns restrained laterally by struts, it shall be the clear distance between consecutive struts in each vertical plane; provided that to be an adequate support, two such struts shall meet the column at approximately the same level, and the angle between vertical planes through the struts shall not vary more than 15 degrees from a right angle. Such struts shall be of adequate dimensions and anchorage to restrain the column against lateral deflection.

4. In columns restrained laterally by struts or beams, with brackets used at the junction, it shall be the clear distance between the floor and the lower edge of the bracket, provided that the bracket width equals that of the beam or strut and is at least half that of the column.

(*b*) For rectangular columns, that length shall be considered which produces the greatest ratio of length to depth of section.

1103—Spirally reinforced columns

(*a*) *Allowable load*—The maximum allowable axial load, *P*, on columns with closely spaced spirals enclosing a circular concrete core reinforced with vertical bars shall be that given by formula (11).

$$P = A_g \ (0.225f_c' + f_s p_g) \ \dotfill \ (11)$$

Wherein f_s = nominal allowable stress in vertical column reinforcement, to be taken at 40 percent of the minimum specification value of the yield point; *viz.*, 16,000 psi for intermediate grade steel and 20,000 psi for rail or hard grade steel.*

(*b*) *Vertical reinforcement*—The ratio p_g shall not be less than 0.01 nor more than 0.08. The minimum number of bars shall be six, and the minimum bar size

---

*Nominal allowable stresses for reinforcement of higher yield point may be established at 40 percent of the yield point stress, but not more than 30,000 psi, when the properties of such reinforcing steels have been definitely specified by standards of ASTM designation. If this is done, the lengths of splice required by Section 1103(c) shall be increased accordingly.

shall be #5. The center to center spacing of bars within the periphery of the column core shall not be less than 2½ times the diameter for round bars or three times the side dimension for square bars. The clear spacing between individual bars or between pairs of bars at lapped splices shall not be less than 1½ in. or 1½ times the maximum size of the coarse aggregate used. These spacing rules also apply to adjacent pairs of bars at a lapped splice; each pair of lapped bars forming a splice may be in contact, but the minimum clear spacing between one splice and the adjacent splice should be that specified for adjacent single bars.

(c) *Splices in vertical reinforcement*—Where lapped splices in the column verticals are used, the minimum amount of lap shall be as follows:

1. For deformed bars with concrete having a strength of 3000 psi or more, 20 diameters of bar of intermediate or hard grade steel. For bars of higher yield point, the amount of lap shall be increased one diameter for each 1000 psi by which the allowable stress exceeds 20,000 psi. When the concrete strengths are less than 3000 psi, the amount of lap shall be one-third greater than the values given above.

2. For plain bars, the minimum amount of lap shall be twice that specified for deformed bars.

3. Welded splices or other positive connections may be used instead of lapped splices. Welded splices shall preferably be used in cases where the bar size exceeds #11. An approved welded splice shall be defined as one in which the bars are butted and welded and that will develop in tension at least the yield point stress of the reinforcing steel used.

4. Where longitudinal bars are offset at a splice, the slope of the inclined portion of the bar with the axis of the column shall not exceed 1 in 6, and the portions of the bar above and below the offset shall be parallel to the axis of the column. Adequate horizontal support at the offset bends shall be treated as a matter of design, and may be provided by metal ties, spirals or parts of the floor construction. Metal ties or spirals so designed shall be placed near (never more than eight bar diameters from) the point of bend. The horizontal thrust to be resisted may be assumed as 1½ times the horizontal component of the nominal stress in the inclined portion of the bar.

Offset bars shall be bent before they are placed in the forms. No field bending of bars partially embedded in concrete shall be permitted.

(d) *Spiral reinforcement*—The ratio of spiral reinforcement, p', shall not be less than the value given by formula (12).

$$p' = 0.45 \left(\frac{A_g}{A_c} - 1 \right) \frac{f_c'}{f_s'} \quad \dots \dots \dots \dots \dots \dots \dots \dots \dots \dots \dots \dots \dots \dots \dots \dots \dots \quad (12)$$

Wherein f_s' = useful limit stress of spiral reinforcement, to be taken as 40,000 psi for hot rolled rods of intermediate grade, 50,000 psi for rods of hard grade, and 60,000 psi for cold drawn wire.

The spiral reinforcement shall consist of evenly spaced continuous spirals held firmly in place and true to line by vertical spacers, using at least two for spirals

20 in. or less in diameter, three for spirals 20 to 30 in. in diameter, and four for spirals more than 30 in. in diameter or composed of spiral rods ⅝ in. or larger in size. The spirals shall be of such size and so assembled as to permit handling and placing without being distorted from the designed dimensions. The material used in spirals shall have a minimum diameter of ¼ in. for rolled bars or No. 4 AS&W gage for drawn wire. Anchorage of spiral reinforcement shall be provided by 1½ extra turns of spiral rod or wire at each end of the spiral unit. Splices when necessary shall be made in spiral rod or wire by welding or by a lap of 1½ turns. The center to center spacing of the spirals shall not exceed one-sixth of the core diameter. The clear spacing between spirals shall not exceed 3 in. nor be less than 1⅜ in. or 1½ times the maximum size of coarse aggregate used. The reinforcing spiral shall extend from the floor level in any story or from the top of the footing in the basement, to the level of the lowest horizontal reinforcement in the slab, drop panel or beam above. In a column with a capital, it shall extend to a plane at which the diameter or width of the capital is twice that of the column.

(e) *Protection of reinforcement*—The column spiral reinforcement shall be protected everywhere by a covering of concrete cast monolithically with the core, for which the thickness shall not be less than 1½ in. nor less than 1½ times the maximum size of the coarse aggregate, nor shall it be less than required by the fire protection and weathering provisions of Section 507.

(f) *Isolated column with multiple spirals*—In case two or more interlocking spirals are used in a column, the outer boundary of the column shall be taken as a rectangle the sides of which are outside the extreme limits of the spiral at a distance equal to the requirements of Section 1103(e).

(g) *Limits of section of column built monolithically with wall*—For a spiral column built monolithically with a concrete wall or pier, the outer boundary of the column section shall be taken either as a circle at least 1½ in. outside the column spiral or as a square or rectangle of which the sides are at least 1½ in. outside the spiral or spirals.

(h) *Equivalent circular columns*—As an exception to the general procedure of utilizing the full gross area of the column section, it shall be permissible to design a circular column and to build it with a square, octagonal, or other shaped section of the same least lateral dimension. In such case, the allowable load, the gross area considered, and the required percentages of reinforcement shall be taken as those of the circular column.

1104—Tied columns

(a) *Allowable load*—The maximum allowable axial load on columns reinforced with longitudinal bars and separate lateral ties shall be 80 percent of that given by formula (11). The ratio, p_g, to be considered in tied columns shall not be less than 0.01 nor more than 0.04. The longitudinal reinforcement shall consist of at least four bars, of minimum bar size of #5. Splices in reinforcing bars shall be made as described in Section 1103(c). The spacing requirements for vertical reinforcement in Section 1103(b) shall also apply for all tied columns.

(b) *Combined axial and bending load*—For tied columns which are designed to withstand combined axial and bending stresses, the limiting steel ratio of 0.04 may be increased to 0.08. The amount of steel spliced by lapping shall not exceed a steel ratio of 0.04 in any 3-ft length of column. The size of the column designed under this provision shall in no case be less than that required to withstand the axial load alone with a steel ratio of 0.04.

(c) *Lateral ties*—Lateral ties shall be at least ¼ in. in diameter and shall be spaced apart not over 16 bar diameters, 48 tie diameters, or the least dimension of the column. When there are more than four vertical bars, additional ties shall be provided so that every longitudinal bar is held firmly in its designed position and has lateral support equivalent to that provided by a 90-deg corner of a tie.

(d) *Limits of column section*—In a tied column which for architectural reasons has a larger cross section than required by considerations of loading, a reduced effective area, A_g, not less than one-half of the total area may be used in applying the provisions of Section 1104(a).

1105—Composite columns

(a) *Allowable load*—The allowable load on a composite column, consisting of a structural steel or cast iron column thoroughly encased in concrete reinforced with both longitudinal and spiral reinforcement, shall not exceed that given by formula (13).

$$P = 0.225 \, A_c f_c' + f_s A_s + f_r A_r \dots\dots\dots\dots\dots\dots\dots\dots\dots\dots\dots\dots\dots\dots \quad (13)$$

Wherein f_r = allowable unit stress in metal core, not to exceed 16,000 psi for a steel core; or 10,000 psi for a cast-iron core.

(b) *Details of metal core and reinforcement*—The cross-sectional area of the metal core shall not exceed 20 percent of the gross area of the column. If a hollow metal core is used it shall be filled with concrete. The amounts of longitudinal and spiral reinforcement and the requirements as to spacing of bars, details of splices and thickness of protective shell outside the spiral shall conform to the limiting values specified in Section 1103(b), (c), (d), and (e). A clearance of at least 3 in. shall be maintained between the spiral and the metal core at all points except that when the core consists of a structural steel H-column, the minimum clearance may be reduced to 2 in.

(c) *Splices and connections of metal cores*—Metal cores in composite columns shall be accurately milled at splices and positive provision shall be made for alignment of one core above another. At the column base, provision shall be made to transfer the load to the footing at safe unit stresses in accordance with Section 305(a). The base of the metal section shall be designed to transfer the load from the entire composite column to the footing, or it may be designed to transfer the load from the metal section only, provided it is so placed in the pier or pedestal as to leave ample section of concrete above the base for the transfer of load from the reinforced concrete section of the column by means of bond on the vertical reinforcement and by direct compression on the concrete. Transfer of loads to the metal core shall be provided for by the use of bearing members such as billets, brackets or other positive connections; these shall be provided at the top of the metal core and at intermediate floor levels where required. The column as a whole shall satisfy the requirements of formula (13) at any point; in addition to this, the reinforced concrete portion shall be designed to carry, in accordance with formula (11), all floor loads brought onto the column at levels between the metal brackets or connections. In applying formula (11), the value of A_g shall be interpreted as the area of the concrete section outside the metal core, and the allowable load on the reinforced concrete section shall be further limited to 0.35 $f_c'A_g$. Ample section of concrete and continuity of reinforcement shall be provided at the junction with beams or girders.

(d) *Allowable load on metal core only*—The metal cores of composite columns shall be designed to carry safely any construction or other loads to be placed upon them prior to their encasement in concrete.

1106—Combination columns

(a) *Steel columns encased in concrete*—The allowable load on a structural steel column which is encased in concrete at least 2½ in. thick over all metal (except rivet heads) reinforced as hereinafter specified, shall be computed by formula (14).

$$P = A_r f_r' \left[1 + \frac{A_g}{100 \, A_r} \right] \dotfill (14)$$

The concrete used shall develop a compressive strength, f_c', of at least 2000 psi at 28 days. The concrete shall be reinforced by the equivalent of welded wire mesh having wires of No. 10 AS&W gage, the wires encircling the column being spaced not more than 4 in. apart and those parallel to the column axis not more than 8 in. apart. This mesh shall extend entirely around the column at a distance of 1 in. inside the outer concrete surface and shall be lap-spliced at least 40 wire diameters and wired at the splice. Special brackets shall be used to receive the entire floor load at each floor level. The steel column shall be designed to carry safely any construction or other loads to be placed upon it prior to its encasement in concrete.

(b) *Pipe columns*—The allowable load on columns consisting of steel pipe filled with concrete shall be determined by formula (15).

$$P = 0.25 f_c' \left(1 - 0.000025 \frac{h^2}{K_c^2} \right) A_c + f_r'A_s \dotfill (15)$$

The value of f_r' shall be given by formula (16) when the pipe has a yield strength of at least 33,000 psi, and an h/K_s ratio equal to or less than 120.

$$f_r' = 17,000 - 0.485 \frac{h^2}{K_s^2} \dotfill (16)$$

1107—Long columns

(a) The maximum allowable load, P', on axially loaded reinforced concrete or composite columns having an unsupported length, h, greater than ten times the least lateral dimension, t, shall be given by formula (17).

$$P' = P [1.3 - 0.03\ h/t] \dotfill (17)$$

where P is the allowable axial load on a short column as given by Sections 1103, 1104, and 1105.

The maximum allowable load, P', on eccentrically loaded columns in which h/t exceeds 10 shall also be given by formula (17), in which P is the allowable eccentrically applied load on a short column as determined by the provisions of Section 1109. In long columns subjected to definite bending stresses, as determined in Section 1108, the ratio h/t shall not exceed 20.

1108—Bending moments in columns

(a) The bending moments in the columns of all reinforced concrete structures shall be determined on the basis of loading conditions and restraint and shall be provided for in the design. When the stiffness and strength of the columns are utilized to reduce moments in beams, girders, or slabs, as in the case of rigid frames, or in other forms of continuous construction wherein column moments are unavoidable, they shall be provided for in the design. In building frames, particular attention shall be given to the effect of unbalanced floor loads on both exterior and interior columns and of eccentric loading due to other causes. In computing moments in columns, the far ends may be considered fixed. Columns shall be designed to resist the axial forces from loads on all floors, plus the maximum bending due to loads on a single adjacent span of the floor under consideration.

Resistance to bending moments at any floor level shall be provided by distributing the moment between the columns immediately above and below the given floor in proportion to their relative stiffnesses and conditions of restraint.

1109—Columns subjected to axial load and bending

(a) Members subject to an axial load and bending in one principal plane, but with the ratio of eccentricity to depth e/t no greater than 2/3, shall be so proportioned that

$$\frac{f_a}{F_a} + \frac{f_b}{F_b} \text{ does not exceed unity} \dotfill (18)$$

(b) When bending exists on both of the principal axes, formula (18) becomes

$$\frac{f_a}{F_a} + \frac{f_{bx}}{F_b} + \frac{f_{by}}{F_b} \text{ does not exceed unity} \dotfill (19)$$

where f_{bx} and f_{by} are the bending moment components about the x and y principal axes divided by the section modulus of the transformed section relative to the respective axes, provided that the ratio e/t is no greater than 2/3 in either direction.

(*c*) In designing a column subject to both axial load and bending, the preliminary selection of the column may be made by use of an equivalent axial load given by formula (20).

$$P = N \left(1 + \frac{Be}{t} \right)^* \quad \dots\dots\dots\dots\dots\dots\dots\dots\dots\dots\dots\dots\dots\dots\dots \quad (20)$$

When bending exists on both of the principal axes, the quantity Be/t is the numerical sum of the Be/t quantities in the two directions.

(*d*) For columns in which the load, N, has an eccentricity, e, greater than 2/3 the column depth, t, the determination of the fiber stress f_c shall be made by use of recognized theory for cracked sections, based on the assumption that the concrete does not resist tension. In such cases the modular ratio for the compressive reinforcement shall be assumed as double the value given in Section 601; however the stress in the compressive reinforcement when calculated on this basis, shall not be greater than the allowable stress in tension. The maximum combined compressive stress in the concrete shall not exceed $0.45f_c'$. For such cases the tensile steel stress shall also be investigated.

1110—Wind and earthquake stresses

(*a*) When the allowable stress in columns is modified to provide for combined axial load and bending, and the stress due to wind or earthquake loads is also added, the total shall still come within the allowable values specified for wind or earthquake loads in Section 603(c).

1111—Reinforced concrete walls

(*a*) The allowable stresses in reinforced concrete bearing walls with minimum reinforcement as required by Section 1111(h), shall be $0.25f_c'$ for walls having a ratio of height to thickness of ten or less, and shall be reduced proportionally to $0.15f_c'$ for walls having a ratio of height to thickness of 25. When the reinforcement in bearing walls is designed, placed, and anchored in position as for tied columns, the allowable stresses shall be on the basis of Section 1104, as for columns. In the case of concentrated loads, the length of the wall to be considered as effective for each shall not exceed the center to center distance between loads, nor shall it exceed the width of the bearing plus four times the wall thickness. The ratio p_g shall not exceed 0.04.

---

*For trial computations B may be taken from 3 to 3½ for rectangular tied columns, the lower value being used for columns with the minimum amount of reinforcement. Similarly for circular spiral columns, the value of B from 5 to 6 may be used.

(*b*) Walls shall be designed for any lateral or other pressure to which they are subjected. Proper provision shall be made for eccentric loads and wind stresses. In such designs the allowable stresses shall be as given in Section 305(a) and 603(c).

(*c*) Panel and enclosure walls of reinforced concrete shall have a thickness of not less than 4 in. and not less than 1/30 the distance between the supporting or enclosing members.

(*d*) Reinforced concrete bearing walls of buildings shall be not less than 6 in. thick for the uppermost 15 ft of their height; and for each successive 25 ft downward, or fraction thereof, the minimum thickness shall be increased 1 in. Reinforced concrete bearing walls of two-story dwellings may be 6 in. thick throughout their height.

(*e*) Exterior basement walls, foundation walls, fire walls, and party walls shall not be less than 8 in. thick whether reinforced or not.

(*f*) Reinforced concrete bearing walls shall have a thickness of at least 1/25 of the unsupported height or width, whichever is the shorter.

(*g*) Reinforced concrete walls shall be anchored to the floors, or to the columns, pilasters, buttresses, and intersecting walls with reinforcement at least equivalent to #3 bars 12 in. on centers, for each layer of wall reinforcement.

(*h*) The area of the horizontal reinforcement of reinforced concrete walls shall be not less than 0.0025 and that of the vertical reinforcement not less than 0.0015 times the area of the reinforced section of the wall if of bars, and not less than three-fourths as much if of welded wire fabric. The wire of the welded fabric shall be of not less than No. 10 AS&W gage. Walls more than 10 in. thick, except for basement walls, shall have the reinforcement for each direction placed in two layers parallel with the faces of the wall. One layer consisting of not less than one-half and not more than two-thirds the total required shall be placed not less than 2 in. nor more than one-third the thickness of the wall from the exterior surface. The other layer, comprising the balance of the required reinforcement, shall be placed not less than ¾ in. and not more than one-third the thickness of the wall from the interior surface. Bars, if used, shall not be less than #3 bars, nor shall they be spaced more than 18 in. on centers. Welded wire reinforcement for walls shall be in flat sheet form.

(*i*) In addition to the minimum as prescribed in Section 1111(h) there shall be not less than two #5 bars around all window or door openings. Such bars shall extend at least 24 in. beyond the corner of the openings.

(*j*) Where reinforced concrete bearing walls consist of studs or ribs tied together by reinforced concrete members at each floor level, the studs may be considered as columns, but the restrictions as to minimum diameter or thickness of columns shall not apply.

(*k*) The limits of thicknesses and quantity of reinforcement may be waived where structural analysis shows adequate strength and stability.

CHAPTER 12—FOOTINGS

1201—Scope

(*a*) The requirements prescribed in Sections 1202 to 1209 apply only to isolated footings.*

1202—Loads and reactions

(*a*) Footings shall be proportioned to sustain the applied loads and induced reactions without exceeding the allowable stresses as prescribed in Sections 305 and 306, and as further provided in Sections 1205, 1206, and 1207.

(*b*) In cases where the footing is concentrically loaded and the member being supported does not transmit any moment to the footing, computations for moments and shears shall be based on an upward reaction assumed to be uniformly distributed per unit area or per pile and a downward applied load assumed to be uniformly distributed over the area of the footing covered by the column, pedestal, wall, or metallic column base.

(*c*) In cases where the footing is eccentrically loaded and/or the member being supported transmits a moment to the footing, proper allowance shall be made for any variation that may exist in the intensities of reaction and applied load consistent with the magnitude of the applied load and the amount of its actual or virtual eccentricity.

(*d*) In the case of footings on piles, computations for moments and shears may be based on the assumption that the reaction from any pile is concentrated at the center of the pile.

1203—Sloped or stepped footings

(*a*) In sloped or stepped footings, the angle of slope or depth and location of steps shall be such that the allowable stresses are not exceeded at any section.

(*b*) In sloped or stepped footings, the effective cross section in compression shall be limited by the area above the neutral plane.

(*c*) Sloped or stepped footings shall be cast as a unit.

1204—Bending moment

(*a*) The external moment on any section shall be determined by passing through the section a vertical plane which extends completely across the footing, and computing the moment of the forces acting over the entire area of the footing on one side of said plane.

(*b*) The greatest bending moment to be used in the design of an isolated footing shall be the moment computed in the manner prescribed in Section 1204(a) at sections located as follows:

    1. At the face of the column, pedestal or wall, for footings supporting a concrete column, pedestal or wall.

---

*The committee is not prepared at this time to make recommendations for combined footings —those supporting more than one column or wall.

2. Halfway between the middle and the edge of the wall, for footings under masonry walls.

3. Halfway between the face of the column or pedestal and the edge of the metallic base, for footings under metallic bases.

(c) The width resisting compression at any section shall be assumed as the entire width of the top of the footing at the section under consideration.

(d) In one-way reinforced footings, the total tensile reinforcement at any section shall provide a moment of resistance at least equal to the moment computed in the manner prescribed in Section 1204(a); and the reinforcement thus determined shall be distributed uniformly across the full width of the section.

(e) In two-way reinforced footings, the total tensile reinforcement at any section shall provide a moment of resistance at least equal to 85 percent of the moment computed in the manner prescribed in Section 1204(a); and the total reinforcement thus determined shall be distributed across the corresponding resisting section in the manner prescribed for the square footings in Section 1204(f), and for rectangular footings in Section 1204(g).

(f) In two-way square footings, the reinforcement extending in each direction shall be distributed uniformly across the full width of the footing.

(g) In two-way rectangular footings, the reinforcement in the long direction shall be distributed uniformly across the full width of the footing. In the case of the reinforcement in the short direction, that portion determined by formula (21) shall be uniformly distributed across a band-width (B) centered with respect to the centerline of the column or pedestal and having a width equal to the length of the short side of the footing. The remainder of the reinforcement shall be uniformly distributed in the outer portions of the footing.

$$\frac{Reinforcement\ in\ band\text{-}width\ (B)}{Total\ reinforcement\ in\ short\ direction} = \frac{2}{(S+1)} \quad \dots \dots \dots \dots \quad (21)$$

In formula (21), S is the ratio of the long side to the short side of the footing.

1205—Shear and bond

(a) The critical section for shear to be used as a measure of diagonal tension shall be assumed as a vertical section obtained by passing a series of vertical planes through the footing, each of which is parallel to a corresponding face of the column, pedestal, or wall and located a distance therefrom equal to the depth d for footings on soil, and one-half the depth d for footings on piles.

(b) Each face of the critical section as defined in Section 1205(a) shall be considered as resisting an external shear equal to the load on an area bounded by said face of the critical section for shear, two diagonal lines drawn from the column or pedestal corners and making 45-deg angles with the principal axes of the footing, and that portion of the corresponding edge or edges of the footing intercepted between the two diagonals.

(c) Critical sections for bond shall be assumed at the same planes as those prescribed for bending moment in Section 1204(b); also at all other vertical planes where changes of section or of reinforcement occur.

(d) Computation for shear to be used as a measure of bond shall be based on the same section and loading as prescribed for bending moment in Section 1204(a).

(e) The total tensile reinforcement at any section shall provide a bond resistance at least equal to the bond requirement as computed from the following percentages of the external shear at the section:

    1. In one-way reinforced footings, 100 percent.

    2. In two-way reinforced footings, 85 percent.

(f) In computing the external shear on any section through a footing supported on piles, the entire reaction from any pile whose center is located 6 in. or more outside the section shall be assumed as producing shear on the section; the reaction from any pile whose center is located 6 in. or more inside the section shall be assumed as producing no shear on the section. For intermediate positions of the pile center, the portion of the pile reaction to be assumed as producing shear on the section shall be based on straight-line interpolation between full value at 6 in. outside the section and zero value at 6 in. inside the section.

(g) For allowable shearing stresses, see Section 305 and 809.

(h) For allowable bond stresses, see Section 305 and 901 to 905.

1206—Transfer of stress at base of column

(a) The stress in the longitudinal reinforcement of a column or pedestal shall be transferred to its supporting pedestal or footing either by extending the longitudinal bars into the supporting member, or by dowels.

(b) In case the transfer of stress in the reinforcement is accomplished by extension of the longitudinal bars, they shall extend into the supporting member the distance required to transfer to the concrete, by allowable bond stress, their full working value.

(c) In cases where dowels are used, their total sectional area shall be not less than the sectional area of the longitudinal reinforcement in the member from which the stress is being transferred. In no case shall the number of dowels per member be less than four and the diameter of the dowels shall not exceed the diameter of the column bars by more than $\frac{1}{8}$ in.

(d) Dowels shall extend up into the column or pedestal a distance at least equal to that required for lap of longitudinal column bars (see Section 1103) and down into the supporting pedestal or footing the distance required to transfer to the concrete, by allowable bond stress, the full working value of the dowel [see Section 906(c)].

(e) The compressive stress in the concrete at the base of a column or pedestal shall be considered as being transferred by bearing to the top of the supporting pedestal or footing. The unit compressive stress on the loaded area shall not exceed the bearing stress allowable for the quality of concrete in the supporting member as limited by the ratio of the loaded area to the supporting area.

(*f*) For allowable bearing stresses see Table 305(a), Section 305.

(*g*) In sloped or stepped footings, the supporting area for bearing may be taken as the top horizontal surface of the footing, or assumed as the area of the lower base of the largest frustum of a pyramid or cone contained wholly within the footing and having for its upper base the area actually loaded, and having side slopes of one vertical to two horizontal.

1207—Pedestals and footings (plain concrete)

(*a*) The allowable compressive unit stress on the gross area of a concentrically loaded pedestal shall not exceed $0.25f_c'$. Where this stress is exceeded, reinforcement shall be provided and the member designed as a reinforced concrete column.

(*b*) The depth and width of a pedestal or footing of plain concrete shall be such that the tension in the concrete shall not exceed $0.03f_c'$, and the average shearing stress shall not exceed $0.02f_c'$ taken on sections as prescribed in Section 1204 and 1205 for reinforced concrete footings.

1208—Footings supporting round columns

(*a*) In computing the stresses in footings which support a round or octagonal concrete column or pedestal, the "face" of the column or pedestal shall be taken as the side of a square having an area equal to the area enclosed within the perimeter of the column or pedestal.

1209—Minimum edge-thickness

(*a*) In reinforced concrete footings, the thickness above the reinforcement at the edge shall be not less than 6 in. for footings on soil, nor less than 12 in. for footings on piles.

(*b*) In plain concrete footings, the thickness at the edge shall be not less than 8 in. for footings on soil, nor less than 14 in. above the tops of the piles for footings on piles.

— — — — — — — — — — — — — — — — —

APPENDIX

ABSTRACT OF REPORT OF ACI-ASCE JOINT COMMITTEE ON ULTIMATE STRENGTH DESIGN*

A600—Notation

(a) Loads and load factors

U = ultimate strength capacity of section

B = effect of basic load consisting of dead load plus volume change due to creep, elastic action, shrinkage, and temperature

L = effect of live load plus impact

W = effect of wind load

E = effect of earthquake forces

K = load factor

M_u = ultimate resisting moment

P_b = load defined by Eq. (A8)

P_o = ultimate strength of concentrically loaded member given by Eq. (A6)

P_u = ultimate strength of eccentrically loaded member

P_u' = maximum axial load on long member given by Eq. (A14)

(b) Cross-sectional constants

A_g = gross area of section

A_s = area of tensile reinforcement

A_s' = area of compressive reinforcement

A_{sf} = steel area to develop compressive strength of overhanging flange in T-sections, defined by Eq. (A5)

A_{st} = total area of longitudinal reinforcement

b = width of a rectangular section or over-all width of flange in T-sections

b' = width of web in T-sections

D = total diameter of circular section

D_s = diameter of circle circumscribing the longitudinal reinforcement in circular section

d = distance from extreme compressive fiber to centroid of tensile reinforcement

d' = distance from extreme compressive fiber to centroid of compressive reinforcement

e = eccentricity of axial load measured from the centroid of tensile reinforcement

e' = eccentricity of axial load measured from plastic centroid of section

e_b' = eccentricity of load P_b measured from plastic centroid of section

f_c' = 28-day cylinder strength

f_s = stress in tensile reinforcement at ultimate strength

f_y = yield point of reinforcement, not to be taken greater than 60,000 psi

k_u = defined by $k_u d$ = distance from extreme compressive fiber to neutral axis at ultimate strength

k_1 = ratio of average compressive stress to 0.85 f_c'

k_2 = ratio of distance between extreme compressive fiber and resultant of compressive stresses to distance between extreme fiber and neutral axis

m = $f_y/0.85\ f_c'$

m' = $m - 1$

p = A_s/bd

p' = A_s'/bd

p_f = $A_{sf}/b'd$

p_t = A_{st}/A_g

p_w = $A_s/b'd$

q = $p f_y/f_c'$

t = flange thickness in T-sections, also total depth of rectangular section

---

*For full report see *Proceedings*, ASCE, V. 81, Paper No. 809, Oct. 1955. Also see ACI JOURNAL, Jan. 1956, *Proc.* V. 52, pp. 505-524.

A601—Definitions and scope

(*a*) This appendix presents recommendations for design of reinforced concrete structures by ultimate strength theories. The term "ultimate strength design" indicates a method of design based on the ultimate strength of a reinforced concrete cross section in simple bending, combined bending and axial load on the basis of inelastic action.

(*b*) These recommendations are confined to design of sections. It is assumed that external moments and forces acting in a structure will be determined by the theory of elastic frames. With the specified load factors, stresses under service loads will remain within safe limits.

A602—General requirements

(*a*) The American Concrete Institute "Building Code Requirements for Reinforced Concrete" shall apply to the design of members by ultimate strength theory except where otherwise provided in this appendix.

(*b*) Analysis of indeterminate structures, such as continuous girders and arches, shall be based on the theory of elastic frames. For buildings of usual types of construction, spans, and story heights, approximate methods such as the use of coefficients recommended in the ACI Building Code are acceptable for determination of moments and shears.

(*c*) Bending moments in compression members shall be taken into account in the calculation of their required strength.

(*d*) In arches the effect of shortening of the arch axis, temperature, shrinkage, and secondary moments due to deflection shall be considered.

(*e*) Attention shall be given to the deflection of members, including the effect of creep, especially whenever the net ratio of reinforcement which is defined as $(p - p')$ or $(p_w - p_f)$ in any section of a flexural member exceeds $0.18 f_c'/f_y$.

(*f*) Controlled concrete should be used and shall meet the following requirements. The quality of concrete shall be such that not more than one test in ten shall have an average strength less than the strength assumed in the design, and the average of any three consecutive tests shall not be less than the assumed design strength. Each test shall consist of not less than three standard cylinders.

A603—Assumptions

Ultimate strength design of reinforced concrete members shall be based on the following assumptions:

(*a*) Plane sections normal to the axis remain plane after bending.

(*b*) Tensile strength in concrete is neglected in sections subject to bending.

(*c*) At ultimate strength, stresses and strains are not proportional. The diagram of compressive concrete stress distribution may be assumed a rectangle, trapezoid, parabola, or any other shape which results in ultimate strength in reasonable agreement with comprehensive tests.

(*d*)   Maximum fiber stress in concrete does not exceed $0.85f_c'$.

(*e*)   Stress in tensile and compressive reinforcement at ultimate load shall not be assumed greater than the yield point or 60,000 psi, whichever is smaller.

A604—Load factors

(*a*)   Members shall be so proportioned that an ample factor of safety is provided against an increase in live load beyond that assumed in design; and strains under service loads should not be so large as to cause excessive cracking. These criteria are satisfied by the following formulas:

> 1. For structures in which, due to location or proportions, the effects of wind and earthquake loading can be properly neglected:

$$U = 1.2B + 2.4L \dotfill \text{(I)}$$

$$U = K(B + L) \dotfill \text{(II)}$$

> 2. For structures in which wind loading must be considered:

$$U = 1.2B + 2.4L + 0.6W \dotfill \text{(Ia)}$$

$$U = 1.2B + 0.6L + 2.4W \dotfill \text{(Ib)}$$

$$U = K(B + L + \tfrac{1}{2}W) \dotfill \text{(IIa)}$$

$$U = K(B + \tfrac{1}{2}L + W) \dotfill \text{(IIb)}$$

> 3. For those structures in which earthquake loading must be considered, substitute E for W in the preceding equations.

(*b*)   The load factor, K, shall be taken equal to 2 for columns and members subjected to combined bending and axial load, and equal to 1.8 for beams and girders subject to bending only.

A605—Rectangular beams with tensile reinforcement only

(*a*)   The ultimate capacity of an under-reinforced section is approached when the tensile steel begins to yield. The steel shall then be assumed to elongate plastically at its yield point stress, thereby reducing the concrete area in compression until crushing takes place. The ultimate strength so obtained is controlled by tension.

(*b*)   The computed ultimate moment shall not exceed that given by:

$$M_u = bd^2f_c' \, q(1 - 0.59q) \dotfill \text{(A1)}$$

in which $q = pf_y/f_c'$.

(*c*)   In Eq. (A1), the maximum ratio of reinforcement shall be so limited that p does not exceed:

$$p = 0.40 \, f_c'/f_y \dotfill \text{(A2)}$$

The coefficient 0.40 is to be reduced at the rate of 0.025 per 1000 psi concrete strength in excess of 5000 psi.

A606—Rectangular beams with compressive reinforcement

(*a*) The ultimate moment shall not exceed that computed by:

$$M_u = (A_s - A_s')f_y d \left[1 - 0.59 \, (p - p')f_y/f_c'\right] + A_s'f_y^* \, (d - d') \quad \text{......} \quad \text{(A3)}$$

(*b*) In Eq. (A3), the maximum ratio of reinforcement shall be so limited that $(p - p')$ does not exceed the values given by Eq. (A2).

A607—T-sections

(*a*) When the flange thickness equals or exceeds the depth to the neutral axis given by $k_u d = 1.30 \, qd$ or the depth of the equivalent stress block (1.18 qd), the section may be designed by Eq. (A1), with q computed as for a rectangular beam with a width equal to the over-all flange width.

(*b*) When the flange thickness is less than $k_u d$ or less than the depth of the equivalent stress block, the ultimate moment shall not exceed that computed by:

$$M_u = (A_s - A_{sf})f_y d \, \left[1 - 0.59 \, (p_w - p_f) \, f_y/f_c'\right] + A_{sf}f_y \, (d - 0.5t) \quad \text{... (A4)}$$

in which A_{sf}, the steel area necessary to develop the compressive strength of the overhanging portions of the flange, is:

$$A_{sf} = 0.85(b - b')t \, f_c'/f_y \quad \text{...} \quad \text{(A5)}$$

(*c*) In Eq. (A4), the maximum ratio of reinforcement shall be so limited that $(p_u - p_f)$ does not exceed the values given by Eq. (A2).

A608—Concentrically loaded short columns

(*a*) All members subject to axial loads shall be designed for at least a minimum eccentricity:

For spirally reinforced columns, the minimum eccentricity measured from the centroidal axis of column shall be 0.05 times the depth of the column section. For tied columns, the minimum eccentricity shall be 0.10 times the depth.

(*b*) The maximum load capacity for concentric loads for use in Eq. (A10) is given by the formula:

$$P_o = 0.85f_c' \, (A_g - A_{st}) + A_{st} \, f_y \quad \text{.................................} \quad \text{(A6)}$$

A609—Bending and axial load: Rectangular section

(a) The ultimate strength of members subject to combined bending and axial load shall be computed from the equations of equilibrium, which when k_u is less than unity may be expressed as follows:

$$P_u = 0.85f_c' \, bdk_u k_1 + A_s' \, f_y^* - A_s f_s \quad \text{............................} \quad \text{(A7a)}$$

$$P_u e = 0.85f_c' \, bd^2 \, k_u k_1 \, (1 - k_2 k_u) + A_s' \, f_y^* \, (d - d') \quad \text{..............} \quad \text{(A7b)}$$

In Eq (A7a) and (A7b), k_2/k_1 shall not be taken as less than 0.5, and k_1 shall not be taken greater than 0.85 for $f_c' \leq 5000$ psi. The coefficient 0.85 is to be reduced at the rate of 0.05 per 1000 psi concrete strength in excess of 5000 psi.

---

*Correction for concrete area displaced by compressive reinforcement may be made by subtracting 0.85 f_c' from f_y in this term only.

(b) It shall be assumed that the maximum concrete strain is limited to 0.003 so that the section is controlled by tension when:

$$P_u \leqq P_b = 0.85 \, k_1 \quad \left(\frac{90,000}{90,000 + f_v}\right) f_c' \, bd + A_s' \, f_v^* - A_s f_v \quad \dots \dots \dots \dots \text{(A8)}$$

k_1 being limited as for Eq. (A7a) and (A7b). The section is controlled by compression when P_u exceeds P_b.

(c) When the section is controlled by tension, the ultimate strength shall not exceed that computed by:

$$P_u = 0.85 f_c' \, bd \left\{ p'm' - pm + (1 - e/d) \right.$$
$$\left. + \sqrt{(1 - e/d)^2 + 2 \left[(e/d) \, (pm - p'm') + p'm' \, (1 - d'/d) \right]} \right\} \quad \text{(A9)}$$

(d) When the section is controlled by compression, a linear relationship between axial load and moment may be assumed for values of P_u between that given as P_b by Eq. (A8) and the concentric ultimate strength P_o given by Eq. (A6). For this range the ultimate strength may be computed by either Eq. (A10) or (A11):

$$P_u = \frac{P_o}{1 + [(P_o/P_b) - 1] \, e'/e_b'} \quad \dots \dots \dots \dots \dots \dots \dots \dots \dots \dots \dots \dots \dots \text{(A10)}$$

$$P_u = \frac{A_s' f_v}{e'/(d - d') + \frac{1}{2}} + \frac{btf_c'}{(3te'/d^2) + 1.18} \quad \dots \dots \dots \dots \dots \dots \dots \dots \text{(A11)}$$

A610—Bending and axial load: Circular sections

(a) The ultimate strength of circular sections subject to combined bending and axial load may be computed on the basis of the equations of equilibrium taking into account inelastic deformations, or by the empirical formulas Eq. (A12) and (A13):

When tension controls:

$$P_u = 0.85 f_c' D^2 \left[\sqrt{\left(\frac{0.85 \, e'}{D} - 0.38 \right)^2 + \frac{p_t m D_s}{2.5D}} - \left(\frac{0.85 \, e'}{D} - 0.38 \right) \right] \dots \text{(A 12)}$$

When compression controls:

$$P_u = \frac{A_{st} f_v}{\frac{3e'}{D_s} + 1} + \frac{A_g f_c'}{\frac{9.6De'}{(0.8D + 0.67D_s)^2} + 1.18} \quad \dots \dots \dots \dots \dots \dots \dots \dots \dots \text{(A13)}$$

A611—Long members

(a) When the unsupported length, L, of an axially loaded member is greater than 15 times its least lateral dimension, the maximum axial load, P_u', shall be determined by one of the following methods:

1. $P_u' = P_o(1.6 - 0.04L/t)$ .... (A14)

*Correction for concrete area displaced by compressive reinforcement may be made by subtracting 0.85 f_c' from f_v in this term only.

2. A stability determination for P_u' may be made with an apparent reduced modulus of elasticity used for sustained loads, such as the method recommended in the report of ACI Committee 312, "Plain and Reinforced Concrete Arches" (ACI JOURNAL, May 1951, *Proc.* V. 47, p. 681).

Design Tables
and
Curves

TABLE E.1.   Tied Column Capacities*

$$P \text{ (kips)} = (0.18 f_c' A_g + 0.8 f_s A_s) \div 1000$$

		Load on Bars Min.: $0.008 f_s A_g \div 1000$ Max.: $0.032 f_s A_g \div 1000$				Load on Concrete $0.18 f_c' A_g \div 1000$				
	Gross Area A_g	$f_s = 16,000$		$f_s = 20,000$		f_c'				
Column Size		Min.	Max.	Min.	Max.	2000	2500	3000	3750	5000
10	12	15	61	19	77	43	54	65	81	108
	14	18	72	22	90	50	63	76	95	126
	16	20	82	26	102	58	72	86	108	144
	18	23	92	29	115	65	81	97	122	162
12	12	18	74	23	92	52	65	78	97	130
	14	22	86	27	108	60	76	91	113	151
	16	25	98	31	123	69	86	104	130	173
	18	28	111	35	138	78	97	117	146	194
	20	31	123	38	154	86	108	130	162	216
14	14	25	100	31	125	71	88	106	132	176
	16	29	115	36	143	81	101	121	151	202
	18	32	129	40	161	91	113	136	170	227
	20	36	143	45	179	101	126	151	189	252
	22	39	158	49	197	111	139	166	208	277
16	16	33	131	41	164	92	115	138	173	230
	18	37	147	46	184	104	130	156	194	259
	20	41	164	51	205	115	144	173	216	288
	22	45	180	56	225	127	158	190	238	317
	24	49	197	61	246	138	173	207	259	346
18	18	41	166	52	207	117	146	175	219	292
	20	46	184	58	230	130	162	194	243	324
	22	51	203	63	253	143	178	214	267	356
	24	55	221	69	276	156	194	233	292	389
	26	60	240	75	300	168	211	253	316	421
20	20	51	205	64	256	144	180	216	270	360
	22	56	225	70	282	158	198	238	297	396
	24	61	246	77	307	173	216	259	324	432
	26	67	266	83	333	187	234	281	351	468
	28	72	287	90	356	202	252	302	378	504
22	22	62	248	77	310	174	218	261	327	436
	24	68	270	84	338	190	238	285	356	475
	26	73	293	92	366	206	257	309	386	515
	28	79	315	99	394	222	277	333	416	554
24	24	74	295	92	369	207	259	311	389	518
	26	80	319	100	399	225	281	337	421	562
	28	86	344	108	430	242	302	363	454	605
26	26	87	346	108	433	243	304	365	456	608
	28	93	373	116	466	262	328	393	491	655
28	28	100	401	125	502	282	353	423	529	706
30	30	115	461	144	576	324	405	486	608	810
32	32	131	524	164	655	369	461	553	691	922
34	34	148	592	185	740	416	520	624	780	1040
—	—	128	512	160	640	360	450	540	675	900

Load on Bars (kips) = $0.8 f_s A_s \div 1000$

Bar Size	Number of Bars Intermediate Grade: $f_s = 16,000$										Bar Size	Number of Bars Rail or Hard Grade: $f_s = 20,000$									
	4	6	8	10	12	14	16	18	20	22		4	6	8	10	12	14	16	18	20	22
#5	16	24	32	40	48	56	63	71	79	87	#5	20	30	40	50	60	69	79	89	99	109
#6	23	34	45	56	68	79	90	101	113	124	#6	28	42	56	70	85	99	113	127	141	155
#7	31	46	61	77	92	108	123	138	154	169	#7	38	58	77	96	115	134	154	173	192	211
#8	40	61	81	101	121	142	162	182	202	223	#8	51	76	101	126	152	177	202	227	253	278
#9	51	77	102	128	154	179	205	230	256	282	#9	64	96	128	160	192	224	256	288	320	352
#10	65	98	130	163	195	228	260	293	325	358	#10	81	122	163	203	244	285	325	366	407	447
#11	80	120	160	200	240	280	320	360	400	440	#11	100	150	200	250	300	349	399	449	499	549

* From *Reinforced Concrete Design Handbook*, ACI, 1955.

REINFORCED CONCRETE FUNDAMENTALS

TABLE E.2. Spiral Column Capacities*

$$P \text{ (kips)} = (0.225 f_c'A_g + f_sA_s) \div 1000$$

		Square Columns												Round Columns									
		Load on Bars				Load on Concrete $0.225f_c'A_g \div 1000$							Load on Bars				Load on Concrete $0.225f_c'A_g \div 1000$					
		$f_s=16{,}000$		$f_s=20{,}000$									$f_s=16{,}000$		$f_s=20{,}000$						
Col. Size	Gross Area A_g	†Min. Load	‡Max. Load	†Min. Load	‡Max. Load	2000	2500	3000	3750	5000		Gross Area A_g	†Min. Load	‡Max. Load	†Min. Load	‡Max. Load	2000	2500	3000	3750	5000
---	---	---	---	---	---	---	---	---	---	---	---	---	---	---	---	---	---	---	---	---	---
14	196	31	122	39	152	88	110	132	165	221		154	25	122	31	152	69	87	104	130	173
15	225	36	150	45	187	101	127	152	190	253		177	28	150	35	187	80	99	119	149	199
16	256	41	150	51	187	115	144	173	216	288		201	32	150	40	187	91	113	136	170	226
17	289	46	175	58	218	130	163	195	244	325		227	36	175	45	218	102	128	153	192	255
18	324	52	200	65	250	146	182	219	273	365		254	41	200	51	250	114	143	172	215	286
19	361	58	200	72	250	162	203	244	305	406		284	45	200	57	250	128	159	191	239	319
20	400	64	225	80	281	180	225	270	337	450		314	50	225	63	281	141	177	212	265	354
21	441	71	225	88	281	198	248	298	372	496		346	55	225	69	281	156	195	234	292	390
22	484	77	250	97	312	218	272	327	408	544		380	61	250	76	312	171	214	257	321	428
23	529	85	275	106	343	238	298	357	446	595		415	66	275	83	343	187	234	280	350	467
24	576	92	275	115	343	259	324	389	486	648		452	72	275	90	343	204	254	305	382	509
25	625	100	300	125	374	281	352	422	527	703		491	79	300	98	374	221	276	331	414	552
26	676	108	324	135	406	304	380	456	570	760		531	85	324	106	406	239	299	358	448	597
27	729	117	324	146	406	328	410	492	615	820		573	92	324	115	406	258	322	387	483	644
28	784	125	349	157	437	353	441	529	661	882		616	98	349	123	437	277	346	416	519	693
29	841	135	349	168	437	378	473	567	710	946		661	106	349	132	437	297	372	446	557	743
30	900	144	374	180	468	405	506	608	760	1013		707	113	374	141	468	318	398	477	596	795
31	961	154	399	192	499	433	540	648	811	1081		755	121	399	151	499	340	424	510	637	849
32	1024	164	399	205	499	461	576	691	864	1151		804	129	399	161	499	362	452	543	678	905
33	1089	174	424	218	531	490	613	735	919	1225		855	137	424	171	531	385	481	577	722	962

Load on Bars, A_s (kips) $= f_sA_s \div 1000$ (Max. $A_s = 0.08A_g$)

Number of Bars

Bar Size	6	7	8	9	10	11	12	13	14	15	16	17	18	19	20	21	22	23	24	25	26
Intermediate Grade: $f_s = 16{,}000$																					
#5	30	35	40	45	50	55	60	64	69	74	79	84	89	94	99	104	109	114	119	124	129
#6	42	49	56	63	70	77	84	92	99	106	113	120	127	134	141	148	155	162	169	176	183
#7	58	67	77	86	96	106	115	125	134	144	154	163	173	182	192	202	211	221	230	240	250
#8	76	88	101	114	126	139	152	164	177	190	202	215	228	240	253	266	278	291	303	316	329
#9	96	112	128	144	160	176	192	208	224	240	256	272	288	304	320	336	352	368	384	400	416
#10	122	142	163	183	203	224	244	264	285	305	325	346	366	386	406	427	447	467	488	508	528
#11	150	175	200	225	250	275	300	324	349	374	399	424	449	474	499	524	549	574	599	624	649
Rail or Hard Grade: $f_s = 20{,}000$																					
#5	37	43	50	56	62	68	74	81	87	93	99	105	112	118	124	130	136	143	149	155	161
#6	53	62	70	79	88	97	106	114	123	132	141	150	158	167	176	185	194	202	211	220	229
#7	72	84	96	108	120	132	144	156	168	180	192	204	216	228	240	252	264	276	288	300	312
#8	95	111	126	142	158	174	190	205	221	237	253	269	284	300	316	332	348	364	379	395	411
#9	120	140	160	180	200	220	240	260	280	300	320	340	360	380	400	420	440	460	480	500	520
#10	152	178	203	229	254	279	305	330	356	381	406	432	457	483	508	534	559	584	610	635	660
#11	187	218	250	281	312	343	374	406	437	468	499	531	562	593	624	655	686	718	749	780	811

* From *Reinforced Concrete Design Handbook*, ACI, 1955.
† Minimum area of reinforcement $0.01A_g$.
‡ With 1½-in. concrete protection and maximum number of maximum size bars arranged in one outer ring.

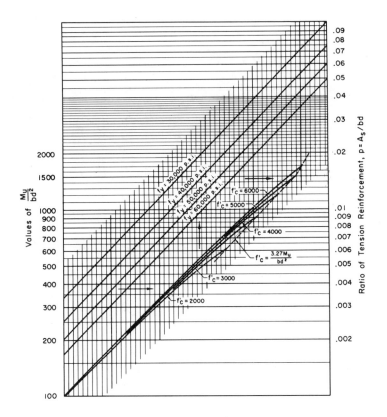

Fig. E.1. Chart for ultimate strength of rectangular beams. (From Ref. 5 of Chap. 3, ACI.) Enlarged copies (about 12 in. by 12 in.) of Fig. E.1 and Figs. E.20 through E.33 are available from the American Concrete Institute, P.O. Box 4754, Redford Station, Detroit 19, Mich., at $2.00 per set.

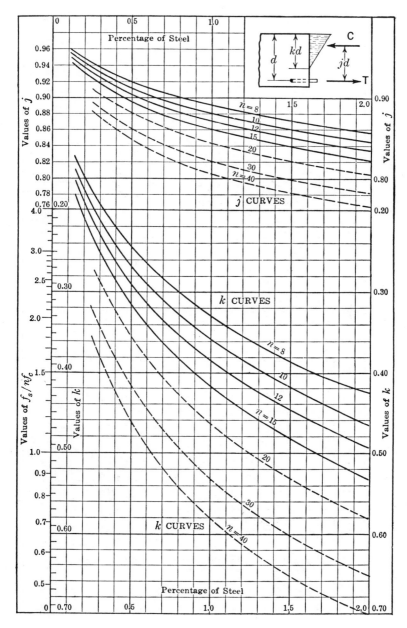

Fig. E.2. Values of k and j for rectangular beams, working stress values. (From Ref. 2 of Chap. 4.)

DESIGN TABLES AND CURVES

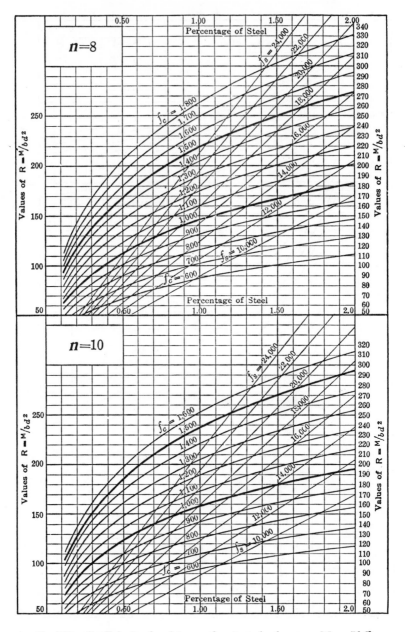

Fig. E.3. Coefficients of resistance of rectangular beams. $M = Rbd^2$. (From Ref. 2 of Chap. 4.)

REINFORCED CONCRETE FUNDAMENTALS

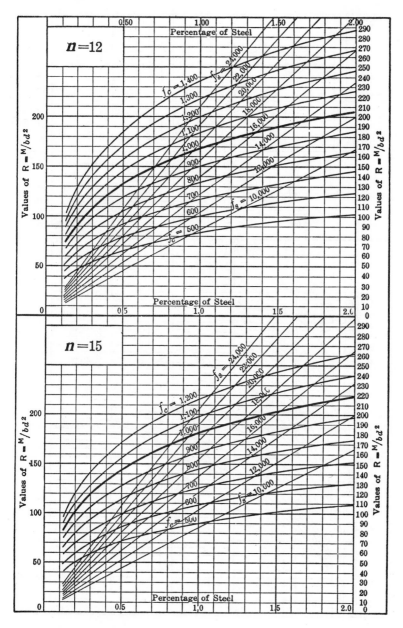

Fig. E.4. Coefficients of resistance of rectangular beams. $M = Rbd^2$. (From Ref. 2 of Chap. 4.)

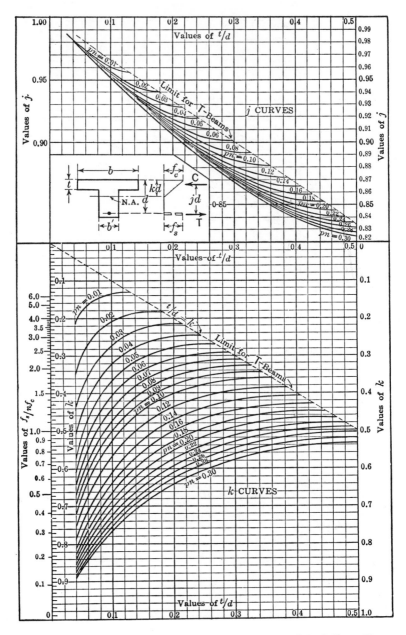

Fig. E.5. Values of k and j for T-beams. (From Ref. 2 of Chap. 4.)

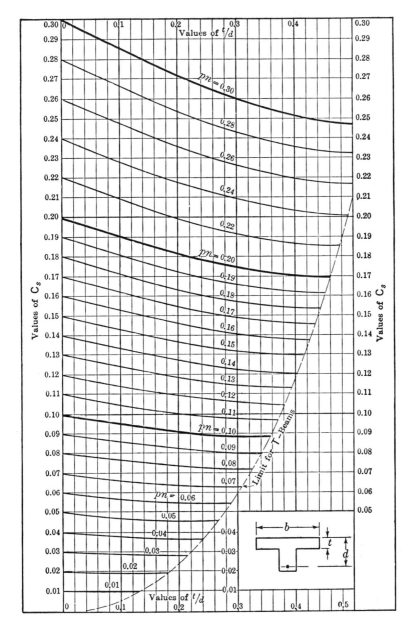

Fig. E.6. Coefficients of resistance of T-beams with respect to the steel.
$M_s = C_s(f_s/n)bd^2$. (From Ref. 2 of Chap. 4.)

DESIGN TABLES AND CURVES

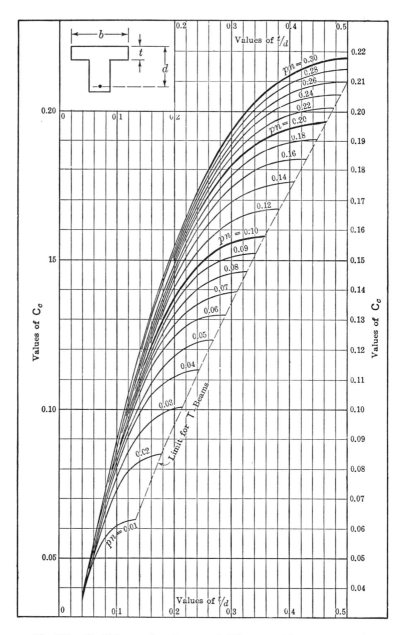

Fig. E.7. Coefficients of resistance of T-beams with respect to the concrete. $M_c = C_c f_c b d^2$. (From Ref. 2 of Chap. 4.)

REINFORCED CONCRETE FUNDAMENTALS

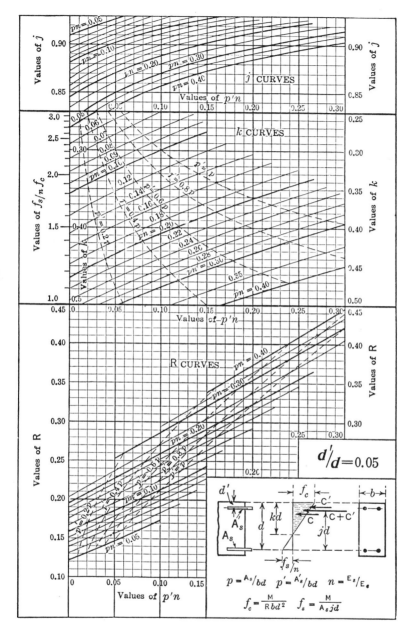

Fig. E.8. Rectangular beams reinforced for compression, *elastic* analysis. $M = f_c R b d^2$. (From Ref. 2 of Chap. 4.)

DESIGN TABLES AND CURVES

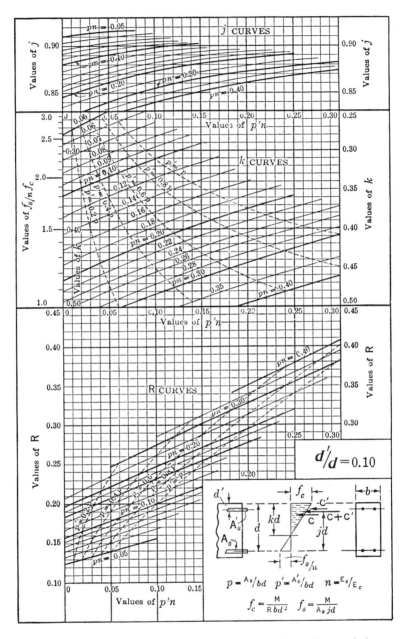

Fig. E.9. Rectangular beams reinforced for compression, *elastic* analysis. $M = f_c R b d^2$. (From Ref. 2 of Chap. 4.)

REINFORCED CONCRETE FUNDAMENTALS

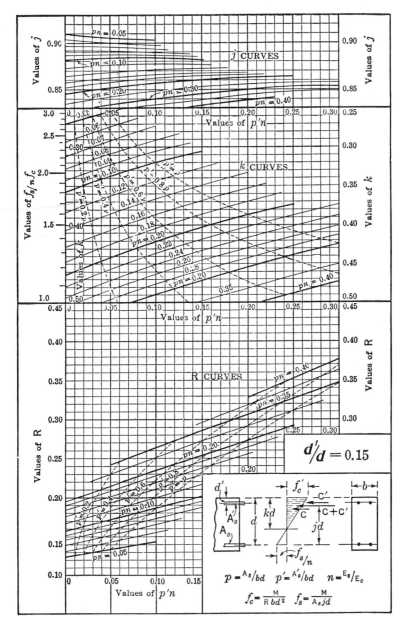

Fig. E.10. Rectangular beams reinforced for compression, *elastic* analysis. $M = f_c R b d^2$. (From Ref. 2 of Chap. 4.)

DESIGN TABLES AND CURVES

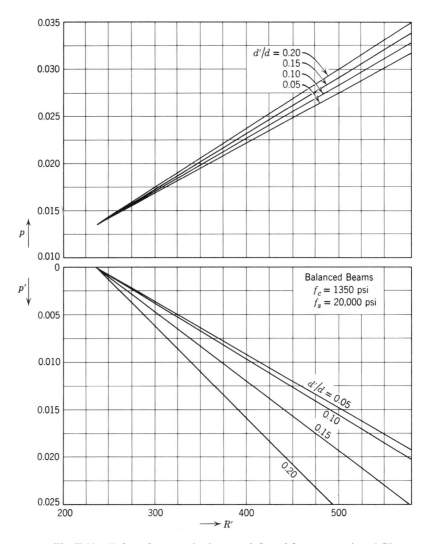

Fig. E.11. *Balanced* rectangular beams reinforced for compression, ACI Code.

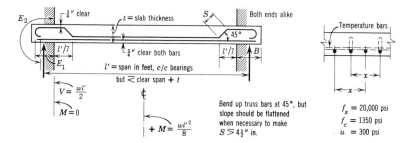

E_1 = 6-in. minimum for bottom bars.

E_2 = 17 bar diameters* (straight if possible, bent if necessary).

B = ordinarily 4-in. minimum but sufficient in any case to keep the bearing pressure on the wall within the allowable for the material of which the wall is made.

x = distance between consecutive bottom bars = distance between consecutive truss bars = distance between *pairs* of bars.

Alternate bars are trussed as shown. (Sometimes only every fourth bar is trussed on outer end.)

* This embedment theoretically develops the bar on the basis of $L = \dfrac{f_s D}{4u} = \dfrac{20,000 D}{4 \times 300} = 16\frac{2}{3} D$. Recent pullout tests have indicated little or no stress in bars beyond a 10- to 13-diameter embedment.

Fig. E.12. Detailing of bars for simple span slabs tabulated in *CRSI Design Handbook.*

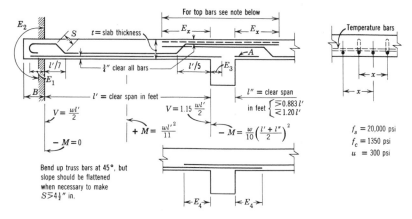

$E_1 = $ 6-in. minimum for bottom bars.

$E_2 = $ 17 bar diameters* (straight if possible, bent if necessary).

$E_3 = $ 6-in. minimum with $\frac{2}{3}\%$ reinforcement.

$E_4 \geq \begin{Bmatrix} 17 \text{ bar diameters} \\ l'/15\dagger \end{Bmatrix}$ with balanced reinforcement.

$E_x = $ to meet ACI Art. 902a extend at least one-third of top bars $l'/3$ and the remainder $l'/6$; if necessary increase extension until bars are anchored $17D$ past point of max. stress (bend-down points).

$B = $ ordinarily 4-in. minimum and sufficient in any case to keep the bearing pressure on the wall within the allowable for the material of which the wall is made.

$x = $ distance between consecutive bottom bars $=$ distance between consecutive truss bars $=$ distance between *pairs* of bars.

$A = $ bottom bar in adjoining span, not shown.

* This embedment theoretically develops the bar on the basis of $L = \dfrac{f_s D}{4u} = \dfrac{20{,}000D}{4 \times 300} = 16\tfrac{2}{3}D$. Recent pullout tests have indicated little or no stress in bars beyond a 10- to 13-diameter embedment.

† Embedment of bottom bars at interior support is determined by the fact that some of the bottom bars are required for compressive reinforcement. The exact length varies. The maximum is that which will develop the full compression in the bars at the higher unit stress permitted by the ACI Code, Art. 706b, and which will at the same time extend the needed distance across the moment curve. The capacity of the slab may be determined by shear, bond, or flexure. The recommendation for E_4 will cover the worst condition. The user may at his option work out the needs of any particular problem.

Fig. E.13. Detailing of bars for end span slabs tabulated in *CRSI Design Handbook*.

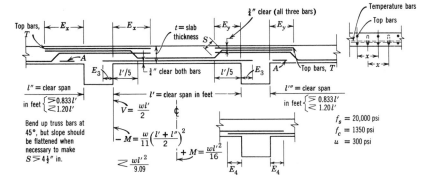

E_3 = 6 in. minimum with $\frac{2}{3}\%$ reinforcement.

E_4 = not less than 17 bar diameters, nor less than $l''/15$,* with balanced reinforcement.

$E_x = E_y$ = to meet ACI, Art. 902a, extend at least one-third of the top bars $l'/3$ and remainder at least $l'/6$; if necessary increase extension until bars are anchored 17 dias. past point of max. stress (bend-down points).

x = distance between consecutive bottom bars = distance between consecutive truss bars = distance between *pairs* of bars.

T = additional top bars, one over each meeting pair of bottom bars, that is, one for each set of straight and truss bars.

A = bottom bar in adjoining span, not shown.

* Embedment of bottom bars at interior support is determined by the fact that some of the bottom bars are required for compressive reinforcement. The exact length varies. The maximum is that which will develop the full compression in the bars at the higher unit stress permitted by the ACI Code (20,000 psi) and which will at the same time extend the needed distance across the moment curve. The capacity of the slab may be determined by shear, bond, or flexure. The recommendation for E_4 will cover the worst condition. The user may at his option work out the needs of any particular problem.

Fig. E.14. Detailing of bars for interior span slabs tabulated in *CRSI Design Handbook*.

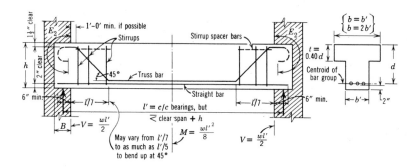

Stresses:

f_s = 20,000 psi.
f_c' = 3000 psi.
f_c = 1350 psi.
u = 300 psi for bottom bars.
= 210 psi for top bars with over 12 in. of concrete under them.

E_1 = 6-in. minimum for bottom bars.

E_2 = 17 bar diameters (24 diameters if $d > 12$ in.) (straight if possible, bent if necessary).

B = ordinarily 8-in. minimum and sufficient in any case to keep the bearing pressure on the wall within the allowable for the material of which the wall is made.

Codes: "Building Code Requirements for Reinforced Concrete," ACI 318–56; also "Manual of Standard Practice for Detailing Reinforced Concrete Structures," ACI 315–57.

Fig. E.15. Detailing of bars for simple span beams tabulated in *CRSI Design Handbook*.

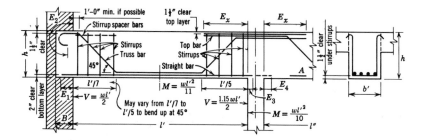

Stresses and Codes same as for Fig. E.15.

E_1 = 6-in. minimum for bottom bars.

E_2 = 17 bar diameters, usually requiring a semicircular hook. (24 bar diameters for depths over 12 in.)

E_3 = bottom bar to extend 6 in. into the support where not counted for compression steel.

E_4 = when counted for compression steel, bottom bars must lap bars of adjoining span 20 diameters.

E_x = $l'/4$ or $l''/4$ or 17 bar dias. (24 dias., $d >$ 12 in.) past bend-down point, whichever is greatest.

ACI Art. 902a requires the extending of top bars past innermost position of point of inflection $l/16$, d, or half-bond length; if point of inflection is at $l/5$ of center-to-center span, if beam depth is $l/12$, and if column face is $l/15$, the given ratios, which are easily applied, work out fairly well, but must be checked for actual use.

B = ordinarily 8-in. minimum and sufficient in any case to keep the bearing pressure on the wall within the allowable for the material of which the wall is made.

A = bars in adjoining span, not shown.

Fig. E.16. Detailing of bars for end span beams tabulated in *CRSI Design Handbook*.

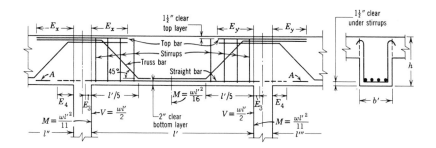

Stresses and Codes same as for Fig. E.15.

E_3, E_4, E_x, and A same as for Fig. E.16.

$E_y = l'/4$, or $l'''/4$, or $17D$ ($24D$ if $d > 12$ in.) past bend-down point, whichever is greatest.

Fig. E.17. Detailing of bars for interior span beams tabulated in *CRSI Design Handbook*.

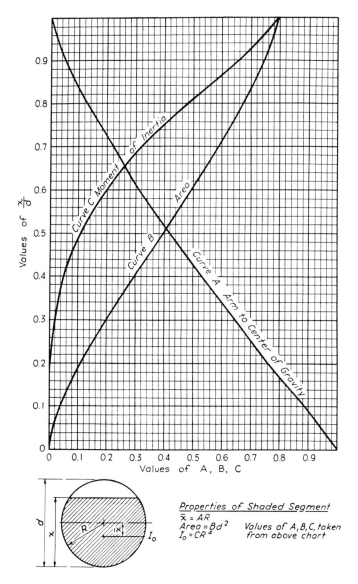

Fig. E.18. Constants for properties of circular segments. (Courtesy Prof. J. R. Shank, Ohio State University.)

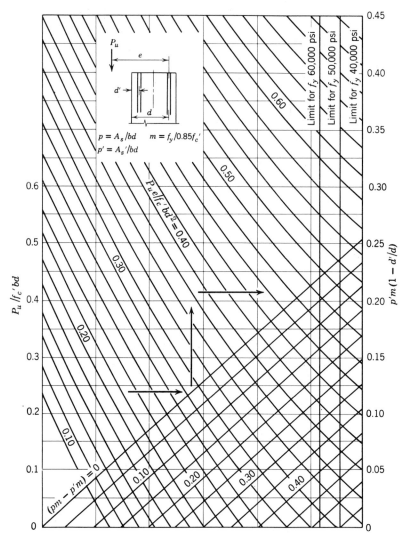

Fig. E.19. Chart for ultimate strength of eccentrically loaded rectangular members *failing in tension*. (From Ref. 2 of Chap. 13, ACI.)

REINFORCED CONCRETE FUNDAMENTALS

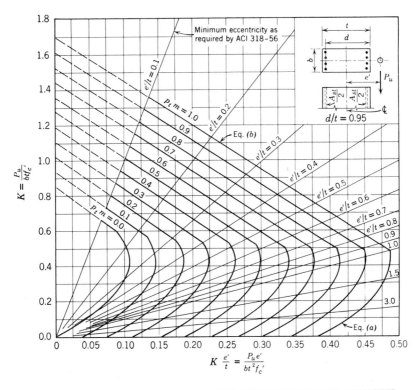

$$(a) \quad P_u = 0.85 f_c' b d \left\{ 1 - p - \frac{e}{d} + \sqrt{\left(1 - \frac{e}{d}\right)^2 + 2p \left[m' \left(1 - \frac{d'}{d}\right) + \frac{e}{d}\right]} \right\}$$

$$(b) \quad P_u = \frac{2 A_s' f_y'}{\dfrac{2e'}{(d - d')} + 1} + \frac{b t f_c'}{\dfrac{3 t e'}{d^2} + 1.18}$$

Fig. E.20

Figs. E.20–E.23. Whitney's chart for eccentrically loaded rectangular members failing in compression or tension. (From Ref. 6 of Chap. 13, ACI.)

Enlarged copies (about 12-in. by 12-in.) of Fig. E.1 and Figs. E.20 through E.33 are available from the American Concrete Institute, P.O. Box 4754, Redford Station, Detroit 19, Mich., at $2.00 per set.

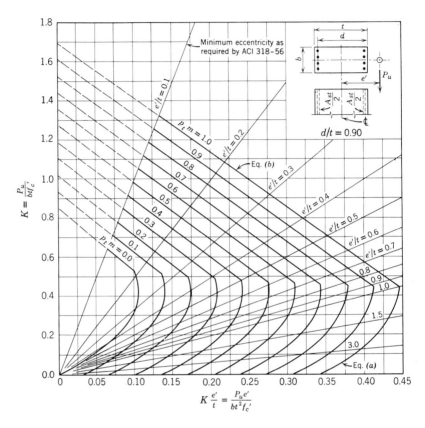

$$(a) \quad P_u = 0.85f_c'bd \left\{ 1 - p - \frac{e}{d} + \sqrt{\left(1 - \frac{e}{d}\right)^2 + 2p\left[m'\left(1 - \frac{d'}{d}\right) + \frac{e}{d}\right]} \right\}$$

$$(b) \quad P_u = \frac{2A_s'f_y'}{\dfrac{2e'}{(d - d')} + 1} + \frac{btf_c'}{\dfrac{3te'}{d^2} + 1.18}$$

Fig. E.21.

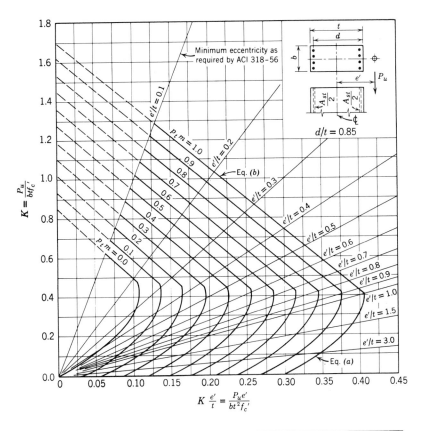

$(a) \quad P_u = 0.85 f_c' b d \left\{ 1 - p - \dfrac{e}{d} + \sqrt{\left(1 - \dfrac{e}{d}\right)^2 + 2p \left[m' \left(\left(1 - \dfrac{d'}{d}\right) + \dfrac{e}{d}\right) \right]} \right\}$

$(b) \quad P_u = \dfrac{2A_s' f_y'}{\dfrac{2e'}{(d - d')} + 1} + \dfrac{b t f_c'}{\dfrac{3 t e'}{d^2} + 1.18}$

Fig. E.22.

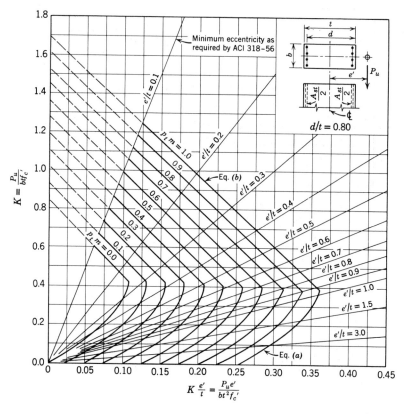

(a) $P_u = 0.85 f_c' b d \left\{ 1 - p - \dfrac{e}{d} + \sqrt{ \left(1 - \dfrac{e}{d} \right)^2 + 2p \left[m' \left(1 - \dfrac{d'}{d} \right) + \dfrac{e}{d} \right] } \right\}$

(b) $P_u = \dfrac{2 A_s' f_y'}{\dfrac{2e'}{(d - d')} + 1} + \dfrac{b t f_c'}{\dfrac{3te'}{d^2} + 1.18}$

Fig. E.23.

REINFORCED CONCRETE FUNDAMENTALS

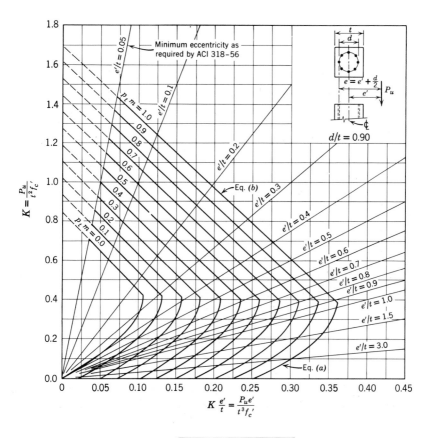

$$\text{(a)} \quad P_u = 0.85t^2f_c'\left\{\sqrt{\left(\frac{e'}{t} - 0.5\right)^2 + 0.67\frac{d}{t}p_tm} - \left(\frac{e'}{t} - 0.5\right)\right\}$$

$$\text{(b)} \quad P_u = \frac{A_{st}f_y'}{\dfrac{3e'}{d} + 1} + \frac{A_gf_c'}{\dfrac{12.0te'}{(t + 0.67d)^2} + 1.18}$$

Fig. E.24.

Figs. E.24–E.27. Whitney's chart for eccentrically loaded rectangular members with spiral core failing in compression or tension. (From Ref. 6 of Chap. 13, ACI.)

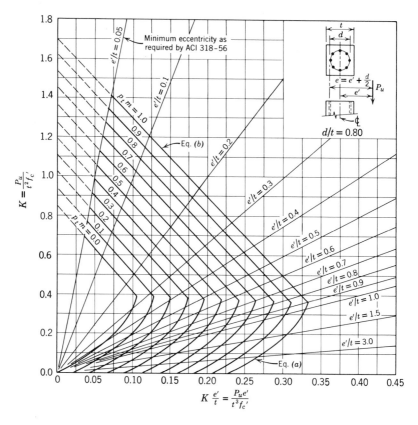

$$(a) \quad P_u = 0.85t^2f_c' \left\{ \sqrt{\left(\frac{e'}{t} - 0.5\right)^2 + 0.67\frac{d}{t}\,p_t m} - \left(\frac{e'}{t} - 0.5\right) \right\}$$

$$(b) \quad P_u = \frac{A_{st}f_y'}{\dfrac{3e'}{d} + 1} + \frac{A_g f_c'}{\dfrac{12.0te'}{(t + 0.67d)^2} + 1.18}$$

Fig. E.25.

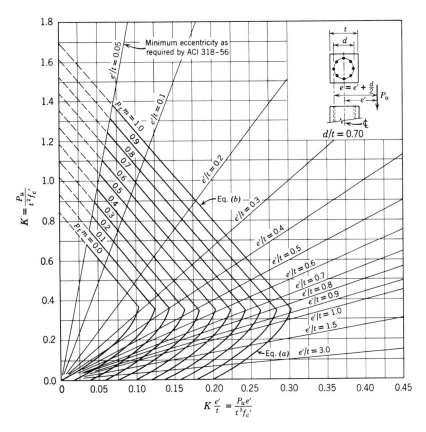

$$(a) \quad P_u = 0.85t^2f_c' \left\{ \sqrt{\left(\frac{e'}{t} - 0.5\right)^2 + 0.67\frac{d}{t}p_tm} - \left(\frac{e'}{t} - 0.5\right) \right\}$$

$$(b) \quad P_u = \frac{A_{st}f_y'}{\dfrac{3e'}{d} + 1} + \frac{A_gf_c'}{\dfrac{12.0te'}{(t + 0.67d)^2} + 1.18}$$

Fig. E.26.

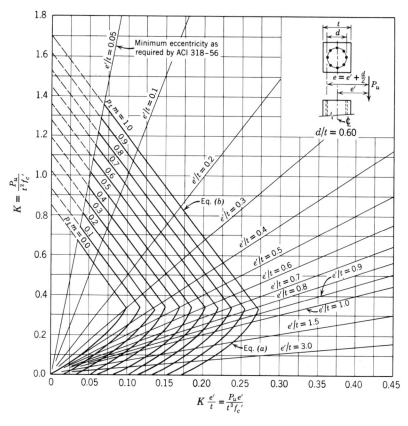

$$(a) \quad P_u = 0.85t^2f_c' \left\{ \sqrt{\left(\frac{e'}{t} - 0.5\right)^2 + 0.67\frac{d}{t}p_t m} - \left(\frac{e'}{t} - 0.5\right)\right\}$$

$$(b) \quad P_u = \frac{A_{st}f_y'}{\dfrac{3e'}{d} + 1} + \frac{A_g f_c'}{\dfrac{12.0te'}{(t + 0.67d)^2} + 1.18}$$

Fig. E.27.

REINFORCED CONCRETE FUNDAMENTALS

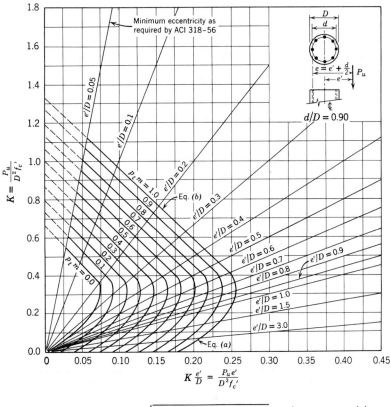

$$(a) \quad P_u = 0.85 D^2 f_c' \left\{ \sqrt{\left(\frac{0.85e'}{D} - 0.38 \right)^2 + \frac{dp_tm}{2.5D}} - \left(\frac{0.85e'}{D} - 0.38 \right) \right\}$$

$$(b) \quad P_u = \frac{A_{st}f_y'}{\dfrac{3e'}{d} + 1} + \frac{A_gf_c'}{\dfrac{9.6De'}{(0.8D + 0.67d)^2} + 1.18}$$

Fig. E.28.

Figs. E.28–E.31. Whitney's chart for eccentrically loaded circular members failing in compression or tension. (From Ref. 6 of Chap. 13, ACI.)

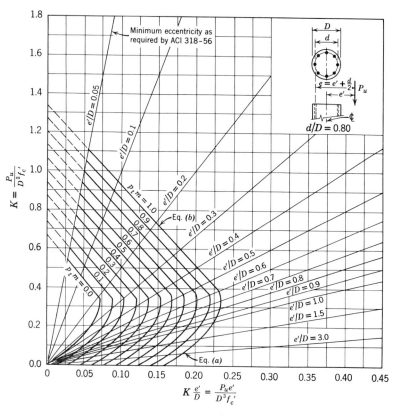

$$(a) \quad P_u = 0.85 D^2 f_c' \left\{ \sqrt{\left(\frac{0.85e'}{D} - 0.38 \right)^2 + \frac{dp_t m}{2.5D}} - \left(\frac{0.85e'}{D} - 0.38 \right) \right\}$$

$$(b) \quad P_u = \frac{A_{st} f_y'}{\dfrac{3e'}{d} + 1} + \frac{A_g f_c'}{\dfrac{9.6 D e'}{(0.8D + 0.67d)^2} + 1.18}$$

Fig. E.29.

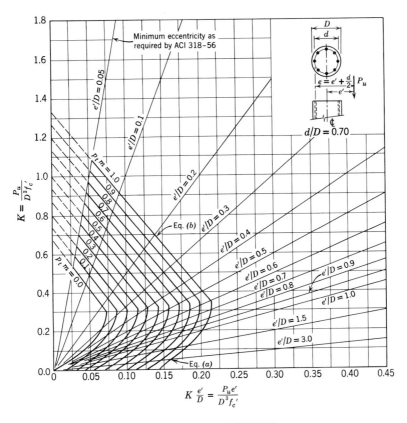

$$(a) \quad P_u = 0.85 D^2 f_c' \left\{ \sqrt{\left(\frac{0.85e'}{D} - 0.38 \right)^2 + \frac{dp_t m}{2.5D}} - \left(\frac{0.85e'}{D} - 0.38 \right) \right\}$$

$$(b) \quad P_u = \frac{A_{st}f_y'}{\dfrac{3e'}{d} + 1} + \frac{A_g f_c'}{\dfrac{9.6De'}{(0.8D + 0.67d)^2} + 1.18}$$

Fig. E.30.

DESIGN TABLES AND CURVES

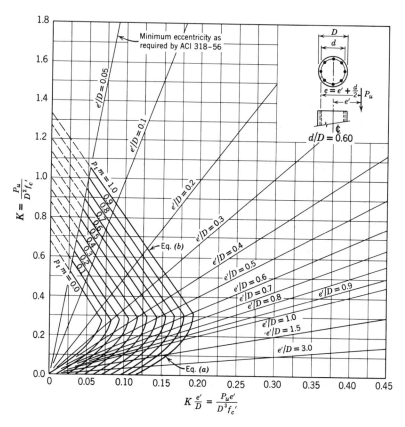

$$(a) \quad P_u = 0.85 D^2 f_c' \left\{ \sqrt{\left(\frac{0.85e'}{D} - 0.38 \right)^2 + \frac{dp_t m}{2.5D}} - \left(\frac{0.85e'}{D} - 0.38 \right) \right\}$$

$$(b) \quad P_u = \frac{A_{st} f_y'}{\dfrac{3e'}{d} + 1} + \frac{A_g f_c'}{\dfrac{9.6De'}{(0.8D + 0.67d)^2} + 1.18}$$

Fig. E.31.

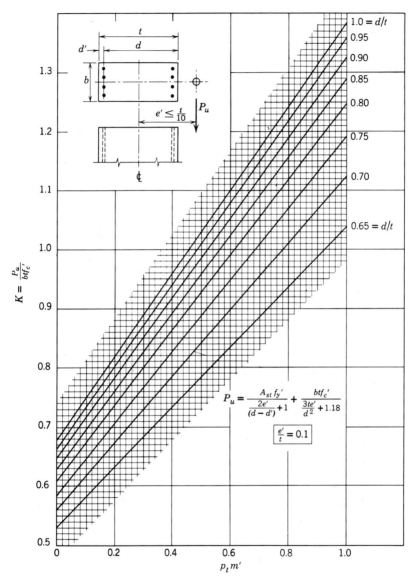

Fig. E.32. Chart for rectangular column with minimum eccentricity. (From Ref. 6 of Chap. 13, ACI.)

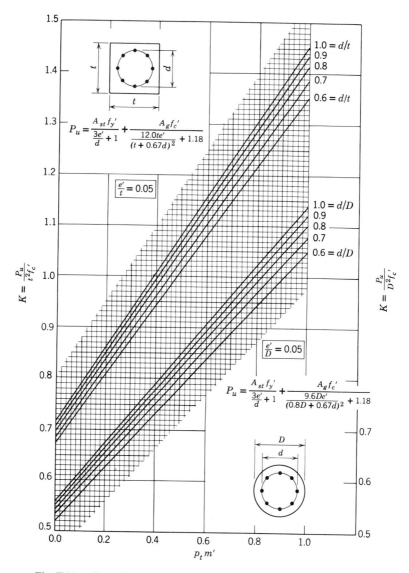

Fig. E.33. Chart for circular and rectangular columns with spirals and minimum eccentricity. (From Ref. 6 of Chap. 13, ACI.)

REINFORCED CONCRETE FUNDAMENTALS

General Index

Note: Items applying exclusively to ultimate strength, limit design, and yield-line theory are in the Special Index which follows this section.

Reinforcing steel, plain bars, 14
  hooks required, 521
  rust, 504
  shrinkage, 510
  sizes, standard bars, 15, 16
  spacer bars, 187
  spacing, 504
  splices, 129, 505
  stop points, variable depth, 183
  stress, (at) diagonal crack, 132
    effective in compression, 71
  temperature steel, 187, 510
  yield points, 14
Retaining walls, active soil pressure,
    165
  cantilever walls, base length, 173
    design, 171
    dowels to stem, 182
    heel design, 177
      under overload, 178
    joining stem, heel, toe, 181
    key to soil, 182
    shear key, stem to base, 181
    stem design, 172
    stem steel detailing, 183
    toe design, 179
  counterfort, 165
  deflection, minimum, 169
  drainage, 188
  reaction distribution, 173
  reaction pressures, 175
  surcharge, 169
  temperature steel, 185
  wall types, 163

Shear, allowable stresses, 139
  coefficients, 508
  diagram, as simple beam plus con-
    tinuity, 441
    continuity shear from moment
      diagram, 444
  stress formula, 135
  torsion, 157
  ultimate strength design, 159
  varying depth members, 150
  See also Diagonal tension
Shear key, 181
Shrinkage steel, 510
  parallel to joists, 511

Sign conventions, angles in moment
    distribution, 455
  beam bending moments, 453
  moment distribution, joint signs,
    453, 454
Slab band, 321
  See also Flat slabs
Slabs, bar bends, continuous slabs, 207
  bars around openings, 335
  bond stress, 207
  concentrated load distribution, 326
    transverse steel, 332
  conduit, embedded, 335
  continuous one-way, 205
  design strip, 77
  highway load design, 329
  moment coefficients, 507
  one-way, 191
    design example, 196
  openings through, 335
    strengthening around, 335
  shear coefficients, 508
  spacing steel, 207
  temperature steel, 207
  transverse moment, concentrated
    loads, 328
  transverse steel, concentrated loads,
    332
  yield-line theory. See Special Index
  See also Flat slabs, Two-way slabs
Slump test, 3
Soil pressure, active, 165
  coefficient K_A, 168
  Coulomb theory, 166
  effect of deflection, 169
  equivalent fluid weight, 168
  passive, 170
  Rankine theory, 166
  rigid walls, 169
  surcharge, 169
Span length, 508
Spiral. See Columns, (with) spiral
Splices. See Reinforcing steel
Stiffness, 453
Stirrups, anchorage, 154, 518
  beam length requiring, 153
  bent bars, 141, 518
  combined, vertical and inclined, 144

Stirrups, continuous rectangular beams, 223, 517
  continuous T-beams, 221
  design, vertical, 145, 152
  inclined, effective length, 144
    limitations, 140
  maximum spacing, 142, 144, 519
  minimum ratio, 143, 153, 519
  (in) negative moment zone, 222
  number, theoretical, 146
    excess over theoretical, 155
  spacing, desirable, 146
    slide-rule method, 148, 156
  spacing curve, 154
  spacing formula, inclined, 143
    vertical, 142, 518
  specification extension, 517
  standard hook, 152
  truss analogy, 140
  types, 140, 518
    mixed, 519
  vertical, design, 145, 152
Stress distribution, 17
Stresses, allowable, compression steel, 510
  concrete, 501
  earthquake, 506
  steel, 502
  wind, 506
Supervision of construction, 496

T-beams, allowable moment, 81
  analysis, 77
    approximate, 80
    exact, 78
  continuous, bar selection, 212
    bending bars, 212, 214
    bond, 219
    compression steel, 208
      bond, 220
      stop point, 218
    design, example, 207
      negative moment section, 208
      positive moment section, 210
    end spans, 223
    irregular spans, 223
    points of inflection, 210, 213
    stirrups, 221

T-beams, continuous, stopping bars, 212, 214
  design charts, 91, 120, 565, 566
  design example, 111
  design procedure, 196
  f_c, approximate, 113
  flange steel, 510
  flange width, 509
  formulas, 87
  isolated, 510
  jd, approximate, 82, 111
  k and j charts, 564
  wedge of stress, evaluation, 79, 80
Temperature steel, 510
Tests, loading existing structures, 495
Ties, column, 33
  compression steel, 222, 510
Top bar, definition for bond, 501
Torsion, 157
Transformed area, bars in circle,
    cracked section, 351
    uncracked section, 345
  beams, 69
  columns, 39
  effective, 40
    in compression, 70
  limitations for compression, 41
Two-way slabs, 229
  approximate analysis, 232
  bar placement sequence, 235
  beam loads, 516
  beams, Method 1, 241
    Method 2, 246
  bond, Method 1, 241
    Method 2, 246
  deflection patterns, 230
  depth, use of average, 237
  design examples, Method 1, 237
    Method 2, 243
  design strips, 233, 240, 515
  elastic analysis, 230
    approximations in, 232
  exterior corners, 248, 512
  inflection points, 512
  Method 1, 234, 512
  Method 2, 235, 243, 514
  minimum thickness, 237, 238
  modified elastic analysis, 223
  moments, 513, 515

Two-way slabs, moments, on beams, 513
  openings, 335
  reinforcing, arrangement, 513
  shear, 246, 513, 516
    on beams, 513
  thickness, minimum, 512
  types, 511

Ultimate strength theory. *See* Special
  Index

Waffle slab. *See* Flat slabs
Walls, 545
  openings, use of corner bars, 336
Water-cement ratio, 3
Wedge of stress, 78, 80
Wind forces, 506
Working stresses. *See* Beams, allow-able stresses; Bond, allowable stresses; etc.

Yield-line theory. *See* Special Index

Special Index:

ULTIMATE STRENGTH AND OTHER NONWORKING LOAD METHODS

This index lists only items applying exclusively to these methods. Routine items applying to all methods, such as bar spacing and cover, are in the General Index.